Fundamentals of
ENGINEERING
ELECTRONICS

By WILLIAM G. DOW

FUNDAMENTALS OF
ENGINEERING ELECTRONICS
Second Edition

MICROWAVE ELECTRON TUBES (*in preparation*)

FUNDAMENTALS OF
PHYSICAL ELECTRONICS (*in preparation*)

Fundamentals of
ENGINEERING
ELECTRONICS

—— SECOND EDITION ——

WILLIAM G. DOW
Professor of Electrical Engineering
University of Michigan

New York · JOHN WILEY & SONS, Inc.
London · CHAPMAN & HALL, Ltd.

Library of Congress Catalog Card Number: 52–10760

PRINTED IN THE UNITED STATES OF AMERICA

PREFACE

The reception accorded the first edition, and the results obtained in employing it as a textbook primarily for undergraduate electrical engineering courses at the University of Michigan, have added substantial strength to the author's convictions as to the merits of its general plan.

For both editions, the most important broad objective has been to make it relatively easy for any student of electrical engineering, and more particularly those planning a life work in electronic *circuit* engineering, to achieve a reasonably complete and satisfactory understanding of the internal functioning of the electron devices that serve as the active elements in electronic circuits. Although primarily a textbook, it should also be useful as a reference book for electron tube and electronic circuit engineers in industrial and government work.

It has been found not particularly difficult to impart a satisfactory quality of understanding of the noncircuit aspects of electron devices to electrical engineering students, in spite of their tendency to have much greater familiarity with the circuit aspects. The noncircuit phenomena sometimes seem strange, to both students and instructors, but they are not difficult to employ. For example, the author finds that students in the junior year achieve competence in the useful employment of the quantum-mechanical energy-level diagrams of Chapters VIII and XIII somewhat more rapidly than they achieve competence in the use of amplifier equivalent circuits, Chapters IX and X. In the author's judgment, the basic energy-level concepts presented in Chapters VIII and XIII form a necessary part of any even partially adequate treatment of semiconductors and gaseous-conducting devices. Without these basic concepts, such studies can be only very superficial.

It is realized, of course, that each instructor may not wish to use all the material. Selections can easily be made in accordance with the emphasis desired.

Important changes relative to the first edition are as follows:

The meter-kilogram-second system of units is employed throughout, in accordance with accepted engineering practice.

v

The analysis of the behavior of space-charge-control tubes, in Chapters IV, V, and VI, retains the same basis in conformal analysis as in the first edition, but it has been modernized by the introduction of the *equivalent electrostatic circuit* and *equivalent grid sheet potential* concepts. The treatment thus becomes completely quantitative for simple geometries, including that of the filamentary-cathode planar triode. The results are in agreement with modern engineering practice.

Various added detail aspects of space-charge-control devices include microphonics in filamentary-cathode triodes, an extension of the tetrode analysis to a more complete discussion of secondary emission phenomena in any tube, pentagrid tube principles, the upper limit to transconductance per ampere, and introduction of the uhf "figure of merit."

An analytical treatment of the dependence of interelectrode and input and output capacitances on space-charge-control tube geometry is given; this follows naturally from the equivalent electrostatic circuit analysis.

In Chapter XI, Introduction to Microwave Electron Tube Principles, a statement is presented of the basic new principles that must be employed in electron tubes designed for uhf and microwave frequency ranges. These principles include the effects of electron transit time on electron interaction efficiency, input loading, and input-to-output phase angles, the induced current concept, and an introduction to klystrons, magnetron oscillators, and traveling wave amplifiers.

The study of energy-level diagrams in metals has been extended to cover the basic aspects of semiconductor energy-level diagrams and their general relation to the behavior of transistors (semiconductor amplifying devices). The Fermi distribution function is introduced and the Fermi energy level discussed.

In the study of amplifier circuit principles, Chapters IX and X, the current generator equivalent circuit is introduced and its convenience emphasized; Thévenin's and Norton's circuit theorems are described and their manner of use indicated; and analytical treatments of negative feedback and the cathode follower circuit are given. Brief studies of the grid separation amplifier circuit and of Class C amplifier behavior in general appear in Chapter XI, preliminary to the study of transit time effects.

A derivation of the Maxwell-Boltzmann velocity distribution equation from basic principles is included.

The discussions of mean free paths and drift velocities of electrons and ions in gaseous-conducting devices have been closely correlated and made more easily useful in a quantitative sense.

An analytical presentation is given of the criterion for voltage break-down, in a gas at low pressure, including correlation with Paschen's law and the similitude behavior of "Townsend's α."

In order to make possible the inclusion of these new features in a volume of about the same size as the first edition, certain omissions of first-edition material have been made. For the most part, however, the material so left out has been incorporated into the manuscripts for two new companion books, *Fundamentals of Physical Electronics* and *Microwave Electron Tubes*, to be published in the near future.

The author wishes to express appreciation of the many helpful comments made by users of the first edition, also of the very thoughtful and constructive evaluations and criticisms made during the preparation of the manuscript for the second edition by Gunnar Hok, J. R. Black, J. S. Needle, P. H. Rogers, and H. W. Welch, all of the teaching and research staff of the Department of Electrical Engineering at the University of Michigan.

W. G. Dow

Ann Arbor, Michigan
August, 1952

CONTENTS

CONTENTS xiii

TABLES

INTRODUCTION

0.1 Text Material.[1c]* The study of electronics requires attention to the internal behavior of electron tubes and kindred circuit elements, and to the analysis of circuits employing such devices. Electron tubes are of two kinds: vacuum tubes, which are evacuated to as high a degree as practical engineering considerations permit, and gas tubes, which depend on gas content at a low pressure for their functioning. Kindred electron devices usually employ semiconductors. Examples are silicon and germanium rectifying diodes, photosensitive semiconductor devices, and semiconductor amplifiers.

In this textbook the various fundamental physical principles underlying the operation of electron devices are introduced as the need arises. This requires extensive application of electric and magnetic field principles. It also requires a working knowledge of the simpler aspects of quantum mechanics as applied to metals, semiconductors, and gases, as well as an introduction to the kinetic behavior of gas particles. Experience has shown that these noncircuit concepts, though perhaps strange to electrical engineering students, are considerably easier to learn to use effectively than are a-c circuit principles as applied to complex networks.[1c]

The author considers Chapter XIII, which deals with energy-level diagrams of atoms and introduces the elementary principles of the quantum theory, to be one of the essential items in any first course in electronics. The fundamental concepts of this material, although unfamiliar to students of electrical engineering, are very easy to understand and to employ usefully; without them the study of gaseous conduction and photosensitive devices drops to the level of a superficial survey treatment.

Advances in the electronic arts have made desirable a considerable expansion in text content as compared with the first edition of *Fundamentals of Engineering Electronics*. This expansion has resulted in the preparation of two somewhat advanced text and reference books, in addition to the present revision published under the original title. The titles of the new books are *Fundamentals of Physical Electronics* and *Microwave Electron Tubes*. The following objectives have governed the allocation of both old and new material between the three books:

* For itemized periodical and book references, see the bibliography, page 585.

1

(a) To make available, in this revised form of *Fundamentals of Engineering Electronics*, a relatively compact coverage of material of primary importance for a first undergraduate electronics course in a well-rounded electrical engineering curriculum, including also, where space permits and continuity considerations indicate, a modest amount of engineering reference material; and

(b) To present in the other two books more advanced material, of primary value for graduate study and reference.

Each of these books is self-contained, but complementary references to the others are frequently made.

0.2 Bibliography. Beginning on page 585 bibliographical references are presented, grouped according to text chapters. The reference items have been selected partly for general study, partly to support specific statements in the text. In general there may be more items in the bibliography than are referred to directly in the text.

In the coding of references to the bibliography, the notation $3a, f$, B, D–116, E–VI refers the reader to periodical articles a and f, and to books B, D, and E, with particular reference to page 116 in book D, and to Chapter VI in book E, all listed in the Chapter III portion of the bibliography.

Textbooks of general value dealing with mathematics and theoretical physics, including electromagnetic field theory, are grouped with the bibliographical material for Chapter I, and books on vacuum laboratory technology under Chapter II.

0.3 Symbolism; Vectors and Scalars. In problems dealing with motions of electrons, the mastery of various noncircuit concepts is essential. One element of such mastery is a clear and immediate distinction between vector quantities, which possess the attribute of direction in space, and scalar quantities, which have magnitude but no direction. The student should be sufficiently familiar with the physical nature of noncircuit concepts so that the distinction between field vectors and field scalars is immediate and automatic, regardless of the manner of presentation (for example, by means of the bold-faced type some authors employ). As an aid to the student, many equations in the early chapters have indications in brackets as to whether the equation describes a vector or a scalar quantity.

The symbols for logarithms and exponents are as follows:

$\ln x$ symbolizes the natural logarithm of x.
$\log_{10} x$ symbolizes the logarithm of x to the base 10.
$\exp x$ signifies ϵ^x, where ϵ is the natural logarithm base.

Thus: $\ln \exp x = x$ (0–1)

In some equations, particularly in Table IX, the ϵ^x form is retained for conciseness.

The abbreviations r-f, a-c, d-c, uhf, and rms are for radio-frequency, alternating-current, direct-current, ultra-high-frequency, and root-mean-square, all adjectives.

0.4 The Rationalized Meter-Kilogram-Second System of Units. The rationalized mks (meter-kilogram-second) system of units is employed. For this system the following relations hold in a vacuum: [1A, 1a]

$$D = \epsilon_0 F \quad \text{[vector]} \tag{0-2}$$

$$B = \mu_0 H \quad \text{[vector]} \tag{0-3}$$

where D = electric flux density, coulombs per square meter, a vector quantity.

F = electric field intensity, volts per meter, a vector quantity sometimes called "the electric vector."

ϵ_0 = permittivity of a vacuum, value $1/(36\pi \times 10^9)$ = 8.85×10^{-12} farad per meter, a scalar. $\hspace{1cm}$ (0-4)

B = magnetic flux density, webers per square meter, a vector.

H = magnetic field intensity, amperes per meter, a vector quantity sometimes called "the magnetic vector."

μ_0 = permeability of a vacuum, value $4\pi \times 10^{-7}$ henry per meter, a scalar. $\hspace{1cm}$ (0-5)

Coulomb's law becomes

$$f = \frac{q_1 q_2}{4\pi\epsilon_0 r^2} \quad \text{[vector]} \tag{0-6}$$

where f is the force in newtons (a vector, joules per meter) between point charges q_1 and q_2 (coulombs) located r meters apart. The electric field intensity F at distance r from point charge q_1 is therefore

$$F = \frac{q_1}{4\pi\epsilon_0 r^2} \quad \text{[volts per meter, vector]} \tag{0-7}$$

The corresponding electric flux density is

$$D = \frac{q_1}{4\pi r^2} \quad \text{[coulombs per square meter, vector]} \tag{0-8}$$

As $4\pi r^2$ is the area of the surface of a sphere of radius r, this may be written

Total flux = Area $\times D = 4\pi r^2 D = q_1$ $\hspace{1cm}$ [scalar] $\hspace{1cm}$ (0-9)

It is apparent from this equation that each coulomb of charge gives rise to one flux line. Thus the word coulomb signifies charge and flux magnitude identically; charge and flux are merely words describing different aspects of a single quantitative concept.

Useful conversion relationships are:

$$1 \text{ volt} = 10^8 \text{ abvolts} = 1/300 \text{ statvolt}$$
$$1 \text{ ampere} = 0.1 \text{ abampere} = 3 \times 10^9 \text{ statamperes}$$
$$1 \text{ weber per square meter} = 10,000 \text{ gausses}$$
$$1 \text{ newton} = 10^7 \text{ dynes}$$
$$1 \text{ joule} = 10^7 \text{ ergs}$$

The numerical values of the charge q_e on an electron and of the electron's mass m_e are[1A,b]

$$q_e = 1.602 \times 10^{-19} \quad \text{[coulomb per electron]} \quad (0\text{--}10)$$

$$m_e = 9.11 \times 10^{-31} \quad \text{[kilogram per electron]} \quad (0\text{--}11)$$

The ratio m_g/m_e of the mass of a gas particle or ion to the mass of an electron is determined by multiplying the particle's atomic or molecular weight by 1822, the ratio of the mass of a particle of unit atomic weight to the mass of an electron. Mathematically

$$m_g/m_e = 1822 \times \text{Atomic weight} \quad (0\text{--}12)$$

No particles having unit atomic weight exist, the nearest being the hydrogen atom, atomic weight 1.008. (See also Tables I and II.)

0.5   Technique for Conversion between Gaussian and MKS Systems. A convenient method of conversion between systems of units will be illustrated by application to the space-charge-limited current density equation (5–11). It is presumed that the equation is known in Gaussian units and is to be converted into mks units. The conversion steps are as follows:

(a) Write the equation in its given form:

$$J = \frac{\sqrt{2}}{9\pi} \sqrt{\frac{q_e}{m_e}} \frac{E^{3/2}}{s^2} \quad \text{[Gaussian units]} \quad (0\text{--}13)$$

Units as given and desired are:

	Given	Desired	Ratio
J, current density	Statamperes per square centimeter	Amperes per square meter	3×10^5
E, potential	Statvolts	Volts	$\frac{1}{300}$
s, distance	Centimeters	Meters	100
q_e, electronic charge	Statcoulombs	Coulombs	3×10^9
m_e, electronic mass	Grams	Kilograms	1000

(b) Rewrite the equation, substituting empty brackets for the symbols to be converted, labeling the units of each bracket by subscripts:

$$[\qquad]_{\text{sa/sq cm}} = \frac{\sqrt{2}\Big[\qquad\Big]_{\text{sc}}^{\frac{1}{2}}\Big[\qquad\Big]_{\text{sv}}^{\frac{3}{2}}}{9\pi\Big[\qquad\Big]_{\text{gm}}^{\frac{1}{2}}\Big[\qquad\Big]_{\text{cm}}^{2}} \tag{0-14}$$

(c) Insert in each empty bracket the symbol for the type of unit into which conversion is to be made, together with the proper multiplier. It is important to recognize that a symbol is a substitute for a *number* that measures, in proper units, a *definite physical condition*. Thus, when converting statvolts into volts, one should place inside the bracket for voltage the symbol for volts multiplied by $\frac{1}{300}$, for that is the number by which one must multiply the number 600 (which might symbolize, for example, the peak of an a-c 424-volt wave), to secure 2, its measure in statvolts. In the present example this procedure leads to:

$$[J \times 3 \times 10^5]_{\text{sa/sq cm}} = \frac{\sqrt{2}\Big[q_e \times 3 \times 10^9\Big]_{\text{sc}}^{\frac{1}{2}}\Big[E \times \frac{1}{300}\Big]_{\text{sv}}^{\frac{3}{2}}}{9\pi\Big[m_e \times 1000\Big]_{\text{gm}}^{\frac{1}{2}}\Big[s \times 100\Big]_{\text{cm}}^{2}} \tag{0-15}$$

In this form the symbols J, E, q_e, and m_e all stand for values in mks units.

(d) Simplify the expression after removing the brackets:

$$J[3 \times 10^5] = \frac{1}{9\pi}\sqrt{\frac{2q_e}{m_e}}\frac{E^{\frac{3}{2}}}{s^2}\left\{\frac{[3 \times 10^9]^{\frac{1}{2}}[\frac{1}{300}]^{\frac{3}{2}}}{[1000]^{\frac{1}{2}}[100]^2}\right\} \tag{0-16}$$

that is,

$$J = \frac{10^{-9}}{81\pi}\sqrt{\frac{2q_e}{m_e}}\frac{E^{\frac{3}{2}}}{s^2} = 2.33 \times 10^{-6}\frac{E^{\frac{3}{2}}}{s^2} \tag{0-17}$$

This can also be written, in terms of ϵ_0 as given by (0–4), in the (5–11) form, thus:

$$J = \frac{4\epsilon_0}{9}\sqrt{\frac{2q_e}{m_e}}\frac{E^{\frac{3}{2}}}{s^2} \tag{0-18}$$

CHAPTER I

POTENTIAL DISTRIBUTION DIAGRAMS

1.1 A Triode in a Simple Amplifier Circuit. Special attention must be devoted to thermionic grid-controlled vacuum tubes, often called space-charge-control tubes. The simplest such tube, a *triode*, contains three electrodes: grid, anode or plate, and cathode. It is desirable to present certain points of view relative to potential distribution diagrams for triodes and related tubes; however, first a brief discussion of the most important circuit use of a triode will be given.

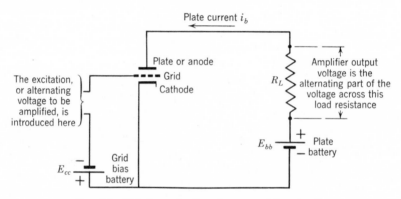

FIG. 1.1 · Triode connections in an amplifier circuit.

Figure 1.1 is a diagram of a circuit that employs a triode like that of Fig. 1.2 for amplifying the variations of more or less irregularly alternating voltages. An a-c voltage whose variations are to be amplified, called the input or *excitation* voltage, is introduced in series with the grid bias battery. The potential difference between grid and cathode therefore consists of a steady (d-c) voltage plus an alternating one. The plate circuit carries (*a*) a direct current, corresponding to zero excitation voltage, plus (*b*) an alternating current that follows the excitation voltage pattern, because of control over electron passage exerted by the grid. The voltage drop in load resistance R_L has corresponding d-c and a-c parts. The latter is the useful *output voltage* of the amplifier; it has the same pattern as the excitation voltage, but on an enlarged scale.

6

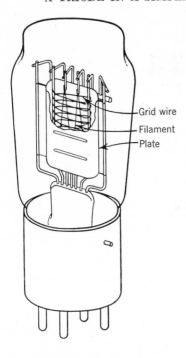

FIG. 1.2 Typical filamentary-cathode planar triode, in a glass envelope. This is called a "planar" device because the filament wires that form the cathode lie in a plane parallel to the plate surfaces.

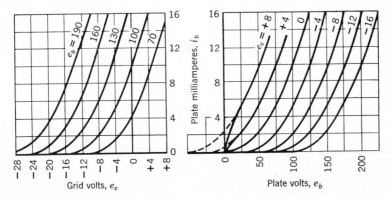

(a) Mutual characteristics, sometimes called transfer characteristics.

(b) Plate characteristics.

FIG. 1.3 Average characteristic curves for a particular filamentary-cathode planar triode, of the general type illustrated in Fig. 1.2. These curves are for the Western Electric type 101-F triode used in telephone repeater service. Note that, *for any type of vacuum tube,* the characteristic curves for any one individual tube may be expected to differ appreciably from the published average characteristics applying to that tube type.

The *voltage gain* of the amplifier is the ratio of the output voltage, that is, the a-c part of the voltage across the load resistance, to the excitation voltage. Numerical problems relative to circuits like that of Fig. 1.1 are solved by using *tube characteristic curves*, of the general type illustrated in Fig. 1.3, and with the aid of fictitious a-c equivalent circuits; see Chapter IX.

1.2 Triode Potential Distribution; Space-Charge Control of Plate Current by Grid and Plate Voltages. The region inside the envelope of a vacuum tube is made as nearly perfect a vacuum as is commercially feasible; [2A, B, C, D] this means a pressure of the general order of magnitude of 10^{-6} millimeter of mercury. The cathode surface is made of a substance that is a thermionic emitter; that is, it releases electrons when at a red or white heat. An auxiliary filament or heater circuit, not shown in Fig. 1.1, maintains the required cathode temperature. The exact rate of electron release is not important as long as it is large enough, because the actual flow is electrostatically controlled by the values of plate and grid potentials, not in general by cathode temperature. The cathode must be hot enough to provide the maximum number of electrons likely to be demanded per second by the electrostatic control (space-charge control) under normal conditions, yet not so hot as to destroy the electron-emitting properties of the cathode surface. In general the normal cathode temperature sets an upper limit to the tube current.

Consider conditions within a triode that has parallel-plane cathode and plate surfaces, as illustrated in the top portions of Figs. 1.4a and 1.4b. The solid lines in Fig. 1.4 describe typical point-to-point variations in potential (the potential distributions) within such a "planar" triode when the cathode is cold, so that no electrons are emitted and the tube interior is free from space charge. No current flows under such conditions. The dotted lines in Figs. 1.4a and 1.4b similarly describe potential distributions after the cathode is heated, so that electrons are emitted, and negative space charge does therefore exist between the electrodes. Under such conditions current does flow, because of the movement of the electrons that constitute the space charge.

Thus the solid lies in the four diagrams of Fig. 1.4 represent space-charge-free potential distributions that correspond to four different values of grid voltage. The upper solid line in each diagram describes the space-charge-free potential variation along a path midway between adjacent grid wires; the lower solid line, that along a path through the center of a grid wire.

The general "topography" of space-charge-free potential variation in the planar tube interior can be simulated by a stretched elastic

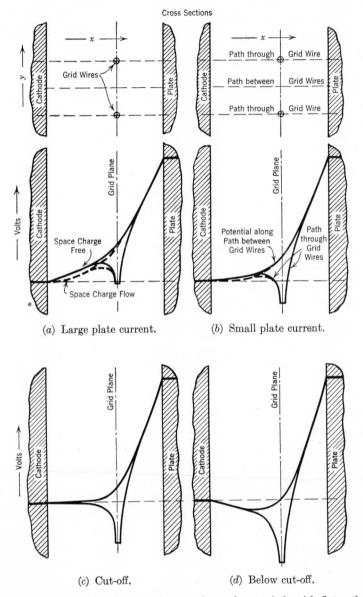

FIG. 1.4   Potential distribution diagrams for a planar triode with flat cathode, at various grid voltages.

membrane. The membrane must initially be tightly stretched between
the edges of two supports in such a way as to give its surface an inclination, the support at one end being higher than that at the other, just
as the plate potential is higher than that of the cathode. Then a
miniature inverted picket fence is lowered, in a vertical plane intermediate between and parallel to the supports, until the ends of the
pickets depress regularly spaced points of the membrane to a level
slightly below that of the lower-support "cathode." The level reached
by the ends of the pickets corresponds to grid potential.

The upper solid line of any one of the potential diagrams of Fig. 1.4
represents the profile of such a stretched membrane in a plane perpendicular to the supports and midway between adjacent pickets.
Each lower solid line represents a profile for a plane similarly located
except that it passes through a picket. To make the analogy satisfactory the membrane must be stretched tightly enough so that after
lowering the pickets the portions of the membrane near the support
are flat inclined surfaces free from wrinkles. This flatness corresponds
to the fact that the space-charge-free electric field in a triode is practically uniform near the cathode and plate surfaces.

A slant in the potential line adjacent to the cathode indicates the
existence there of a potential gradient. The potential gradient is
identical with the negative of electric field intensity and proportional
to the negative of the flux density. The slope of the potential line just
off the cathode is therefore a direct measure of the number of flux lines
that terminate on each unit area of cathode surface, and so of the
electric charge density on the cathode.

The slope of the potential line near the cathode is dependent on the
grid potential, in the manner indicated by the contrasts between the
various diagrams in Fig. 1.4. Therefore the negative charge on the
cathode changes whenever the grid potential is changed, that is, whenever the picket fence is raised or lowered.

As soon as the cathode is heated, the escape of electrons moves the
negative surface charge into the region near to but outside the cathode,
where it becomes space charge. The surface charge before electron
release is represented in Figs. 1.4a and 1.4b by the sharp turns of the
solid potential lines at cathode surfaces. The space charge after
release similarly corresponds to the gradual bends in the dotted potential lines. The total amount of turn, and so the total charge, is
about the same whether on the surface (solid lines) or just outside it
(dotted lines). Therefore the total amount of space charge after electron release is dependent on grid potential.

The flow of space charge constitutes the plate current; the less the
space charge, the smaller the current. Therefore the lowering of the

grid potential from its value in Fig. 1.4*a* to a more negative one in Fig. 1.4*b* results in a decrease in plate current. Thus, by controlling the electrostatic field in the tube, the grid voltage controls the magnitude of the plate current. The plate voltage exerts a similar but less powerful influence. However, the dependence of current on, for

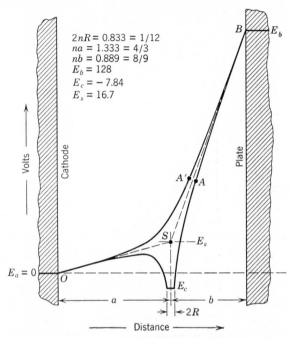

$2nR = 0.833 = 1/12$
$na = 1.333 = 4/3$
$nb = 0.889 = 8/9$
$E_b = 128$
$E_c = -7.84$
$E_s = 16.7$

FIG. 1.5 Mathematically determined potential distribution for a particular planar triode, obtained by using (4–107). The equivalent grid sheet thickness, given by (4–68), is too little to be discernible on this diagram. Compare this diagram with Fig. 4.13*b*. See Section 4.13 for a discussion of limiting magnitudes for this type of representation.

example, the grid potential, is more than linear, because a decrease in the grid potential (*a*) calls for a smaller space charge and (*b*) makes the space charge flow more slowly. The mechanism just described is referred to as "space-charge control" of the current from the cathode.

If the grid potential is low enough to make the off-cathode gradient zero, as in Fig. 1.4*c*, or negative, as in Fig. 1.4*d*, no plate current flows after electron release. The zero-off-cathode gradient condition, Fig. 1.4*c*, corresponds to "cut-off," that is, to the termination at the zero-plate-current axis of a *mutual characteristic curve* of the type illustrated in Fig. 1.3*a*.

Figure 1.5 is a mathematically correct diagram of the space-charge-free version of Fig. 1.4*b*. The uniform field near the cathode has a potential gradient described by the slope of the straight line *OS*. The line *OS* and the similar straight line *SB*, whose slope describes the gradient at the plate, are shown intersecting at a point *S* in the plane of the grid. The potential described by this point of intersection is called the *equivalent grid sheet potential*. It will be shown later that the equivalent grid sheet potential determines the current flow from the cathode.

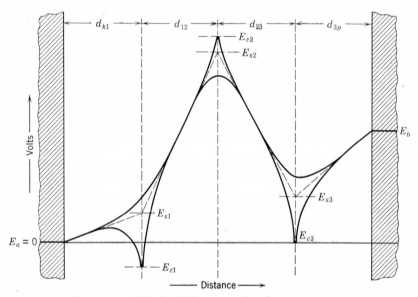

FIG. 1.6 Illustrative space-charge-free potential distribution for a planar pentode. Potentials: of cathode, E_a, zero; of control grid, E_{c1}, somewhat negative; of second grid, E_{c2}, strongly positive; of suppressor grid, E_{c3}, zero; of plate, E_b, any positive value.

The above reasoning and the associated stretched-membrane visual concepts can be extended directly to the study of multigrid tubes. Figure 1.6 illustrates the potential distribution in a space-charge-free planar (i.e., parallel-plane) *pentode* having three grids. The various equivalent grid sheet potentials are indicated.

Before potential distribution diagrams of the types just described can be sketched, the potentials of the various electrodes and all equivalent grid sheet potentials must be known; methods for determining these potentials are given in Chapters IV and V. To sketch the diagram for a pentode, for example, one should:

(*a*) Mark at the various electrode positions the values of grid sheet, grid wire, and plate potentials.

(b) Connect by a straight line the cathode and first grid sheet potentials, by another straight line the first and second grid sheet potentials, and so on, through to the plate.

(c) Sketch in free-hand for each grid the fillets discriminating between paths through and between grid wires.

If the grid wires are large and close together, relative to the electrode spacing, the fillets extend well out into the interelectrode regions; if the grid wires are small and far apart, the fillets extend only very slightly into the interelectrode regions. Note that in each case the upper and lower fillet curves merge into a straight line simultaneously, as for example to the right and upward from points A, A' in Fig. 1.5. This simultaneous merging is required by the mathematics of the potential distribution, as contained in (4–102b) and (4–107).

1.3   Electric Intensity and Potential; Force on an Electron.   The relationship between electric intensity and potential underlies the entire study of electronic devices.[1A]   Its simplest mathematical expressions are:

$$F = -\frac{dE}{ds} \quad \text{[vector]} \tag{1-1}$$

and

$$E_2 - E_1 = -\int_1^2 F \, ds \quad \text{[scalar]} \tag{1-2}$$

The first form described mathematically the fact that electric intensity F is the negative space derivative of electric potential E. The second form indicates that, conversely, the difference of potential between two points in the field is the negative line integral of the intensity along a path (any path) between the two points. In these equations ds is the incremental distance *measured parallel to the direction of the electric force*. If the line integral is taken over a path that is not everywhere parallel to the direction of the electric flux, ds represents only the component in the direction of the field of each increment of the path.

The application of (1–1) and (1–2) to the field intermediate between two parallel metal plates (no grid) is illustrated graphically in Fig. 1.7. Potential is measured vertically, distance horizontally. Potential gradient, that is, the slope of the potential line, is numerically equal to the electric intensity, though of opposite sign. Since the force on an electron of charge q_e in the intermediate region is $q_e F$ newtons, the slope of the potential line is proportional to the force on, and the acceleration experienced by, such an electron.

The potential line of Fig. 1.7a may be likened to the side of a hill (Fig. 1.7b), the top level of the hill corresponding to the potential of

14 POTENTIAL DISTRIBUTION DIAGRAMS

the more positive plate, the bottom level to that of the more negative plate. It is apparent that the force tending to roll a ball down the hill is dependent on the slope, which is merely another name for the gradient or space derivative of the elevation. Similarly the force on an electron is dependent on the slope of the potential line.

In potential diagrams positive potentials correspond to upper levels, and negative potentials to lower levels. Unfortunately, this practice gives electrons the property of "rolling" uphill rather than down.

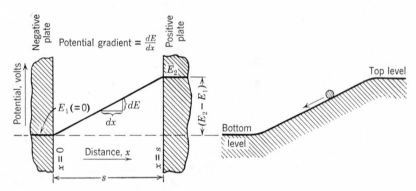

FIG. 1.7a Potential distribution between two parallel metal surfaces.

FIG. 1.7b The force tending to roll a ball down a hill is dependent on the gradient.

The force on an electron is proportional to the slope of the potential line, that is, to the tangent of the angle it makes with the horizontal, whereas the gravitational force on the ball is proportional to the sine of the angle between hillside and horizontal. Therefore the analogy is satisfactory only for comparison with gently sloping hillsides for which the sine and the tangent are nearly the same.

1.4 Poisson's and the Laplace Equations. In many electric circuit elements, for example, inductances and capacitances, it is satisfactory to assume that electric charge exists only on the surfaces of the conductors. In electron devices electric charge may be distributed throughout a volume and must then be measured in units of space-charge density, by stating the number of coulombs per cubic meter.

If the volume charge results from the presence of electrons, the space-charge density is negative; if from the presence of positively charged ions, the space-charge density is positive. If both are present, the space-charge density corresponds to the algebraic sum of their opposite effects. It is often negligibly small in regions having very high concentrations of both kinds of particles.

The general partial differential equation relating potential E, rectangular space coordinates x, y, and z, and space-charge density ρ (coulombs per cubic meter) is

$$\frac{\partial^2 E}{\partial x^2} + \frac{\partial^2 E}{\partial y^2} + \frac{\partial^2 E}{\partial z^2} = -\frac{\rho}{\epsilon_0} \quad \text{[scalar]} \qquad (1\text{--}3)$$

This is known as *Poisson's equation.** Many engineering problems deal with fields in which there is no space charge; for such fields

$$\frac{\partial^2 E}{\partial x^2} + \frac{\partial^2 E}{\partial y^2} + \frac{\partial^2 E}{\partial z^2} = 0 \qquad (1\text{--}4)$$

This is called the *Laplace equation.** It applies in any interelectrode region from which space charge is absent and in which the dielectric constant is everywhere uniform. The general problem of electrostatic field analysis is that of finding solutions of (1–4) that satisfy boundary conditions imposed by electrode geometry and potentials; see Chapter IV for methods.

The electric field in the region between the infinitely extending parallel plates of Fig. 1.7a is said to be *one-dimensional*. It is obvious that the equipotentials are all perfectly flat surfaces perpendicular to the x-coordinate direction. Explorations confined to travel in the y and z directions will discover no change in potential, so that the last two terms of the left-hand sides of (1–3) and (1–4) drop out; Poisson's and the Laplace equations in one dimension are

$$\frac{d^2 E}{dx^2} = -\frac{\rho}{\epsilon_0} \qquad (1\text{--}5)$$

and

$$\frac{d^2 E}{dx^2} = 0 \qquad (1\text{--}6)$$

Figure 1.7a indicates that the slope of the space-potential line is the potential gradient, dE/dx. The expression d^2E/dx^2 is merely a way of writing

$$\frac{d}{dx}\left(\frac{dE}{dx}\right)$$

which is the space rate of change of slope, called the *flexion*, of the potential curve. Equation (1–6) therefore requires that the potential

* See bibliographical references 1B through 1G.

distribution curve for a one-dimensional field in a region free from space charge must be a straight line, for only a line that is straight has zero flexion. If in any region the space-potential line is curved, either space charge is present, or the field is not one-dimensional, or both.

Poisson's equation (1–3) will be derived by reference to the small rectangular volume $dx\,dy\,dz$ of Fig. 1.8 within which the space-charge density is ρ. Electric flux density D_x enters the left-hand $dy\,dz$ surface, and flux density $D_x + (\partial D_x/\partial x)\,dx$ leaves the right-hand $dy\,dz$ surface.

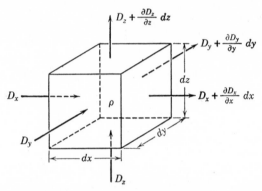

FIG. 1.8   Electric flux densities entering and emerging from a small rectangular volume $dx\,dy\,dz$ within which the space-charge density is ρ coulombs per cubic meter.

Therefore, the excess of the amount of flux leaving the right-hand $dy\,dz$ surface over that entering the left-hand $dy\,dz$ surface is

$$\left(D_x + \frac{\partial D_x}{\partial x}\,dx\right) dy\,dz - (D_x)\,dy\,dz = \frac{\partial D_x}{\partial x}\,dx\,dy\,dz \qquad (1\text{–}7)$$

The overall excess of flux leaving over that entering is obtained by adding to this expression two similar terms employing $\partial D_y/\partial y$ and $\partial D_z/\partial z$; this sum is of course equal to the total charge $\rho\,dx\,dy\,dz$ within the small volume, because each coulomb terminates one flux line.   Therefore

$$\frac{\partial D_x}{\partial x}\,dx\,dy\,dz + \frac{\partial D_y}{\partial y}\,dx\,dy\,dz + \frac{\partial D_z}{\partial z}\,dx\,dy\,dz = \rho\,dx\,dy\,dz \qquad (1\text{–}8)$$

Cancellation of $dx\,dy\,dz$ gives

$$\frac{\partial D_x}{\partial x} + \frac{\partial D_y}{\partial y} + \frac{\partial D_z}{\partial z} = \rho \qquad (1\text{–}9)$$

Of course

$$\frac{\partial D_x}{\partial x} = \epsilon_0 \frac{\partial F_x}{\partial x} = -\epsilon_0 \frac{\partial}{\partial x}\left(\frac{\partial E}{\partial x}\right) = -\epsilon_0 \frac{\partial^2 E}{\partial x^2} \qquad (1\text{--}10)$$

and similarly for $\partial D_y/\partial y$ and $\partial D_z/\partial z$. This permits conversion of the D's into E's, leading to (1–3).

1.5   Poisson's and the Laplace Equations in Two Dimensions. The plate and cathode surfaces of Fig. 1.4 are considered infinite in extent and the grid wires infinitely long. Hence an exploration confined to travel along a line parallel to a grid wire will discover no variation in potential. Only the x and y gradients $\partial E/\partial x$ and $\partial E/\partial y$ have values, so the fields in Fig. 1.4 are said to be *two-dimensional*. Poisson's and the Laplace equations in rectangular coordinates for a two-dimensional field are

$$\frac{\partial^2 E}{\partial x^2} + \frac{\partial^2 E}{\partial y^2} = -\frac{\rho}{\epsilon_0} \qquad \text{[scalar]} \qquad (1\text{--}11)$$

and

$$\frac{\partial^2 E}{\partial x^2} + \frac{\partial^2 E}{\partial y^2} = 0 \qquad (1\text{--}12)$$

The second x derivative of the potential, $\partial^2 E/\partial x^2$, may in general have a value, so the potential profiles in the x direction have flexion, either (A) in a one-dimensional field due to the presence of space charge, as along the dotted lines near the cathodes of Figs. 1.4a and 1.4b, or (B) in a two- or three-dimensional field with or without space charge, as along the curved parts of the solid lines in the same figures, or along the dotted lines in the neighborhood of the grid. In cases of type A,

(A)
$$\frac{\partial^2 E}{\partial x^2} = -\frac{\rho}{\epsilon_0} \qquad (1\text{--}13)$$

In cases of the two-dimensional (B) type, without space charge,

(B)
$$\frac{\partial^2 E}{\partial x^2} = -\frac{\partial^2 E}{\partial y^2} \qquad (1\text{--}14)$$

Near the plate and cathode of a parallel-plane triode, Fig. 1.4, the field is one-dimensional, in that the potential varies only with exploration in the x direction. Correspondingly, *before* the entrance of electron-borne space charge the space-potential line near the cathode is *straight*, as described by the solid lines. The *dotted* line in Fig. 1.4a is *curved* near the cathode because it describes the potential distribution *after* electrons are permitted to enter and establish a strong negative space charge just outside the cathode.

In the neighborhood of the grid, Fig. 1.4, all the solid (space-charge-free condition) lines are curved. Their curvature indicates that in that region the field is not one-dimensional, as the potential varies along a path from one grid wire over an intermediate hill to the next wire.

Equation (1–14) indicates that if, in a space-charge-free two-dimensional field, the flexion of the x profile is positive (convex downward) that of the y profile must be negative (convex upward). This is suggestive of the "topography" of a saddle.

1.6 Surface- and Space-Charge Density in Potential Diagrams. The electric field of Fig. 1.7a terminates in surface charges at the two plates; at each surface the abrupt change in the potential gradient, that is, in the slope of the potential line, is a direct measure of the *surface-charge density.*

The lines of electric flux between the plates terminate at the metal surfaces. Flux lines terminate only on electric charges; one flux line ends on each coulomb of charge. Therefore the charge density on a terminal surface must be equal to the flux density, and hence proportional to the electric field intensity and the potential gradient that exists just outside the surface. Mathematically, at the negative plate,

$$F = \frac{\sigma}{\epsilon_0} \quad \text{or} \quad \frac{dE}{dx} = -\frac{\sigma}{\epsilon_0} \quad \text{[vector]} \qquad (1\text{–}15)$$

Here σ is surface-charge density in coulombs per square meter; it is a vector quantity directed perpendicular to the surface.

Equation (1–15) can be adapted to indicate in a single expression the relation between field properties and surface charges at *both* plates by using the *change* in field intensity and gradient experienced in passing through the surface from left to right (in the direction of an increase in x) as follows:

$$\Delta F = +\frac{\sigma}{\epsilon_0} \quad \text{or} \quad \Delta \left(\frac{dE}{dx}\right) = -\frac{\sigma}{\epsilon_0} \qquad (1\text{–}16)$$

At the left-hand plate the gradient increases from zero inside to a positive value outside, so that its change is positive; the surface charge is negative, as called for by (1–16). At the right-hand plate the gradient changes from a positive value outside to zero inside, so that the change in crossing the surface in the plus x direction is negative; the surface charge is positive, as demanded by the equation.

Thus the change in potential gradient in passing through a surface is a direct measure of the charge density on the surface. The space charge in a one-dimensional field may be thought of as consisting of many very thin layers of space charge; the space-charge density in successive layers may or may not be the same. If the layers are thin enough, they resemble surface charges.

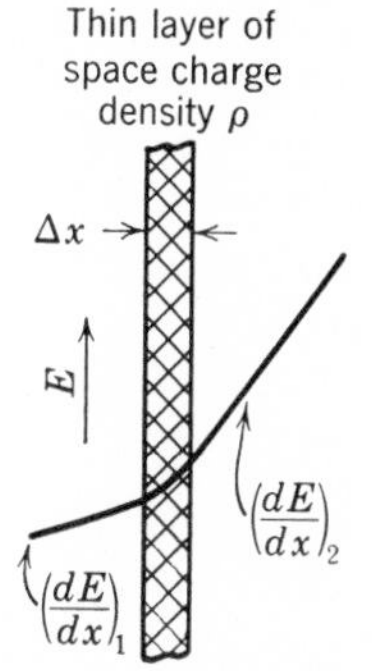

Figure 1.9 illustrates the potential change in passing through one such thin layer. If the charge content of the layer is σ coulombs per unit area, (1–16) can be applied to relate the gradient's change in traversing the layer to the charge content as follows:

Thin layer of space charge density ρ

FIG. 1.9 Change in potential gradient in passing through a thin layer of space charge.

$$\Delta\left(\frac{dE}{dx}\right) = \left(\frac{dE}{dx}\right)_2 - \left(\frac{dE}{dx}\right)_1 = -\frac{\sigma}{\epsilon_0} \quad (1\text{–}17)$$

The layer's charge content can also be described by stating the space-charge density ρ within it. To do this the symbol σ must be replaced by $\rho\,\Delta x$, this being the charge within a unit area of the layer, of thickness now specified as Δx. With this change, (1–17) becomes

$\left(\frac{dE}{dx}\right)_1$ and $\left(\frac{dE}{dx}\right)_2$ signify the slopes of the potential line.

$$\left(\frac{dE}{dx}\right)_2 - \left(\frac{dE}{dx}\right)_1 = \Delta\left(\frac{dE}{dx}\right) = -\frac{\rho\,\Delta x}{\epsilon_0} \quad \text{[vector]} \quad (1\text{–}18)$$

If the thickness of the layer of charge approaches zero as a limit, the potential gradient change $\Delta(dE/dx)$ and the thickness Δx are written $d(dE/dx)$ and dx; (1–13) results.

1.7 Potential Diagrams for One-Dimensional Fields in Regions Containing Space Charge. Figure 1.10 illustrates a shape the potential distribution curve in the one-dimensional region between two parallel plates may have when the intermediate region contains *uniform* space-charge density. The situation so represented *can never persist,* but it is serviceable for illustrative purposes. Two successive integrations of (1–13), based on a constant value for ρ and with the origin at the negative plate, show that the potential line in Fig. 1.10 must be a parabola. The first constant of integration is σ_1, the surface-charge density at the more negative plate. The second integration constant is zero.

The *convex-downward* flexion of the potential line in Fig. 1.10 corresponds to a *negative* space charge such as would result from a uniform concentration of electrons. A uniform *positive* space charge would result in a parabola *convex upward*. The sharp bend at the left-hand end can be described as convex downward; correspondingly the surface

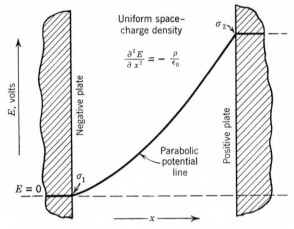

Fig. 1.10   Typical potential distribution in a one-dimensional region containing space-charge density.

charge is negative. At the right-hand surface there is a sharp convex-upward bend, indicating a positive surface charge.

If interelectrode space charge is due to electrons, they must move in response to the force exerted on them by the electric field whose form

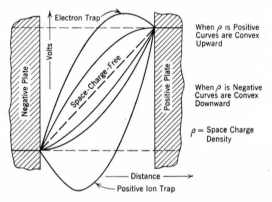

Fig. 1.11   Potential distributions for various values of uniform space-charge density, parallel plane electrodes.

they help to determine. For that reason a *uniform electron concentration can ordinarily exist only for an extremely short time.*

Whether space-charge density is uniform or not, the flexion of the potential line is at every point, for one-dimensional geometry, proportional to the negative of the space-charge density, and an abrupt change of slope at a surface is a direct measure of surface-charge density.

Figure 1.11 illustrates a variety of uniform space-charge-density conditions, all with the same plate potential, but with varying amounts and kinds of space charge. Of particular interest is the uppermost curve, corresponding to a rather large *positive* space-charge density. If a single electron were set free in such a field, it would be accelerated toward the highest point of this curve, the vertex of the parabola. An electron introduced without any initial velocity at any point where the potential is above that of the positive plate could not escape to either plate. Because of its inertia, such an electron would oscillate near the vertex, like a ball at the bottom of a parabolic trough. Enough electrons so placed would partially or wholly neutralize the positive space charge.

1.8 Spherical and Cylindrical Coordinates. Occasionally the following general forms taken by Poisson's equation when referred to spherical and cylindrical coordinate systems are useful [1G-90] (see also Chapter I in *Fundamentals of Physical Electronics*).

Cylindrical coordinates, as in Fig. 1.12:

$$\frac{1}{r}\frac{\partial}{\partial r}\left(r\frac{\partial E}{\partial r}\right) + \frac{1}{r^2}\frac{\partial^2 E}{\partial \phi^2} + \frac{\partial^2 E}{\partial z^2} = -\frac{\rho}{\epsilon_0} \qquad \text{[scalar]} \qquad (1\text{--}19)$$

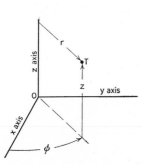

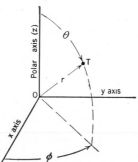

FIG. 1.12 Cylindrical co-ordinates of the point T.   FIG. 1.13 Spherical coordinates of the point T.

Spherical coordinates, as in Fig. 1.13:

$$\frac{1}{r^2}\frac{\partial}{\partial r}\left(r^2\frac{\partial E}{\partial r}\right) + \frac{1}{r^2 \sin\theta}\frac{\partial}{\partial \theta}\left(\sin\theta\frac{\partial E}{\partial \theta}\right)$$

$$+ \frac{1}{r^2 \sin^2\theta}\frac{\partial^2 E}{\partial \phi^2} = -\frac{\rho}{\epsilon_0} \qquad \text{[scalar]} \qquad (1\text{--}20)$$

Many electron tubes employ cylindrical electrodes; if all equi-potentials are cylinders, so that the potential varies only with the radial distance from the axis of symmetry, Poisson's equation becomes

$$\frac{1}{r}\frac{d}{dr}\left(r\frac{dE}{dr}\right) = -\frac{\rho}{\epsilon_0} \qquad \text{[scalar]} \qquad (1\text{-}21)$$

also expressible as

$$\frac{d^2E}{(d\ln r)^2} = -\frac{\rho r^2}{\epsilon_0} \qquad (1\text{-}22)$$

If there is no space charge, but there is present an on-axis line charge of τ coulombs per meter of axial length, the electric flux density (coulombs per unit area) is a purely radial vector, of value

$$D = \frac{\tau}{2\pi r} \;;\, \text{also,}\; F = \frac{\tau}{2\pi\epsilon_0 r} = -\frac{dE}{dr} \qquad \text{[vector]} \qquad (1\text{-}23)$$

If any two equipotential cylinders are at potentials E_1 and E_2 and radii r_1 and r_2, respectively, integration of this equation shows that

$$E_2 - E_1 = -\frac{\tau}{2\pi\epsilon_0}\ln\frac{r_2}{r_1} \qquad \text{[scalar]} \qquad (1\text{-}24)$$

The potential E at any radius r between r_1 and r_2 is then related to other quantities as follows:

$$\frac{E - E_1}{E_2 - E_1} = \frac{\ln r/r_1}{\ln r_2/r_1} \qquad (1\text{-}25)$$

Thus the potential distribution in such a region is logarithmic.

Figure 1.14 illustrates the logarithmic potential distribution in a space-charge-free cylindrical diode. Figure 4.19 illustrates the potential distribution in a cylindrical pentode. Note the similarities and contrasts between Figs. 4.19 and 1.6; in Fig. 4.19 the lines joining equivalent grid sheet potentials are logarithmic curves rather than straight lines.

In sketching these logarithmic curves, it is convenient to note that at the point whose radius is the *geometric* mean between the inner and outer radii, the potential is the *arithmetic* mean between the potentials of the inner and outer cylinders.

The first terms of (1–3), (1–19), and (1–20) represent Poisson's equation in the three potential distributions that are symmetrical about a

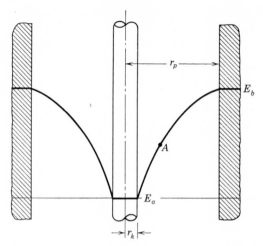

FIG. 1.14 Space-charge-free potential distribution in a cylindrical diode. At point A the potential is the arithmetic mean between E_a and E_b; the radius at A is the geometric mean between r_k and r_p.

plane, a line, and a point, respectively. For these three symmetries, Poisson's equation can be written: [15b]

$$\frac{d^2E}{dr^2} + \frac{k}{r}\frac{dE}{dr} = -\frac{\rho}{\epsilon_0} \qquad \text{[scalar]} \qquad (1\text{-}26)$$

where $k = 0$ for planar symmetry, $k = 1$ for cylindrical symmetry about a line, and $k = 2$ for spherical symmetry about a point.

PROBLEMS

1. In Fig. 1.11, potential difference between the plates is 300 volts; spacing 1.5 cm. Uniform space-charge density, sufficient to make the potential gradient be zero just outside the negative plate, exists between the plates. Find: (*a*) space-charge density; (*b*) electron concentration; (*c*) potential gradient adjacent to the positive plate; (*d*) surface-charge density on the positive plate; (*e*) space charge (coulombs) within a volume that extends from one plate to the other, of cross-sectional area 1 sq cm; (*f*) acceleration experienced by an electron at a point midway between the plates.

2. Potential distribution between a pair of infinite parallel plates 1.5 cm apart is given by $E = 2.25x^{4/3}$. Find the new answers to (*d*) and (*e*), Prob. 1; evaluate the quantity $\rho\sqrt{E}$ at $x = 0.75$ cm, also at $x = 1.5$ cm.

3. Midway between grid-wire centers, Fig. 1.4*a*, the *space-charge-free* value of flexion d^2E/dx^2 of the x-profile potential distribution is 6×10^7 volts per meter squared. According to Poisson's equation the introduction of flowing negative space charge (electrons) makes the algebraic sum of the x- and y-profile flexions become

more positive. If the total change due to introduction of space charge is equally divided between the two flexions, what is the value of each at the specified point when ρ is $-(\frac{1}{3}) \times 10^{-4}$ coulomb per cubic meter?

4. Two concentric cylinders have radii $r_a = 0.04$ cm, $r_b = 0.60$ cm, and potentials $E_a = 0$, $E_b = +360$ (in volts). Find: (a) τ_a, the charge on the inner cylinder (coulombs per meter); (b) surface-charge densities on the two electrodes; (c) potential gradient just outside the inner cylinder, and just inside the outer one. (d) Plot a curve of E vs. r.

CHAPTER II

ELECTRON BALLISTICS

2.1 Acceleration Due to an Electric Field. Under certain conditions
electrons may escape from metal boundaries.   If electric or magnetic
fields exist in the region into which they escape, and if there is a vacuum
sufficiently high [2A, B, C, D] so that collisions with gas particles are relatively rare, these fields will control the subsequent movements of the
electrons. This chapter analyzes types of electron motion that take
place when the number of electrons escaping is so small that their
charges and movements have negligible effects on the fields.

Imagine a few electrons to be released from the more negative of
two parallel flat electrodes, Fig. 1.7a, between which there is a considerable difference of potential.   Each electron experiences a force f
whose magnitude in newtons is the product of its charge $(-q_e)$ by the
electric field intensity F; thus

$$f = -q_e F = +q_e \frac{dE}{dx} \qquad \text{[vector]} \qquad (2\text{-}1)$$

Just as a ball on a hillside is accelerated toward the bottom of the
hill at a rate dependent on the slope (i.e., elevation gradient), so an
electron is accelerated toward the region of high potential; thus

$$\frac{dv}{dt} = -\frac{q_e F}{m_e} = +\frac{q_e}{m_e}\frac{dE}{dx} \qquad \text{[meters per (second)}^2\text{, vector]} \quad (2\text{-}2)$$

This is a rearrangement of the force equation

$$f = -q_e F = +m_e \frac{dv}{dt} \qquad \text{[newtons, vector]} \qquad (2\text{-}3)$$

If the electric field is uniform, the acceleration is constant. This corresponds to a ball on a hill of constant slope; the time to travel a given
distance and the average and final velocities may be calculated by the
familiar laws governing uniformly accelerated motion.   Behavior in a
nonuniform field may be treated by integration, as in the case of a ball
on a curved slope.

2.2 Velocity and Potential; the Electron Volt. The kinetic energy
acquired by a ball on a hill is independent of local variations in slope,

being related rather to the total vertical distance traveled, that is, to the decrease in potential energy. A "falling" electron, like such a ball, continually converts potential energy of position into kinetic energy, and the gain of one kind must equal the loss of the other.

Electric potential difference between two points is by definition the work expended in moving a unit charge from one point to the other. Therefore the change (in joules) of potential energy during an electron's movement is the product of the potential difference E through which it moves (volts) by its charge q_e (coulombs). Equating this to the kinetic energy gained gives

$$Eq_e = \tfrac{1}{2}m_e v^2 \qquad \text{[joules, scalar]} \qquad (2\text{--}4)$$

Thus an electron that has "fallen" through a certain potential difference E has definite values of kinetic energy and velocity, regardless of the manner of variation of potential between the starting and end points, or of the direction of the velocity, provided the potential distribution remains constant during the electron's flight.

The energy possessed by an electron that has "fallen" through a potential difference of 1 volt is a convenient *unit of energy*, called the *electron volt*. This unit is applicable even when the energy measured is not at all the result of movement of a charged particle in an electric field. For example, the average kinetic energy of thermal motion possessed by molecules of air at 40° C is conveniently specified as 0.0675 electron volt. This means that their average kinetic energy is that gained by an electron in traversing 0.0675 volt; it does not indicate at all that an electron or an electric field has any part in creating an air molecule's energies.

If the energy E in electron volts of an electron is known, its velocity can be calculated by solving (2–4) for the velocity, giving

$$v = \sqrt{\frac{2q_e}{m_e}}\,\sqrt{E} = 5.93 \times 10^5 \sqrt{E} \qquad \text{[meters per second, vector]} \quad (2\text{--}5)$$

It is frequently desirable to determine the velocity of an *atom* or *molecule* whose energy in electron volts is known. Equation (2–5) indicates that the velocity is inversely proportional to the square root of the mass, so that for these heavier particles

$$v = \frac{5.93 \times 10^5 \sqrt{E}}{\sqrt{m_g/m_e}} \qquad \text{[vector]} \qquad (2\text{--}6)$$

Here m_g is the mass and m_g/m_e the *mass ratio* of the particle concerned; see (0–12).

2.3 Directed Energies; Velocity Measurable in Square-Root Volts.

The direction of the velocity possessed by an electron is important. Suppose, for example, that the "electron gun" (devices so described are used in cathode-ray apparatus) shoots a beam of electrons at an angle into the uniform field between the plates of Fig. 2.1. Each entering electron initially possesses an x-directed velocity component v_x, and a y-directed component v_y. The former remains constant; the latter is modified by uniform downward acceleration due to the field.

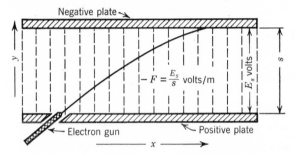

FIG. 2.1 Electron trajectory in a uniform electric field.

The trajectory is parabolic, as in the exactly analogous case of a ball thrown upward at an angle against the force of gravity.

Only the y-directed velocity is effective in aiding the electrons to reach the upper plate. For example, if E_s is 200 volts, the beam can reach the upper plate only if initially $v_y \geqq 5.93 \times 10^5 \times \sqrt{200}$; that is, the initial vertical velocity must exceed $\sqrt{200} = 14.14$ *square-root volts*. The horizontal velocity may be anything at all without affecting the vertical travel. If the initial vertical energy is exactly 200 electron volts a grazing contact occurs (at the vertex of the parabola) at the upper electrode.

The two initial velocity components may conveniently be described as $\sqrt{E_x}$ and $\sqrt{E_y}$ square-root volts. The total velocity is $\sqrt{v_x{}^2 + v_y{}^2}$, or, in square-root volts,

$$\text{Total velocity} = \sqrt{\sqrt{E_x}^2 + \sqrt{E_y}^2} = \sqrt{E_x + E_y} \quad \text{[vector]} \quad (2\text{--}7)$$

If, for example, $\sqrt{E_x}$ is $\sqrt{400} = 20$, and $\sqrt{E_y}$ is $\sqrt{300} = 17.32$, the total initial velocity in meters per second is $5.93 \cdot 10^5 \times \sqrt{400 + 300} = 5.93 \cdot 10^5 \times \sqrt{700}$. The initial angle with the horizontal is arc tan $\sqrt{300/400} =$ arc tan 0.866. The electron gun is said to be delivering 700-volt electrons, and the electron beam is called a 700-volt beam.

The gun must contain provisions for accelerating electrons through a potential difference of 700 volts.

The time required to reach the upper plate depends entirely on the initial upward velocity and can be obtained by integration after writing (2–5) in the form

$$dt = \frac{1}{5.93 \cdot 10^5} \frac{1}{\sqrt{E_y}} \, dy \qquad \text{[scalar]} \qquad (2\text{–}8)$$

Here $\sqrt{E_y}$ describes the vertically upward velocity at any point after leaving the gun. In this example E_y is a linear function of y, because the field is uniform; if the initial value of E_y is E_{y0}, the vertical velocity at any ordinate y is $+\sqrt{E_{y0} + yF}$ square-root volts, and the time of flight to the top plate is

$$t = \frac{1}{5.93 \cdot 10^5} \int_{y=0}^{y=s} \frac{dy}{\sqrt{E_{y0} + yF}} \qquad \text{[scalar]} \qquad (2\text{–}9)$$

which is easily evaluated; note that F here has a negative value. The distance traveled in the x direction is of course $v_x t$, where $v_x = 5.93 \cdot 10^5 \sqrt{E_x}$.

2.4　Electron Deflection in Passing through Grids; Electron Rejection from the Plate Region.[2a]　Figure 2.2a illustrates the space-charge-free potential distribution in a triode with plate and cathode at a common potential, and the grid positive. Figure 2.2b is a cross section showing the electrode arrangement. Suppose that a few electrons are released at the cathode with negligible initial velocities. Most of these electrons cannot reach the plate, for, as indicated by the trajectories shown in Fig. 2.2b, each one experiences as it passes the grid a slight sideways deflection which converts part of the energy of x-directed motion that it has received from the field into y-directed motion. It must miss the plate by just the amount of energy so converted.

For example, consider an electron at T, traveling along the trajectory drawn through that point. Because it started from the cathode with zero initial velocity, it possesses at T just E_T electron volts of kinetic energy. This is enough, if properly directed, to get the electron to the plate. But E_y electron volts of this is associated with y-directed motion. The electron possesses, at T, $E_T - E_y$ electron volts of x-directed motion, but the plate is E_T volts away, so that the electron must fail to reach the plate by just E_y volts.

One of the trajectories shown is the straight-line path of electrons that pass just midway between grid wires, so experiencing no deflection; only these can reach the plate. All others, after passing the grid, follow parabolic trajectories whose vertex is slightly to the left of the plate. They are unable subsequently to return to the cathode for the same reason that prevents them from reaching the plate. They must oscillate back and forth, like a ball rolling down one side and up the

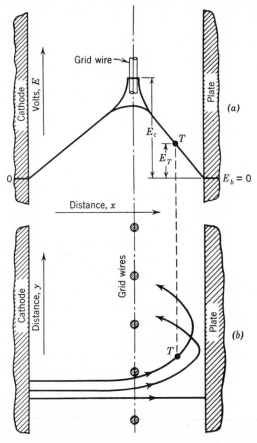

FIG. 2.2   Deflection of electrons in passing through a grid.

other of a trough, until finally they happen to strike the grid and pass on into the grid circuit. The period of oscillation can be calculated by proper integration of (2–8).

A situation very similar to this exists near zero plate voltage in tetrodes and pentodes; see Fig. 6.15b. For such tubes, the slopes of plate characteristic curves, as they rise from zero with increasing but small voltages, are dependent partly on the degree of dispersion experienced by the electrons in traversing the grid region, because each increment of plate voltage makes it easier for deflected electrons to reach the plate. The plate is sometimes said to "reject" the electrons at low plate voltages.

If in Fig. 2.2 the plate voltage is considerably positive, all electrons may be expected to reach and enter it, but it is still true as before that any y-directed velocity component acquired by an electron in passing the grid does not subsequently change in value. Manipulation of grid and plate voltages therefore permits focusing the electrons into narrow bands at various distances from grid toward plate.

2.5 Electron Flight-Line Diagrams; Transit Angle. Imagine a planar diode with a constant plate potential of E_s volts; Fig. 2.3b

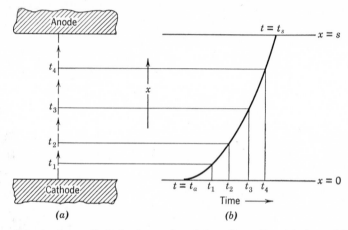

(a)　　　　　　　　　　(b)

FIG. 2.3　A planar diode having a d-c plate voltage E_s. (a) A straight-line electron trajectory. (b) A curved flight line describing the motion of a single electron, starting from the cathode with zero initial velocity and being accelerated toward the anode by a uniform electric field.

illustrates the distance and time coordinates of a "flight-line diagram" for this arrangement. The single flight line of Fig. 2.3b represents the distance-time history of a single electron released from the cathode with zero initial velocity at time $t = t_a$. The straight vertical line from cathode to plate in Fig. 2.3a represents the actual space trajectory. The electron is accelerated through the electric field F that is constant and uniform. The equation of the flight line is obtained by integrating (2–2) twice and is

$$x = -\frac{1}{2}\frac{q_e F}{m_e}(t - t_a)^2 \qquad (2\text{–}10)$$

The constants of integration are zero; the first one because the electron has zero velocity at time $t = t_a$, the second because $x = 0$ at the cathode.

Figure 2.4b is the flight-line diagram, sometimes called an "Applegate" diagram, corresponding to the passage of a steady current of electrons through a field assumed constant and uniform. (The current flow is assumed to be small enough so that space-charge distortion of the field is not important.)

Each of the flight lines in Fig. 2.4b may be thought of as *a line of constant charge*. Thus the electron-borne charge that has passed some

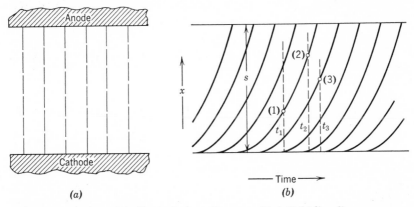

(a)   (b)

FIG. 2.4   (a) A straight-line trajectory diagram. (b) A flight-line diagram, sometimes called an "Applegate" diagram. Both correspond to a steady flow of electrons in an essentially uniform field region between cathode and anode of a planar diode having a d-c plate potential E_s. The electrons leave the cathode with zero initial velocities.

chosen point previous to moment (1) along a given flight line is just the same amount that has passed a farther point previous to a later moment (2) on the same flight line.

The slope of a flight line is proportional to the velocity of electron travel at the point and moment selected for examination. The space rate of change of slope, that is, the flexion, is proportional to the acceleration. The flight lines in Fig. 2.4b are parabolas because the electric field and therefore the acceleration are uniform.

A-c variations of voltage and current may be superposed on the type of motion illustrated in Fig. 2.4. In *small-signal* apparatus, for example, radio receiving devices, the a-c voltages and currents are small relative to the d-c quantities, and the corresponding ultra-high-frequency (uhf) analysis is called a "small-signal" theory.

In ultra-high-frequency (uhf) devices, surveyed briefly in Chapter XI, the *transit time* required for an electron's passage through an interelectrode space, as $t_s - t_a$ in Figs. 2.3 and 2.4, is at least a measurable fraction of the a-c cyclic period, and may be many cycles. In small-signal apparatus the effect on transit time of the a-c voltage variations are not important, so that the transit times are calculated on the basis of the d-c voltages and potential distributions. Thus the *transit angle* in a small-signal uhf device is the transit time for d-c flow expressed in electrical radians or electrical degrees; on this basis, for Fig. 2.4,

$$\text{Transit angle} = 2\pi f(t_s - t_a) \quad \text{[radians]}$$
$$\text{Transit angle} = 360f(t_s - t_a) \quad \text{[electrical degrees]}$$

(2–11)

where f is the frequency of the small uhf signal superposed on the d-c flow.

To determine the transit time for Fig. 2.4, note first that the electric field is uniform; therefore the electrons pursue uniformly accelerated motion. The average velocity between points such as 1 and 2 is, then, *for uniformly accelerated motion,*

$$\text{Average velocity between 1 and 2} = \frac{v_1 + v_2}{2} \quad (2\text{–}12)$$

where v_1 and v_2 are the velocities at points 1 and 2. The electron transit time for passage between points 1 and 2 is of course

$$t_2 - t_1 = \frac{\text{Distance traversed}}{\text{Average velocity}} \quad (2\text{–}13)$$

In Fig. 2.4 the electrons start from rest, and each traverses a distance s, with terminal velocity given by (2–5) as

$$v_s = 5.93 \times 10^5 \sqrt{E_s} \quad \text{[vector]} \quad (2\text{–}14)$$

Use of these facts in (2–12) and (2–13) gives the cathode-to-plate transit time, *in the absence of space charge,* as

$$t_s - t_a = \frac{s}{\frac{1}{2} \times 5.93 \cdot 10^5 \sqrt{E_s}} \quad (2\text{–}15)$$

The same result is obtainable by letting $x = s$, $t = t_s$ in (2–10).

It will be shown in Chapter V that the "space-charge-limited" conditions existing normally in a planar diode create a potential distribution of the nature

$$E = Kx^{4/3} \quad \text{[scalar]} \quad (2\text{–}16)$$

where K is a constant dependent on current density. Therefore, for the Fig. 2.4 arrangement, E_s would be given by

$$E_s = Ks^{4/3} \quad \text{[scalar]} \quad (2\text{–}17)$$

The electron transit time, if subject to (2–16), can be found by integrating the following form of (2–5):

$$dt = \frac{1}{5.93 \cdot 10^5 \sqrt{E}} dx \qquad (2\text{–}18)$$

with (2–16) used for E; integration is carried out between $x = 0$, $t = t_a$ at the cathode, and $x = s$, $t = t_s$ at the anode. The constant K is eliminated by using (2–17). The result is

$$t_s - t_a = \frac{s}{\frac{1}{3} \times 5.93 \cdot 10^5 \sqrt{E_s}} \qquad (2\text{–}19)$$

Thus in the usual space-charge-limited (2–16) condition, the electron transit time is half again as large as that in (2–15) for the space-charge-free condition.

For a planar triode or a multigrid tube, as for example Fig. 1.6, the electron transit time from cathode to control grid is found in the same way as between cathode and anode of a planar diode. The cathode-to-first-grid spacing is used for s, and the equivalent grid sheet potential E_{s1} for E_s, in (2–19).

In determining the transit times or transit angles for planar triodes and multigrid tubes it is usually permissible to ignore space charge everywhere except between the cathode and the control grid, for reasons discussed in Chapter V. It will be shown later, in connection with (4–97), how to determine the equivalent sheet potentials for a pentode having a potential distribution as in Fig. 1.6. The transit times are then determined by assuming that the electrons pass each grid with the velocity corresponding to the equivalent grid sheet potential at that grid, and that they experience uniformly accelerated motion between grids, also between the last grid and the plate, because in those regions the electric field is essentially uniform. Thus, in (2–12) and (2–13), t_1 and v_1 may symbolize the time and velocity at an electron's passage of the first grid of Fig. 1.6, and t_2 and v_2 the time and velocity at passage of the second grid. Then

$$\left.\begin{array}{l}\text{Average velocity between}\\ \text{grids 1 and 2}\end{array}\right\} = 5.93 \cdot 10^5 \left(\frac{\sqrt{E_{s1}} + \sqrt{E_{s2}}}{2} \right) \qquad (2\text{–}20)$$

where E_{s1} and E_{s2} are equivalent grid sheet potentials for the first and second grids.

In cylindrical tubes, the potential distribution is logarithmic; therefore the motion is not uniformly accelerated. Hence precise determination of transit time requires integration of (2–18) in rather difficult form. Frequently, however, it is possible to obtain a quick approximation to transit time by means of a mental estimate of the time-of-flight average of the square root of the potential, which may then be used in (2–13).

2.6   Large-Signal UHF Electron Transit Analysis. [2b, 11C, E, I, N, P]   An important situation related to the operation of *large-signal* uhf electron tubes (see also Chapter XI) is illustrated in Fig. 2.5. The time variation of plate voltage, illustrated in Fig. 2.5b, is of the type

$$e_b = E_b + E_{pm} \cos 2\pi f t \qquad \text{[scalar]} \qquad (2\text{–}21)$$

Here e_b is the instantaneous plate potential, E_b is the d-c component of plate potential (negative in this illustration), and E_{pm} is the maximum value of the sinusoidal a-c component, of frequency f. E_{pm} may be as large as or larger than E_b. Figure 2.5a is a flight-line diagram for this new condition of a uniform but not constant field. Plate spacing is s.

Prior to moment AA in Fig. 2.5a no electrons leave the cathode, because the electric gradient is negative. Between moments AA and BB the rate of electron emergence from the cathode is assumed constant, as indicated by equal spacing of the flight lines at the cathode. Between BB and $A'A'$ there is again no emergence of electrons from the cathode.

To start the determination of the flight-line equation (2–21) is combined with (2–2), and with the fact that $-F = e_b/s$, to give

$$\frac{m_e}{q_e} \frac{d^2 x}{dt^2} = \frac{E_b}{s} + \frac{E_{pm}}{s} \sin 2\pi f t \qquad \text{[vector]} \qquad (2\text{–}22)$$

Separation of variables, and use of v for dx/dt, gives

$$\frac{m_e}{q_e} \int_{v=v_a}^{v=v} dv = \int_{t=t_a}^{t=t} \left(\frac{E_b}{s} + \frac{E_{pm}}{s} \sin 2\pi f t \right) dt \qquad \text{[vector]} \quad (2\text{–}23)$$

The limits of integration represent the beginning point and an indefinite later point *along some one flight line;* thus

The lower limit states conditions at
departure from cathode as
$$\begin{Bmatrix} t = t_a \\ v = v_a \end{Bmatrix} \qquad (2\text{–}24)$$

The upper limit indicates conditions
at some later moment as
$$\begin{Bmatrix} t = t \\ v = v \end{Bmatrix} \qquad (2\text{–}25)$$

In the Fig. 2.5a problem the initial electron velocities are zero, so for all flight-line equations $v_a = 0$. The first integration is straightforward after substituting ω for $2\pi f$, and the result can be expressed

$$v = \frac{dx}{dt} = \frac{q_e}{m_e \omega s}[E_b(\omega t - \omega t_a) - E_{pm}(\cos \omega t - \cos \omega t_a)] \quad (2\text{--}26)$$

Separation of variables for the second integration is easily accomplished; rearrangement prior to the second integration gives

$$\int_{x=0}^{x=x} dx = \frac{q_e}{m_e \omega^2 s}\left[E_b \int_{\omega t = \omega t_a}^{\omega t = \omega t} (\omega t - \omega t_a)d(\omega t - \omega t_a) \right.$$

$$\left. - E_{pm}\int_{\omega t = \omega t_a}^{\omega t = \omega t}(\cos \omega t - \cos \omega t_a)d\omega t \right] \quad (2\text{--}27)$$

This second integration yields

$$\frac{x}{s} = \frac{q_e}{m_e \omega^2 s^2}[\tfrac{1}{2}E_b(\omega t - \omega t_a)^2 + E_{pm}(\omega t - \omega t_a)\cos \omega t_a$$

$$- E_{pm}(\sin \omega t - \sin \omega t_a)] \quad (2\text{--}28)$$

The student should verify this form; the analysis is extended in Chapters IV and V of *Microwave Electron Tubes*.

It is convenient in such an analysis to refer to the quantity t as "clock time," and to the quantity $t - t_a$ as "transit time." Any given point and moment may then be unambiguously characterized in any one of three distinct ways, as follows:

(a) By stating a distance x from the cathode, and a clock time t; or

(b) By stating t_a, the moment of origin of some definite flight line, and the transit time $t - t_a$ to the point and moment to be designated; or,

(c) By stating a clock time t and a transit time $t - t_a$.

Note that in Fig. 2.5:

(1) Moment BB corresponds to a point of inflection on each flight line, because at that moment the electric field, therefore also the acceleration, is zero.

(2) The electrons leaving the cathode later than moment CC do not reach the anode but return to the cathode.

(3) It is not possible in this large-signal case to state a clearly defined single value of "transit time" $(t_s - t_a)$ or "transit angle" $2\pi f(t_s - t_a)$ characterizing in any simple way the time of flight of *all* the electrons, for the complete passage from cathode to plate. Such simple characterization is possible only for a small-signal situation.

(4) The kinetic energy in electron volts possessed by an electron at any point and moment during flight is proportional to its v^2 at that point and moment, and may be very different indeed from the potential at that point and moment relative

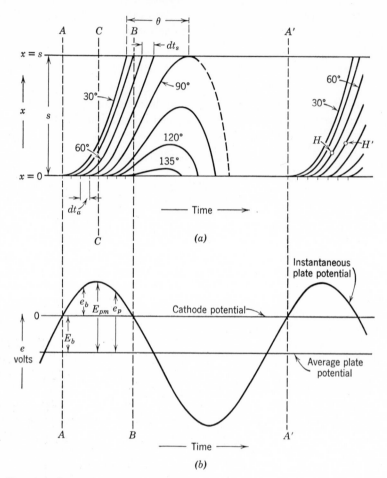

Fig. 2.5 Large-signal long-transit-time electron flow in a planar diode, with uniform electric field between the plates.

(a) Flight-line ("Applegate") diagram, for electron flow subject to the time-varying anode voltage described by (b). The slopes of the flight lines are proportional to electron velocities. Return of some electrons to the cathode with substantial velocities indicates that "back-heating" of the cathode is taking place, the heating being due to the kinetic energies of the returning electrons.

(b) The large-signal ultra-high-frequency voltage applied to the anode, causing the electron motions described by the flight lines in (a).

to the cathode of electron origin. This difference between the potential and the electron-volt energy arises from the fact that the kinetic energy is acquired during flight through a *changing* field, whereas the potential is the line integral of the field as it exists at the stated moment. Similarly, the energy dissipated by an electron on arrival at plate or cathode is proportional to its v^2 at the moment of arrival, and is therefore, from the equations given above, very different indeed from the potential of the electrode at the moment of impact. This is one of the most striking consequences of operation at frequencies such that transit times of individual electrons are substantial fractions of the cyclic period. As an example, the electrons that return to the cathode dive into it with high velocities, as indicated by the slopes of the flight lines. Yet the cathode potential remains constant at zero. Thus the device illustrated in Fig. 2.5 is experiencing *cathode back-heating* due to the return of electrons to the cathode with substantial kinetic energies.

(5) The first electrons to reach the plate arrive with substantially higher velocities than do the later ones.

(6) Although the rate of departure of electrons from the cathode is uniform between AA and BB, their rate of arrival at the plate is highly nonuniform.

The above discussion is based on planar diode geometry, but it applies equally well to the region between cathode and grid of a planar triode. The equivalent grid sheet potential of the triode plays the same part in the triode analysis that plate potential does in the diode analysis. See Chapter XI for brief discussions of some of the consequences of this type of behavior in a triode.

2.7 Analogy between Electron Trajectories and Light-Ray Paths; Electron Optics. There is an important analogy between the laws governing the trajectories of electrons and those governing paths taken by light rays.[14C] Because of this analogy the study of electron trajectories is sometimes called "electron optics." This title is particularly apt in relation to the precise focusing of electron rays in cathode-ray tubes, as surveyed very briefly in Chapter III, and discussed in detail in Chapter II of *Fundamentals of Physical Electronics*, and various other books.[3A, B, C, D, E, F, G, H, I]

A basic law governing passage of a ray of light through refractive media is that the path taken between any two chosen points along a ray is such as to require the least *time* for passage. The similar basic law for electron trajectories is that the path taken between any two chosen points will be such as to involve the least *action*, the quantity action being defined as the line integral of momentum, taken along the path of flight between the beginning and end points.

The analogy may be illustrated by Fig. 2.6, which illustrates passage of an electron ray from one completely field-free region into another similar region, across a boundary consisting of two close and completely penetrable and equipotential surfaces. Figure 2.6a contains vector diagrams of the electron-ray velocity components before and after passing from the E_1 potential region to the E_2 potential region. Since the only electric field experienced between A and B causes a deceleration *solely in the x direction*, the $\sqrt{E_y}$ velocity vectors are identical for the two regions. However, the total velocity vectors

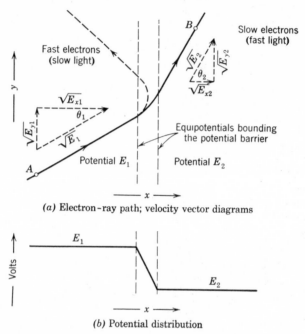

(a) Electron-ray path; velocity vector diagrams

(b) Potential distribution

FIG. 2.6   Deflection of an electron ray by a potential barrier or of a light ray by a change in the velocity of propagation.

must have the values $\sqrt{E_1}$ and $\sqrt{E_2}$. It is therefore apparent that

$$\frac{\sin \theta_2}{\sin \theta_1} = \frac{\sqrt{E_y/E_2}}{\sqrt{E_y/E_1}} = \sqrt{\frac{E_1}{E_2}} \qquad (2\text{--}29)$$

This is precisely the type of formula relating the sines of the angles to the refractive indices in the case of passage of a ray of light from one transparent substance to another, e.g., from water into glass or vice versa.[14B, C]

Note that the electron ray is shown passing from a high-velocity to a low-velocity region; in so doing it is bent *away* from the normal to the surface. The analogous light ray would be bent away from the normal in passing *to* a high-velocity *from* a low-velocity region, as from water into air. If the electrons were to pass from A to B by a straight-line path between these two points, the action, that is, the line integral of momentum, would be greater than along the path shown. This is because they would travel a greater distance at a high velocity, and a less distance at a low velocity, as compared with the actual path taken. This illustrates the "least action" principle.

By way of contrast, suppose that the boundary between fast and slow *light* be thought of as the shore line between a shallow pond on the left and dry land on the right. A man can walk more rapidly on the dry land than in the pond. Therefore a man wishing to walk from A to B in the least time would follow the light-ray type of "trajectory" shown rather than travel a straight-line path from A to B. This illustrates the "least time" principle that governs a light ray.

If the potential difference between E_1 and E_2 were sufficiently great, the electron ray would be reflected, as indicated by the dashed line returning into E_1. Evidently the angle of reflection must equal the angle of incidence, since the value of $\sqrt{E_y}$ is unchanged, and the total velocity is of course unchanged. This again represents agreement with the behavior of a light ray.

The analogy between electron-ray and light-ray behavior can be extended almost indefinitely, limited only by usability rather than theoretical considerations.

2.8 Step-by-Step Trajectory Determination Methods in Electric Fields.[2c, 3A, B, C, D, E] There are a number of step-by-step methods for determining the trajectories of electrons in nonuniform electric fields. The first requirement for any of them is the determination of the configuration of the nonuniform field itself. For two-dimensional fields this can often be done by conformal transformation methods, discussed in Chapter IV. Other methods available include free-hand flux mapping [1A, 7F] (frequently useful when a quick and approximate determination is wanted), electrolytic tank methods,[4b, 2c] and fluid flow mapping techniques.[4c]

One very useful method of step-by-step trajectory determination will be described by reference to Fig. 2.7. Assume that the trajectory has been previously determined through the portion AG, in the field having equipotentials E_1, E_2, E_3, E_4, etc. The plane of the paper contains the trajectory section AG and the electric field vector GM, which is perpendicular to E_2 and to E_3. It is assumed that the trajectory section GB may be sufficiently closely approximated by an arc of a circle. It is desired to determine the radius r of this arc, centered at some point O along the line GHN perpendicular to AG at G.

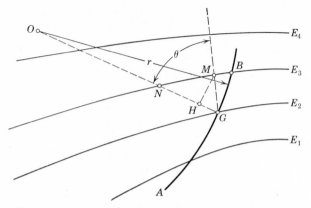

FIG. 2.7   Step-by-step determination of electron trajectory, in a nonuniform electric field, as a succession of arcs of circles between equipotentials.

The inward radial force is of course due to the component of electric field strength in the direction GHN and equals the centrifugal force; thus

$$\frac{m_e v^2}{r} = q_e \frac{E_3 - E_2}{\overline{GM}} \cos \theta \quad \text{[vector]} \quad (2\text{--}30)$$

The average kinetic energy during flight from G to B can be stated

$$\frac{m_e v^2}{2} = \frac{E_3 + E_2}{2} q_e \quad \text{[scalar]} \quad (2\text{--}31)$$

And of course

$$\overline{GM} = \overline{GN} \cos \theta \quad (2\text{--}32)$$

Combination of these three expressions gives

$$r = \frac{E_3 + E_2}{E_3 - E_2} \overline{GN} = \overline{GO} \quad (2\text{--}33)$$

Thus the point O can now be located along GHN, if the potentials are known, and the circular arc GB can be drawn. The process is then repeated with B as a starting point, and so on indefinitely.

Another step-by-step method is based on the assumption, illustrated in Fig. 2.8, that the volume between any two equipotential surfaces is a field-free "equipotential block." The potential of each block is taken as the mean value between the two bounding equipotentials. Thus at passage from one block to the next an electron ray experiences "refraction," similar in nature to that of a light beam in entering a piece of glass.

In Fig. 2.8, an electron ray that approaches along AG at an angle θ_{12} with the normal to E_2 departs at an angle θ_{23}, such that

$$\frac{\sin \theta_{23}}{\sin \theta_{12}} = \frac{\sqrt{E_1 + E_2}}{\sqrt{E_2 + E_3}} \qquad (2\text{-}34)$$

Graphical construction is initiated by striking from G an arc HS of any radius, and extending AG to intersection N on the arc. This determines the length of the normal ND to the line GMS. The line GMS is

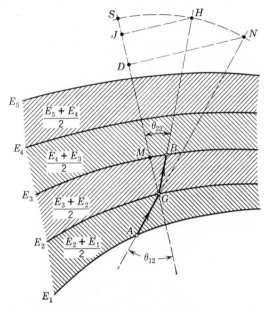

FIG. 2.8 Step-by-step determination of trajectories, in a nonuniform electric field, as a succession of straight lines within equipotential blocks.

perpendicular to the E_2 surface. The direction of the new trajectory section GB is determined by requiring that the normal HJ to GMS be related to ND as follows:

$$\frac{\overline{HJ}}{\overline{ND}} = \frac{\overline{GH} \sin \theta_{23}}{\overline{GN} \sin \theta_{12}} = \sqrt{\frac{E_1 + E_2}{E_2 + E_3}} \qquad (2\text{-}35)$$

The process may then be repeated from B as a starting point.

For both these step-by-step methods the zero of potential must be chosen so that the electron ray has zero velocity at the equipotential for which $E = 0$.

2.9 Mass: A Property Due to Electric and Magnetic Fields.[1C, D, 1F–176]

The electric field between the plates of a condenser represents storage of energy; so also does the electric field due to its own charge that surrounds an electron. Likewise the magnetic field that surrounds a moving electron represents energy storage, in a form similar to that in an inductance carrying a current.

Mass is a manifestation of energy; the interdependence is indicated by the equation

$$m_e = \frac{W_e}{c^2} \tag{2–36}$$

which relates the electron's mass m_e to the energy storage W_e (joules) in its electric field. c is the velocity of light, 3×10^8. If the charge on an electron is assumed to be distributed uniformly over a hollow sphere of radius a,

$$W_e = \frac{\text{Charge} \times \text{Potential}}{2} = \frac{1}{2} \times q_e \times \frac{q_e}{4\pi\epsilon_0 a} = \frac{q_e^2}{8\pi\epsilon_0 a} \tag{2–37}$$

On combining the last two equations, and introducing numerical values for m_e, q_e, c, and ϵ_0, the radius is found to be about

$$a = 1.4 \times 10^{-15} \quad [\text{meter}] \tag{2–38}$$

It is very unlikely that the charge on an electron is distributed uniformly around a spherical shell, so that (2–37) cannot be more than a first approximation to the true expression relating dimensions to energy storage.

2.10 Increase of Electron Mass at Large Velocities.[3k, 1C, D, 1F–176]

The energy stored in a moving electron's magnetic field also contributes to its mass. In general, then, the total mass m of an electron is

$$m = \frac{W_e}{c^2} + \frac{W_m}{c^2} \quad [\text{scalar}] \tag{2–39}$$

where W_m is the magnetic energy storage. At standstill there is no magnetic field, so that W_m is zero; only W_e/c^2 remains. Hence m_e, which was identified with W_e/c^2 in the preceding paragraph, is called the "rest mass" of an electron.

If an electron's velocity approaches that of light, as happens in some engineering devices, the contribution of the magnetic term W_m/c^2 is not negligible. Determination of mass at these high velocities starts with the observation that in all cases W_m is the stored-up form of the kinetic energy Eq_e acquired by the electron in traversing the potential difference E of an accelerating field.   That is,

$$\frac{W_m}{c^2} = \frac{Eq_e}{c^2} \qquad \text{[scalar]} \tag{2-40}$$

The electron's mass can therefore be expressed as

$$m = m_e + \frac{Eq_e}{c^2} \qquad \text{[scalar]} \tag{2-41}$$

Since the rest mass m_e is a constant,

$$\frac{dm}{dt} = \frac{d}{dt}\left(\frac{Eq_e}{c^2}\right) = \frac{1}{c^2}\frac{d}{dt}(Eq_e) \qquad \text{[scalar]} \tag{2-42}$$

But the rate of change of energy $d(Eq_e)/dt$ is power, and the power input to the electron is the accelerating force f times the velocity, so that

$$\frac{dm}{dt} = \frac{fv}{c^2} \qquad \text{[scalar]} \tag{2-43}$$

When acting on a particle of changing mass, force is rate of change of momentum; therefore

$$\frac{dm}{dt} = \frac{v}{c^2}\frac{d(mv)}{dt} \qquad \text{or} \qquad dm = \frac{v}{c}d\left(\frac{mv}{c}\right) \tag{2-44}$$

If the indicated differentiation is carried out, and the resulting expression is separated according to the variables m and v/c and integrated with an integration constant $\ln A$, there results

$$\ln m = \ln \frac{1}{\sqrt{1 - (v^2/c^2)}} + \ln A \tag{2-45}$$

or

$$m = \frac{m_e}{\sqrt{1 - (v^2/c^2)}} \tag{2-46}$$

for, when $v = 0$, $m = m_e = A$.   Thus the electron's mass approaches an infinite value as its velocity approaches that of light.

If an electron that has already acquired a high velocity is introduced into an electric field, its acceleration is obtained from an equation between the field force and the rate of change of momentum.   Mathematically,

$$f = \frac{d}{dt}(mv_f) \qquad \text{[vector]} \tag{2-47}$$

where v_f is the velocity in the direction of the force. The electron's mass m is dependent on its total velocity v. It is convenient to treat two distinct conditions: (a) the electric field is perpendicular to the direction of the electron's initial motion; and (b) the electric field is in the direction of the initial motion.

In the first case the added velocity, being a differential increment normal to the original, does not change the total velocity, for the vector resulting from the addition of a very small velocity at right angles to a very large one has the same length as the large one (see Fig. 2.9a).

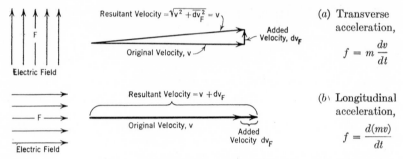

FIG. 2.9 Transverse and longitudinal acceleration of a high-velocity electron.

Hence the mass remains constant at the value given by (2–46), and (2–47) becomes

$$f = \frac{m_e}{\sqrt{1 - (v^2/c^2)}} \frac{dv_f}{dt} \quad \text{[vector]} \quad (2\text{--}48)$$

This has the general form, force = mass × acceleration, and gives rise to the name "transverse mass," m_t, of value

$$m_t = \frac{m_e}{\sqrt{1 - (v^2/c^2)}} \quad \text{[scalar]} \quad (2\text{--}49)$$

which must be used in determining a high-speed electron's acceleration in a direction normal to its existing motion.

In the second case the change in velocity adds its full value to the existing velocity, for the very small vector is added as an extension to a very large one (see Fig. 2.9b); dv_f becomes simply dv, and, since m is now affected by the change in total velocity, the time derivative of the momentum contains dv/dt in one term, dm/dt in the other. The force expression simplifies to

$$f = \frac{m_e}{[1 - (v^2/c^2)]^{3/2}} \frac{dv}{dt} \quad \text{[vector]} \quad (2\text{--}50)$$

which gives rise to the concept "longitudinal mass," m_l, of value

$$m_l = \frac{m_e}{[1 - (v^2/c^2)]^{3/2}} \quad \text{[scalar]} \quad (2\text{-}51)$$

The longitudinal mass is of academic interest only. Calculations of the nature suggested by the name are accomplished by setting up an expression similar to (2–4) but more general in application. The expression $v = ds/dt$, in which ds stands for a differential increment of distance, can be rearranged to read $dt = ds/v$, and this value of dt substituted into (2–50). Both sides can then be integrated, the left side (in the form $q_e F\, ds$) with respect to distance, the right side with respect to velocity; there is no constant of integration if the electron is considered to be initially at rest. The result is [3k]

$$Eq_e = m_e c^2 \left[\frac{1}{\sqrt{1 - (v^2/c^2)}} - 1 \right] \quad \text{[scalar]} \quad (2\text{-}52)$$

For velocities small enough so that $(v/c) \ll 1$, a binomial expansion reduces (2–52) to (2–4).

Equation (2–52) can be rearranged into the form

$$\sqrt{1 - \frac{v^2}{c^2}} = \frac{1}{1 + (Eq_e/m_e c^2)} \quad (2\text{-}53)$$

or, numerically,

$$\sqrt{1 - \frac{v^2}{c^2}} = \frac{1}{1 + (E/511{,}000)} \quad (2\text{-}54)$$

If this expression is solved for v, it gives the velocity as a function of the accelerating potential, as follows:

$$v = c \sqrt{1 - \frac{1}{[1 + (E/511{,}000)]^2}} \quad \text{[vector]} \quad (2\text{-}55)$$

Equation (2–54) also permits expression of the transverse mass, which must be used in estimating response to magnetic or transverse electric fields, in terms of the accelerating potential, in the following form:

$$m_t = \frac{m_e}{\sqrt{1 - (v^2/c^2)}} = m_e \left(1 + \frac{E}{511{,}000} \right) \quad (2\text{-}56)$$

This equation indicates that the percentage of increase in transverse mass is directly proportional to the accelerating voltage; an electron that has been accelerated through a potential difference of 51,000 volts has a mass 10 per cent greater than its rest mass. These relations have been demonstrated experimentally.

2.11 Force on an Electron Moving in a Magnetic Field. A moving electron is a form of electric current and, like a conductor carrying a current, experiences in a magnetic field a force perpendicular to the field and to the direction of movement of charge. The force f on an electron having velocity v, in a field of magnetic flux density B (webers per square meter) perpendicular to the velocity, is the vector product of these two mutually perpendicular vectors. For this simple situation

$$f = -Bq_e v \quad \begin{bmatrix} \text{newtons, a vector perpendicular} \\ \text{to both } B \text{ and } v \end{bmatrix} \quad (2\text{·}57)$$

This is closely related to the familiar expression

$$f = Bil \quad (2\text{–}58)$$

which describes the force on a conductor l meters long carrying i amperes at right angles to the field. For if the conductor contains, in each meter of length, N electrons that are free to travel, and if their average velocity of electron advance is v, (2–57) requires that the force on the l meters of conductor length shall be

$$\text{Force on the wire} = -Bq_e v(Nl) = B(-Nq_e v)l \quad (2\text{–}59)$$

This is identical with (2–58), for $-Nq_e v$ is the current i.

The directional sense of the magnetic force on an electron is obtained by the same method used for determining the direction of the force on a conductor in a magnetic field, bearing in mind that an upward-moving electron corresponds to a downward-flowing current. As illustrated in Fig. 2.10, an upward motion of the electrons in a magnetic field whose flux lines are pointed toward the reader results in a force toward the left; this is in accord with the minus sign in (2–57), for a right-handed coordinate system as illustrated in Fig. 2.17.

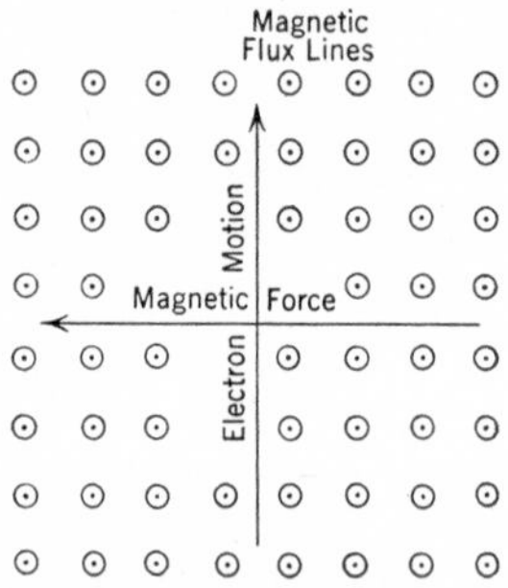

FIG. 2.10 Direction of magnetic force on a moving electron.

In a great many problems no ambiguity results from failing to carry along the minus sign in (2–57), because physical considerations can always be used to determine the direction of the force.

2.12 Path Circular or Helical in a Uniform Magnetic Field; the Larmor Angular Velocity. The force on and acceleration of an electron in a magnetic field are at every instant at right angles to the existing velocity; therefore, the total velocity remains constant. If the magnetic field is uniform, the acceleration normal to the velocity is of constant magnitude. The simultaneous existence of constant linear electron velocity and uniform electron acceleration at right angles to the direction of motion requires travel in a circular path.

If the original velocity is not normal to the direction of the field, the *velocity component parallel to the field* is not affected either in direction or magnitude, while the *velocity component normal to the field* continually changes direction, remaining constant in magnitude. The resulting path is a helix combining uniform circular motion with translation parallel to the axis of rotation.

Equations for the circular motion are derived by equating centripetal force to the magnetic force. If r is the radius of the circle,

$$\frac{m_e v^2}{r} = Bq_e v \qquad \text{[vector product of two vectors]} \qquad (2\text{--}60)$$

or

$$r = \frac{m_e}{q_e}\frac{v}{B} \qquad \text{[vector ratio of two vectors]} \qquad (2\text{--}61)$$

This equation permits expression of the radius in terms of the electron's kinetic energy, E_v electron volts, and the flux density; thus,

$$r = \frac{9.11 \cdot 10^{-31} \times 5.93 \cdot 10^5 \; \sqrt{E_v}}{1.602 \cdot 10^{-19} \qquad B} = 3.37 \times 10^{-6} \frac{\sqrt{E_v}}{B} \qquad (2\text{--}62)$$

This expresses the very great sensitivity of an electron's motion to magnetic fields.

The radius of the path for heavier particles having the same energy is larger in proportion to the *square root* of the mass ratio; this fact is made use of in the determination of the masses of particles of atomic magnitude in the mass spectrograph, and for isotope separation.

Angular velocity ω (radians per second) in the circular path is v/r; on substituting this in (2–61) it appears that

$$\omega = \frac{Bq_e}{m_e} = 1.76 \times 10^{11} B \qquad \begin{bmatrix} \text{cyclotron angular velocity,} \\ \text{radians per second, for an} \\ \text{electron} \end{bmatrix} \qquad (2\text{--}63)$$

The quantity Bq_e/m is sometimes called the "cyclotron angular velocity" because as applied to ions it is the angular velocity in the cyclotron type of nuclear particle accelerator (see Prob. 13, page 61). Equation (2–63) indicates that for an electron the angular velocity depends only on the magnetic field strength and not at all on the electron's linear velocity; it also gives the angular velocity around the axis of the helix, in case of helical motion. The *Larmor* angular velocity ω_l, frequently employed in atomic physics, is just half the cyclotron angular velocity, that is,

$$\omega_l = \frac{Bq_e}{2m_e} = 0.88 \times 10^{11}B \qquad \begin{bmatrix} \text{Larmor angular} \\ \text{velocity, radians} \\ \text{per second} \end{bmatrix} \qquad (2\text{-}64)$$

For high-energy electrons, the transverse mass is used in these equations.

2.13   Electron Motion in the Presence of Uniform Electric and Magnetic Fields at Right Angles.[1F]   Figure 2.11 illustrates a region containing a uniform electric field and a uniform magnetic field, the two being at right angles to one another. The magnetic flux lines are directed toward the reader, that is, in the $+z$ direction. If an electron beam is shot upward from the gun, the magnetic field tends to deflect it toward the left, the magnetic force on each electron being given by (2-57). The electric field exerts an oppositely directed force, its magnitude given by (2-1).

If these two forces are equal, the electrons of the beam are not deflected, and they travel vertically with constant velocity, just as though neither field were present. The conditions for no deflection are obtained by equating the two force expressions, with the following result:

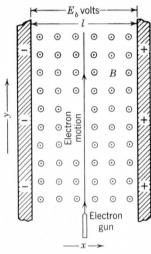

FIG. 2.11   Straight-line electron motion with balanced uniform electric and magnetic fields.

$$Bv = -F \qquad \text{[vector product of two vectors]} \qquad (2\text{-}65)$$

In the above illustration the electrons have been thought of as moving upward with constant velocity, and the magnetic field as standing still. It is reasonable to expect that the important matter is the relative velocity between the two, and such a point of view leads to a correct prediction of the motion. If the magnetic field is made to move downward with a velocity v, related to B and F according to (2-65), an electron released into the field with zero velocity must stand still; the stationary electric and moving magnetic fields completely neutralize one another.

It is more in accord with the usual presentation of electromagnetic theory to say that the motion of the magnetic field "generates" an electric field equal and opposite to that already existing, that is, of value

$$F_{gen} = +Bv \quad \text{[vector]} \quad (2\text{-}66)$$

and that the electron stands still because the net electric field is zero. Because the electron's velocity is zero, the magnetic field exerts no force; the effect of the motion of the magnetic field itself has been taken account of in terms of a "generated electric field." The "generated voltage" E_{gen} over the entire region between the plates, their separation being l, is of course $-F_{gen}l$, that is

$$E_{gen} = -Blv \quad \text{[scalar product of the vectors } l \text{ and } Bv] \quad (2\text{-}67)$$

In cgs units, with B in gausses and E_{gen} in volts, this is the familiar relation

$$E_{gen} = -Blv \times 10^{-8} \quad \text{[scalar]} \quad (2\text{-}68)$$

Thus the relative motion between magnetic field and electron needed to avoid movement in response to the applied electric field is exactly that needed to generate a voltage numerically equal to E_{gen} in a wire stretched from one electrode to the other. The internal electric field produced by the moving magnetic field is the exact analogue of the generated voltage, sometimes called "back voltage" or "counter electromotive force," in a d-c motor. The electron's motion is zero when the generated field is equal to the applied field, for exactly the same reason that the armature current in a motor is zero when the generated voltage is equal to the applied voltage.

2.14 Cycloidal and Trochoidal Motion.[2d, e, 1F] In general, for fields as illustrated in Fig. 2.11, an electron's initial velocity is not such as to make the opposing electric and magnetic forces equal and opposite, and the electron pursues some sort of curved path. The type of motion in any particular case can be predicted by recognizing that it must be a composite of (a) the motion necessary to counteract magnetically the electric force and (b) circular or helical motion as produced by the magnetic field alone.

Suppose the magnetic field of Fig. 2.11 to be moving vertically downward with just the velocity necessary to generate a "back" field equal and opposite to the applied field; the velocity must be as given by (2-65). If now an electron is introduced with some initial velocity, it will pursue a circular path, for the motion of the magnetic field just destroys the effect of the applied electric field; only the normal effect of velocity in a magnetic field remains. The relative motion between the electron and the magnetic field is now a composite of circular and translational types.

A case of particular interest is that in which the circular motion has the same velocity as the translational, both having the balanced-force value

$$v = -\frac{F}{B} \qquad \text{[vector ratio of two vectors]} \qquad (2\text{--}69)$$

The radius of the circular motion is obtained by using this in (2–61); it is

$$r = \frac{m_e}{q_e}\frac{F}{B^2} = \frac{F}{\omega B} \qquad (2\text{--}70)$$

The angular velocity ω produced by the magnetic field is independent of the electron's linear velocity and is given by (2–63).

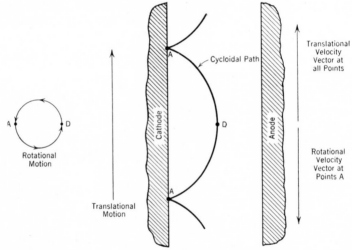

Fig. 2.12 Cycloidal path of an electron in uniform electric and magnetic fields; zero initial velocity.

Now suppose that an observer rides with the moving magnetic field. Not being conscious of his own downward motion, he thinks the electron is moving upward. To him it appears to have circular motion superposed on straight-line upward travel of equal velocity, with resultant cycloidal motion of the type illustrated in Fig. 2.12. The cusps at points A indicate periodic recurrence of zero relative velocity, owing to the two relative-velocity components being momentarily equal and opposite.

Only the relative motion has significance. Therefore the electron's movement relative to the observer and to the magnetic field must be the same whether they are moving or stationary. Thus the cycloid in Fig. 2.12 also illustrates the path pursued by an electron released with zero initial velocity into a stationary combined field. The point of release is the first of the periodically recurring points A.

Such a path as is illustrated in Fig. 2.12 would be traced by a point on the rim of a wheel, of radius given by (2–62), rolling along the plane surface (cathode) from which the electron is initially released. The center of the wheel translates at just the velocity, given by (2–69), necessary to counteract magnetically the electric force due to the applied field.

If the electron's initial velocity is not zero, its path may be that traced by the end of a spoke that either extends beyond or fails to reach the rim of the wheel, which must have the same radius and roll at the same speed as before. See Fig. 2.13. There are several distinct steps in the prediction of the type of motion that must result from specified values of field strength and initial velocity, as follows:

(a) The translational velocity, the radius to rim of the rolling wheel, and the angular velocity are all independent of the electron's initial velocity, and so are determined exactly as in the simpler case of zero initial velocity.

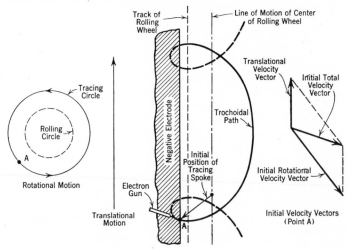

Fig. 2.13   Trochoidal path of an electron in uniform electric and magnetic fields, initial velocity not zero.

(b) As illustrated for the start-off point A, Fig. 2.13, the initial magnitude and direction of the circular velocity component must be such that vector combination of it with the translational velocity gives the initial velocity whose direction and magnitude are specified in the statement of the problem.

(c) The length L of the spoke that traces the path is determined from the general relation $\omega = v/L$, where ω is known from (a) and v is the circular velocity, whose magnitude remains constant at the initial value found as described in (b). The initial position of the tracing spoke is, of course, perpendicular to the initial circular-velocity vector.

(d) The far end of the initial position of the spoke identifies the position of the line of motion of the rolling wheel's center. Since the radius to the rim is known, the track can be located and the path graphically or mathematically constructed.

In the simple cycloidal motion of Fig. 2.12, for any given electrode spacing there is a particular value of magnetic field strength that makes the electrons just graze a plate surface located parallel to the cathode. The kinetic energy at the outer extreme, D in the figure, is all due to vertical velocity of twice the translational value, for at this point the circular and translational motions are equal in direction as well as in magnitude. The electric field strength can be expressed as E_b/s, where s is the spacing between the plates, and E_b the plate potential. The resulting cut-off relation between voltage, spacing, and field strength necessary to produce grazing contact at the plate surface is

$$E_b = \frac{q_e}{2m_e} B^2 s^2 \qquad \text{[cut-off, planar geometry]} \qquad (2\text{--}71)$$

If the magnetic field is weaker than this, all electrons originating at the cathode enter the plate; if stronger than this, no electrons enter the plate.

The relations derived above can be obtained without recourse to the relative-velocity imagery by solving the following pair of differential equations of the electron's motion: [2d, 1C, 1F-238]

$$m_e \frac{d^2x}{dt^2} = -Bq_e \frac{dy}{dt} + q_e F \qquad \text{[vector]} \qquad (2\text{--}72)$$

$$m_e \frac{d^2y}{dt^2} = +Bq_e \frac{dx}{dt} \qquad \text{[vector]} \qquad (2\text{--}73)$$

Here t is time, and x and y are horizontal and vertical coordinates, all measured from the instant and point of electron release or ejection. For zero initial velocity, Fig. 2.12, dx/dt and dy/dt are both zero when t is zero. The results of the solution for this case are

$$x = \frac{F}{\omega B} (1 - \cos \omega t) \qquad (2\text{--}74)$$

$$y = \frac{F}{\omega B} (\omega t - \sin \omega t) \qquad (2\text{--}75)$$

where ω is given by (2-63).

2.15   Motion in Combined Fields at Any Angle.[1F–238]   To determine
an electron's motion subject to a uniform electric field F and a uniform
magnetic field B not at right angles to one another, resolve F into two
components respectively parallel and perpendicular to B. The component of F parallel to B will impart uniformly accelerated motion
parallel to B, acceleration as given by (2–2); the magnetic field will
have no effect on that motion. The projection of the trajectory on a
plane perpendicular to B will be a cycloid or trochoid, just as described
in the preceding section. Of course the component of F normal to B
must be used in the equations determining the trochoidal motion.

**2.16   Magnetic Cut-Off, for Motion between Concentric Cylinders
with Axial Magnetic Field.**[2f] Cylindrical electrode arrangements remotely similar to that shown in Fig. 2.14 are used as uhf "magnetron
oscillators," surveyed briefly in Section 11.9.*   In this figure the
magnetic field is uniform and parallel to the axis. If the cathode radius
is small relative to that of the anode, an electron released at the cathode
without initial velocity pursues an approximately circular path and
returns ultimately to the cathode, as shown. The reason for this is
that except in the near neighborhood of the cathode the linear velocity
is nearly constant. Figure 2.14b illustrates the variation of potential
in such a region (no space charge), and Fig. 2.14c the corresponding
variation in total velocity. There is a very rapid growth of velocity
in the near neighborhood of the cathode, but after the electron emerges
from that region its velocity, therefore also the radius of curvature of
its path, changes very little. Over most of the trajectory the velocity
is very nearly that corresponding to anode potential E_b.

Such a device is said to be in the cut-off condition when the relation
between magnetic field strength B, anode potential E_b, and tube
geometry is such as to cause the circular trajectory just to graze the
anode.[2f]   An approximate relation between these quantities for the
cut-off condition is obtained by observing that the radius given by
(2–61) must then be $r_p/2$, and that the velocity appearing in (2–61) is
obtained by using in (2–5) the potential E_b. The approximate relation
so obtained is

$$E_b \cong \frac{q_e}{8m_e} B^2 r_p{}^2 \qquad \text{[at magnetic cut-off]} \qquad (2\text{--}76)$$

This indicates that, if for given values of r_p and B the anode potential
E_b is less than the (2–76) value, no electrons will reach the anode. If
E_b is greater than the (2–76) value, all electrons will strike and enter

* Electron behavior in magnetron oscillator tubes is discussed in detail in Chapter
VIII of *Microwave Electron Tubes*, and in various other books.[11C, D, I, P]

the anode. Thus in an ideal case the cut-off relation represents a sharp discontinuity in plate current as a function of plate voltage. Equation (2–76) is reasonably accurate if the cathode radius is very small relative to the anode radius; (2–92) is the complete expression.

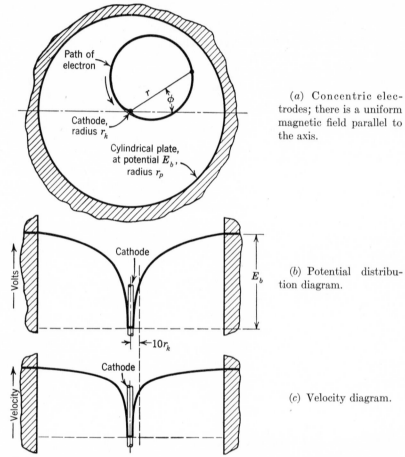

(a) Concentric electrodes; there is a uniform magnetic field parallel to the axis.

(b) Potential distribution diagram.

(c) Velocity diagram.

🔲 Fig. 2.14 Approximately circular path of an electron that originates with zero initial velocity at the surface of a small-diameter cathode, in a region having a radial electric field and a uniform axially directed magnetic field.

2.17 Inertial-Force Equations in Cylindrical Geometry. For a rectangular coordinate system the inertial reactions of an electron to any force on it, whether electric or magnetic, are expressed by the following familiar forms:

$$x\text{-directed force} = m_e \frac{d^2x}{dt^2} \qquad (2\text{-}77a)$$

$$y\text{-directed force} = m_e \frac{d^2 y}{dt^2} \qquad (2\text{-}77b)$$

$$z\text{-directed force} = m_e \frac{d^2 z}{dt^2} \qquad (2\text{-}77c)$$

In considering an electron's motion in cylindrical coordinates, as in Fig. 1.12 and Fig. 2.14, it is desirable to have in mind the similar inertial-force equations for such coordinates. The relations are

$$\text{Outward radial force} = m_e \frac{d^2 r}{dt^2} - m_e r \left(\frac{d\phi}{dt} \right)^2 \qquad (2\text{-}78)$$

$$\text{Tangential force} = m_e \frac{1}{r} \frac{d}{dt} \left(r^2 \frac{d\phi}{dt} \right) \qquad (2\text{-}79)$$

$$\text{Axially directed force} = m_e \frac{d^2 z}{dt^2} \qquad (2\text{-}80)$$

The first of these is familiar in that it contains a centrifugal-force term, in addition to the $d^2 r/dt^2$ term.

To verify the tangential-force equation, note first that torque (or, more correctly, the moment of the force) is the time rate of change of angular momentum, just as force is the time rate of change of linear momentum; that is,

$$\text{Moment of the force} = \frac{d \text{ (Angular momentum)}}{dt}$$

$$= \frac{\begin{Bmatrix} d \text{ (Moment of inertia} \\ \times \text{ Angular velocity)} \end{Bmatrix}}{dt} \qquad (2\text{-}81)$$

This may be written

$$r \times \text{Tangential force} = \frac{d}{dt} \left(m_e r^2 \frac{d\phi}{dt} \right) \qquad (2\text{-}82)$$

which rearranges immediately into (2–79). Here, of course,

$$m_e r^2 = \text{Moment of inertia of the electron at radius } r \qquad (2\text{-}83)$$

and angular velocity is $d\phi/dt$.

Note that in rotary motion, such as is here being implied, the term *acceleration* is defined as a ratio of force to mass, *not* as a velocity component's time derivative. Thus the *radial acceleration is not* $d^2 r/dt^2$ *but is* (*2–78*) *divided by* m_e; similarly tangential acceleration is (2–79) divided by m_e. Thus radial *acceleration*, being defined in terms of force, can be described relative to the acceleration due to gravity (so many g's), even though the motion is purely tangential, as in a centrifuge.

2.18   The Complete Equation for Magnetic Cut-Off. The complete equation for magnetic cut-off is obtained by integration of the tangential-force relation (2–79) in the geometry of Fig. 2.14. Because the electric field is wholly radial, there will be no electric field component of the tangential force. There will, however, be a tangential magnetic force on the electron, given by

$$\text{Tangential magnetic force} = Bq_e \frac{dr}{dt} \qquad (2\text{–}84)$$

The tangential magnetic and inertial forces must be equal; therefore, from (2–79) and (2–84)

$$Bq_e r \frac{dr}{dt} = m_e \frac{d}{dt}\left(r^2 \frac{d\phi}{dt}\right) \qquad (2\text{–}85)$$

which can also be stated

$$\frac{Bq_e}{2m_e} \frac{dr^2}{dt} = \frac{d}{dt}\left(r^2 \frac{d\phi}{dt}\right) \qquad (2\text{–}86)$$

After canceling a dt, this can be integrated into

$$\frac{Bq_e r^2}{2m_e} = r^2 \frac{d\phi}{dt} + \text{Constant} \qquad (2\text{–}87)$$

For an electron starting with zero velocity from the cathode:

$$\text{When } r = r_k, \frac{d\phi}{dt} = 0 \qquad (2\text{–}88)$$

With the integration constant evaluated by means of this boundary condition, (2–87) becomes

$$\frac{d\phi}{dt} = \frac{Bq_e}{2m_e}(r^2 - r_k{}^2) \qquad (2\text{–}89)$$

The tangential kinetic-energy equation, for any radius, is

$$\text{Tangential kinetic energy} = \frac{1}{2}m_e r^2 \left(\frac{d\phi}{dt}\right)^2 = E_\phi q_e \qquad (2\text{–}90)$$

where E_ϕ is defined as the kinetic energy in electron volts associated with the electron's tangential motion. Elimination of $d\phi/dt$ between the last two equations leads to

$$E_\phi = \frac{q_e}{8m_e} B^2 r^2 \left(1 - \frac{r_k{}^2}{r^2}\right)^2 \qquad (2\text{–}91)$$

This is a rather remarkable relation, of very great importance in the theory of magnetron oscillators. It implies that the electron's tangential kinetic energy is a function only of the magnetic field strength and the radial position and *is completely independent of the electric field*, if any exists, as long as there is no tangential electric field component.

At the grazing point of an electron's trajectory, Fig. 2.14, all the kinetic energy is due to tangential motion, and the kinetic energy in electron volts is just the anode potential. Therefore the complete equation for magnetic cut-off is obtained by using r_p for r, and E_b for E_ϕ, in (2–91), and is

$$E_b = \frac{q_e}{8m_e} B^2 r_p{}^2 \left(1 - \frac{r_k{}^2}{r_p{}^2}\right)^2 \qquad \begin{bmatrix} \text{the complete equation} \\ \text{for magnetic cut-off} \end{bmatrix} \quad (2\text{–}92)$$

Because E_ϕ, and therefore E_b for cut-off, is independent of the detail nature of the radial electric field, this cut-off equation is equally valid whether space charge is present or not, except that the space charge must have an axially symmetric distribution.

2.19   Trajectory Types in a Space-Charge-Free Cylindrical Magnetron.   Figure 2.15 illustrates a geometry to which the inertial equations (2–78) and (2–79) apply because it is a cylindrical system.   A d-c

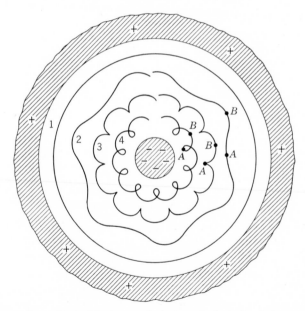

FIG. 2.15   Several possible types of electron trajectories between concentric cylinders, magnetic field parallel to the axis, outer cylinder electrically positive. Electrons initially introduced at any arbitrary location and velocity, as by means of an electron gun. This physical arrangement is sometimes called a smooth-bore cylindrical diode magnetron.

potential difference is applied between the inner and outer electrodes, and a magnetic field is established parallel to the axis. The inner electrode is not a cathode, because electrons are introduced at an arbitrary location and velocity, as from an electron gun. The differential equation (2–86) applies, but the (2–88) boundary condition does not apply; thus the constant of integration is not that incorporated

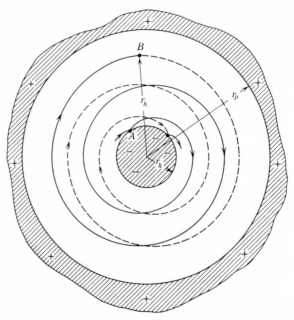

Fig. 2.16 Out-and-in spiral electron motion in a structure like that of Fig. 2.15, magnetic field parallel to axis. Period of local out-and-in motion many times that of circulation around the axis. This motion is indicated as originating in a cusp at a central cathode; thus the motion resembles trajectory (3) of Fig. 2.15 more nearly than any of the others.

into (2–89). Thus (2–89), and therefore also (2–91), does not apply to the Fig. 2.15 situation, at least not with the meaning given them in relation to Fig. 2.14.

The setting up and solution of the differential equations for the type of motion illustrated in Fig. 2.15 are carried out in Chapter VIII of *Microwave Electron Tubes*. The types of trajectories indicated by the solution are shown in the figure. The (1) trajectory is a circle concentric with the axis; the (2), (3), and (4) trajectories have local generally rotational motions superposed on a circulation around the axis. There exists here a family resemblance to the linear, trochoidal, and cycloidal motions described in connection with Figs. 2.12 and 2.13. If the period of the local rotational motion becomes long relative to that of the circulatory motion, an out-and-in spiral motion occurs; see Fig. 2.16. The local rotational motions in Fig. 2.15 are not truly circular.

2.20 Motions in Irregular Space-Varying Fields. In any space-varying combination of electric and magnetic fields, an *electron* obeys the following general differential equations of motion:

$$\frac{d^2x}{dt^2} = \frac{q_e}{m_e}\left[+\frac{\partial E}{\partial x} - \left(B_z\frac{dy}{dt} - B_y\frac{dz}{dt}\right)\right] \qquad (2\text{--}93a)$$

$$\frac{d^2y}{dt^2} = \frac{q_e}{m_e}\left[+\frac{\partial E}{\partial y} - \left(B_x\frac{dz}{dt} - B_z\frac{dx}{dt}\right)\right] \qquad (2\text{--}93b)$$

$$\frac{d^2z}{dt^2} = \frac{q_e}{m_e}\left[+\frac{\partial E}{\partial z} - \left(B_y\frac{dx}{dt} - B_x\frac{dy}{dt}\right)\right] \qquad (2\text{--}93c)$$

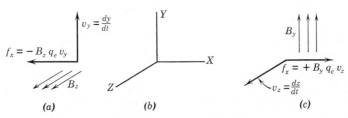

Fig. 2.17 Rectangular-coordinate forces, showing sense relations, on an *electron* moving in a magnetic field, illustrating the equation

$$m_e\frac{dx^2}{dt^2} = -q_e\left(B_z\frac{dy}{dt} - B_y\frac{dz}{dt}\right)$$

(a) Force component *to the left*, due to forward flux and upward velocity components; compare Fig. 2.10.

(b) The right-handed coordinate system used.

(c) Force component *to the right*, due to upward flux and forward velocity components.

where B_x, B_y, and B_z are the components of the magnetic flux density; see Fig. 2.17 for sense relations. Some methods of solution are dealt with in Chapter II, on Electron Optics, in *Fundamentals of Physical Electronics*.

It is important to bear in mind that passage through a magnetic field neither adds to nor subtracts from an electron's linear velocity; the magnetic field does no work on the electron.

PROBLEMS

1. The average thermal-motion kinetic energy of air molecules at 40° C is 0.0675 electron volt (from Section 7.3). Three-fifths of this energy is due to translational motion, the remainder to rotation and vibration of the dumbbell-like molecules. Find the velocity of a molecule (N_2) of nitrogen (atomic weight in Table II) having the average 40° C translational energy. (This is the rms, not average, velocity; see Chapter XII.)

2. In Fig. 2.1, $s = 0.025$ meter, $E_s = 50$; plates are infinite in extent. State where, with what velocity components, and after what time electrons strike one or the other electrode if the gun shoots 100-volt electrons at angles with horizontal of (a) 30°, (b) 45°, (c) 60°, (d) 90°.

3. In Fig. 2.2, an electron with zero initial velocity starts from a cathode point almost but not quite opposite a grid-wire center, and so experiences considerable y-directed acceleration before reaching the grid plane. Assume that it crosses the grid plane at a point 64 volts above the cathode potential, its y-directed velocity component at the grid-plane crossing being 40×10^5 meters per sec; it experiences no y-directed acceleration after the grid-plane crossing. $E_b = +300$; plate 4 mm beyond grid plane. Find: (a) x-directed velocity component at grid-plane crossing; (b) x-directed and y-directed velocity components on hitting the plate; (c) grid-plane-to-plate transit time; (d) y-directed motion during (c); (e) energy (electron volts) delivered to the plate.

4. Positive-grid triode potential distribution as in Fig. 2.18; potential at T is $+150$, and $E_b = -50$, relative to the cathode. (a) How close can an electron

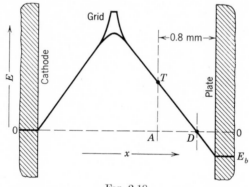

Fig. 2.18

with zero initial velocity get to the plate? (b) A particular electron advances only to T before turning back; state magnitude and direction of its velocity, also its acceleration, at T.

5. An electron crosses the grid plane with the velocity components of Prob. 3, experiencing no y-directed acceleration thereafter: (a) if $E_b = +10$, how close will it get to the plate; (b) what must E_b be to make it reach the plate?

6. Parallel plates A and B, of infinite extent, at $x = x_a$, $x = x_b$, are at potentials $E_a = 0$, E_b. An electron enters the interplate region via a hole in A at $y = 0$, $z = 0$, with velocity V_a in the x, y plane, at angle θ with the y axis. Derive equations for the electron's x, y coordinates as a function of time.

7. An electron moves in the $+x$ direction along a potential distribution given by $E = Ax^{5/3}$, starting with zero velocity at $x = 0$. Derive an equation for its flight line (x in terms of t).

8. In Fig. 2.19, potential is $+400$ volts within and $+100$ outside region $DBSB'D'$, relative to the cathode of the electron ray MT, which enters parallel

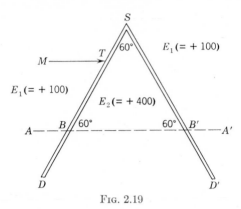

Fig. 2.19

to AA' and penetrates the 300-volt barrier at T. Determine the ray's path from T to its crossing of AA', stating the angle with AA' of each portion of the path.

9. Starting from rest, an electron is accelerated from one plane electrode toward another by a 200-volt battery, whose polarity is reversed without loss of time 10^{-9} sec after the voltage is first applied. Electrode separation is 1.5 cm. On which electrode will the electron terminate its flight, and after how long a time?

10. Concentric cylindrical electrodes have radii 1.5 and 4.5 mm. Radial field strength is 830,000 volts per meter at $r = 3$ mm, the outer cylinder more positive.

(a) Find the voltage between the inner and outer conductors.

(b) An electron pursues a circular path of 3-mm radius, and concentric with the inner conductor. An axial magnetic field provides the radially inward force necessary to maintain the motion. The radially outward centrifugal force is half the outward electric force. Find the kinetic energy of the electrons (in electron volts) and the magnetic field strength.

11. 300-volt electrons are projected into a uniform magnetic field of 100 gausses. The electron beam makes a 30° angle with the direction of the magnetic field. Find the diameter and pitch of the helical beam trajectory.

12. A 100-gauss magnetic field exists within a solenoidal current-carrying coil. An electron gun protrudes through the coil, as through one plate in Fig. 2.1.

(a) If the gun is perpendicular to and aimed toward the axis, what beam energy will make the electrons emerge through a hole in the coil 90° around its circumference from the gun's location?

(b) What angle of inclination of gun with axis, and what beam energy, will make the electrons emerge through a hole still 90° around the circumference but shifted 5 cm axially from the gun's location?

13. In a *cyclotron* a strong magnetic field makes ions pursue successive semicircular paths of increasing radii, the overall motion being spiral. After each semicircle the ions traverse a short portion of arc exposed to a tangential accelerating electric field; thus in each semicircle the energy is greater than during the last one. The electric field reverses periodically, to encourage rotation of the same sense at the start and end of each semicircle. With heavy hydrogen ions (atomic weight 2) and a 16,000-gauss magnetic field, what is the accelerating electric field's frequency? If each electric field passage adds 25,000 electron volts of ion energy, how much time elapses between an ion's central entrance and its rim emergence as a 5,000,000-volt ion? State the radius of the last semicircle before emergence. What would this be with argon ions?

14. With gun and fields as in Fig. 2.11, let $F = 1500$ volts per cm, $B = 100$ gausses. What beam energy (electron volts) at emergence from the gun will make the electrons pursue (a) a straight-line path, (b) a cycloidal path. (c) How far to one side of the gun's axis would the cycloid cusps lie?

15. (a) State an electron's transverse mass at a velocity half that of light. (b) Through what potential must it "fall" to acquire this velocity? (c) State its arc radius and rotational period on entering a 1000-gauss magnetic field.

16. A *proton* is accelerated through 900 volts, then injected into a 1 weber per square meter magnetic field, its motion at injection making a 30° angle with the magnetic field. For the resulting helical motion, find: (a) the radius; (b) the time per turn; (c) the pitch. (d) What is the proton's energy 10^{-7} sec after entering the field?

17. An electron is emitted with zero velocity from a plane surface into an accelerating gradient of 50 volts per cm and a 500-gauss transverse magnetic field. For the resulting cycloidal path state: (a) maximum travel in the direction of the electric field; (b) velocity at the point of maximum distance from the emitting plane; (c) elapsed time between departure from and return to the emitting plane.

18. A particle of mass $3m_e$ and charge $2q_e$ is accelerated through 900 volts, then projected into a uniform magnetic field of flux density B, at 30° with the Z axis, 90° with the Y axis; see Fig. 2.20. B is perpendicular to the YZ plane.

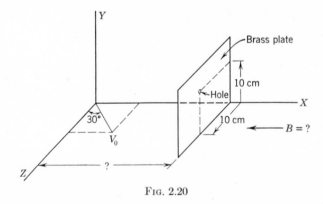

FIG. 2.20

A brass plate having a small hole lies parallel to the YZ plane. The hole is 10 cm from the XY plane and from the XZ plane. Find the flux density B, and the distance from the YZ plane to the plate, that will make the particle go through the hole.

19. Coordinates and fields as in Fig. 2.21; the electron gun delivers electrons at the origin, aimed in the $-x$ direction. Magnetic field in the $-z$ direction; an electric field exerts a force on the electrons in the $+y$ direction. Trochoidal motion, as indicated.   Find: (a) translational velocity; (b) time to traverse each loop; (c) radius to rim of the rolling wheel; (d) rotational component of velocity; (e) beam energy on emergence from the gun.

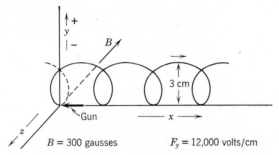

FIG. 2.21   Trochoidal trajectory.

20. Describe the effect, in Prob. 19, of adding an electric field component exerting a force in the $-z$ direction.

21. Consider an electron motion of the looping trochoidal type, F and B being uniform and at right angles.   At one extreme lateral position T_1 the electrons are moving faster than but in the same direction as the translational motion; total kinetic energy 1600 electron volts.   At the other extreme position T_2, the motion is opposite to the direction of the translational motion; total kinetic energy 900 electron volts.   Radius of the tracing spoke is 1.7 cm.   Find: (a) electric field strength; (b) translational velocity; (c) rotational velocity, at end of the tracing spoke.   (d) Sketch the trajectory *approximately to scale.*

CHAPTER III

CATHODE-RAY DEVICES

3.1   Cathode Ray: A Name for a Beam of Electrons.   A small beam of electrons in a vacuum, which may be ejected from an "electron gun," is called a *cathode ray* because it emerges from a cathode and in many ways resembles a ray of light.

Cathode rays are used in devices for measuring rapidly changing voltages and currents,[3a, b, c, d, i] in television apparatus,[3A, D, j] in high-speed switching devices,[3l] for presentation of radar information,[3J, f] in the electron microscope,[3C] in the production of X rays, and in general for a variety of experimental and industrial purposes.   The behavior of cathode-ray devices can be analyzed by studying trajectories of individual electrons according to principles developed in Chapter II. Focusing arrangements are usually necessary; see Section 3.6.

3.2   The Cathode-Ray Tube.   Devices called cathode-ray tubes are used for television picture presentation, for displaying radar information, and, in the form of the cathode-ray oscilloscope tube, for displaying and measuring a-c voltage and current wave forms.   Figure 3.1a illustrates a simple cathode-ray tube geometric arrangement.   The cathode ray originates at the cathode, passes through a circular hole in a disk which serves as a control grid to govern beam intensity, then through an accelerating field established by one or more hollow cylindrical anodes.   The compact triode-like assembly of the cathode, control grid, and accelerating anodes is called the electron gun.   The accelerating anodes may be shaped so as to provide a focusing radial electric field component, or focusing magnetic fields may be used; see Section 3.6.   After leaving the gun the electron passes through either electric or magnetic deflecting fields and finally terminates on a sensitized surface.   This surface is usually a layer of *phosphor* material, which fluoresces to produce light under electron impact, but it may be a photographic film (inside the vacuum envelope).   The fluorescent trace is viewed by looking at the exposed end of the tube from the outside.

In a cathode-ray oscilloscope tube a voltage to be measured may be connected to a pair of deflecting plates that establish between them an electrostatic deflection field.   As the beam passes between the plates, it experiences a transverse acceleration. The resulting bend in the trajectory makes the electrons strike the screen well to one side of the zero-deflection location, the distance from the zero being proportional to the potential difference between the deflecting plates. If instead of deflecting plates a current-carrying coil is used, so placed that its magnetic field produces a bend in the beam's path, the deflection from the zero position is a measure of the current in the coil. Usually de-

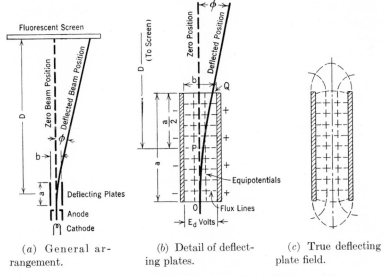

(a) General arrangement.

(b) Detail of deflecting plates.

(c) True deflecting plate field.

FIG. 3.1 Electrostatic deflection of the beam of a cathode-ray tube.

flecting plates are located inside the vacuum envelope, and deflecting coils outside the envelope, for reasons of engineering convenience.

The necessary time-axis motion of the trace of the oscilloscope beam is obtained by producing a time-varying deflection (caused either electrically or magnetically) at right angles to the deflection that provides measurement information.

In a television picture tube the deflection-field circuitry is arranged so as to make the beam trace out a "raster," that is, an array of closely spaced parallel straight lines. Variations in beam intensity, caused by picture-signal variations in the cathode-ray tube control-grid voltage, convert the uniform raster into a television picture.[3D, N]

In a radar "A scope" or "B scope" the tube measures, as in a cathode-ray oscilloscope tube, the time of occurrence of a voltage or current variation, usually a short pulse producing a short-duration large-amplitude "pip" on the screen. In the "B scope" the time-sweep motion is circular and the pip deflection radial. The "PPI" (plan position indicator) radar display uses in effect a raster of radial lines that are, however, extremely close together because the circumferential traverse requires several seconds. Beam intensity control provides the trace brilliance variation that gives plan position information.

3.3 Voltage Sensitivity.[3J, M, a, d, f, g, h] Electrostatic deflection of the trace on a cathode-ray tube is proportional to the voltage to be measured, inversely proportional to the accelerating voltage, and dependent on geometrical arrangement. Figure 3.1b is a detail of the electron's path in the immediate vicinity of deflecting plates of length a, spacing b. The actual form of the field at the two extremities of the plates is shown in Fig. 3.1c, but a sufficiently accurate analysis of the beam trajectory can be obtained by assuming a uniform field up to the end of the plates and zero field beyond.

The electrons enter the deflecting field with a velocity that depends on the accelerating or beam voltage according to (2–5) or (2–55). While in the deflecting field each electron has (a) constant velocity in the original direction and (b) uniformly accelerated motion in the direction of the field force, that is, at right angles to the original direction. The resulting path between the plates is parabolic.

The vertex of the parabola is at O, the entrance to the transverse field. The vertical component v_a of the velocity remains constant, the transverse component v_t increasing uniformly with time. The path continues to be parabolic to the point of emergence from between the plates. There the deflecting field ends, v_t becomes constant at a value which will be called v_d, and the trajectory straightens out into a direct line at an angle ϕ with the original direction. The deflection of the beam's terminus on the screen from the zero location depends on the angle ϕ and the distance D from the center of the plates to the screen. For a truly parabolic path the tangent to the trajectory at the point of emergence Q passes through P, the midpoint of the field.

One component of the ultimate straight-line motion is v_a; the other is v_d. The deflection x on the screen is dependent on these velocity components by way of the angle ϕ, as follows:

$$x = D \tan \phi = D \frac{v_d}{v_a} \tag{3-1}$$

If the accelerating voltage is small, the deflection for a given transverse field is correspondingly large, for each electron then moves very slowly through the deflecting field and is exposed for a long time (a/v_a) to the transverse acceleration dv_t/dt. The dependence of v_d on time of exposure is expressed mathematically by the equation

$$v_d = \frac{a}{v_a} \frac{dv_t}{dt} \tag{3-2}$$

On using (2-2) for relating the transverse acceleration to the field, recognizing that the strength of the electric field between the plates is E_d/b, and using (2-5) to express the incoming velocity in terms of the accelerating or anode voltage E_a, (3-1) becomes

$$x = D\frac{a}{2b}\frac{E_d}{E_a} \tag{3-3}$$

E_d is of course the voltage applied to the plates in order to be measured. If E_a is large enough so that the electron's mass is appreciably more than the rest mass, the incoming velocity and the mass factor in the acceleration should be expressed as in (2-55) and (2-56).

3.4 Magnetic Sensitivity.[3J, M, a, d, f, g, h] Magnetically produced deflection in a cathode-ray oscilloscope varies in direct proportion to the

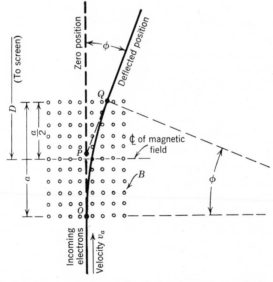

FIG. 3.2 Magnetic deflection of the electron beam in a cathode-ray tube.

strength of the magnetic field, varies inversely as the square root of the accelerating voltage, and is dependent on geometrical proportions. Figure 3.2 is a detail of the bend in the electron beam as it passes through the magnetic field substituted for the electric deflecting field of Fig. 3.1. The magnetic field is directed at right angles to the

desired deflection. Analysis is based on the reasonably satisfactory
assumption of a sharply bounded magnetic field having a value B
within a restricted region and zero value elsewhere.

Each electron pursues a circular arc of radius r while in the magnetic field; radii drawn to the path at O and Q are perpendicular
respectively to the initial and deflected beam positions. Hence the
total angle of arc traversed between these radii is the same as the
deflection angle ϕ. The deflection is usually small enough so that the
point P obtained by backward projection of the outgoing beam direction may be identified with the midpoint of the field, from which D is
measured; it is also small enough so that the angle ϕ is indistinguishable
from tan ϕ and from a/r, where a is the length of the magnetic field.
As with the electric deflecting field

$$x = D \tan \phi \qquad (3\text{–}4)$$

Since $\tan \phi = \phi = a/r$, the deflection can be evaluated by using (2–62)
for the radius, as follows:

$$x = D\frac{a}{r} = D\frac{aB \times 10^6}{3.37\sqrt{E_a}} \qquad (3\text{–}5)$$

Here B is stated in webers per square meter, and distances are in meter
units. E_a is the accelerating voltage.

3.5 Phosphors.[3J, K, L, M, d, e, i, 15H, I, J, r] Visual observation of the
beam's trace on a metal or glass screen is made possible by coating the
screen with a properly chosen fluorescent material. Such fluorescent
materials are called "phosphors" and are similar to the coatings on the
interior surfaces of fluorescent lights. The manufacture of phosphors
has become a highly specialized art. Three of the simpler phosphors
are:

Zinc silicate (willemite, Zn_2SiO_4)	Green trace
Calcium sulphide (CaS)	Nearly white when strong, green when faint
Calcium tungstate ($CaWO_4$)	Blue

Phosphors may be classified according to a substantial variety of
properties, including:

(a) Color of trace, in relation to visual or photographic spectral response.

(b) Brightness of trace, for given electron energy and phosphor thickness.

(c) Persistence of the trace after excitation by the beam has stopped; thus there
are "short-persistence" and "long-persistence" phosphors.

(d) Nature of the law governing rate of decay; for example, the light from some
phosphors decays as an inverse exponential function of time, from others approximately as an inverse power function of time.

(e) Electrical conductivity of the phosphor layer.

(f) Methods that can be used for "erasing" a long-persistence trace before it disappears normally.

(g) Life of the phosphor coating for given electron energy; this property measures the resistance to "burning holes" in the phosphor layer by an intense beam maintained for a long time at a given spot.

(h) Difficulty of manufacture and use in cathode-ray tubes.

For television cathode-ray picture tubes a white trace is desirable. For cathode-ray oscilloscope tubes maximum brightness is more important than color. Green phosphors presently available give greater brightness than any others, in terms of visual response; therefore, cathode-ray oscilloscope tubes used for visual observation usually have green-trace phosphors. If the trace is to be photographed, tubes having blue-trace phosphors may be used because photographic films are usually more sensitive to blue than to green light.

The choice of phosphor for any particular purpose may be a complex applicational problem whose optimum solution is a compromise. The following descriptions of typical needs illustrate this.

(a) A cathode-ray oscilloscope tube is to be used for displaying visually, or for photographically recording,[3J, M, e, h, i] a single-trace event. That is, each event observed happens just once, giving rise to a single trip of the "spot" across the screen at a very fast "writing speed." The time between successive events is long compared with the longest persistence of commercially available phosphors, but the duration of each event is very brief, perhaps a fraction of a microsecond. This calls for a phosphor of maximum brightness and the longest persistence obtainable. Also, high beam energy is indicated, with a correspondingly low deflection sensitivity. Thus, if the signal to be measured is small, very substantial signal voltage amplification at high frequencies must be provided. The necessary beam energy would quickly destroy the phosphor coating if the beam were allowed to rest on one spot for even a very brief time, so that intensity controls synchronized with time-axis motion must be provided to suppress brilliance except during rapid writing.

(b) A cathode-ray tube is to display visually a pattern that recurs rapidly but whose shape changes slowly, as in the simple horizontal range scale (A scope) radar [3J, f] presentation; another example is the presentation of the output wave form of a radio-frequency amplifier under test, unmodulated. This application requires only moderate brightness, as the trace recurs often, and a long-persistence phosphor can be used, because the pattern changes only slowly. The beam energy need not be high, so that substantial deflection sensitivity is easily obtainable, and phosphor burn-out is not a problem.

(c) Requirements are the same as in (b), except that the pattern changes with substantial rapidity, as in a television picture tube. Here a short-persistence phosphor must be used, to permit rapid changing of the picture.

(d) The radar plan position indicator (PPI) [3J, f] requires that the trace persist for just about one rotation of the scanning antenna, usually a matter of from 1 to 5 seconds. Thus a specific time persistence is needed. The ideal would be a phosphor whose brightness persists with little change for a specific time, then disappears abruptly. No such phosphors exist, so a compromise choice is necessary.

The compromise should provide the required persistence without excessive initial-trace brilliance, because excessive initial-trace brilliance is psychologically disturbing to the observer. One approach is to use a phosphor in which the initial trace is of a color having relatively poor visual response (blue or blue-violet), which excites a long-persistence trace of a color having good visual response (white, yellow, or green).

Electrical conductivity of the phosphor is of consequence because the return circuit for the electrons of the cathode ray is through the phosphor itself to the sides of the tube.

It is common practice to use a camera to record the phosphor trace, where permanence of the information displayed is needed.[3J, M, e, h, i]

3.6 Production and Focusing of the Beam. The cathode from which the electrons emerge is usually a heated thermionic emitting surface, although it may be the unheated negative terminal of a glow discharge at a very low gas pressure. The thermionic emitter provides a beam with high electron concentration, with good visual and photographic sensitivities at moderate accelerating potentials, and requiring special focusing provisions in order to secure a fine trace. A cold-cathode beam [3k] operates with a high accelerating voltage, usually over 40,000 volts, and so has rather limited voltage sensitivity. It has satisfactory photographic sensitivity and is kept focused easily because of its low electron concentration.

Space-charge control (similar to current control in a triode) of the intensity of the beam from the electron gun's thermionic cathode is obtained by means of a "grid" (actually a disk with a central hole) between the cathode and an accelerating electrode.

The electrons of the beam tend to diverge because of the lateral components of their initial small random velocities and because of the radially outward electric force on them due to their own space charge. Focusing of the beam to produce a brilliant, narrow trace on the viewing screen requires that these effects be either negligible or compensated for by forces tending toward convergence. In cold-cathode instruments satisfactory focusing can be obtained by using a pinhole to select a fine pencil of rays.

The concentrated beam from a thermionic cathode requires the application of electron optical principles to produce sharp focusing; see Chapter II in *Fundamentals of Physical Electronics*, and various books on electron optics.[3A, B, C, D, E, F, G, H, I] The radial variation of potential due to the space charge of a cylindrical electron beam of uniform concentration is illustrated in Fig. 3.3; the gradient encourages divergence. In the absence of focusing provisions there results a moderate spreading of electron paths, shown in Fig. 3.4a. Such a

beam may be focused by a converging field which gives the outer electrons a radially inward component of velocity. This converging field
may be produced electrostatically,
magnetostatically, or by gas
focusing.[3A, D, E, J, M, a, d, f, g, m]

The left half of Fig. 3.4b illustrates a converging electrostatic
field between a focusing cylinder
and a cylindrical anode. The right
half shows the response to this field
of an otherwise divergent beam.
Several radial cross sections of the
space-charge-free potential in this
region are shown in Fig. 3.4c; they
indicate the presence of a pro-

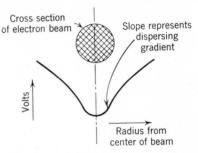

FIG. 3.3   Potential variation within
and near an electron beam, due to the
beam's own space charge.

nounced central high-potential "channel." The steepness of the sides of
the channel in the lower-potential sections measures the potential gradient
producing a radially inward force. In the 1-1 potential line the downward shift from the top to the bottom boundary of the shaded region

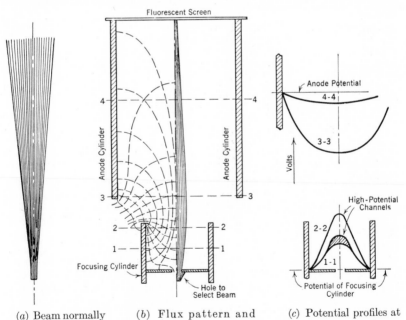

(a) Beam normally
diverging; no focus-
ing field.

(b) Flux pattern and
beam, in convergent focusing field.

(c) Potential profiles at
locations 1-1, 2-2, 3-3, 4-4,
of (b).

FIG. 3.4   Electrostatic focusing of a cathode-ray tube beam.

is the result of the space charge of the beam. A similar shift, not shown, occurs in the other sections.

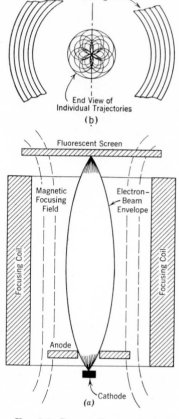

(b)

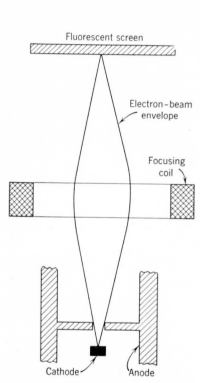

Fig. 3.5 Short-coil magnetostatic focusing arrangement. Potential of the region between anode and screen is that of the anode. Envelope only of the beam is shown. Individual trajectories are straight lines except within the magnetic field, where they are sections of helices.

Fig. 3.6 Long-coil magnetostatic focusing of a cathode-ray tube beam. Potential of the region between anode and screen is that of the anode. In (a) the envelope only of the beam is shown; individual trajectories are helical in nature, with a pitch equal to the distance between anode and screen. In (b) the nature of individual trajectories is shown, detailed more fully in Fig. 3.7.

The electron beam may be magnetostatically focused by means of a "short" coil carrying a d-c current,[3A, C, D, a] the axis of the coil coinciding with the zero-deflection beam position; this is illustrated in Fig. 3.5.

The convergence of the beam in short-coil focusing may be thought of as due to the electrons following a small portion only of the complete helical trajectory involved in "long-coil" magnetostatic focusing; see Fig. 3.6.

Figure 3.6a illustrates the nature of a "long-coil" focusing field and the envelope in this field of an otherwise divergent beam.[3A, C, D, a] As the electrons emerge from a hole in the anode, already with somewhat divergent (initial) velocities, they enter a magnetic field that is parallel

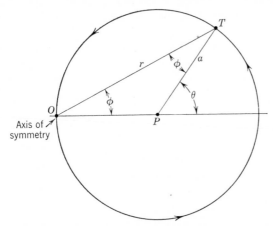

FIG. 3.7   End view of the helical trajectory of an electron undergoing "long-coil" focusing, as in Fig. 3.6. Note that $\phi = \theta/2$ and $d\theta/dt = 2\omega_l$; therefore $d\phi/dt = \omega_l$.

to the zero-deflection axis. Each electron whose radially outward velocity is appreciable pursues a helical path which in one complete revolution brings it back to a point on the axis, as indicated in Fig. 3.6b. Electrons having large initial outward velocities have large diameter paths. Because the time for completing a turn around the helix is dependent only on the magnetic field strength and not at all on velocity, all return to the axis after the same length of time. As all have the same axial velocity, they return to a common focus. If the magnetic field is of sufficient axial extent, there may be more than one focus. Satisfactory results have been obtained with cathode-ray devices in which the deflection plates are placed near the first focus, the fluorescent screen at the second.

Figure 3.7 is a detail end view of the trajectory of an electron experiencing long-coil focusing. In the isosceles triangle OPT, $\phi + \phi + (180° - \theta) = 180°$; therefore $\phi = \theta/2$. Therefore $d\phi/dt = \frac{1}{2} d\theta/dt$. But, from (2–63) and (2–64), $d\theta/dt = 2\omega_l$; therefore $d\phi/dt$ is constant at the value ω_l for Fig. 3.7 and for all the electrons in Fig. 3.6.

In long-coil focusing, the general direction of travel of the beam as a whole is determined *by the direction of the magnetic flux*. If deflecting plates or coils are used near a first focus and result in deflection of a beam's position at that location, the deflection on a screen at the second focus will be the same *distance* as the deflection actually taking place while within the deflecting field at the first focus. This is because the axis of helical motion, therefore the general direction of motion of the beam, after passing the deflecting field is the same as that before entering it. As a result the deflection at the screen or photographic plate is very small; however, the focusing can be excellent in quality, susceptible of substantial optical magnification without loss of definition.

3.7   Gas Focusing. Beam concentration may be obtained or aided by *gas focusing*, usually by employing one of the inert gases at a very low pressure, as in the tube devised by J. B. Johnson.[3a] The strength of the focusing action is dependent on the nature and concentration of the gas, the concentration of electrons within the beam, and the accelerating voltage. The focusing action may be adjusted by changing beam intensity until the focus is satisfactory. With too weak or too intense a beam the electrons tend toward convergence beyond or short of the screen. Some devices which depend primarily on electrostatic or magnetostatic focusing contain a little inert gas to contribute to the sharpness of focus.

The mechanism of gas focusing is as follows:

If there is appreciable gas present, yet not enough to cause serious scattering of the electrons of the beam, some atoms lying in the beam's path are ionized, each atom so affected giving rise to one atom and one electron. In this situation, for reasons discussed in Section 15.7, the probability of immediate recombination to re-form neutral gas particles is very remote, so that there come into being in the path of the beam a swarm of approximately equal numbers of positive ions and of low-energy electrons. The electrons formed by ionization are called low-energy ones by contrast with those of the electron beam. The ions and low-energy electrons are produced equally rapidly; therefore, if there is to be an equilibrium state, they must disperse laterally at equal rates. Lateral dispersion occurs because of random velocities. The electrons, being lighter, have much higher lateral components of random velocities than do the ions.

Thus the electrons "run out" laterally more rapidly than the ions, leaving a positively charged high-potential channel in the beam region. The gradient at the sides of this channel aids ion dispersion and retards electron dispersion; the strength of the positive space charge in the channel builds up until this effect of the radial gradient just balances the tendency of the electrons to disperse more rapidly than ions because of their greater random velocities. (This mechanism is similar to that leading to the potential distribution in Fig. 15.2b.) The existence of the high-potential channel is of course responsible for the focusing of the high-energy electrons, just as focusing results from the differently caused high-potential channel of Fig. 3.4c.

3.8   Time-Axis Motion.   The need for a cyclic time axis in a cathode-ray oscilloscope trace makes it desirable for the beam to move with constant velocity at right angles to the deflection produced by the voltage or current to be measured.   This motion can be produced by a second pair of deflecting plates, called sweep plates.   If the time-axis motion takes place at a uniform velocity, the record has a *linear* time scale, which is advantageous in interpreting the voltage and current variations.   Usually the time-axis motion should repeat periodically, requiring a deflecting-plate voltage of sawtooth wave form.

Television cathode-ray tubes frequently employ magnetic deflection for producing the raster pattern; this requires a deflection-coil current having a sawtooth wave form.

A typical sawtooth time-axis deflection voltage, employed to produce electrostatically the time-axis motion for observing cyclic phenomena, is shown in Fig. 3.8*a*.   Ideally the slant portion should be a straight

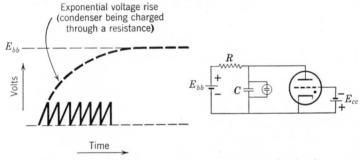

(*a*) Time axis voltage wave form.   (*b*) Gas tube circuit.

Fig. 3.8   A simple circuit using a thyratron (a gas triode) as a switch to produce a sawtooth voltage for the time axis of a cathode-ray oscilloscope.   Usually an amplifier is introduced between the condenser C and the time-axis plates.

line of controllable slope, and the amplitude independent of slope. The abrupt drop should occur with extreme rapidity, in order to make the return trace of the beam faint enough to avoid confusing the forward trace.

Figure 3.8*b* is a sweep circuit sometimes used.   The actual sawtooth voltage it produces may be quite modest in amplitude, of the order of 15 to 30 volts, and then be amplified before application to the time-axis deflection plates.   Control of the amplifier gain permits control of the time-axis voltage amplitude without disturbing the circuit responsible for producing the proper wave form.   In operation, the condenser C is charged through the resistance R while the thyratron (a gas triode used as a switch; see Section 18.9) is held in the nonconducting state by the negative bias on its grid. However, at a critical voltage, determined by the thyratron's grid control curve (see Fig. 18.11), the thyratron becomes conducting and discharges the condenser to a low voltage. The plate current in the thyratron then becomes very small, with the result that it again becomes an open switch, and the condenser is again charged through the resistance R. This cycle of events is repeated indefinitely.

With R and C the resistance and the capacitance in series during the charging period, and e_b and E_{bb} the instantaneous and ultimate values of tube plate voltage that is applied (after being amplified) to the time-axis deflection plates, the circuit equation for the dotted line in Fig. 3.8a is

$$e_b = E_{bb}\left(1 - \exp\frac{-t}{RC}\right) \tag{3-6}$$

time t being measured from the beginning of the voltage rise. This makes the initial rate of rise of each sawtooth have the value

$$\left(\frac{de_b}{dt}\right)_{t=0} = \frac{E_{bb}}{RC} \qquad \text{[volts per second]} \tag{3-7}$$

The *time constant RC* (seconds) thus controls the rise rate. The time-axis frequency is the (3–7) rate divided by the voltage difference between the lowest point and the crest of the sawtooth.

Figure 3.9b illustrates another gas tube circuit that has been used to produce time-axis voltages and for industrial control timing purposes; illustrative potentials are indicated. As in Fig. 3.8, the thyratron is a grid-controlled gas rectifier and as such acts like a switch; it is not a device capable of controlling current magnitudes. While in a conducting state the voltage from cathode to anode (called the "tube drop") is small relative to other voltage used in this particular circuit, and the current magnitudes are therefore controlled entirely by the external circuit. Note that this is a relatively high-voltage circuit, in contrast with Fig. 3.8b.

The sweep plates are connected across the condenser; the time-axis motion results from the sawtooth rise and fall of the cathode potential e_a, as in Fig. 3.9a. During the slant-line declining period the thyratron is not conducting; it is an open switch, and the condenser C therefore discharges through the resistance R according to the circuit equation

$$e_a = E_{bb}\exp\left(-\frac{t}{RC}\right) \tag{3-8}$$

The time t is measured from the beginning of the decline. This relation makes the initial rate of decline be

$$\frac{de_a}{dt} = -\frac{E_{bb}}{RC} \tag{3-9}$$

The grid potential is held at a constant value E_c by the potential divider R_1, R_2. During the condenser-discharge period the cathode

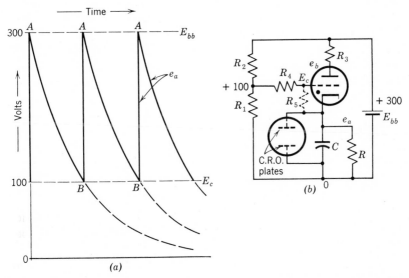

FIG. 3.9 (a) Sawtooth voltage suitable for producing time-axis motion of the beam of a cathode-ray tube, with (b) a circuit that employs a thyratron to produce the sawtooth wave form. This circuit is also used for timing purposes in industrial electronic control apparatus. See also Figs. 18.17 and 18.18.

potential e_a is higher than E_c; therefore the tube remains an open switch. When in its slant decline e_a reaches E_c, the tube becomes conducting, that is, a closed switch; the grid loses control, as discussed in a later thyratron analysis, and the condenser is abruptly charged to the potential E_{bb}. With the condenser fully charged, the thyratron becomes a nonconductor, for reasons discussed in Section 18.16. The cathode potential then declines along the exponential curve again, and the process repeats indefinitely.

Obviously the circuit as illustrated does not produce an exactly linear time-axis motion, because e_a declines exponentially, not linearly. The lower E_c is dropped toward zero, the worse the nonlinearity becomes. By replacing R with a pentode suitably connected, the condenser discharge current can be held constant during the decline, giving a linear time-axis motion. Adjustment of the frequency of the saw-tooth variation is accomplished by changing C and R; such changes do not alter the amplitude.

3.9 Cathode Rays as Current Carriers.[31] A cathode ray or electron beam represents an electric convection current, flowing within the tube in whatever direction, or to whatever electrode the internal electric and magnetic fields may order; these fields are subject to the control of the operator. The beam current in a cathode-ray television or oscilloscope tube may be extremely small, or it may be as much as 100 microamperes; the choice of magnitude is based on convenience and effectiveness in producing a visual or photographic image. For some other requirements the currents in electron beams are measured in milliamperes, and developments in prospect will employ electron beams carrying many amperes.[3A, m] A fraction of a milliampere is sufficient to operate sensitive electronic devices and relays, so that even a small-current beam has the potentialities of an extremely fast and flexible switching device, depending on current-receiving arrangements within the tube. It appears probable that future developments in the communication and electronic computer arts will make continuing use of electron-beam devices as current carriers and switching means.[31, m]

One of the important uses of electron beams having high beam densities is to serve as current-carrying elements in uhf and microwave electron tube amplifiers and oscillators, operating at frequencies between 300 and 30,000 megacycles per second. Klystrons and traveling-wave amplifier tubes are illustrative types, see Chapter XI; also see Chapters II, VI, and VII in *Microwave Electron Tubes.*

3.10 Television Camera Tubes.[3A, D, N, d, j] An important application of the current-carrying properties of electron beams is in television pick-up tubes, that is, camera tubes. In some such tubes the fluorescent screen is replaced by a "mosaic" which is, in effect, a more or less random array of an extremely large number of very tiny condensers, which have one plate (the outer one) in common. The other plate of each consists of a localized bit of photoelectrically sensitive material. Under influence of field controls the beam *scans* this surface line by line as a draftsman crosshatches a section; the screen must be completely scanned from top to bottom many times a second.

Optical lenses focus an image of the action to be televised on the photoelectrically sensitive surface. Between successive visits of the electron scanning beam each localized part of the surface acquires, photoelectrically, a charge proportional to the local light intensity and to the time since the last visit. At the beam's passage, each tiny condenser is discharged through the beam and an external circuit connected to the metal backing plate common to all the condensers.

The current in this external circuit thus varies rapidly, corresponding to the changing light intensity at points successively scanned. Secondary emission techniques (see Section 6.7) may be used to amplify these changes. The variation pattern is broadcast over a high-frequency carrier wave and made to control the beam intensity in a cathode-ray television receiver picture tube. The receiver's beam scans a fluorescent screen in synchronism with the scanning by the transmitter's beam of the action image. There is thus produced on the receiving screen a light image that follows faithfully the local brightnesses and darknesses of the action image.

New and interesting problems of research and development relative to cathode-ray tubes appear in the art and science of color television.[3j]

PROBLEMS

1. (a) If, in Fig. 3.1, $a = 10$ mm, $b = 2$ mm, what value of E_d would make the electrons of a 6000-volt beam just hit the end of one of the plates? (b) Demonstrate that the vertex P of the angle ϕ lies half way between the ends of the plates.

2. If, in Fig. 3.2, $a = 2$ cm, $\phi = 10°$, how far above the field center line is P?

3. If in a cathode-ray oscilloscope a deflecting voltage E_d and a magnetic flux density B produce equal deflections when $E_a = 3000$, what is the ratio of the deflections due to the same E_d and B when $E_a = 2000$, geometry unchanged?

4. Write an equation for the Fig. 3.3 potential distribution for a uniform-space-charge-density 20-μa 1000-volt electron beam, diameter 2 mm, also for the radial force on the electrons, in terms of the radius.

5. In Fig. 3.6, with a 1000-volt beam, what magnetic field will focus the electrons 10 cm beyond the anode? At greatest beam divergence an electron is 5 mm from the axis; what was its trajectory angle at the anode? Neglect space charge.

6. In Fig. 3.4, given that on-axis potentials are: 4900 volts at 4–4, 3600 at 3–3, 3025 at 2–2, 2500 at 1–1; also, the axial angle of the outermost trajectory is 7° diverging at 1–1, 2° converging at 4–4.

(a) Find the outer-electron radial velocities at 1–1 and 4–4.

(b) Find the work done (electron volts) on an outer-trajectory electron by the radial field component during flight from 1–1 to 4–4.

(c) Along-axis spacings from cathode are: to 1–1, 2 mm; to 2–2, 4 mm; to 3–3, 7 mm; to 4–4, 12 mm. Draw the along-axis potential distribution.

(d) Using (c), find the 1–1 to 4–4 transit time.

7. In a "post-acceleration" cathode-ray oscilloscope [3h] the fluorescent screen is E_s volts above, cathode E_a volts below, the deflecting-plate potential. Longitudinal field between deflecting-plate location and screen assumed uniform. The given E_d makes the deflection 3 cm and the deflecting-plate-to-screen transit time t_1 sec, when $E_s = 0$. With E_d the same, but $E_s = E_a$, find the new deflection, the new transit time t_2 (in terms of t_1), and the factor of spot brilliance increase.

8. In Fig. 3.6, given a 2° outer-trajectory axial angle at entrance to focusing field, and a 1300-volt beam. (a) What magnetic field will make the maximum beam diameter 2 mm?   (*b*) State the electron kinetic energy (electron volts) of outermost electrons due to axial motion; (*c*) to circular motion.   (*d*) Determine helical motion rotational frequency.   (*e*) At what anode-to-screen distance will the first focus appear at the screen?

9. Electric deflecting plates are placed at the first focus, in Fig. 3.6.   Between the plates the electric deflecting and magnetic focusing fields provide brief exposure to "combined uniform fields at right angles."   Describe the relation of the motion while between the plates, and afterward, to the considerations of Section 2.13.

CHAPTER IV

ELECTROSTATIC FIELDS IN SPACE-CHARGE CONTROL TUBES

4.1 Conformal Transformations. The analysis of two-dimensional electric and magnetic fields is facilitated by *conformal transformation* [1B, C, Q, R, S, 1G–III, 3C, 4A, a] of the actual coordinate system to an equivalent one which makes the properties of the field determinable by comparison with familiar geometries. Such treatment greatly simplifies the study of the electric field within a triode, a tetrode, or a pentode, in the absence of space charge; the effects of space charge can be considered subsequently.

If x and y are the coordinates of the original two-dimensional field, and x' and y' those of the new equivalent field, the useful type of transformation is such that the underlying two-dimensional differential equation

$$\frac{\partial^2 E}{\partial x^2} + \frac{\partial^2 E}{\partial y^2} = 0 \tag{4–1}$$

transforms into the similar one

$$\frac{\partial^2 E}{\partial x'^2} + \frac{\partial^2 E}{\partial y'^2} = 0 \tag{4–2}$$

That is, the Laplace equation must be satisfied in both the actual and equivalent systems. All transformations that can be described by an equation of the following general type satisfy this requirement and are called *conformal transformations:*

$$x + jy = f(x' + jy') \tag{4–3}$$

Here j is the complex-number operator, that is, $j = \sqrt{-1}$, and $f(x' + jy')$ may be any function of $x' + jy'$. It might, for example, be convenient in a particular case to use

$$x + jy = (x' + jy')^{3/2} \tag{4–4}$$

It will now be demonstrated that any transformation of the (4–3) type makes the potential E satisfy the Laplace equation in both sys-

tems if it does in either of them.   To broaden the utility of this demonstration, it will deal similarly with the electric flux ψ.

Figure 4.1 illustrates a portion of a *uniform* two-dimensional electric
field.   The potential E (volts) increases linearly with x from a reference
equipotential at which $E = 0$.   The flux content ψ (coulombs per meter

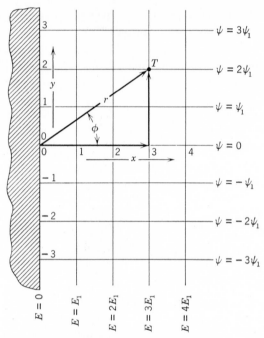

FIG. 4.1   Uniform electric field; total electric flux ψ coulombs per meter of depth,
measured relative to a reference flux line for which $\psi = 0$; potential E measured
relative to a reference equipotential for which $E = 0$.

of depth) between any given flux line and the reference flux line ($\psi = 0$)
increases linearly with y.   It is evidently permissible to write, for this
field,

$$E - j\frac{\psi}{\epsilon_0} = -F(x + jy)   \text{[scalar]}   \qquad (4\text{–}5)$$

where F is the constant electric field strength.   Now separate real and
imaginary parts, and differentiate the real part relative to x and the
imaginary part relative to y, obtaining

$$\frac{\partial E}{\partial x} = -F   \qquad \frac{\partial \psi}{\partial y} = +\epsilon_0 F = +D   \text{[vectors]}   \qquad (4\text{–}6)$$

where D is the constant flux density.   These are familiar relations.

The Laplace equations in both E and ψ,

$$\frac{\partial^2 E}{\partial x^2} + \frac{\partial^2 E}{\partial y^2} = 0 \qquad \frac{\partial^2 \psi}{\partial x^2} + \frac{\partial^2 \psi}{\partial y^2} = 0 \qquad (4\text{--}7)$$

are satisfied, since all derivatives vanish.

Thus it has been established that (4–5) describes the potential and flux in the simplest imaginable electric field, and that both E and ψ satisfy the Laplace equation in this field. This field can be conformally transformed into a new one by introduction of (4–3) into (4–5). It will now be demonstrated that in this new field configuration both E and ψ still satisfy the Laplace equation.

On using (4–3) in (4–5) there results

$$E - j\frac{\psi}{\epsilon_0} = f(x' + jy') \qquad (4\text{--}8)$$

where the $-F$ of (4–5) has been absorbed into the general form of the function f. Partial differentiations of (4–8) relative to x' and y' give

$$\frac{\partial E}{\partial x'} - \frac{j}{\epsilon_0}\frac{\partial \psi}{\partial x'} = \frac{df}{d(x' + jy')}\frac{\partial(x' + jy')}{\partial x'} = \frac{df}{d(x' + jy')} \qquad (4\text{--}9)$$

$$\frac{\partial E}{\partial y'} - \frac{j}{\epsilon_0}\frac{\partial \psi}{\partial y'} = \frac{df}{d(x' + jy')}\frac{\partial(x' + jy')}{\partial y'} = j\frac{df}{d(x' + jy')} \qquad (4\text{--}10)$$

Second similar differentiations lead to

$$\frac{\partial^2 E}{\partial x'^2} - \frac{j}{\epsilon_0}\frac{\partial^2 \psi}{\partial x'^2} = \frac{d^2 f}{[d(x' + jy')]^2} \qquad (4\text{--}11a)$$

$$\frac{\partial^2 E}{\partial y'^2} - \frac{j}{\epsilon_0}\frac{\partial^2 \psi}{\partial y'^2} = -\frac{d^2 f}{[d(x' + jy')]^2} \qquad (4\text{--}11b)$$

If these equations are added, the right-hand terms cancel, giving zero; the real and the imaginary parts of the left-side sum must therefore each be zero. This proves that the Laplace relation is satisfied for both E and ψ in the *new* coordinate system, that is

$$\frac{\partial^2 E}{\partial x'^2} + \frac{\partial^2 E}{\partial y'^2} = 0 \qquad \frac{\partial^2 \psi}{\partial x'^2} + \frac{\partial^2 \psi}{\partial y'^2} = 0 \qquad (4\text{--}12)$$

This shows, as a by-product concept, that in any *two-dimensional* field configuration the flux lines can alternatively describe equipotentials, and vice versa, because both E and ψ satisfy the Laplace relation.

It is not difficult to show that the expression

$$E = \int_{\phi=-\pi}^{\phi=+\pi} f(z + jr \cos \phi) \, d\phi \qquad (4\text{--}13)$$

describes a potential that satisfies the Laplace equation in the axially symmetric polar coordinate form

$$\frac{1}{r} \frac{\partial}{\partial r} \left(r \frac{\partial E}{\partial r} \right) + \frac{\partial^2 E}{\partial z^2} = 0 \qquad (4\text{--}14)$$

for the coordinate system of Fig. 1.12. The potential configuration is completely defined when the function $f(z + jr \cos \phi)$ is stated. For example, one might study the fields for

$$f(z + jr \cos \phi) = z + jr \cos \phi \qquad (4\text{--}15)$$

and

$$f(z + jr \cos \phi) = \frac{1}{z + jr \cos \phi} \qquad (4\text{--}16)$$

This set of concepts is useful in the study of three-dimensional but cylindrically symmetric fields.

Returning again to the two-dimensional case, any point such as T in Fig. 4.1 can be described as having

The field property $\qquad\qquad\qquad\qquad\qquad E - j\dfrac{\psi}{\epsilon_0}$ $\quad$ (4–17a)

The rectangular coordinate property $\qquad x + jy$ $\quad$ (4–17b)

The polar coordinate property $\qquad\qquad r \exp j\phi$ $\quad$ (4–17c)

Just as the quantity $x + jy$, in relation to Fig. 4.1, describes a vector terminating at T whose horizontal and vertical components are x, y, so $x' + jy'$ describes similarly a vector terminating at T'' with x', y' horizontal and vertical components in a transformed system. Every vector in the original coordinate system has its counterpart in the transformed system. But (4–3) requires that the *field* property $E - j(\psi/\epsilon_0)$ must be the same at T'' as at T.

Figure 4.2 illustrates graphically the basic concepts of a conformal transformation. The left-hand diagram represents, not an electric field, but a sheet of graph paper ruled rectangularly, coordinates being x and y relative to a central origin O. Now let the sheet of paper be cut along the heavy horizontal line from the origin to the extreme left and progressively opened up along the cut by a systematic bending of the coordinate lines, of the nature indicated by Figs. 4.2b and 4.2c.

Each of the coordinate lines becomes a curve, as illustrated by those for $x = a$ and $y = b$.

Any such systematic bending of the original pattern is the equivalent of a transformation of coordinates. The particular kinds of bending that lead to Figs. 4.2b and 4.2c correspond to conformal transformations. It is characteristic of the conformal treatment that 90° intersections of the original coordinate lines remain 90° intersections after transformation, with the exception of unique points ("singular points"),

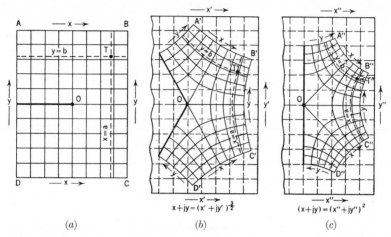

(a)   (b)   (c)

Fig. 4.2 Conformal transformation of a rectangular sheet marked with rectangular coordinates.

such as the origin in Fig. 4.2. Initially square blocks become "curvilinear squares" of the type used in freehand mapping of electric and magnetic fields.[1A-VI, 7F] The smaller the square block considered, the more nearly it retains the original shape.

The point T in Fig. 4.2a has the coordinates $x = a$ and $y = b$. The point T' to which T transforms in Fig. 4.2b can also be identified as that for which $x = a$ and $y = b$, or it can be described in the new coordinates as the point for which $x' = a'$ and $y' = b'$. The point T is the terminus of the vector $a + jb$, horizontal and vertical components being a and b; the point T' is similarly the terminus of the vector $a' + jb'$, with horizontal and vertical components a' and b' in the new system. The specific relation between Figs. 4.2b and 4.2a is expressed by (4–4), the two vectors being so related that

$$a + jb = (a' + jb')^{3/2} \qquad (4\text{--}18)$$

An identical relation exists between any two corresponding points or vectors; that is the meaning of (4–4).

Figures 4.2a and 4.2c are related by the equation

$$x + jy = (x'' + jy'')^2 \qquad (4\text{–}19)$$

The mathematical equations of the curved lines on Fig. 4.2c, into which the original straight coordinate lines are transformed, can be obtained by expansion into the form

$$x + jy = x''^2 - y''^2 + j2x''y'' \qquad (4\text{–}20)$$

Real and imaginary parts can then be separately equated, so that the relations

$$x = x''^2 - y''^2 \qquad (4\text{–}21a)$$

$$y = 2x''y'' \qquad (4\text{–}21b)$$

describe the positions taken on the x'', y'' coordinates by the original x, y lines.

It is often desirable to describe conformal transformations in polar coordinates. The vector terminating at any point such as T, Figs. 4.2a and 4.3a, is equally well described by the expressions $x + jy$ and $r \exp j\phi$, r being the radius vector and ϕ the angle with the axis, as in Fig. 4.1; that is,

$$r = \sqrt{x^2 + y^2} \qquad (4\text{–}22a)$$

$$\phi = \arc \cos \frac{x}{r} = \arc \sin \frac{y}{r} \qquad (4\text{–}22b)$$

$$x = r \cos \phi \qquad (4\text{–}22c)$$

$$y = r \sin \phi \qquad (4\text{–}22d)$$

Similarly the vector terminating at T' in the transformed diagram can be described as $r' \exp j\phi'$, related to $x' + jy'$ as $r \exp j\phi$ is to $x + jy$. It is helpful to recall that the product of two polar vectors $r_1 \exp j\phi_1$ and $r_2 \exp j\phi_2$ is the vector $r_1 r_2 \exp j(\phi_1 + \phi_2)$. Figures 4.3a, 4.3b, and 4.3c represent a sheet of graph paper ruled with polar coordinates and given exactly the treatment illustrated in Fig. 4.2, that is,

$$r \exp j\phi = (r' \exp j\phi')^{3/2} \qquad (4\text{–}23)$$

$$r \exp j\phi = (r'' \exp j\phi'')^2 \qquad (4\text{–}24)$$

Figures 4.2 and 4.3 contrast two different ways of marking a stretchable sheet; the cutting and stretching are exactly the same in the two illustrations.

If an electric field such as that of Fig. 4.1 is drawn on the original graph paper of Fig. 4.2a, with the zeros of potential and flux coinciding with the origin, the lines of constant x and y become equipotentials and flux lines in Figs. 4.2b and 4.2c. Then, referring to (4–21a) and (4–21b), one may write, for Fig. 4.2c,

$$E = A(x''^2 - y''^2) \qquad (4\text{–}25)$$

$$\psi/\epsilon_0 = A(2x''y'') \qquad (4\text{–}26)$$

These relations individually satisfy the Laplace equation.

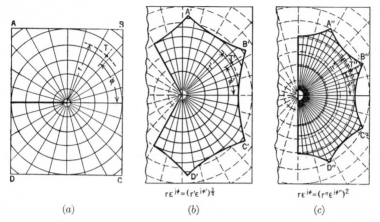

$$r\epsilon^{j\phi} = (r'\epsilon^{j\phi'})^{\frac{3}{4}} \qquad\qquad r\epsilon^{j\phi} = (r''\epsilon^{j\phi''})^2$$

$$(a) \qquad\qquad (b) \qquad\qquad (c)$$

FIG. 4.3 Conformal transformation of a rectangular sheet marked with polar coordinates.

The original x, y graph may have drawn on it the equipotential and flux-line pattern of a field more complex than Fig. 4.1, for example, the concentric-cylinder pattern of Fig. 4.4a. Such a pattern must, in the

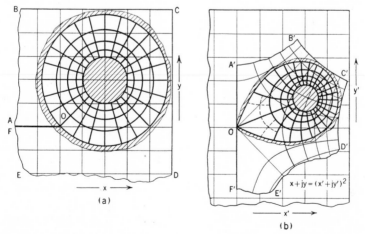

$$x + jy = (x' + jy')^2$$

$$(a) \qquad\qquad\qquad (b)$$

FIG. 4.4 Conformal transformation of an electrostatic field map, originally cylindrical.

absence of space charge, satisfy (4–7) in the interelectrode region and possess at the electrode surfaces whatever potentials the problem requires. If the transformation is a conformal one, the transformed equipotentials and flux lines will also satisfy (4–7) and will fit the altered locations of the original boundaries.

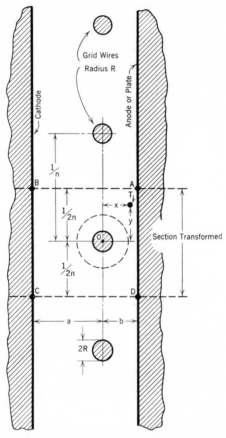

FIG. 4.5   Planar triode with flat cathode. x and y are coordinates of any point T relative to origin at grid-wire center. n grid wires per meter.   Points A, B, C, D on this W-plane representation transform to points A', B', C', D' on the Z-plane representation, Fig. 4.6.

Figures 4.4a and 4.4b illustrate the transformation of the flux pattern between concentric circular cylinders on the x, y graph into that between corresponding oval-sectioned cylinders at the same potential difference on the x, y set. If, as in this figure, the bending of the coordinate lines on which the field is mapped corresponds to a conformal

transformation, the total charge on each electrode, the potentials between them, all capacitances, total energy storage, and all other overall properties of the electric field carry over without change from one
representation to the other.   The potential gradients, surface-charge
densities, energy storages per unit volume, and other detail quantities

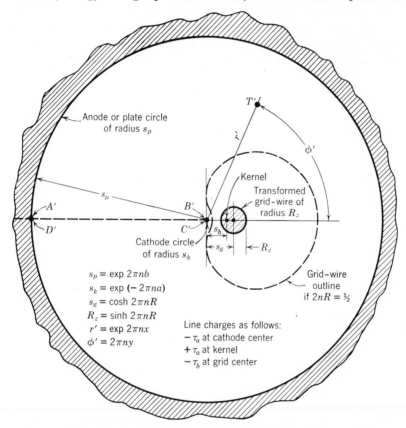

FIG. 4.6   Transformed or Z-plane representation of section $ABCD$ of the triode
of Fig. 4.5.

are modified.   Either field can, however, be completely understood,
from analysis of the other.

4.2   Conformal Transformation for a Planar Triode.[1B, C, Q, R, S, 4A, D, a, d, e, f, g]*
Figure 4.5 represents the three electrodes of a parallel-plane or
planar triode, drawn on x, y, r, ϕ coordinates; this representation will
be called the W plane.   The grid-wire radius is R, the center distance

* This manner of applying a conformal transformation to a triode is due to
Vodges and Elder.[4d]

between grid wires $1/n$, the distance from grid plane to cathode a, and from grid plane to plate b. Figure 4.6 represents a restricted portion of the same set of electrodes transformed to an x', y', r', ϕ' coordinate set, located on the Z plane. The conformal transformation used is

$$2\pi nx + j2\pi ny = \ln(x' + jy') \tag{4-27}$$

The x, y origin is taken at the center of a W-plane grid wire. The determination of the Z-plane to W-plane coordinate relationship is best approached by mixing the rectangular and polar notations; thus

$$2\pi nx + j2\pi ny = \ln(r' \exp j\phi') \tag{4-28}$$

$$= \ln r' + j\phi' \tag{4-29}$$

Separation of the real and imaginary parts shows that

$$r' = \exp 2\pi nx \tag{4-30}$$

$$\phi' = 2\pi ny \tag{4-31}$$

Note that the *grid plane* transforms to a *cylinder* at radius

$$r' = \exp 0 = 1 \tag{4-32}$$

Therefore the W-plane origin transforms to the point

$$r' = 1$$

$$\phi' = 2\pi n \times 0 = 0 \tag{4-33}$$

This point *is not at the geometrical center* of the Z-plane grid figure. $2\pi n$ is chosen as the multiplier for x and jy in order to make $\phi' = \pi$ when $y = 1/2n$, thus limiting the Z-plane representation to a portion of the W plane that extends half-way from the origin to each adjacent grid-wire center.

The cathode surface becomes, on the Z plane, a very small circle of radius $s_k = \exp(-2\pi na)$; the plate becomes a very large circle of radius $s_p = \exp(+2\pi nb)$. Ordinarily the distances a and b from grid plane to cathode and plate are at least equal to or greater than the grid spacing $1/n$, that is, ordinarily,

$$\frac{a}{1/n} = an > 1 \qquad \frac{b}{1/n} = bn > 1 \tag{4-34}$$

On applying these limits it appears that the radius of the cathode circle is ordinarily *smaller* than $\exp(-2\pi)$, or about $\frac{1}{500}$, and the radius of the plate circle is correspondingly *greater* than 500, on a scale for which the grid plane is represented by a circle at unit radius. In subsequent analytical treatment approximations will be used that deteriorate rapidly as to validity as an and bn become appreciably less than unity; see also Section 4.13.

The grid wire transforms to a figure that is essentially circular [4d] if the W-plane grid diameter is not more than about one-sixth or one-fifth of the center distance between grid wires. The Z-plane grid-wire figure crosses the horizontal axis ($\phi' = 0$) at extreme inner and outer points; the radii to the crossing points are

$$\text{Innermost:} \quad s_1 = \exp(-2\pi nR) \tag{4-35}$$

$$\text{Outermost:} \quad s_2 = \exp(+2\pi nR) \tag{4-36}$$

The radius of the transformed grid-wire figure, for those cases in which it can be considered circular, is

$$R_z = \tfrac{1}{2}(s_2 - s_1) = \tfrac{1}{2}[\exp(2\pi nR) - \exp(-2\pi nR)]$$

$$= \sinh 2\pi nR \tag{4-37}$$

The quantity $2nR$ will be called the *shadow fraction*, as it describes the extent to which the cathode lies in the shadow of the grid wires. It is the ratio of the grid-wire diameter $2R$ to the distance $1/n$ between grid-wire centers.

If $2nR$ is not greater than perhaps $\tfrac{1}{5}$ or $\tfrac{1}{6}$, the Z-plane grid figure is essentially circular. The dashed circle and dashed Z-plane grid figure in Figs. 4.5 and 4.6 are drawn for $2nR = \tfrac{1}{2}$.

4.3 Placement of Charges To Satisfy Triode Boundary Conditions.[4d] The space-charge-free electric field within a triode like that of Fig. 4.5 can be analyzed in terms of the Z-plane coordinates of Fig. 4.6 and subsequently discussed in terms of the real coordinates. This analysis must take into account the fact that at normal operating voltages the potential of the plate is much higher, and that of the grid a little lower, than that of the cathode; there must be provision for negative charges on the grid and cathode, and for a positive charge on the plate.

The electrode boundaries in Fig. 4.6 are, of course, equipotential surfaces, and the electric field is zero within each electrode. For purposes of study, let it be imagined that these metallic bodies are removed from the diagram and in one's mind, but a memory retained as to where the boundaries used to be; thus on the diagram there now may be electric fields within the former electrode boundaries. If line charges now are appropriately located within these former boundaries, the boundaries can be made equipotentials in the field of the line charges. The voltages of these equipotentials may be made identical with the voltages of the cathode, grid, and plate by proper choice of charge magnitudes. Then the electric field and potential distribution in the regions between the former electrode boundaries will be exactly the same as they would be in the Z-plane construction with metallic electrodes. Equations for potential distributions, potential gradients, charge densities, etc., can be written in terms of the line charges and Z-plane dimensions and, by using the conformal transformation coordinate relations, applied directly to the real tube. In this way a complete knowledge of electrostatic field details is obtained.

Because the Z-plane cathode cylinder is very small, it is an equipotential, regardless of the effect of grid and plate charges, if a line charge (usually negative) of $-\tau_a$ coulombs per meter length is located along its axis. This line charge may then be *imaged* in the grid cylinder in order to keep the latter an equipotential. To this end there must be located at the *kernel* of the Z-plane grid circle a line charge $+\tau_a$ equal and opposite to that at the cathode center. The kernel is at radius s_h, where

$$s_g s_h = 1 \tag{4–38}$$

This condition is illustrated in Fig. 4.6 and also in Fig. 4.7.

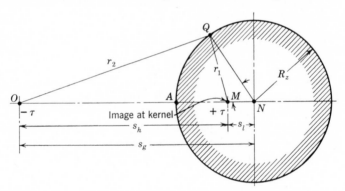

FIG. 4.7   Image of a line charge $-\tau$ in a cylinder.

The proof of (4–38) is dependent on an image relation, applicable either in imaging a point in a sphere or a line in a cylinder, to the effect that the product of the distances from the inside and outside charge locations to the center of the sphere or cylinder is equal to the square of the latter's radius. The demonstration of this image-charge position relation will now be given for the line and cylinder.

The circle of Fig. 4.7 represents a cylindrical surface of radius R_z. It is to be demonstrated that it is an equipotential surface of the electric field produced by two line charges, $-\tau$ and $+\tau$, that are parallel to and in a plane with the cylinder axis, provided that

$$\overline{ON} \cdot \overline{MN} = \overline{NQ}^2 \qquad (4\text{--}39)$$

Note that if this relation is satisfied

$$\frac{\overline{ON}}{\overline{NQ}} = \frac{\overline{NQ}}{\overline{MN}} \qquad (4\text{--}40)$$

Therefore OQN and MQN are similar triangles, as they have a common angle with proportional adjacent sides; thus also

$$\frac{\overline{MQ}}{\overline{OQ}} = \frac{\overline{NM}}{\overline{NQ}} = \frac{\overline{NQ}}{\overline{NO}} \qquad (4\text{--}41)$$

Q is any point on the cylinder; A is a point on the cylinder and in the plane of the charges. The potential difference between Q and A owing to $-\tau$ is

$$E_Q - E_A = -\frac{-\tau}{2\pi\epsilon_0} \ln \frac{\overline{OQ}}{\overline{OA}} \qquad (4\text{--}42)$$

Owing to $+\tau$ it is

$$E_Q - E_A = -\frac{+\tau}{2\pi\epsilon_0} \ln \frac{\overline{MQ}}{\overline{MA}} \qquad (4\text{--}43)$$

Owing to *both*,

$$E_Q - E_A = -\frac{-\tau}{2\pi\epsilon_0} \ln \frac{\overline{OQ}}{\overline{OA}} - \frac{+\tau}{2\pi\epsilon_0} \ln \frac{\overline{MQ}}{\overline{MA}}$$

$$= -\frac{+\tau}{2\pi\epsilon_0} \ln \frac{\overline{MQ} \cdot \overline{OA}}{\overline{MA} \cdot \overline{OQ}} \qquad (4\text{--}44)$$

The cylinder is to be an equipotential; therefore $E_Q - E_A$ must be zero, and therefore, from (4–44),

$$\frac{\overline{MQ} \cdot \overline{OA}}{\overline{MA} \cdot \overline{OQ}} = 1 \qquad (4\text{--}45)$$

From Fig. 4.7 this may be written

$$\frac{\overline{MQ}(\overline{ON} - \overline{NQ})}{\overline{OQ}(\overline{NQ} - \overline{NM})} = 1 \qquad (4\text{--}46)$$

that is,

$$\frac{\overline{MQ}\ \overline{NQ}\left(\dfrac{\overline{ON}}{\overline{NQ}}-1\right)}{\overline{OQ}\ \overline{NM}\left(\dfrac{\overline{NQ}}{\overline{NM}}-1\right)}=1 \tag{4-47}$$

This is satisfied if (4–41) is satisfied. This completes the desired demonstration.

Equation (4–39) may be written

$$s_g s_l = R_z{}^2 \tag{4-48}$$

If, in (4–48), $s_g - s_h$ is used for s_l, and it is recognized that

$$s_g{}^2 - R_z{}^2 = \cosh^2 2\pi nR - \sinh^2 2\pi nR = 1 \tag{4-49}$$

equation (4–38) results.

With just the two line charges $-\tau_a$ and $+\tau_a$ present, the electric field near cathode and grid is as illustrated in Fig. 4.8. The cathode

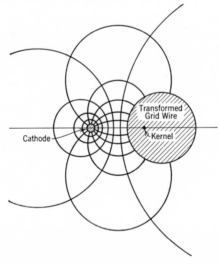

Fig. 4.8 Z-plane triode flux pattern with equal and opposite charges on cathode and grid; none on plate. The plate circle is remote with center at cathode.

charge is negative, as under normal conditions; but the plate has as yet no charge, and the grid has a positive charge. By locating a third line charge $-\tau_b$ along the grid-cylinder axis, these disagreements with normality can be corrected *without disturbing the equipotential nature of the grid figure*. The quantity $-\tau_a$ usually has a negative numerical value, and $+\tau_b$ a positive one. However, when the grid voltage is below the cut-off value, as in Fig. 1.4d, $-\tau_a$ has a positive numerical value; similarly $+\tau_a$ may have a negative value.

The Z-plane plate circle is so very remote from the grid circle that both grid and cathode figures, so also *all three* line charges, are for all practical purposes at the axis of the plate cylinder. Hence the electric field in the neighborhood of the plate may be treated as though due to the net grid-and-cathode charge $-\tau_b$ located along the plate-cylinder axis. Such a field terminates in a charge $+\tau_b$ coulombs per meter of cylinder length, distributed uniformly over the interior of the plate cylinder.

The array of three line charges, $-\tau_a$, $+\tau_a$, and $-\tau_b$, detailed in Fig. 4.9, makes all the Z-plane electrode boundaries equipotential for

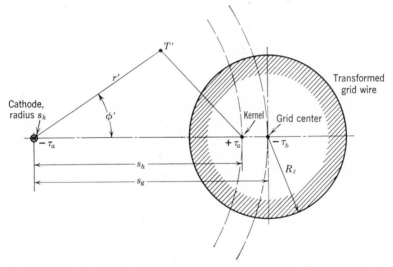

Fig. 4.9   Detail of placement of Z-plane charges in Fig. 4.6. Plate circle remote with center at cathode. Dashed-line circles through $+\tau_a$ and $-\tau_b$ turn out to be the inner and outer faces of the Z-plane representation of the "equivalent grid sheet"; see (4–100).

any and all values of $\pm\tau_a$ and τ_b; that is, the *geometrical* boundary conditions are satisfied. The charges on the electrodes, in coulombs per meter length of the Z-plane figure, are: cathode, $-\tau_a$; plate, $+\tau_b$; grid, $+\tau_a - \tau_b$.

4.4   The Electrostatic Equivalent Circuit of a Triode.[5h, 11E]   The overall electrostatic properties of any arrangement of three electrodes in charge-free space, whether in a vacuum or elsewhere, can be represented diagrammatically by three properly chosen condensers arranged

in delta, or three other properly chosen condensers arranged in star.[15b]
A triode is such a set of electrodes; its true geometry and equivalent
star and delta electrostatic circuits can be diagrammed as in Fig. 4.10.
"Equivalence" means that if these three items, a, b, and c of the figure,
were placed in three identical boxes, with three leads brought out
identically from each one, no external capacitance measurements could

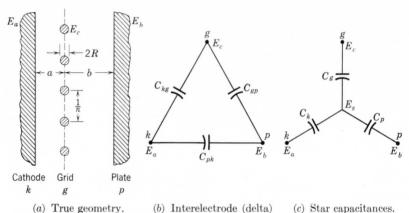

<table>
<tr><td>Cathode</td><td>Grid</td><td>Plate</td></tr>
<tr><td>k</td><td>g</td><td>p</td></tr>
</table>

(a) True geometry.   (b) Interelectrode (delta)   (c) Star capacitances.
                           capacitances.

FIG. 4.10   Triode electrostatic circuits.

distinguish between them.   Interrelations between the star and delta
capacitances are obtained by elementary a-c circuit principles; typical
equations are

$$C_{kg} = \frac{C_k C_g}{C_k + C_g + C_p} \tag{4-50}$$

$$C_k = \frac{C_{kg} C_{gp} + C_{gp} C_{pk} + C_{pk} C_{kg}}{C_{gp}} \tag{4-51}$$

Two other pairs of similar relations are obtained by symmetrical
rearrangement of symbols.

The potential of the central junction in Fig. 4.10c is symbolized as
E_s, and called the equivalent grid sheet potential, for reasons which
will appear later.*

---

* The use here of the star equivalent electrostatic circuit [5h] is an outgrowth of
Llewellyn's type of treatment; see Figs. 1, 5, and 8 in his book,[11E] similar in principle
to Figs. 4.13b, 4.10b, and 4.10c (the star diagram) presented here.   The use of
the "equivalent grid sheet" or "equivalent grid plane" concept is believed due to
L. A. Hazeltine originally.   It was first brought to the author's attention in two
lecture series, by B. J. Thompson and F. B. Llewellyn, given at the University of
Michigan in the summer of 1937.

There is no net charge on the electrodes of a vacuum tube before it is connected into a circuit. The connection of batteries or other voltage sources merely results in the transfer of charge from one electrode to another, the total net charge on the k, g, p electrodes combined remaining zero. Therefore, the sum of the charges on the three condensers C_k, C_g, C_p is always zero. This is expressed by the following equation:

$$(E_s - E_a)C_k + (E_s - E_c)C_g + (E_s - E_b)C_p = 0 \qquad (4\text{--}52)$$

where E_a, E_c, and E_b denote cathode, grid, and plate potentials respectively. The solution for E_s is

$$E_s = \frac{E_a C_k + E_c C_g + E_b C_p}{C_k + C_g + C_p} \qquad (4\text{--}53)$$

In most interesting cases $E_a = 0$, so the first term in the numerator drops out.

4.5   Equations for the Star Capacitances.   The values of the star capacitances will now be established in terms of the planar triode dimensions. These values will first be obtained per grid section, that is, for the whole Z-plane diagram of Fig. 4.6, and therefore for the portion $ABCD$ of Fig. 4.5. Considering Fig. 4.10c to refer to a single grid section, suppose that capacitances C_g and C_p are to be determined with the cathode disconnected, that is, "floating." This condition, chosen because of convenience in analysis, corresponds in Fig. 4.6 to that of no charge on the cathode, that is, $\pm\tau_a = 0$. This zero-cathode-charge condition is called the *cut-off* condition. The electric field in the Z-plane grid and cathode region is then qualitatively as shown in Fig. 4.11, although most true Z-plane geometries have cathodes much smaller than here indicated. The grid-to-cathode and grid-to-plate potential differences are, for this condition,

$$E_a - E_c = -\frac{-\tau_b}{2\pi\epsilon_0}\ln\frac{s_g}{R_z} \qquad (4\text{--}54)$$

$$E_b - E_c = -\frac{-\tau_b}{2\pi\epsilon_0}\ln\frac{s_p}{R_z} \qquad (4\text{--}55)$$

so that

$$\frac{E_a - E_c}{E_b - E_c} = \frac{\ln\dfrac{s_g}{R_z}}{\ln\dfrac{s_p}{R_z}} \qquad (4\text{--}56)$$

With no connection made to the cathode, C_g and C_p are, circuitwise, just two capacitances in series; therefore

$$(E_s - E_c)C_g = (E_b - E_c)\frac{1}{\dfrac{1}{C_g} + \dfrac{1}{C_p}} \tag{4-57}$$

Because there is no charge on the cathode, C_k is uncharged, so that $E_s = E_a$. Therefore the last equation gives immediately an expres-

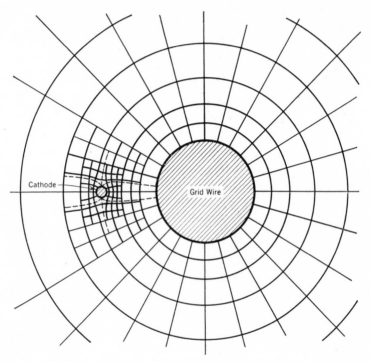

FIG. 4.11 Z-plane representation of the electric field map, in the neighborhood of grid and cathode, for a triode at cut-off. No charge on cathode (see Fig. 1.4c). Cathode size greatly exaggerated.

sion for the ratio $(E_a - E_c)/(E_b - E_c)$ under the cut-off condition. Comparison with the previous equation then shows that

$$\frac{\ln \dfrac{s_g}{R_z}}{\ln \dfrac{s_p}{R_z}} = \frac{\dfrac{1}{C_g}}{\dfrac{1}{C_g} + \dfrac{1}{C_p}} \tag{4-58}$$

This is one of two relations between the geometry and these C's needed to evaluate the C's.

In the Z-plane figure, the capacitance between grid and plate under this zero-cathode-charge condition is the ratio of τ_b to $E_b - E_c$, obtainable from (4-55). This capacitance is also that of C_g and C_p of Fig. 4.10c in series. Equating the expressions for capacitance obtained in these two ways gives the second of the two needed relations as

$$\frac{2\pi\epsilon_0}{\ln \dfrac{s_p}{R_z}} = \frac{1}{\dfrac{1}{C_g} + \dfrac{1}{C_p}} \qquad (4\text{-}59)$$

Division of this by the previous equation gives

$$C_g = \frac{2\pi\epsilon_0}{\ln \dfrac{s_g}{R_z}} \qquad \text{[farads per meter per grid section]} \qquad (4\text{-}60)$$

which when used in (4-59) leads to

$$C_p = \frac{2\pi\epsilon_0}{\ln \dfrac{s_p}{s_g}} \qquad \text{[farads per meter per grid section]} \qquad (4\text{-}61a)$$

To complete the picture, note from (4-64) below that

$$C_k = \frac{2\pi\epsilon_0}{\ln \dfrac{1}{s_k s_g}} \qquad (4\text{-}61b)$$

Multiplication of (4-60, 4-61a) by n gives capacitance values per square meter of cathode area (also of plate area); in W-plane dimensions:

$$C_p = \frac{2\pi\epsilon_0 n}{2\pi nb - \ln \cosh 2\pi nR} \qquad \text{[farads per square meter]} \qquad (4\text{-}62)$$

$$C_g = \frac{2\pi\epsilon_0 n}{\ln \coth 2\pi nR} \qquad \text{[farads per square meter]} \qquad (4\text{-}63)$$

From mathematical symmetry C_k must be the same as C_p except that a replaces b; therefore

$$C_k = \frac{2\pi\epsilon_0 n}{2\pi na - \ln \cosh 2\pi nR} \qquad \text{[farads per square meter]} \qquad (4\text{-}64)$$

To show graphically the simple relationship between Z-plane geometry and C_p, C_g, imagine the Z-plane grid figure to be removed and replaced by a hollow cylindrical metal sheet concentric with the Z-plane origin, having an outer radius s_g, an inner radius s_h (that is, $1/s_g$), and a thickness $s_g - s_h$. Equation (4–61a) shows that the capacitance between this concentric conducting sheet and the anode is C_p, expressed per grid section. Similarly from (4–61b) the capacitance between the sheet and the cathode is C_k, expressed per grid section.

Equations (4–62) and (4–64) can be written

$$C_p = \cfrac{\epsilon_0}{b\left(1 - \cfrac{\ln \cosh 2\pi nR}{2\pi nb}\right)} = \cfrac{\epsilon_0}{b - \cfrac{\ln \cosh 2\pi nR}{2\pi n}} \qquad (4\text{–}65)$$

$$C_k = \cfrac{\epsilon_0}{a\left(1 - \cfrac{\ln \cosh 2\pi nR}{2\pi na}\right)} = \cfrac{\epsilon_0}{a - \cfrac{\ln \cosh 2\pi nR}{2\pi n}} \qquad (4\text{–}66)$$

in farads per square meter. Since $na > 1$, $nb > 1$, and $2nR > \frac{1}{5}$ or so, the $\ln \cosh 2\pi nR$ terms in the parentheses are small relative to unity and can in most cases be neglected without introducing appreciable error. For such cases very good approximate expressions are

$$C_p \cong \frac{\epsilon_0}{b} \qquad C_k \cong \frac{\epsilon_0}{a} \qquad \text{[farads per square meter]} \qquad (4\text{–}67)$$

which are capacitances for parallel-plate condensers of spacings b and a respectively. Thus C_p is very nearly *the capacitance between the anode and a flat electrode located at the plane of the grid*, and C_k very nearly *that between the cathode and the same flat electrode at the plane of the grid*.

More precisely, C_p, as given by (4–65), is the capacitance between the plate and a flat equivalent grid sheet, replacing the grid, *centered on the grid plane*, and having a half-thickness given by

$$\text{Equivalent grid sheet half-thickness} = \frac{\ln \cosh 2\pi nR}{2\pi n} \qquad (4\text{–}68)$$

C_k, as given by (4–66), is the capacitance between the cathode and this same equivalent grid sheet.

Figure 4.12 is primarily a *circuit diagram* identical in principle with the star diagram, Fig. 4.10c, in that it contains capacitances C_k, C_p, and C_g respectively between cathode, plate, grid, and the imaginary central electrode, called the equivalent grid sheet. It is, however, drawn so as to indicate the relationship between C_k, C_p, and the actual geometry. This indicates why C_g may somewhat facetiously be called the capacitance between the grid wires and the plane in which they lie.

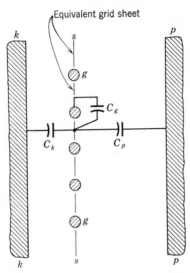

FIG. 4.12   Positional diagram of the star electrostatic circuit of a triode, illustrating the equivalent grid sheet concept.

4.6   Construction of Triode Potential Distribution Diagrams. Figure 4.13a is still another circuit diagram identical in principle with the star diagram, Fig. 4.10c, in that it represents the three capacitances C_k, C_p, C_g, properly assembled in a circuit. In this diagram, however, C_k and C_p (but not C_g) are shown as having precisely their correct dimensions. That is, the spacings in C_k and C_p are as given by the denominators of (4–65) and (4–66). Furthermore, these capacitances are shown as being separated by a grid sheet whose half-thickness is given by (4–68), thus making the total cathode-to-anode spacing $a + b$ as in the real tube. In this representation it is imagined that voltages E_c and E_b are applied just as in the real tube; the voltages across C_k and C_p must be $E_s - E_a$ and $E_b - E_s$, where E_s is as in (4–53).

The flat electrodes of the C_k and C_p capacitances in this figure have the same areas as the cathode and plate of the real tube. As there is complete electrostatic equivalence as to charge-to-voltage ratio between the real geometry and such a star equivalent electrostatic circuit as this, the charges and charge densities on cathode and plate surfaces must be the same in Fig. 4.13a as in the real tube. Therefore the potential gradients within the C_k, C_p capacitances of this figure must be the same as the potential gradients immediately adjacent to cathode and plate in the real tube. Furthermore, the cathode and plate are spaced apart precisely the same distance as in the real tube, because of the choice of half-thickness of the center sheet. Therefore Fig. 4.13a

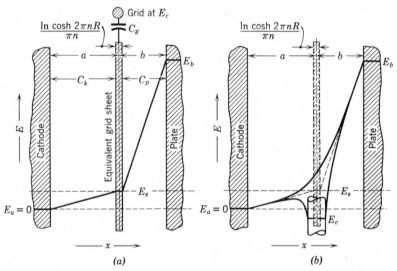

FIG. 4.13   Diagrammatic representation of the equivalent grid sheet concept for a planar triode, no space charge.

(a) Construction lines between cathode, anode, and equivalent grid sheet in a fictitious structure representative of the star electrostatic circuit, Fig. 4.10c. These lines describe correctly the potential gradients adjacent to cathode and plate.

(b) Potential distribution in the real triode, showing relation of equivalent grid sheet potential to grid fillets and to gradients at cathode and anode.

can be used as a starting point for constructing the potential distribution diagram for the real tube, shown in Fig. 4.13b; see also the shapes in Fig. 1.4.

Thus in order to sketch such a potential distribution diagram as Fig. 4.13b, one should, as indicated in less detail in connection with Fig. 1.5:

(a) Knowing the tube geometry, determine C_k, C_g, C_p from (4–64) or (4–67); (4–63); and (4–62) or (4–67).

(b) Knowing the tube potentials, determine E_s from (4–53). In general E_a in this equation will be zero.

(c) Sketch the electrode diagram as in Fig. 4.13b, using the equivalent grid sheet thickness as given by (4–68), and grid-wire diameter $2R$. Usually the equivalent grid sheet thickness is too little to be represented on the diagram.

(d) Draw straight construction lines between E_s at grid sheet faces, and E_a, E_b at cathode and plate faces, as in Figs. 4.13a and 4.13b. These lines describe correctly the potential gradients adjacent to the flat cathode and plate surfaces.

(e) Sketch in the fillets describing potential variations along paths through and between grid wires, based on whatever information is available and usable as to fineness of grid structure; see particularly (4–109). Equations for these potential distribution curves are derived in Section 4.12, and given by (4–107), but the stretched elastic membrane concept used in introducing Fig. 1.4 is adequate for sketching fillets for most purposes. The fillets in Fig. 1.5 are mathematically c orrect.

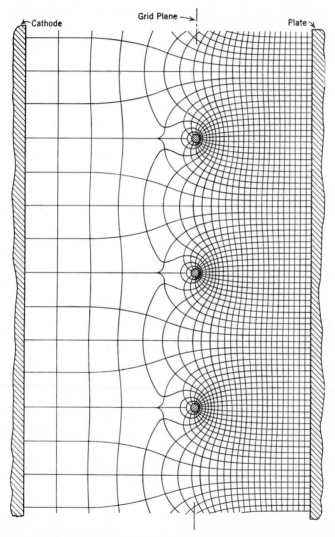

FIG. 4.14   Typical space-charge-free electric field map for a planar triode, normal voltages. See Section 4.13 for a discussion of limiting magnitudes, for the analytical method of Section 4.12 used in obtaining this figure.

Figure 4.14 illustrates the electric flux and equipotential map for a typical set of voltages as applied to a planar triode, space-charge-free conditions. See Section 4.13 for a discussion of limitations to the validity of this type of analysis.

The important result of the preceding analysis is the demonstration that, with a, b, n, and $2nR$ given specific values, the potential gradients set up near cathode and plate by any specified set of voltage and the corresponding value of E_s will be the same in the grid sheet construction diagram, Fig. 4.13a, as in the real tube, Fig. 4.13b, for space-charge-free conditions. It will be shown later that the equivalent grid sheet potential E_s determines the electron current flow from the cathode, under normal space-charge-limited current conditions.

4.7   Amplification Factor for a Planar Triode. It is important to note that C_g is in most cases many times larger than either C_k or C_p. The ratio C_g/C_p will in Section 5.7 be shown to be, for a negative-grid triode, an important quantity called the *amplification factor* (not to be confused with the voltage or power gain per stage; see Chapter IX). Thus for a planar triode the amplification factor μ is, from (4–63) and (4–62),[4d, e, j, 4B–178, 4D, 5h, i, j, k, l]

$$\mu = \frac{C_g}{C_p} = \frac{2\pi nb - \ln \cosh 2\pi nR}{\ln \coth 2\pi nR} \tag{4–69}$$

A very good approximation is obtained by omitting $\ln \cosh 2\pi nR$ in the numerator; thus,

$$\mu \cong \frac{2\pi nb}{\ln \coth 2\pi nR} \tag{4–70}$$

The term $\ln \cosh 2\pi nR$ is, in general, small relative to $2\pi nb$ but not relative to $\ln \sinh 2\pi nR$, and therefore must be retained in any expansion of the form $\ln \coth 2\pi nR$ in the denominator, even though it is discarded in the numerator.

Many commercial triodes approach closely enough to true planar geometry to make these equations closely approximate measured μ's.

By means of the substitution $C_g/C_p = \mu$, and using $E_a = 0$, (4–53) can be converted into the following extremely useful expression:

$$E_s = \frac{E_c + \dfrac{E_b}{\mu}}{1 + \dfrac{1}{\mu} + \dfrac{1}{\mu}\dfrac{C_k}{C_p}} \tag{4–71}$$

Thus it appears that the equivalent grid sheet potential is proportional to the quantity $E_c + \dfrac{E_b}{\mu}$. It is shown in Sections 5.4 and 5.10, particularly in equation (5–36), that in a planar triode the electron current flow is proportional to $E_s{}^{3\!/\!2}$, therefore to $\left(E_c + \dfrac{E_b}{\mu}\right)^{3\!/\!2}$. When this quantity is just zero, the current is just barely zero, and the cathode charge is zero. As indicated in Section 4.5, this is called the cut-off condition. Thus, for a negative-grid triode,

$$\text{At cut-off:} \quad \mu = -\frac{E_b}{E_c} \tag{4–72}$$

4.8 Geometrical Dependence of Star Capacitances for a Cylindrical Triode.[4d, i, j, 5h]
Equation (4–63) for C_g depends only on the grid struc-

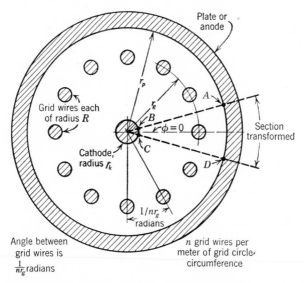

FIG. 4.15 Cylindrical triode with grid wires parallel to the axis. Region $ABCD$ transforms to $A'B'C'D'$ of Fig. 4.6.

ture, not on its placement. It is therefore reasonable to consider that in a cylindrical triode, such as is shown in Fig. 4.15, the value of C_g per unit axial extent is obtainable by multiplying C_g per unit area by $2\pi r_g$, the area per unit length. Thus, for a cylindrical triode,

$$C_g = \frac{4\pi^2 \epsilon_0 n r_g}{\ln \coth 2\pi n R} \quad \text{[farads per meter]} \tag{4–73}$$

where r_g is the grid cylinder radius and R and n have meanings as heretofore. Following the logical conclusions drawn from (4–67), the values of C_k and C_p should be the capacitances between a cylindrical electrode at the grid radius and the cathode and plate cylinders, respectively. Thus for a space-charge-free cylindrical triode, approximately, in farads per meter,

$$C_k \cong \frac{2\pi\epsilon_0}{\ln\dfrac{r_g}{r_k}} \qquad C_p \cong \frac{2\pi\epsilon_0}{\ln\dfrac{r_p}{r_g}} \qquad (4\text{–}74)$$

where r_k and r_p are cathode and plate radii. Equations (4–74) are, like (4–67), very nearly true for most interesting cases. This adaptation of the planar analysis is equally valid whether the grid wires are wound helically or lie parallel to the axis.

4.9   Conformal Transformation for Cylindrical Triodes. If the grid wires are straight and parallel to the axis, being spaced at equal circumferential intervals at grid radius r_g, a conformal transformation can be made which leads to precisely the same Z-plane figure as the planar treatment.[4d, e, i, j, 5h]   Figure 4.15 represents a cross section of such a cylindrical triode. There are n grid wires per meter of grid-circle circumference, so that the total number of grid wires is $2\pi nr_g$. The shadow fraction is $2nR$ as before. The field is to be conformally transformed into that of Fig. 4.6 in such a way that the entire circumference of the Z-plane grid circle corresponds to a sector of the W plane that includes just one grid wire, located at the middle of the sector transformed. The total angle of the actual grid circle is 2π radians, and it contains $2\pi nr_g$ grid wires, so that the angle corresponding to one grid-wire sector is $1/nr_g$ radians. This is the value that the W-plane angle ϕ must have when the Z-plane angle ϕ' is 2π radians, so that

$$\phi = \frac{1}{2\pi nr_g}\phi' \qquad (4\text{–}75)$$

The satisfactory transformation equation is

$$\ln\left(\frac{x+jy}{r_g}\right) = \frac{1}{2\pi nr_g}\ln(x'+jy') \qquad (4\text{–}76)$$

This can also be written

$$\ln\left(\frac{r}{r_g}\exp j\phi\right) = \frac{1}{2\pi nr_g}\ln(r'\exp j\phi') \qquad (4\text{–}77)$$

which expands into

$$\ln\frac{r}{r_g} + j\phi = \frac{1}{2\pi nr_g}\ln r' + \frac{j\phi'}{2\pi nr_g} \qquad (4\text{–}78)$$

This is in form to provide the desired relation between the angles, as specified by (4–75). The r_g factor in the denominator of the *left-hand side* logarithms of (4–76), (4–77), and (4–78) is introduced for convenience; it makes the grid-cylinder radius serve as a unit of measurement for the true tube dimensions and leads to the equation

$$\ln r' = 2\pi n r_g \ln \frac{r}{r_g} \tag{4–79}$$

for radius conversion between the two figures.

The meanings given to the Z-plane dimensions by this transformation of Fig. 4.15 are as follows:

$$\text{Cathode radius:} \quad \ln s_k = 2\pi n r_g \ln \frac{r_k}{r_g} \tag{4–80}$$

$$\text{Plate radius:} \quad \ln s_p = 2\pi n r_g \ln \frac{r_p}{r_g} \tag{4–81}$$

Inner and outer extremes of the transformed grid wire occur at s_1 and s_2, where

$$\ln s_1 = 2\pi n r_g \ln \left(1 - \frac{R}{r_g} \right) \tag{4–82}$$

$$\ln s_2 = 2\pi n r_g \ln \left(1 + \frac{R}{r_g} \right) \tag{4–83}$$

In all ordinary cases $R/r_g \ll 1$; therefore

$$\ln \left(1 \pm \frac{R}{r_g} \right) \cong \pm \frac{R}{r_g} \tag{4–84}$$

By the use of this relation, (4–82) and (4–83) simplify to

$$\ln s_1 \cong -2\pi n R \quad \text{or} \quad s_1 \cong \exp\left(-2\pi n R\right) \tag{4–85}$$

$$\ln s_2 \cong +2\pi n R \quad \text{or} \quad s_2 \cong \exp\left(+2\pi n R\right) \tag{4–86}$$

These are the same as (4–35) and (4–36) so that, for the usual cases in which $R/r_g \ll 1$,

$$s_g \cong \cosh 2\pi n R \tag{4–87}$$

$$R_z \cong \sinh 2\pi n R \tag{4–88}$$

as in the planar triode transformation. These are now applicable to determine the C_g per grid section (4–60). Multiplication by the number of grid sections, $2\pi n r_g$, gives (4–73). This verifies the concept used in setting up (4–73).

By using (4–81) in (4–61a) it is seen that the cylindrical geometry counterpart of (4–65) is, in W-plane dimensions,

$$C_p = \frac{2\pi\epsilon_0}{\ln \dfrac{r_p}{r_g} - \dfrac{\ln \cosh 2\pi nR}{2\pi n r_g}} \qquad \text{[farads per meter]} \qquad (4\text{–}89)$$

and similarly

$$C_k = \frac{2\pi\epsilon_0}{\ln \dfrac{r_g}{r_k} - \dfrac{\ln \cosh 2\pi nR}{2\pi n r_g}} \qquad (4\text{–}90)$$

For C_g, see (4–73).

A study of (4–89) and (4–90) will show that the equivalent grid sheet is now a cylinder such that

$$\text{Cylindrical grid sheet outer radius} = r_g(\cosh 2\pi nR)^{1/2\pi n r_g} \quad (4\text{–}91a)$$

$$\text{Cylindrical grid sheet inner radius} = \frac{r_g}{(\cosh 2\pi nR)^{1/2\pi n r_g}} \quad (4\text{–}91b)$$

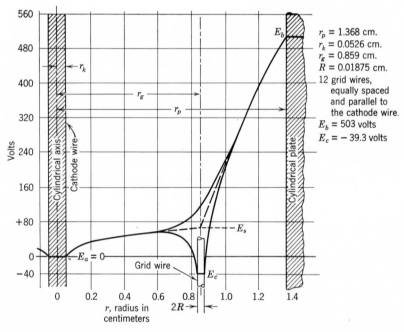

FIG. 4.16 Space-charge-free potential distribution diagram for a cylindrical triode; obtained using (4–112), therefore mathematically correct for the type of construction in which the grid wires are parallel to the tube axis; correct as to general indication of fillet size for helically wound grids.

When $2\pi n r_g = 1$, the actual triode is identical with the Z-plane triode.

It is now possible to construct a potential distribution diagram for a cylindrical triode, as shown in Fig. 4.16, by essentially the same procedure that was used in constructing the potential diagrams for a planar triode, Figs. 1.5 and 4.13b. The most obvious change in going from the planar potential distribution diagram to the cylindrical one is that the construction lines, as from E_s at the grid sheet to E_a, E_b at cathode and plate, must be logarithmic curves rather than straight lines; see Section 1.8.

Experiments have shown [4d] that the effect of a grid on space-charge-limited current values is the same, for a given shadow fraction, grid-wire diameter, and grid location, for a helically wound grid as for one having straight grid wires parallel to the axis. It is therefore reasonable to assume that (4–73), (4–89), (4–90), and (4–91) can be employed with equal validity for either type of structure.

4.10 Amplification Factor for Cylindrical Triodes. For a cylindrical triode, as for a planar triode, the amplification factor μ is C_g/C_p; thus from (4–73) and (4–89),[4d, 4B, D]

$$\mu = \frac{C_g}{C_p} = \frac{2\pi n r_g \ln \dfrac{r_p}{r_g} - \ln \cosh 2\pi n R}{\ln \coth 2\pi n R} \qquad (4\text{–}92)$$

As in the planar case, the $\ln \cosh 2\pi n R$ term in the numerator is relatively unimportant.

As a practical matter, hardly any commercial tubes employ cylindrical geometries that are sufficiently regular to make (4–92) give a μ that is even approximately correct.

4.11 Electrostatic Equivalent Circuits for Multigrid Tubes.[4g, h, j, 5h] In establishing the Z-plane boundary conditions, Fig. 4.6, the process was to remove mentally the electrode boundaries, then locate line charges in ways that make equipotentials coincide with the remembered boundary locations. In the field of $\pm\tau_a$ and $-\tau_b$, in Fig. 4.6, the equipotentials approach circles for very large values of r', also for very small values of r'. This corresponds to the fact that, in Fig. 4.14, the electric flux map approaches a uniform field more and more closely with increasing distance from the grid structure, either to the right or to the left. The factor that determines the (4–34) limitation that na and nb must not be less than perhaps unity or so is this approach to uniformity of the electric field. If na or nb are too small, the equipotentials at plate and cathode locations will not be Z-plane circles and therefore not straight lines in the W plane.

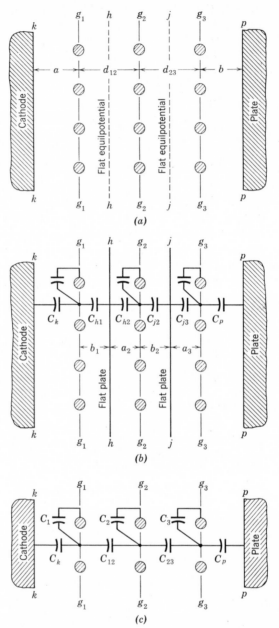

Fig. 4.17   The pentode illustrated in (a) is, in (b), resolved into three triodes, in order to demonstrate the pentode equivalent electrostatic circuit of (c).

Figure 4.17a illustrates a planar pentode in which the grids are separated far enough so that there will in fact be a region between grids 1 and 2, also between grids 2 and 3, in which the electric field is essentially uniform; see Section 4.13 and equation (4–34). This means that a plane such as hh can be found which will correspond to a *large-radius* circular equipotential in a transformation based on the first grid, and to a *small-radius* circular equipotential in a transformation based on the second grid. A similar plane equipotential jj between grids 2 and 3 is also determinable.

If, now, in such an electron-free tube, flat uncharged plates are introduced at arbitrary uniform-field locations hh and jj, no disturbance of the field whatever results. But in that case there exist three triodes, as suggested in Fig. 4.17b, whose capacitances are all completely known. (Figure 4.17b is patterned after Fig. 4.12.) Since the plates at hh and jj are uncharged, condensers C_{h1} and C_{h2} have equal charges, as do C_{j2} and C_{j3}. Thus it is possible to combine C_{h1} and C_{h2} into C_{12}, and C_{j2} and C_{j3} into C_{23}, by simple series capacitance relationships. The plates hh and jj are then dispensed with, having served the purpose of clarification of logic. Figure 4.17c results. A simpler presentation of this electrostatic equivalent circuit for a pentode appears in Fig. 4.18. It is reasonably evident, from comparison with Fig. 4.13 and (4–65) and (4–66), that in precise form

$$C_k = \frac{\epsilon_0}{a - \dfrac{\ln \cosh 2\pi n_1 R_1}{2\pi n_1}} \tag{4-93}$$

$$C_{12} = \frac{\epsilon_0}{d_{12} - \dfrac{\ln \cosh 2\pi n_1 R_1}{2\pi n_1} - \dfrac{\ln \cosh 2\pi n_2 R_2}{2\pi n_2}} \tag{4-94}$$

$$C_{23} = \frac{\epsilon_0}{d_{23} - \dfrac{\ln \cosh 2\pi n_2 R_2}{2\pi n_2} - \dfrac{\ln \cosh 2\pi n_3 R_3}{2\pi n_3}} \tag{4-95}$$

$$C_p = \frac{\epsilon_0}{b - \dfrac{\ln \cosh 2\pi n_3 R_3}{2\pi n_3}} \tag{4-96}$$

where n_1, R_1 and n_2, R_2, etc., have obvious meanings, and a, b, and the d's are as in Fig. 4.17a.

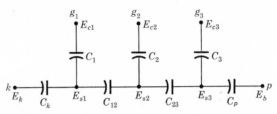

Fɪɢ. 4.18   The electrostatic equivalent circuit of a pentode. E_{s1}, E_{s2}, E_{s3} are equivalent grid sheet potentials. In general, C_1, C_2, C_3 are individually much larger than C_k, C_{12}, C_{23}, C_p.

In most cases the grid sheets are of negligible thickness; therefore the ln cosh $2\pi n R$ terms are unimportant relative to a, d_{12}, d_{23}, and b. The complete set of capacitance equations in its most useful form is therefore, per unit area,

$$C_k \cong \frac{\epsilon_0}{a} \qquad C_1 = \frac{2\pi \epsilon_0 n_1}{\ln \coth 2\pi n_1 R_1}$$

$$C_{12} \cong \frac{\epsilon_0}{d_{12}} \qquad C_2 = \frac{2\pi \epsilon_0 n_2}{\ln \coth 2\pi n_2 R_2}$$

$$C_{23} \cong \frac{\epsilon_0}{d_{23}} \qquad C_3 = \frac{2\pi \epsilon_0 n_3}{\ln \coth 2\pi n_3 R_3}$$

(4–97)

$$C_p \cong \frac{\epsilon_0}{b}$$

Three expressions similar to (4–52) can be written applying to Fig. 4.18, one for each grid sheet junction point. With all electrode potentials given, these three simultaneous equations permit the determination of E_{s1}, E_{s2}, and E_{s3}, the three equivalent grid sheet potentials. C_1, C_2, and C_3 are in general much larger than C_k, C_{12}, C_{23}, and C_p. By use of the q-plane concept of Figs. 5.4 and 5.5, E_{s1} may be found without solving a set of simultaneous algebraic equations.

Thus the procedure described for constructing a potential distribution diagram for a planar triode is extendable to a planar pentode, the placement of the construction lines being determined by the values of E_{s1}, E_{s2}, and E_{s3} as outlined in connection with Fig. 1.6. The space-charge-limited current from the cathode is determined by the equivalent grid sheet potential of the first grid.

The extension to a *cylindrical* pentode is left as an exercise for the student. Figure 4.19 illustrates in a mathematically correct form the final results of such an extension. The potential distribution near the

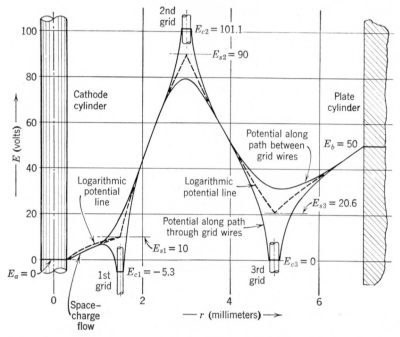

FIG. 4.19 Typical potential distribution in a cylindrical pentode; fillets mathematically determined by means of (4-112).

cathode has been drawn, according to a method described in connection with Fig. 5.7, to represent the normal condition of space-charge-limited current flow.

4.12   Triode Potential Distribution Equations.[4f, g, h, 5h] It is desirable to be able to determine mathematically the details of the electric field in the nonuniform region near the grid wires. Consider a general point T in Fig. 4.5, T' in Figs. 4.6 and 4.9. Its potential relative to the cathode can be stated on the basis of (1-24) as follows.

The contribution due to $-\tau_a$ is

$$E_T - E_a = -\frac{-\tau_a}{2\pi\epsilon_0}\ln\frac{r'}{s_k} \qquad (4\text{-}98a)$$

That due to $+\tau_a$ is

$$E_T - E_a = -\frac{+\tau_a}{2\pi\epsilon_0}\ln\frac{\sqrt{r'^2 + s_h^2 - 2r's_h\cos\phi'}}{s_h \pm s_k} \qquad (4\text{-}98b)$$

That due to $-\tau_b$ is

$$E_T - E_a = -\frac{-\tau_b}{2\pi\epsilon_0}\ln\frac{\sqrt{r'^2 + s_g^2 - 2r's_g\cos\phi'}}{s_g \pm s_k} \qquad (4\text{-}98c)$$

The $\pm s_k$ in the denominators indicates that the point on the cathode whose potential is being referred to might equally well be distant s_k *toward* the grid or s_k *away from* the grid, from the Z-plane origin. Or the cathode point of reference might be on the cathode surface just above or below the origin. But the boundary conditions require that *all* these points have the same potential; that can be true only if s_k is ignorable relative to s_h and s_g in (4–98b) and (4–98c). That is reasonably true if $na > 1$, for then $s_k < \exp(-2\pi)$, that is, $s_k < 0.0025$, whereas s_h and s_g are of the order of unity. Therefore the $\pm s_k$ terms will be dropped. The charge $+\tau_b$ uniformly distributed over the plate circle will produce no electric field within the plate circle, and therefore will not affect the potential difference between T and the cathode. To obtain $E_T - E_a$ due to all charges, one may add the three (4–98) contributions algebraically, as will be done in a later paragraph.

It is convenient to express the final result, for the near-to-the-grid potential distribution, relative to the equivalent grid sheet potential E_s rather than relative to the cathode potential E_a. This requires that E_a be eliminated in favor of E_s. This will be accomplished by making use of the fact that E_a and E_s are the terminations of the cathode-to-grid straight construction line in Fig. 4.13, also of the logarithmically shaped Z-plane counterpart of this construction line.

It is apparent that in Fig. 4.13

$$E_s - E_a = \begin{bmatrix} \text{Potential gra-} \\ \text{dient be-} \\ \text{tween cath-} \\ \text{ode and grid} \end{bmatrix} \begin{bmatrix} \begin{pmatrix} \text{Value of } x \text{ at} \\ \text{the near} \\ \text{face of the} \\ \text{grid sheet} \end{pmatrix} - \begin{pmatrix} \text{Value} \\ \text{of } x \\ \text{at the} \\ \text{cathode} \end{pmatrix} \end{bmatrix} \quad (4\text{--}99)$$

It is convenient to use a Z-plane rather than this W-plane form of this relation to eliminate E_a. To obtain the Z-plane form, the Z-plane boundaries of the equivalent grid sheet must be determined.

From (4–68), the W-plane location of the two faces of the equivalent grid sheet are at

$$x = \pm \frac{\ln \cosh 2\pi nR}{2\pi n} \; ; \text{that is, } 2\pi nx = \pm \ln \cosh 2\pi nR \quad (4\text{--}100a)$$

Use of this in the transformation equation (4–30) relating r' to x shows that the inner and outer faces of the equivalent grid sheet appear on the Z-plane representation at the following locations:

At the outer
face of the $\Big\}$ $r' = \exp(+\ln \cosh 2\pi nR) = \cosh 2\pi nR = s_g$ $\quad (4\text{--}100b)$
grid sheet

At the inner face of the grid sheet $\Big\} r' = \exp\left(-\ln\cosh 2\pi nR\right) = \dfrac{1}{s_g} = s_h$ (4–100c)

These inner and outer cylindrical surfaces bounding the Z-plane equivalent grid sheet are the dashed circles of Fig. 4.9.

It is apparent now that the Z-plane counterpart of (4–99) is

$$E_s - E_a = -\frac{-\tau_a}{2\pi\epsilon_0}\ln\frac{s_h}{s_k} \qquad (4\text{–}101)$$

Note that this is dependent only on the cathode charge $-\tau_a$, and not at all on τ_b, just as in (4–99) only the potential gradient described by the slope of the cathode-to-grid construction line is involved.

Note that in obtaining this relationship between E_a and E_s only the construction line, *not the actual potential distribution*, has been employed.

Addition of the three (4–98) contributions to $E_T - E_a$ gives

$$E_T - E_a = -\frac{-\tau_a}{2\pi\epsilon_0}\ln\frac{r'}{s_k} + \frac{-\tau_a}{2\pi\epsilon_0}\ln\frac{\sqrt{r'^2 + s_h{}^2 - 2r's_h\cos\phi'}}{s_h}$$

$$+ \frac{+\tau_b}{2\pi\epsilon_0}\ln\frac{\sqrt{r'^2 + s_g{}^2 - 2r's_g\cos\phi'}}{s_g} \qquad (4\text{–}102a)$$

Elimination of E_a by the use of the preceding equation, and of s_h by means of the substitution $s_h = 1/s_g$, followed by rearrangement into convenient form, leads to the following very useful equation for the potential distribution, relative to E_s:

$$E_T - E_s = +\frac{-\tau_a}{2\pi\epsilon_0}\ln\sqrt{1 + \frac{1}{r'^2 s_g{}^2} - \frac{2}{r's_g}\cos\phi'}$$

$$+ \frac{+\tau_b}{2\pi\epsilon_0}\ln\sqrt{1 + \frac{r'^2}{s_g{}^2} - \frac{2r'}{s_g}\cos\phi'} \qquad (4\text{–}102b)$$

In planar geometry, at a point for which r' is very large ($r' \gg s_g$), this reduces to

$$E_T - E_s \cong \frac{+\tau_b}{2\pi\epsilon_0}\ln\frac{r'}{s_g} \qquad (4\text{–}103a)$$

$$\cong \frac{+\tau_b n}{\epsilon_0}\left(x - \frac{\ln\cosh 2\pi nR}{2\pi n}\right) \qquad (4\text{–}103b)$$

where x is numerically positive. At a point for which r' is very small

$$E_T - E_s \cong \frac{-\tau_a}{2\pi\epsilon_0} \ln \frac{1}{r's_g} \qquad (4\text{--}104a)$$

$$\cong \frac{-\tau_a n}{\epsilon_0} \left(-x - \frac{\ln \cosh 2\pi nR}{2\pi n} \right) \qquad (4\text{--}104b)$$

where x is numerically negative.

Equations (4–103) and (4–104) are, of course, the equations of the straight construction lines in Fig. 4.13b, so that

$$-\frac{-\tau_a n}{\epsilon_0} = \begin{cases} \text{the slope of the cathode-to-grid construction} \\ \quad \text{line, therefore the potential gradient de-} \\ \quad \text{scribed by that line} \end{cases} \qquad (4\text{--}105a)$$

$$+\frac{+\tau_b n}{\epsilon_0} = \begin{cases} \text{the slope of the grid-to-plate construction} \\ \quad \text{line, therefore the potential gradient de-} \\ \quad \text{scribed by that line} \end{cases} \qquad (4\text{--}105b)$$

Because potential gradient and electric flux density are related by the proportionality factor ϵ_0, the quantities $-\tau_a n$ and $\tau_b n$ are the flux densities in the respective regions, and are therefore also surface-charge densities in coulombs per unit area, at W-plane plate and cathode surfaces. They may therefore also be identified with the charges on the star per-unit-area capacitances C_k and C_p of Fig. 4.10c; thus

$$(E_s - E_a)C_k = -(-\tau_a n) \qquad (4\text{--}106a)$$

$$(E_s - E_b)C_p = -\tau_b n \qquad (4\text{--}106b)$$

These equations represent the simple and direct way of finding the charge factors for use in the triode potential distribution expressions. It is often desirable to use the complete equations (4–62), (4–64), or (4–61) for C_k, C_p, rather than using (4–67).

Note that for triode conditions commonly considered $-\tau_a$ is negative and τ_b positive, making the (4–105) potential gradients positive in both regions.

In determining the potential distributions in the neighborhoods of the various grids of tetrodes or pentodes, the appropriate adaptation of (4–105) to determine the charge factors is recommended, as being less subject to confusion of concept than is the adaptation of (4–106).

In order to determine the *equations* for the fillets in Figs. 4.13b (also Figs. 1.5, 1.6, 4.16, and 4.19), ϕ' must be given the value zero for the path through grid-wire centers and the value π for the path midway between grid wires. The fillet equation becomes

$$E_T - E_s = + \frac{1}{2\pi n} \frac{(-\tau_a n)}{\epsilon_0} \ln \left| 1 \pm \frac{1}{r' s_g} \right|$$

$$+ \frac{1}{2\pi n} \frac{\tau_b n}{\epsilon_0} \ln \left| 1 \pm \frac{r'}{s_g} \right| \quad (4\text{-}107)$$

where the minus signs refer to the through-grid-wire paths and the plus signs to between-grid-wire paths. From (4–105) $+\tau_b n/\epsilon_0$ is known because it is the voltage gradient of the construction line to the right of the grid in Fig. 4.13, and $-(-\tau_a)n/\epsilon_0$ is that of the construction line to the left of the grid, or (4–106) may be used.

The equation for the potential profile in the plane of the W-plane grid-wire centers is obtained by letting $r' = 1$ in (4–102), ϕ' being the position variable. Thus, in the plane of the grid centers

$$E_T - E_s = \left(+ \frac{-\tau_a n}{\epsilon_0} + \frac{+\tau_b n}{\epsilon_0} \right) \frac{1}{2\pi n} \ln \sqrt{1 + \frac{1}{s_g^2} - \frac{2 \cos \phi'}{s_g}} \quad (4\text{-}108a)$$

The quantity in parentheses is the algebraic difference between the gradients of the two adjacent construction lines. Therefore, if the two gradients are identical, as when there is no charge on the grid, the parenthetical quantity is zero. In that case the plane containing the grid centers is an equipotential.

Equations (4–106) may be introduced into (4–52), and the resulting expression solved for the sum of the charges $-\tau_a n$ and $\tau_b n$. Introduction of this sum converts (4–108a) to

$$E_T - E_s = \frac{(E_s - E_c)C_g}{2\pi\epsilon_0 n} \ln \sqrt{1 + \frac{1}{s_g^2} - \frac{2 \cos \phi'}{s_g}} \quad (4\text{-}108b)$$

Introduction of (4–63) for C_g reduces this to

$$E_T - E_s = \frac{E_s - E_c}{\ln \coth 2\pi n R} \ln \sqrt{1 + \frac{1}{s_g^2} - \frac{2 \cos \phi'}{s_g}} \quad (4\text{-}108c)$$

as the most convenient expression for the potential distribution in the plane containing the grid centers.

For any set of charges, the potential at the point midway between grid wires is obtained by letting $\phi' = 0$ in (4–108a) or (4–108c), or by letting $r' = 1$ in the positive-sign version of (4–107). Thus with T at the point midway between grid wires:

$$E_T - E_s = \left(+ \frac{-\tau_a n}{\epsilon_0} + \frac{+\tau_b n}{\epsilon_0} \right) \frac{1}{2\pi n} \ln \left(1 + \frac{1}{s_g} \right) \qquad (4\text{–}109a)$$

Also, as derived from (4–108c),

$$E_T - E_s = \frac{E_s - E_c}{\ln \coth 2\pi n R} \ln \left(1 + \frac{1}{\cosh 2\pi n R} \right) \qquad (4\text{–}109b)$$

For the usable range of values of $2nR$, from zero to about $\frac{1}{5}$, the factor $\ln [1 + (1/\cosh 2\pi n R)]$ varies only from 0.693 to about 0.604. Thus the first form, (4–109a), indicates that the potential at the point midway between grid wires differs from E_s by an amount which is:

(a) Proportional to the algebraic difference between the slopes of the adjacent construction lines.

(b) Proportional to the spacing $1/n$ between grid-wire centers.

(c) Proportional to a declining but very insensitive function of the shadow fraction, this function being $\ln [1 + (1/s_g)]$.

A good approximation to (4–109a) is obtained by using $s_g = 1$, giving for the point midway between grid wires

$$E_T - E_s \cong \left(\frac{-\tau_a n}{\epsilon_0} + \frac{\tau_b n}{\epsilon_0} \right) \frac{0.105}{n} \qquad (4\text{–}110)$$

This permits a quick estimate of the midway-between-grid-wire potential, useful in sketching fillets in a diagram such as Fig. 4.13b, with $\tau n / \epsilon_0$ values obtained from (4–105).

As (4–102b) and forms derived from it express potentials relative to E_s, they apply in the neighborhood of any grid in a tetrode or pentode, with adjacent construction-line gradients, shadow fractions, and grid spacings given the proper value for each grid. See, however, the comments made a few lines below (4–106) regarding the application to multigrid tubes.

Equation (4–102b) and many forms derived from it are stated for Z-plane rather than W-plane geometry, and therefore apply equally well to cylindrical and planar W-plane geometry, except that in the application to cylindrical geometry the cylindrical transformations apply, and the following expressions serve the purposes which (4–105) and (4–106) accomplish in the planar case:

Charge, per unit length, located
   outside of grid, including all grid $\Big\} = +\tau_b \cdot 2\pi n r_g = -(E_s - E_b)C_p$
   sections $\qquad (4\text{–}111a)$

FIG. 4.20 Flux map for a negative-grid cylindrical triode, space-charge-free condition, obtained by a fluid flow technique.[4c] Note the clarity of definition of the singular points and ease of measuring ratio of cathode charge to grid charge. (Courtesy of Professor A. D. Moore, Dept. of Electrical Engineering, University of Michigan.)

Charge, per unit length, located
inside of grid, including all grid
sections

$$= -\tau_a \cdot 2\pi nr_g = -(E_s - E_a)C_k$$

$$(4-111b)$$

where $2\pi nr_g$ is, for axial grid wires, the total number of grid wires around the circumference.

Thus (4–107) for the fillets becomes, for cylindrical geometry,

$$E_T - E_s = + \frac{-\tau_a \cdot 2\pi nr_g}{4\pi^2 \epsilon_0 nr_g} \ln \left| 1 \pm \frac{1}{r's_g} \right|$$

$$+ \frac{+\tau_b \cdot 2\pi nr_g}{4\pi^2 \epsilon_0 nr_g} \ln \left| 1 \pm \frac{r'}{s_g} \right| \quad (4-112)$$

The quantities $\tau_b \cdot 2\pi nr_g$ and $-\tau_a \cdot 2\pi nr_g$ are the charges on the electrostatic equivalent circuit capacitances that are located respectively to the right and left of the grid sheet junction, in cylindrical-geometry diagrams comparable with Figs. 4.12, 4.17, and 4.18. Equation (4–108a) should be correspondingly modified for convenience in use.

The fillet equations for cylindrical geometry apply formally only for grid wires lying parallel to the axis. However, for practical purposes, they indicate relatively well the nature of the fillets for any orientation of grid wires, as long as shadow fraction, grid spacing (normal to grid wires), and grid placement are unchanged.

Equation (4–102b) and various forms derived from it were employed in the numerical computations for Figs. 1.5, 4.14, 4.16, and 4.19. See also the flux map of Fig. 4.20, obtained by a fluid flow technique.

4.13 Limitations to the Correctness of Equivalent Electrostatic Circuit Relations. It is useful to review the limitations to which the equivalent electrostatic circuit relations are subject, as follows:

(a) The Z-plane grid figure of Fig. 4.6 is treated as though it were a perfect circle; actually it is very nearly circular as long as the shadow fraction $2nR$ does not exceed $\frac{1}{6}$. Fair results are obtainable as long as $2nR$ does not appreciably exceed $\frac{1}{5}$.

(b) The analysis assumes that the plate circle is remote enough from the grid location to make the Z-plane electric field adjacent to the plate essentially uniform, that is, $s_p \gg s_g$. This is necessary in order to make all cathode and grid charges appear to be located at the axis of the system, as viewed by an observer located at the plate circle. The requirement $s_p \gg s_g$ is about the same as $s_p \gg 1$; a convenient way of insuring that $s_p \gg 1$ is to impose the limitation $nb > 1$, as discussed in connection with (4–34). This is sometimes too severe a limitation. For example, in Fig. 1.5, also in Fig. 4.14, $nb = \frac{8}{9}$, so that (4–34) is not quite satisfied, yet the conformal analysis gives very satisfactory results, because s_p exceeds s_g by a ratio great enough to make the electric field essentially uniform adjacent to the cathode. This is demonstrated in Fig. 1.5 by the almost complete merging of the fillets with the straight construction line before the plate is reached; in Fig. 4.14 the flux map adjacent to the plate quite obviously represents a uniform field.

(c) In order similarly to make the electric field be essentially uniform adjacent to the W-plane cathode, the analysis must assume that the cathode is remote enough from the grid so that the Z-plane cathode circle is not much more than a point, on a scale that represents the details of the grid-circle location and size satisfactorily. This requirement $s_k \ll s_g$ is not greatly different from $s_k \ll 1$, leading to $na > 1$ as in (4–34). Just as for the $nb > 1$ limitation, this is sometimes too severe a restriction.

Most commercial triodes whose geometry is sufficiently regular to encourage any attempt to apply the conformal analysis will be found to satisfy the limitations stated as to $2nR$, na, and nb.

When the cathode is so close to the grid that the $na > 1$ limitation is definitely not satisfied but $2nR$ is small enough to make the Z-plane grid figure essentially circular, a more extensive imaging procedure may sometimes be employed to study the field details in an adequately quantitative manner.[4h, 5h, j, k, l] In such cases the electric field is not uniform adjacent to the cathode, and the surface-charge density varies along the cathode surface.

4.14. Triode Interelectrode Capacitances.[4k] In Fig. 4.10b the delta capacitances C_{kg}, C_{gp}, and C_{pk} are the contributions of the active electrode structure to the *interelectrode capacitances* of the tube (some-times called the *direct interelectrode capacitances*).

Discussions in previous sections of this chapter have dealt only with portions of the tube geometry actively related to the control of the flow of electrons, exclusive of the electrode-supporting structure and lead-in wires. In dealing with an actual tube, a capacitance bridge may be used to measure first the capacitance between k and g, p connected together, then that between p and g, k connected together, and then that between g and p, k connected together. These measurements interpreted in the light of the circuits of Figs. 4.10b and 4.10c permit the statement of *measured* values of C_{kg}, C_{gp}, and C_{pk}, also of C_k, C_g, and C_p. These measured values will include the contributions from electrode-supporting structures and lead-in wires and will be larger than values calculated from (4–62), (4–63), (4–64), or (4–67). Such measurements are usually made with the cathode unheated, therefore not emitting electrons.

There is another principle of capacitance measurement, not particu-larly useful practically, which is very illuminating as to the nature of interelectrode capacitances, and provides the basis for the formal definition of the term "interelectrode capacitance." If one terminal of an a-c supply source is connected to the plate of a triode, the other to the grid and also to the cathode, an a-c ammeter in the *cathode* lead-in connection measures the current to C_{pk} only. With the a-c voltage, the measured cathode current, and the frequency known, C_{pk} is determinable. Note that the ammeter must *not* carry the grid lead-in current, if the objective is to determine C_{pk}. *Thus it is in principle possible to measure an individual interelectrode capacitance,* by simultaneous observation of one a-c voltage and one a-c current.

The ratio between the current and the voltage determined in this way is called the *short-circuit transfer admittance* between two electrodes involved, and the interelectrode capacitance is "the capacitance determined from the short-circuit transfer admittance," according to definitions given in the 1950 *Standards on Electron Tubes* of the Institute of Radio Engineers.[4k] In these *Standards*, this definition of interelectrode capacitance in terms of short-circuit transfer admittance is a specialization of more general statements as to the nature of *electron-tube admittances*. These statements deserve careful study because of the extensions of concept they introduce.

To calculate from the geometry of the triode the contributions, to the interelectrode capacitances, of the electron-controlling portions of the structure, the star capacitances C_k, C_g, and C_p of Fig. 4.10c are determined from the geometry; the contributions to the interelectrode capacitances are then obtained by means of (4–50) and its two symmetrical counterparts.

A method for evaluating the effect of space charge on interelectrode capacitance under certain important conditions appears in Section 5.6.

4.15 Interelectrode Capacitances of Multigrid Tubes.[4k] In this section it will be shown how the interelectrode capacitances of the electron-controlling portions of a multigrid tube can be calculated from the geometry.

If a fourth electrode is added to a triode, there will be six interelectrode capacitances, consisting of three having a delta relationship to the original three electrodes, plus one capacitance from each of the original three to the fourth electrode. The three capacitances having the delta relationship to the original three electrodes will have their value changed by the introduction of the fourth electrode. If the tube becomes a pentode, there must then be six interelectrode capacitances associated with the first four electrodes, plus one from each of the first four to the fifth electrode, making a total of ten.

A useful form of schematic diagram showing the ten interelectrode capacitances of a pentode appears in Fig. 4.21a. The corresponding electrostatic equivalent circuit appears in Fig. 4.21b, modified from Fig. 4.18. The arrangement of an a-c voltage source, voltmeter, ammeter, and set of connections shown dotted in Fig. 4.21a is designed to measure the short-circuit transfer admittance Y_{kg_1} due to C_{kg_1}, thus permitting a direct determination of C_{kg_1}. Of course Y_{kg_1} is the ratio of the ammeter current to the generator voltage. No other current

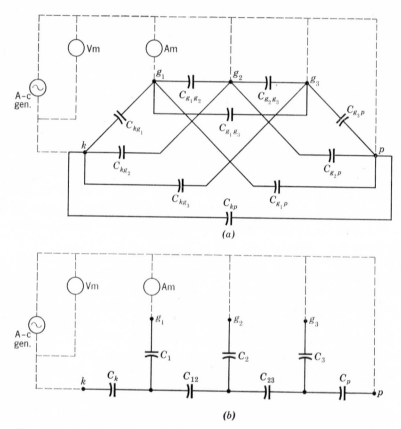

Fig. 4.21   Pentode electrostatic circuits. (a) Interelectrode capacitances for a pentode, with circuit (dotted), illustrating a not practical but very instructive circuit for measuring C_{kg_1}. (b) Same measuring circuit as in (a), applied to the equivalent electrostatic circuit.

than that to C_{kg_1} flows through the ammeter to electrode g_1, because g_2, g_3, and p are all at the same potential as g_1.

The measurement method indicated by Fig. 4.21 is not an experimentally useful method of determining C_{kg_1}, but the principles involved clarify the nature of interelectrode capacitances; it corresponds exactly to the concepts involved in the definition of interelectrode capacitance.

As the electrostatic equivalent circuit of Fig. 4.21b does in fact represent the electrostatic relationships between the electrodes, and measuring arrangements are the same in the two circuit diagrams shown in the figure, the ratio of the ammeter current to the generator voltage must be the same for the two circuits. This ratio can be *calculated* easily from Fig. 4.21b, if C_k, C_1, C_{12}, C_2, C_{23}, etc., are all known, by using series-parallel methods of circuit reduction. When so calculated, this ratio permits determination of C_{kg1} in Fig. 4.21a. Thus the interelectrode capacitance C_{kg_1} of Fig. 4.21a can be analytically determined from Fig. 4.21b, if the C's in the latter figure are known.

A similar method can of course be used for determining any of the other interelectrode capacitances of Fig. 4.21a, by employing the known values of the C's of Fig. 4.21b. The dependence of these C's on geometry is given by (4–97). Note that the *seven* C's of Fig. 4.21b are thus used to find the *ten* C's of Fig. 4.21a.

4.16   Determination of Input and Output Capacitance Currents. In the usual pentode amplifier circuit, purely d-c potentials are applied to the second and third grids, so that these two electrodes may be considered as being at r-f ground potential. The important uses of interelectrode capacitance values, given in commercial tube manuals, are to permit calculation in particular circuits of the capacitive currents drawn by the first grid and the plate. For this purpose the r-f voltages from first grid to cathode and from plate to cathode are presumed to be known. The various capacitive currents can then be calculated by a method employing the "input capacitance," the "output capacitance," and the grid-plate capacitance. According to the 1950 *Standards on Electron Tubes* of the Institute of Radio Engineers: [4k]

The *input capacitance* is "the short-circuit transfer capacitance between the input terminal and all other terminals, except the output terminal, connected together. (Note: This quantity is equivalent to the sum of the interelectrode capacitances between the input electrode and all other electrodes except the output electrode.)"

The *output capacitance* is "the short-circuit transfer capacitance between the output terminal and all other terminals, except the input terminal, connected together." This is, of course, equivalent to the sum of the interelectrode capacitances between the output electrode and all other electrodes except the input electrode.

In the usual pentode amplifier, according to these definitions,

$$\text{Input capacitance} = C_{kg_1} + C_{g_1g_2} + C_{g_1g_3} \qquad (4\text{–}113)$$

$$\text{Output capacitance} = C_{pk} + C_{pg_2} + C_{pg_3} \qquad (4\text{–}114)$$

The input and output currents may be determined as follows:

(a) The portion of the input capacitive current that is due to the input capacitance is determined as the current caused to flow in the input capacitance by the r-f grid voltage, which appears across that capacitance.

(b) The portion of the input capacitive current that is due to the grid-plate capacitance is determined as the r-f current caused to flow in C_{g_1p} by the r-f grid and plate voltages in combination. In the common simple amplifier, having a 180° input-to-output phase shift, the potential of the plate swings down during the same portion of the cycle that the potential of the first grid swings up. Therefore the total r-f voltage across C_{g_1p} is the numerically additive sum of the two r-f voltages. Because the plate r-f voltage may be 10 to 100 times larger than the grid r-f voltage, this input capacitive current through C_{g_1p} may be many times larger than the (a) contribution, unless C_{g_1p} is extremely small. An important design feature of any good pentode is that C_{g_1p} is kept small.

(c) The total input capacitive current is obtained as the numerically additive sum of the (a) and (b) contributions, if the amplifier phase shift is 180°.

(d) The portion of the output capacitive current that is due to the output capacitance is determined as the current caused to flow in the output capacitance by the r-f plate voltage, which appears across that capacitance.

(e) The portion of the output capacitive current due to the grid-plate capacitance is just the current found in (b) above. This is usually much less than the (d) current.

(f) The total output capacitive current is the numerically additive sum of the (d) and (e) contributions, if the amplifier phase shift is 180°.

This same type of procedure may be employed with a triode or a tetrode. For the triode, the (b) contribution to input current is likely to be undesirably large, as the values of C_{gp} for a triode are usually not small. The fact that C_{g_1p} for a tetrode, or a pentode, can be made very small represents one of the overriding advantages of a pentode or tetrode as compared with a triode, for high-gain r-f amplification. The advantage accrues partly from the fact that the triode's large input capacitive current can produce a positive feedback (the "Miller effect"), causing undesired oscillatory behavior ("parasitic oscillations").

PROBLEMS

1. Dimensions of a certain planar triode (Fig. 4.5) are: $a = 0.16$ cm, $b = 0.08$ cm, $2nR = 0.12$, $n = 10$ per cm; cathode area 2 sq cm. Find: (a) star capacitances C_k, C_g, C_p (see Fig. 4.10); (b) amplification factor; (c) interelectrode capacitances; (d) input, output, and grid-plate capacitances (Sections 4.14, 4.16).

2. For the triode of Prob. 1, let $E_b = 250$, $E_c = -17.5$.

(a) Evaluate the equivalent grid sheet potential E_s (no space charge).

(b) On a diagram like Fig. 1.5, construct a potential distribution diagram for these voltages, carefully and to scale. *Use appropriate straight construction lines;* sketch fillets to distinguish between potential distribution along a path through grid-wire centers and that along a path passing midway between grid wires.

(c) Sketch potential distribution in the grid-wire plane [consistent with (b)].

(d) For $E_b = 250$, $E_c = -70$, repeat (a) and (b).

(e) For $E_b = 250$, at what E_c will $E_s = 0$ (the cut-off condition)?

3. Planar triode: $C_k = 9$, $C_p = 3$, $C_g = 21$ ($\mu\mu$f); cathode area 4 sq cm; no space charge. (a) If $E_c = -8$, what value of E_b will make the potential gradient at the cathode be zero? (b) Shadow fraction is 0.15; find the number of grid wires *per centimeter.*

4. Planar tetrode: electrode spacings are: cathode to grid, 1.5 mm; control grid to second grid, 2.5 mm; second grid to plate, 2.0 mm. Equivalent grid sheet potentials are: $E_{s1} = +9$, $E_{s2} = +70$; electrode potentials are: $E_{c1} = -3$, $E_{c2} = +80$, $E_b = +40$.

(a) Sketch carefully *to scale*, using straight construction lines, a potential distribution diagram for potential along paths through and between grid wires; no space charge.

(b) Sketch the equivalent electrostatic circuit; label the capacitances. Cathode surface area 3 sq cm. Find the capacitance magnitudes; to find C_1 and C_2, note that there is no net charge at the s_1 and s_2 junctions.

(c) Find the input, output, and grid-plate (C_{g1p}) capacitances.

5. Planar pentode: cathode surface area 4 sq cm. In the equivalent electrostatic circuit, Fig. 4.18, $C_1 = 20$, $C_2 = 30$, $C_3 = 10$, $C_k = 6$, $C_{12} = 3$, $C_{23} = 2$, $C_p = 4$ ($\mu\mu$f).

(a) Find the spacings between the various electrodes; also, with shadow fractions $\frac{1}{6}$ for the first and second grids, $\frac{1}{12}$ for the third grid, find grid-wire spacing and diameter for all grids.

(b) Find input, output, and grid-plate (C_{g1p}) capacitances.

6. Tube of Prob. 5: $E_{s1} = +10$, $E_{c1} = -10$, $E_{c3} = 0$, $E_b = +60$; find E_{s2}, E_{s3}, E_{c2}.

7. Planar pentode: electrode spacings are: cathode to grid, 1 mm; control grid to screen, 2 mm; screen to suppressor grid, 2.5 mm; suppressor grid to plate, 1.5 mm. Potentials are: $E_{c1} = -10$, $E_{c2} = +120$, $E_{c3} = 0$, $E_b = +60$, $E_{s1} = +10$, $E_{s2} = +100$, $E_{s3} = +30$.

(a) Construct carefully *to scale*, using straight construction lines, the cathode-to-anode potential distribution diagram, with carefully sketched fillets.

(b) Sketch the potential distribution in the control grid plane consistent with (a).

8. Cylindrical triode dimensions: $r_k = 1$ mm, $r_g = 3$ mm, $r_p = 6$ mm, length of active structure 2 cm. Shadow fraction 0.10; $n = 20$ grid wires per cm. Find: (a) capacitances C_k, C_g, C_p, in the equivalent electrostatic circuit; (b) amplification factor; (c) input, output, and grid-plate capacitances.

9. Cylindrical triode such that: $r_k = 1$ mm, $r_g = 10$ mm, $r_p = 30$ mm, amplification factor 20, active axial length 10 cm, shadow fraction 0.10. Determine C_p, C_k, C_g, R, n; also the input, output, and grid-plate capacitances.

10. Cylindrical pentode; electrode radius values, $r_k = 1$, $r_{g1} = 3$, $r_{g2} = 5$, $r_{g3} = 8$, $r_p = 12$ (mm). Electrode and equivalent grid sheet potentials: $E_{c1} = -20$, $E_{c2} = +230$, $E_{c3} = 0$, $E_b = 150$; $E_{s1} = +10$, $E_{s2} = +200$, $E_{s3} = +20$.

(a) Sketch to scale the cathode-to-plate potential distribution diagram, showing construction lines (logarithmic) and carefully sketched fillets.

(b) Find all grid-wire spacings and diameters, if $2n_1R_1 = 2n_2R_2 = \frac{1}{6}$, $2n_3R_3 = \frac{1}{12}$.

11. Two infinitely extending flat grids lie parallel to each other, separated by spacing s. Their wire-to-wire spacings are of the same magnitude $1/n$, but the grid-wire radii R_1 and R_2 are not the same. Shadow fractions are less than $\frac{1}{5}$ for both grids.

(a) Express the capacitance between these two grids, per unit area, for ns values such that equivalent electrostatic circuit concepts apply.

(b) Below what value of ns do these concepts cease to be satisfactory approximations? Justify your answer analytically.

(c) Determine the (a) capacitance for ns values such that equivalent electrostatic circuit concepts do not apply—that is, there is no region between them for which the field is essentially uniform. (This requires placement of equal Z-plane charges at mutual kernels of two grid figures.)

(d) Is there a theoretical lower limit to ns for the (c) procedure?

12. A "grid" of parallel wires 1 cm in diameter and spaced 2 meters apart is supported 10 meters above the ground.

(a) Sketch and dimension the corresponding Z-plane figure, treating the ground as the cathode of Fig. 4.5; there is no "plate" and no plate charge.

(b) Sketch and dimension the Z-plane figure obtained by treating the ground as the plate of Fig. 4.5; there is no "cathode" and no cathode charge.

(c) Draw the "electrostatic equivalent circuit"; evaluate its capacitances.

(d) State each wire's charge (coulombs per meter), at 30,000 volts above ground.

(e) Find potential difference between ground and a point midway between two adjacent wires, using the Z-plane diagram in (a), then that in (b).

13. A certain Z-plane representation shows: (1) a plate, $s_p = 200$; (2) a grid wire, $s_g = 1.071$, $R_z = 0.389$; (3) a very small cathode circle, center at $\phi' = \pi$, $r' = 1.002$ (approximately 1.00), radius $R_k = 0.0628$. (This cathode *is not located at the Z-plane origin;* there is no electrode at the Z-plane origin.)

(a) Using $n = 10$ wires per cm, sketch and dimension the W-plane figure.

(b) A W-plane point T lies midway between the plate and the grid plane, and $\frac{1}{4}$ of the distance from one grid wire to the next. State x, y, r', ϕ' at T; locate T' on the Z plane.

(c) The cathode circle is so small that three line charges, $-\tau_a$ inside the cathode, and $+\tau_a$, $-\tau_b$ inside the grid, establish the boundary equipotentials. Show that radius from Z-plane origin to the charge $+\tau_a$ must now be 1 rather than $1/s_g$.

(d) Express the star C's, also the amplification factor and E_s, in terms of dimensions and E_b, E_c.

14. In Fig. 4.5, let $a = b = 1/2n$, and $R = 1/3n$. Sketch the Z-plane cathode, anode, and grid (be careful) approximately to scale. Locate on the Z plane these points: $x = 0$, $y = \pm R$; $x = \pm R$, $y = 0$; $x = 0$, $y = 0$.

15. Planar triode, shadow fraction $\frac{1}{5}$, grid-wire radius 0.1 mm.

(a) Determine grid-wire spacing and equivalent grid sheet thickness.

(b) In the uniform field region well beyond the grid the potential gradient is 40 volts per mm; in the similar region away from the grid toward the cathode it is 10 volts per mm. On a diagram of volts vs. distance, in which grid-wire diameter and grid sheet thickness are marked, draw straight construction lines describing these gradients, terminating respectively on the two faces of the equivalent grid sheet and at the equivalent grid sheet potential E_s (here the reference potential).

(c) Use the given potential gradients to determine τ_a and τ_b (line charges per grid section) in the triode potential distribution equations.

(d) Determine the potential difference between the equivalent grid sheet and a grid wire by using grid-wire-surface coordinates in the potential distribution equation. Locate the grid-wire potential on the (b) diagram.

PROBLEMS 127

(e) Plot near-the-grid potential distribution curves through and between grid wires, by use of triode potential distribution equations. Carry each way from the grid until fillets and construction lines merge. (Neither cathode nor plate is involved in this problem.)

16. In the Prob. 1 planar triode, let $E_b = 250$. Select E_c from among the following: -17.5, -35, -52.5, -70 (volts). Using this value, find E_s and the gradients in the uniform-field regions each way from the grid. Then:

(a) Determine the values of $-\tau_a$ and $-\tau_b$, in the Z-plane diagram.

(b) Calculate points for and plot curves of the space-charge-free potential distribution (relative to E_s) through and between grid wires. Use for x: -0.16, -0.12, -0.08, -0.04, -0.02, $+0.02$, $+0.04$, $+0.08$ (centimeters).

(c) Plot, to an enlarged scale, near-to-the-grid potential distribution curves; also the straight "construction lines" terminating on the two opposite grid sheet faces. Show grid sheet thickness, also grid-wire diameter, on the diagram.

(d) Set up an equation for the potential distribution, in the plane $y = 1/4n$, and plot on the (b) diagram.

17. Determine r_k, r_g, r_p for a cylindrical triode (Fig. 4.15) that corresponds to the Prob. 1 planar triode. Use 18 equally spaced parallel-to-the-axis grid wires. The shadow fraction, true grid-wire radius, and Z-plane dimensions are as in Prob. 1. Draw potential distribution curves corresponding to those asked for in Prob. 16, using the same E_b and E_c. All potentials of individual plotted points, also E_s, are unchanged. The values of true r at which they are plotted are those corresponding to values of x used in the planar geometry.

18. Check analytically the potential constructions in Figs. 1.5 and 4.16.

19. The cathode of a General Electric FP-110 triode is a W-shaped filament in a plane midway between two parallel-plane electrodes, one being the plate; the other performs the function of the grid in the usual triode. Thus Fig. 4.5 may represent the FP-110 tube, except that the left plate is a "plane-surfaced grid," and n and R are the spacing and filament radius of the grid-like cathode. Suppose that in a tube of this general type plate and plane-surfaced grid are 0.2 cm apart, the grid-like cathode being midway between them. Cathode-wire radius 0.004 cm; 3 wires per cm.

(a) Cathode and plane-surfaced grid are at zero potential, plate $+80$ volts. Sketch the space-charge-free potential distribution along a path from plane-surfaced grid to plate, passing through a cathode wire, also along one passing midway between cathode wires. Use no mathematics; apply principles illustrated in other developments.

(b) Repeat (a) with cathode at zero volts, plate $+80$, plane-surfaced grid -150.

(c) State whether or not plate current will flow in either the (a) or (b) condition, or both, explaining by reference to the diagrams.

(d) Plate at $+80$ volts relative to cathode. Estimate the approximate potential of the plane-surfaced grid at cut-off, explaining by reference to a diagram similar to those asked for in (a) and (b).

20. For a cylindrical triode, determine what value of r_p/r_g will make μ ($= C_g/C_p$) a maximum, if r_k, r_p, n, R remain fixed as r_g is varied.

CHAPTER V

SPACE-CHARGE CONTROL OF CURRENT

5.1 Energy, Flow, and Poisson's Equations. Poisson's equation requires that in a region containing space charge the electric field must vary from point to point; it cannot therefore be everywhere zero. *It must in fact have some value almost everywhere.* The particles that make up the space charge experience a force due to this field, and, if they are free to move, their motion constitutes an electric current. Any region that contains space charge due to unattached particles must therefore also contain an electric current, and there is a definite interdependence between current density, space-charge density, and potential distribution.

Suppose that electrodes as in Fig. 5.1a are maintained at constant potential difference by an external voltage source and that electrons are emitted profusely from the cathode, being then driven to the anode by the electric field. In such a one-dimensional region *Poisson's equation* requires that

$$\frac{d^2E}{dx^2} = -\frac{\rho}{\epsilon_0} \qquad \text{[scalar]} \qquad (5\text{--}1)$$

The *energy equation*

$$Eq_e = \tfrac{1}{2}m_e v^2 \qquad \text{[scalar]} \qquad (5\text{--}2)$$

also written

$$v = \sqrt{\frac{2q_e}{m_e}}\ \sqrt{E} \qquad \text{[vector]} \qquad (5\text{--}3)$$

describes an electron's velocity v at any point for which the potential is E; this velocity evidently increases during flight. This statement of the energy equation implies that zero potential is defined as that of the cathode from which the electrons start, and that they start with negligible initial velocities.

The *equation of flow*

$$J_c = \rho v \qquad \text{[usually just } J = \rho v] \qquad (5\text{--}4)$$

relates convection current density J_c of space-charge flow (amperes per square meter) to space-charge density ρ (coulombs per cubic meter)

128

and velocity v. There is an analogous equality between air flow rate and the product of air density by velocity.

With a definite d-c voltage applied, (5–1), (5–3), and (5–4) determine a definite steady current density $J_c = \rho v$, which has of course the same value at all points between the two flat electrodes. In this equilibrium state the same number of electrons enter any incremental volume per second from the left as leave it from the right. ρv is thus the same for all values of x.

If the voltage applied varies, as when it has an important a-c component, the current density between the electrodes consists of two portions: convection current density J_c, and displacement current density $J_d = \partial D / \partial t = \epsilon_0 \, \partial F / \partial t$, where $\partial D / \partial t$ is the time rate of change of electric flux density at a fixed location. Thus the total current density J_t is

$$J_t = J_c + J_d = \rho v + \epsilon_0 \frac{\partial F}{\partial t} \qquad (5\text{–}5)$$

J_t is, in a one-dimensional (planar) system, the same for all values of x, because of the general principle of continuity of current in an electric circuit.

In the remainder of the present analysis of space charge flow all J symbols will signify simply convection current density, as suggested by the bracket in (5–4), because attention will be limited to circumstances in which the convection current has at any instant the same value at all interelectrode potentials.

Rigorously speaking, this limits the validity of the results of the analysis to electron tube operation at frequencies low enough so that the displacement current density, that is, the current density to the star equivalent electrostatic circuit capacitances, is negligibly small relative to the convection current density. As to physical concept, this implies that for any given instantaneous value of applied voltage the potential distribution and convection current are the same as though the applied voltage were steady at that value. This implication is not satisfied at high frequencies, because it takes time for the space charge density and therefore the potential distribution to change to that required by the new applied potential.

Practically speaking, the results of the analysis are quite acceptably valid *as to the resistive component of the current* until the frequency becomes high enough so that the transit time (see Section 2.5) is an appreciable fraction of the cyclic period. This occurs at perhaps 200 or 300 megacycles, the beginning of the ultra-high-frequency (uhf) range. However, as pointed out by Llewellyn,[11E-50] and discussed in

Section 5.6, also in more detail in Chapter V of *Microwave Electron Tubes*, the results of this analysis cannot be employed to determine the *capacitive* currents in the presence of substantial space charge.

5.2   Zero Gradient at the Cathode a Condition for Maximum Space Charge Consistent with Steady Current Flow. Imagine steady electron current flow to have been established in the planar geometry between two electrodes such as those of Fig. 5.1. In the presence of the space charge then existing the potential distribution curve must be convex downward; the greater the space charge density, the greater the flexion, as discussed in Section 1.4.

One relatively *un*important situation that can then exist is illustrated in Fig. 5.1a. Here the potential gradient just outside the cathode is positive; therefore any electron that is emitted from the cathode experiences immediately an acceleration toward the anode. Thus the cathode current under such conditions is determined by the ability of the cathode to emit electrons. As shown in Chapter VII, the electron-emitting capability of a cathode depends on cathode material and processing, and on cathode temperature. Therefore, under the condition illustrated in Fig. 5.1a, of a positive gradient adjacent to the cathode, the current is said to be *temperature limited*.

It is shown in Chapters VII and XII that electrons emitted from a hot cathode emerge with initial velocities so small that for the purpose of the present analysis they can be considered to have zero velocity at emission.

If, starting with the temperature-limited-current condition of Fig. 5.1a, the temperature of the cathode is slightly increased, anode voltage remaining constant, more current will flow; therefore the space-charge density will become greater, and the potential distribution curve will become more markedly convex downward, as illustrated in Fig. 5.1b. The current is still temperature limited, because the gradient just outside the cathode is still positive. The off-cathode gradient is less positive than before the change.

If the cathode is heated further, there will be a specific cathode temperature at which the off-cathode gradient will just become zero, as in Fig. 5.1c. This will correspond to some definite value of cathode current. If the cathode is still further heated, the space-charge content and the current flow *will not increase* but will remain constant at the values corresponding to the condition of Fig. 5.1c, providing initial electron velocities are ignorably small. Thus raising the temperature of the cathode will *not* give rise to a condition like that of Fig. 5.1d, because an off-cathode dip below cathode potential, as shown there, would stop emergence of electrons from the cathode. If electrons thus

ceased to emerge, the space charge would be reduced by outward electron flow, until the condition of Fig. 5.1c again existed. Thus for any
given electrode geometry and potential, the maximum space charge
consistent with steady current flow corresponds to the existence of a
zero off-cathode gradient, as in Fig. 5.1c.

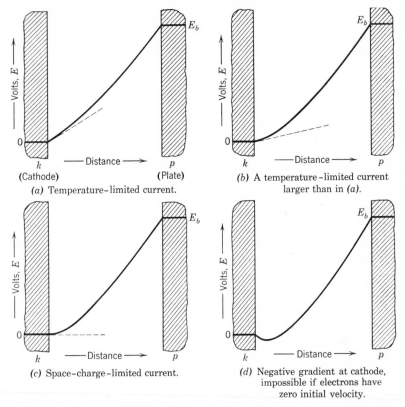

(a) Temperature-limited current.

(b) A temperature-limited current
larger than in (a).

(c) Space-charge-limited current.

(d) Negative gradient at cathode,
impossible if electrons have
zero initial velocity.

FIG. 5.1   Temperature-limited and space-charge-limited potential distributions
in a planar diode.

In summary, if the cathode can supply zero-initial-velocity electrons
at an unlimited rate, the space charge density and the flexion of the
potential distribution curve must grow until the off-cathode potential
gradient becomes zero. They cannot grow beyond that condition,
because any further increase of space charge would shut off electron
emergence from the cathode altogether. Zero gradient at the cathode
is therefore the condition normally reached if the cathode supplies
electrons plentifully and if the initial electron velocities are ignorably
small.

The normally reached zero-off-cathode-gradient condition corresponds to the maximum space charge and maximum current density consistent with steady current flow. This is sometimes called the complete-space-charge condition, and the corresponding current is called the space-charge-limited current.

Thus, in a high-vacuum device, no matter how profuse the electron supply at the cathode may be, *the energy, flow, and Poisson relations establish, for given geometry and electrode potentials, a definite upper limit to the steady current that can be carried by electron movement through a vacuum.*

5.3   Space-Charge-Limited Current Proportional to the $\frac{3}{2}$ Power of the Voltage. In most vacuum tubes the current is normally space charge limited, the cathodes being capable of supplying many more electrons than actually flow. The magnitude of the space-charge-limited current is controlled by electrode geometry and potentials, not by filament temperature.

Under these usual conditions, typified by Fig. 5.1c, there is no surface charge on the cathode; the positive surface charge on the anode is just equal to the total negative space charge. All the negative charge lies between the plates. Poisson's equation indicates a general *proportionality* between potential and space charge if, as here, the integration constants are zero (because the potential and potential gradient are zero at zero distance from the cathode). Therefore *the total space charge under complete-space-charge conditions is proportional to the total voltage, for given geometry.*

The shape of the potential distribution curve for the complete-space-charge state is the same for any overall voltage. That is, the potential at a given distance from the cathode is a definite percentage of the total voltage, regardless of what the total may be. Electron velocity is proportional to the square root of the potential; hence *the velocity of space-charge movement at a given location is proportional to the square root of the total voltage.*

The space-charge content being proportional to the first power of the voltage, and the velocity of its movement to the square root of the voltage, the current, being the product of space-charge density and velocity, *varies as the $\frac{3}{2}$ power* of the voltage for the complete-space-charge condition. This reasoning is applicable strictly to the current between parallel planes, concentric cylinders, and concentric spheres, because in these three geometrical arrangements the electric flux lines and the streamlines of current flow are coincident and straight. It is very nearly applicable for many geometries that seem only very roughly to approximate this requirement.[6A]

The proportionality factor depends on both the general form and detail dimensions of the geometry; it is not the same for concentric cylinders as for the planar geometry of parallel plates.

5.4   Complete-Space-Charge Volt-Ampere Relation; Planar Geometry.   Poisson's, the energy, and the flow equations in combination give for planar geometry the relation

$$\frac{d^2E}{dx^2} = \frac{-J}{\epsilon_0} \sqrt{\frac{m_e}{2q_e}} \frac{1}{\sqrt{E}} \tag{5-6}$$

The electrons are considered to be moving in the direction of increasing x, which corresponds to movement of positive charge in the direction of decreasing x. Therefore the direction of current, following the accepted convention, is negative. Therefore $-J$ has a positive value in (5–6) and subsequent expressions.

To integrate, multiply both sides of (5–6) by the integrating factor dE/dx. Then it is recognized that on the left

$$\frac{dE}{dx}\frac{d^2E}{dx^2} = \frac{1}{2}\frac{d}{dx}\left(\frac{dE}{dx}\right)^2 \tag{5-7}$$

and on the right

$$\frac{1}{\sqrt{E}}\frac{dE}{dx} = 2\frac{d\sqrt{E}}{dx} \tag{5-8}$$

so that the first integration results in

$$\left(\frac{dE}{dx}\right)^2 = \frac{-4J}{\epsilon_0}\sqrt{\frac{m_e}{2q_e}}\sqrt{E} + \text{Constant} \tag{5-9}$$

For the complete-space-charge condition, the potential gradient and potential are both zero when $x = 0$; therefore the integration constant of (5–9) vanishes if $-J$ describes space-charge-limited current. The second integration is straightforward after the square roots of both sides are taken, and the second integration constant is also zero, for the complete-space-charge condition. When solved for the potential, the end expression is

$$E = \left(-\frac{9}{4}\frac{J}{\epsilon_0}\sqrt{\frac{m_e}{2q_e}}\right)^{2/3} x^{4/3} \tag{5-10}$$

Thus under complete-space-charge conditions in planar geometry, the potential varies as the $4/3$ power of the distance from the cathode.

If the spacing between the electrodes of a diode is s, the potential E_s at the anode is obtained by inserting s for x and E_s for E in (5–10). If this is then solved for $-J$, the following expression is derived, for planar space-charge-limited current density:

$$-J = \frac{4\epsilon_0}{9} \sqrt{\frac{2q_e}{m_e}} \frac{E_s^{\,3/2}}{s^2} \tag{5–11}$$

Numerically,

$$-J = 2.33 \times 10^{-6} \frac{E_s^{\,3/2}}{s^2} \qquad \text{[amperes per square meter]} \tag{5–12}$$

Under suitable conditions the reasoning of the preceding paragraphs can be applied to the flow of positive ions instead of electrons; in that case

$$+J = \frac{2.33 \times 10^{-6} E_s^{\,3/2}}{\sqrt{m_g/m_e}\; s^2} \tag{5–13}$$

where m_g and m_e symbolize ion and electron mass.

5.5 Space-Charge-Limited Current in a Planar Triode with a Flat Cathode. In the immediate neighborhood of the cathode of a planar vacuum triode, having a flat surface as its cathode, the initial electron velocities being ignorable, the potential distribution will be of the $4/3$ power nature, as given by (5–10). For each value of J there will correspond some particular $4/3$ power curve, as illustrated in Fig. 5.2. Any one of these curves would, if extended, intersect the near face of the equivalent grid sheet at some definite potential, related to s and J as in (5–12). The actually existing potential curve is the one that intersects the equivalent grid sheet at the equivalent grid sheet potential E_s.

In and beyond the neighborhood of the grid, the potential is usually substantially above its zero value at the cathode. The space-charge density in the neighborhood of the grid is therefore very small, since in and beyond the grid region v is large because $\sqrt{E}$ is large, and ρ therefore is small in inverse ratio to $\sqrt{E}$; for $J = \rho v$, and J is the same for all values of x.

Figure 5.3 illustrates the potential distribution in the cathode and grid region of a triode under complete-space-charge conditions. An observer of limited vision stationed near the grid is aware of a potential structure apparently identical with that of Fig. 4.13b, because at his location space charge is scarcely discernible. However, what he takes to be a straight line from the grid sheet potential E_s to the cathode, as in Fig. 4.13b, is actually only the near-to-the-grid local portion of a $\frac{4}{3}$ power curve originating at the cathode, as in Fig. 5.2. This is the particular $\frac{4}{3}$ power curve that corresponds to the existing value of J. The limited-vision observer near the grid, being quite unaware of space charge, will imagine the cathode to be at the position $k'k'$ in Fig. 5.3,

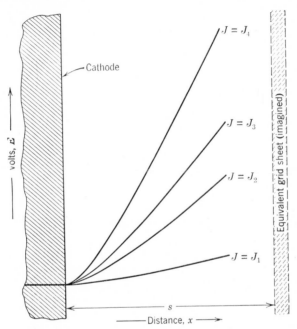

FIG. 5.2   Complete-space-charge potential distribution curves, adjacent to a planar cathode. For each curve $E = Kx^{\frac{4}{3}}$; and each curve is characterized by a unique value of space-charge-limited current density, in accordance with (5–10). Ignorably small initial electron velocities.

rather than at its true location kk. The $k'k'$ plane is located at the intersection between the zero potential level and a straight line tangent to the $\frac{4}{3}$ power curve at the toward-the-cathode face of the equivalent grid sheet. It is easily shown that this intersection point is at one-fourth of the distance from cathode to grid sheet face.

Thus for complete-space-charge conditions in a planar triode the straight line from cathode to grid sheet, in Figs. 1.5 and 4.13b, is replaced by a $\frac{4}{3}$ power curve from cathode to grid sheet.[4B, 5a, f, h, 6A] The fillets in the complete-space-charge case are constructed so as to merge with the $\frac{4}{3}$ power curve on the cathode side of the grid.

The current density J in such a triode is found by determining the equivalent grid sheet potential E_s (taking space charge into account) and then employing this value of E_s and the cathode-grid spacing s in (5–12) or (5–11). In the next section it is shown how to account for space charge in the determination of E_s.

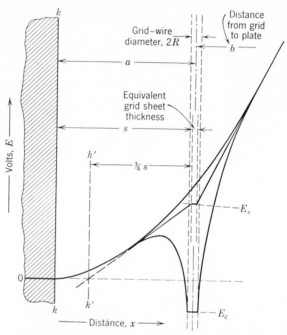

FIG. 5.3. Potential distribution in the neighborhood of cathode and grid of a planar triode with flat cathode; complete space charge. Actual position of cathode is at kk, apparent position is at $k'k'$, to an observer of limited vision stationed at the grid. In most real devices the thickness of the equivalent grid sheet will be a smaller fraction of the grid-wire diameter than is shown here.

5.6   Space-Charge Control of Current in Triodes, Tetrodes, Pentodes; Complete-Space-Charge Capacitance.[*, 4B, C, D, E, 5h, 11E]   By placing a fictitious cathode at $k'k'$, one-fourth closer to the equivalent grid sheet face than the real cathode at kk in Fig. 5.3, and thereafter pursuing the logic of Section 4.6 and Fig. 4.13b, the cathode-grid-region boundary conditions are correctly matched into the grid-plate-region boundaries for the complete-space-charge condition. But this shift

* The method used here for determination of current in space-charge-control tubes is considerably superior to that used in the first edition of this book, although the first-edition concepts were not wrong. The present method agrees as to principles and end results with methods widely used in engineering practice. A complete analysis is given by Llewellyn, in reference 11E. See also footnote in Section 4.4, and references 5a through 5l, especially method comparisons in 5h.

from kk to $k'k'$ is of course the equivalent of increasing the capacitance between cathode and equivalent grid sheet by the factor $\frac{4}{3}$.

Therefore in a planar tube having complete space charge between cathode and grid and ignorable space charge elsewhere, (4–52), (4–53), (4–71) and the corresponding tetrode and pentode relations are usable just as in the space-charge-free case, except that a quantity C_k' is used instead of C_k, where

$$C_k' = \frac{4}{3} C_k \cong \frac{4}{3} \frac{\epsilon_0}{a} \qquad (5\text{–}14a)$$

This value of C_k' is applicable, *for the purpose of finding E_s*, at any frequency below the ultra-high-frequency (uhf) range, that is, below perhaps 200 or 300 megacycles.

If capacitance is defined as the ratio of charge Q to potential, C_k' may be described as the capacitance between cathode and equivalent grid sheet of a triode, or between cathode and plate of a diode, when the current is space-charge limited. C_k' is a linear capacitance, in that it is the same for all values of E_s.

In contrast, Llewellyn [11E–50] has shown that if a space-charge-limited capacitance C_k'' is defined in terms of the ratio of the capacitive component of a-c current to a small-signal applied a-c voltage

$$C_k'' = \frac{3}{5} C_k \cong \frac{3}{5} \frac{\epsilon_0}{a} \qquad \begin{bmatrix} \text{for determining} \\ \text{the capacitive} \\ \text{current} \end{bmatrix} \qquad (5\text{–}14b)$$

Thus in principle this value should be used in the star diagram of Fig. 4.10c in finding the delta interelectrode capacitances of Fig. 4.10b, when the cathode is hot and emitting sufficiently to permit space-charge-limited operation. This (5–14b) value of C_k'' is applicable only below the uhf range; for frequencies above 200 or 300 megacycles transit time effects cause deviations. The difference between (5–14a) for C_k' and (5–14b) for C_k'' may be thought of as a transit time effect that is significant at any frequency for which the displacement component of current in the tube is important. Initial velocity effects may mask this behavior.

Note here the implication that capacitance may be defined as a charge-to-potential ratio ($q = Ce$), or as a ratio of current to rate of change of voltage ($i = C\, de/dt$), or for that matter in terms of energy storage (energy stored = $Ce^2/2$). For the simple "condenser" type of capacitance, these three definitions give identical results; for a space-charge-limited situation they give three different results. Here the electrostatic energy stored in the capacitance, found by volume integration of $\epsilon_0 F^2/2$, is $2QE/5$, instead of the space-charge-free value $QE/2$. The energy present as kinetic energy of the moving electrons is $QE/5$, giving a total for the two kinds of stored energy of $3QE/5$.

The equivalent grid sheet potential e_s for a triode subject to varying electrode voltages, at a frequency below the uhf range, and having complete space charge between cathode and grid, is given by a slightly modified form of (4–53), as follows:

$$e_s = \frac{e_a C_k' + e_c C_g + e_b C_p}{C_k' + C_g + C_p} \tag{5–15}$$

Here e_a, e_c, and e_b are instantaneous values of cathode, grid, and plate potentials, and C_k' is as given by (5–14a). Note that $e_a = 0$, and divide through by C_g; then rearrange into

$$e_s = \frac{e_c + \dfrac{e_b}{C_g/C_p}}{1 + \dfrac{1}{C_g/C_p} + \dfrac{1}{C_g/C_p}\dfrac{C_k'}{C_p}} \tag{5–16}$$

This has the same form as (4–71), if $\mu = C_g/C_p$; see the next section.

The value of e_s for a tetrode or pentode, at any frequency below the uhf range, is found by using the reasoning associated with Figs. 4.17 and 4.18, but using (5–14a) for C_k' to replace C_k, or the q-plane concept of Figs. 5.4 and 5.5 may be used. Having obtained e_s, the space-charge-limited current density at the cathode is given by (5–11) or (5–12), using for s the distance between the cathode surface and the near face of the first-grid equivalent grid sheet. This distance is the denominator of (4–66); usually a sufficiently good approximation is

$$s \cong a \tag{5–17}$$

where a is the spacing from grid-wire centers to the cathode.

Note that the methods of *space-charge-control of current*, described in this section, make it possible to alter the cathode current by varying the potential of a control grid which itself draws no electron-borne current (thus it draws only capacitive current) because its potential is below that of the cathode.

5.7 Triode "Constants." *   The three important vacuum-tube parameters, sometimes called "tube constants," are defined as follows

* See references 4B, C, D, 5a through 5o; also footnote to Section 5.6.

for a triode (see also Section 9.1):

Amplification factor:
$$\mu = -\left.\frac{\partial e_b}{\partial e_c}\right|_{i_b \text{ constant}} \qquad (5\text{–}18)$$

Grid-plate transconductance: [5m]
$$g_m = \left.\frac{\partial i_b}{\partial e_c}\right|_{e_b \text{ constant}} \qquad (5\text{–}19)$$

Plate resistance:
$$r_p = \left.\frac{\partial i_b}{\partial e_b}\right|_{e_c \text{ constant}} \qquad (5\text{–}20)$$

where i_b is plate current, and e_b and e_c are plate and grid potentials. It is shown in Section 5.12 that $\mu = g_m r_p$.

Note that the definition of μ implies that e_b and e_c vary while i_b is held constant. If i_b is constant, so also must the equivalent grid sheet potential e_s be constant; thus, if e_b and e_c are varied in such a way as to hold i_b constant, $\partial e_s/\partial e_c = 0$. Therefore, in order to obtain an expression for μ, (5–16) is differentiated with respect to e_c, and $\partial e_s/\partial e_c$ is placed equal to zero. The result reduces immediately to

$$\mu = -\left.\frac{\partial e_b}{\partial e_c}\right|_{i_b \text{ constant}} = +\frac{C_g}{C_p} \qquad (5\text{–}21a)$$

This becomes, from (4–69),

$$\mu = \frac{2\pi nb - \ln\cosh 2\pi nR}{\ln\coth 2\pi nR} \cong \frac{2\pi nb}{\ln\coth 2\pi nR} \qquad (5\text{–}21b)$$

5.8   Determination of the Triode Equivalent Grid Sheet Potential.
Equation (5–21a) can be used to eliminate C_g/C_p in favor of μ in (5–16), giving

$$e_s = \frac{e_c + \dfrac{e_b}{\mu}}{1 + \dfrac{1}{\mu} + \dfrac{1}{\mu}\dfrac{C_k{'}}{C_p}} \qquad (5\text{–}22)$$

Now use (4–67) and (5–14a) for C_p and $C_k{'}$; the ϵ_0 cancels, giving

$$e_s = \frac{e_c + \dfrac{e_b}{\mu}}{1 + \dfrac{1}{\mu} + \dfrac{1}{\mu}\left(\dfrac{4}{3}\dfrac{b}{a}\right)} \qquad \begin{bmatrix}\text{planar triode,}\\ \text{space-charge-}\\ \text{limited current}\end{bmatrix} \qquad (5\text{–}23)$$

This equation is extensively useful in the engineering design of vacuum tubes. As indicated in Section 5.21, it applies rather well to many planar triodes with filamentary cathodes, as well as to those with flat cathodes.

Because (5–22) and (5–23) describe *electrostatic* field relationships, calculations using them should take into account *contact difference of potential*, as discussed in Section 8.25.

It is left as an exercise for the reader to apply to a cylindrical triode logic similar to that leading to (5–22); it will be found that with C_k' properly chosen (5–22) will still apply. Equation (5–63a) permits evaluation of C_k'.

5.9   Reduction to an Equivalent Diode, to Find E_s; the "q" Plane. *

It is sometimes convenient to find E_s by reducing the triode star circuit of Fig. 5.4a to the particular equivalent diode of Fig. 5.4b, the diode

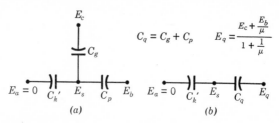

$$C_q = C_g + C_p \qquad E_q = \frac{E_c + \frac{E_b}{\mu}}{1 + \frac{1}{\mu}}$$

(a)   (b)

FIG. 5.4   Reduction of the triode electrostatic circuit to an equivalent diode using the *q*-plane concept.
(a) The original triode star electrostatic circuit.
(b) The equivalent diode circuit.

voltage being E_q. This diode has the properties that, for any pair of values of E_c and E_b, giving rise to a definite voltage E_q:

(a) E_s has the same value as in the triode.

(b) C_q is independent of C_k', and of E_b, E_c.

(c) The dependence of E_q on E_c, E_b, relates to μ but does not involve C_k'.

Figure 5.5a indicates the manner of use of this set of concepts, and the significance of C_q in relation to a location sometimes called the q plane; C_q is the capacitance that would exist between two flat electrodes placed at the grid sheet and at the q-plane locations, respectively. Note that a straight potential line from zero potential at $k'k'$ to E_q at qq passes through E_s at the grid location. In Fig. 5.5b, C_g, C_p, and therefore, of course, μ, are the same as in Fig. 5.5a, but the cathode is more remote, so that C_k' is smaller. The q-plane location, also C_q, and E_q (for given E_c, E_b) are unchanged from Fig. 5.5a, because μ and the grid-plate spacing are unchanged. A straight potential line from E_q at

* This material is based on concepts introduced in a series of lectures given by B. J. Thompson at the University of Michigan in 1937; see also references 5h, c.

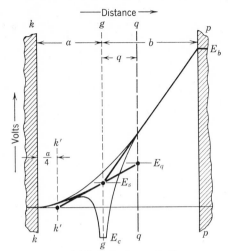

(a) Cathode close to grid

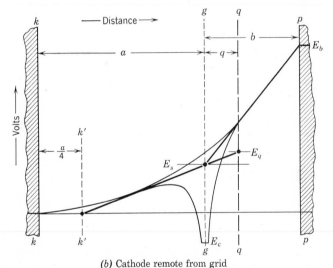

(b) Cathode remote from grid

FIG. 5.5   Use of the q plane and E_q, to determine E_s and locate the construction lines for a triode potential distribution diagram. E_c, E_b, b, μ are alike in (a) and (b).
Procedure:
(1) Find μ by using (5–21b).
(2) From (5–32) determine q, the distance from the plane of the grid gg to the q plane; draw qq, locating the q plane.
(3) From (5–31) determine E_q, and locate E_q on the q plane.   (It is also desirable to locate E_b on the plate, and E_c on the grid plane.)
(4) Locate the intersection of $k'k'$ with the zero-potential base line, ¼ of the distance from cathode to grid plane.
(5) Draw a straight line from the $k'k'$ base line intersection to E_q at the q plane.   This crosses the grid plane at E_s, thus determining E_s.
(6) Connect E_s with E_b.   The two straight slant lines intersecting at E_s (drawn heavy in the diagram) are the construction lines for the potential distribution diagram.
(7) Sketch in the ⅔ power potential line from cathode to E_s, this being tangent to the E_s-to-E_q line at E_s, and having a horizontal tangent at the cathode.
(8) Sketch the fillets in the usual way, merging them with the ⅔ power line between cathode and grid.

qq to zero at the new $k'k'$ location *gives the correct value of E_s* for this new cathode location. This is the meaning of the items a, b, and c above.

To demonstrate mathematical forms for C_q, E_q, and for grid-to-q spacing q, first write, as usual, for Fig. 5.4a,

$$E_s = \frac{E_c + \dfrac{E_b}{\mu}}{1 + \dfrac{1}{\mu} + \dfrac{1}{\mu}\dfrac{C_k'}{C_p}} \tag{5-24}$$

The corresponding expression for Fig. 5.4b is of course

$$E_s = \frac{E_q}{1 + \dfrac{C_k'}{C_q}} \tag{5-25}$$

Item (a) above requires that these give the same E_s; therefore it is required that

$$\frac{E_q}{1 + \dfrac{C_k'}{C_q}} = \frac{E_c + \dfrac{E_b}{\mu}}{1 + \dfrac{1}{\mu} + \dfrac{1}{\mu}\dfrac{C_k'}{C_p}} \tag{5-26}$$

Now let

$$E_q = \frac{E_c + \dfrac{E_b}{\mu}}{M} \tag{5-27}$$

where M is a quantity to be chosen so as not to depend on C_k', in order to satisfy item (b) above. Substitution into the preceding equation, with subsequent cancellation of $E_c + (E_b/\mu)$ and inversion, gives

$$M + M \frac{C_k'}{C_q} = 1 + \frac{1}{\mu} + \frac{1}{\mu}\frac{C_k'}{C_p} \tag{5-28}$$

Inspection now indicates that items (b) and (c) are satisfied if

$$M = 1 + \frac{1}{\mu} \tag{5-29}$$

for then the C_k' cancels and the equation reduces to

$$C_q = (\mu + 1)C_p \quad \text{which is the same as} \quad C_q = C_g + C_p \tag{5-30}$$

Now introduce this value of M into (5–27) to give

$$E_q = \frac{E_c + \dfrac{E_b}{\mu}}{1 + \dfrac{1}{\mu}} \qquad (5\text{–}31)$$

By using the planar capacitance relations $C_p = \epsilon_0/b$ and $C_q = \epsilon_0/q$ (per unit area), (5–30) may be converted into

$$q = \frac{b}{1 + \mu} \qquad (5\text{–}32)$$

This permits location of the q plane if μ and b are known; in general μ will be found directly from the dimensions by using (5–21b).

An important merit of the q-plane procedure is that, with μ and the spacings known, E_s can be found as in Fig. 5.5, without numerically evaluating any of the capacitances. The graphical construction for E_s is the equivalent of the following equation:

$$E_s = E_q \frac{\tfrac{3}{4}a}{\tfrac{3}{4}a + q} = \frac{E_q}{1 + \tfrac{4}{3}(q/a)} \qquad (5\text{–}33)$$

The extension to cylindrical geometry, to obtain and use a q cylinder, is reasonably straightforward, the most important difference being that the $k'k'$ location must be determined somewhat differently; see Section 5.15 for the necessary basic information. Equation (5–26), therefore (5–30) and (5–31), carry over without change into the cylindrical analysis. However, the counterpart of (5–32) involves logarithmic terms, because the (4–89) form (with the ln cosh $2\pi nR$ term omitted) is used in place of (4–67) in establishing the q location. Of course in the cylindrical application logarithmic curves replace the straight lines of Fig. 5.5.

The extension of the q-plane concept to multigrid tubes is completely straightforward. It permits a semigraphical reduction of a multigrid tube (Fig. 4.18) to an equivalent triode, then to an equivalent diode as in Fig. 5.5, and subsequent determination of E_s, without numerical evaluation of any of the capacitances, and without having to solve a set of simultaneous algebraic equations.

Such reduction for a pentode is initiated by replacing the plate and the third grid by a suitably located q electrode at a potential E_q, thus reducing the tube to a tetrode. The μ used in (5–30, 5–31, 5–32) in this operation is of course found by using in (5–21b) the n and R for the third grid, and the spacing from the third grid to the plate for b.

This spacing is used for b, and E_{c_3} for E_c, in (5–30, 5–31, 5–32). The tetrode thus obtained is reduced to a triode by a similar procedure, with subsequent treatment in accordance with Fig. 5.5.

5.10   Space-Charge-Limited Triode Current Determinations; Transconductance.   Equations (5–11) and (5–12) are, from the basis of their derivation, expressions for *cathode* current density, for a planar structure having a flat-surfaced cathode.   In a negative-grid triode there is no grid current; therefore the plate current and grid current have the same value.   Therefore (5–12) can be expressed to give plate current i_b as

$$i_b = 2.33 \times 10^{-6}\, \frac{S}{a^2}\, e_s{}^{3/2} \qquad \text{[negative-grid planar triode]} \quad (5\text{–}34)$$

where S is the cathode surface area.

   a is the cathode-to-grid spacing, as in Figs. 5.3 and 1.5.

Introduction of (5–23) converts this last equation to

$$i_b = 2.33 \times 10^{-6}\, \frac{S}{a^2}\, \frac{\left(e_c + \dfrac{e_b}{\mu}\right)^{3/2}}{\left[1 + \dfrac{1}{\mu} + \dfrac{1}{\mu}\left(\dfrac{4}{3}\dfrac{b}{a}\right)\right]^{3/2}} \qquad \begin{bmatrix} \text{negative-grid} \\ \text{planar triode} \end{bmatrix} \quad (5\text{–}35)$$

This is the equation for a family of plate characteristic curves, as illustrated in Fig. 1.3b.   Ideally each plate characteristic curve should be a $3/2$ power curve.   These relations are essentially *circuit* equations; therefore the minus sign in (5–12) has been omitted, as is customary.[*]

   The above considerations suggest that the equation for *cathode* current i_a for *either* a positive-grid or negative-grid planar triode should be as follows:

$$i_a = 2.33 \times 10^{-6}\, \frac{S}{a^2}\, \frac{\left(e_c + \dfrac{e_b}{\mu}\right)^{3/2}}{\left[1 + \dfrac{1}{\mu} + \dfrac{1}{\mu}\left(\dfrac{4}{3}\dfrac{b}{a}\right)\right]^{3/2}} \qquad \begin{bmatrix} \text{cathode current,} \\ \text{positive or} \\ \text{negative grid,} \\ \text{planar triode} \end{bmatrix} \quad (5\text{–}36)$$

In the positive-grid case, part of the current goes to the grid, part to the plate.   The dashed lines in Fig. 1.3b indicate the cathode current for a positive-grid condition.   This equation is for the most part a

------

* In Fig. 5.3, $J = \rho v$ is numerically negative, because it represents a flow of negative charge in the $+x$ direction, which is the same as the flow of conventional current in the $-x$ direction.   In circuit studies neither $+x$ nor $-x$ has any significance; $+i_b$ is numerically positive because it is defined as conventional current flowing from a high-potential to a low-potential circuit point; see Chapter IX.

satisfactory representation of cathode current for both positive and negative grid voltages; however, see Section 6.3.

The transconductance per unit area of a planar negative-grid triode having a flat-surfaced cathode is the partial derivative, with respect to e_c, of (5–34). Thus, for such a structure

$$g_m = \frac{3}{2} \times 2.33 \times 10^{-6} \frac{S}{a^2} e_s^{1/2} \frac{\partial e_s}{\partial e_c} \qquad (5\text{–}37a)$$

Application of the derivative to (5–23) converts this to

$$g_m = \frac{3}{2} \times 2.33 \times 10^{-6} \frac{S}{a^2} \frac{\left(e_c + \dfrac{e_b}{\mu}\right)^{1/2}}{\left[1 + \dfrac{1}{\mu} + \dfrac{1}{\mu}\left(\dfrac{4}{3}\dfrac{b}{a}\right)\right]^{3/2}} \qquad (5\text{–}37b)$$

(As to contact potential, see Section 8.25.) This can be expressed in terms of i_b by using (5–35) to eliminate the voltage parentheses, thus

$$g_m = \frac{\frac{3}{2}(2.33 \times 10^{-6})^{2/3} S^{2/3}}{1 + \dfrac{1}{\mu} + \dfrac{1}{\mu}\left(\dfrac{4}{3}\dfrac{b}{a}\right)} \frac{S^{2/3}}{a^{4/3}} i_b^{1/3} \qquad (5\text{–}37c)$$

or, numerically,

$$g_m = \frac{264 \times 10^{-6}}{1 + \dfrac{1}{\mu} + \dfrac{1}{\mu}\left(\dfrac{4}{3}\dfrac{b}{a}\right)} \frac{S^{2/3}}{a^{4/3}} i_b^{1/3} \qquad \text{[mhos, planar triode]} \quad (5\text{–}37d)$$

Division of (5–37b) by plate current, (5–35), gives

$$\frac{g_m}{i_b} = \frac{3}{2} \frac{1}{\left(e_c + \dfrac{e_b}{\mu}\right)} \cong \frac{3}{2}\frac{1}{e_s} \qquad \begin{bmatrix} \text{transconductance per} \\ \text{ampere, planar triode} \end{bmatrix} \quad (5\text{–}38)$$

Division of (5–37d) by i_b gives

$$\frac{g_m}{i_b} = \frac{264 \times 10^{-6}}{1 + \dfrac{1}{\mu} + \dfrac{1}{\mu}\left(\dfrac{4}{3}\dfrac{b}{a}\right)} \frac{S^{2/3}}{a^{4/3}} \frac{1}{i_b^{2/3}} \qquad \begin{bmatrix} \text{transconductance per} \\ \text{ampere, planar triode} \end{bmatrix} \quad (5\text{–}39)$$

Thus transconductance per ampere becomes larger as the current becomes smaller; however, see Section 8.19 as to an upper limit to g_m/i_b.

To determine plate resistance r_p, use the (5–47) relation $\mu = g_m r_p$.

5.11   Perveance.   The quantity *perveance*, symbolized here as P, is usually defined, in relation to a space-charge-limited current i, by the relation [6A, B, 5n, o]

$$i = P \times \left(\begin{array}{l}\text{Voltage, or an}\\\text{"equivalent" voltage}\end{array}\right)^{3/2} \qquad (5\text{--}40)$$

There is chance for confusion in applying this to (5–36) or to (5–35) in that the voltage used in (5–40) might conceivably be either the grid sheet potential or the voltage within the (5–35) numerator parentheses.   Thus in any technical study the reader may find it useful to determine carefully whether the author he is following uses perveance as meaning, for a planar triode,

$$P = 2.33 \times 10^{-6} \frac{S}{a^2} \qquad \text{[the voltage in (5--40) being } E_s] \quad (5\text{--}41)$$

or as meaning

$$P = 2.33 \times 10^{-6} \frac{S}{a^2} \frac{1}{\left[1 + \dfrac{1}{\mu} + \dfrac{1}{\mu}\left(\dfrac{4}{3}\dfrac{b}{a}\right)\right]^{3/2}} \qquad \begin{bmatrix}\text{this uses}\\ e_c + \dfrac{e_b}{\mu}\\ \text{in (5--40)}\end{bmatrix} \quad (5\text{--}42)$$

Either is in accord with the basic (5–40) definition of perveance, and usage is not yet fully established; still other voltages might be used.[5h] A designer of tubes is likely to think in terms of the (5–41) definition of P, whereas the user is likely to prefer (5–42).   Fortunately the difference between them is not numerically large, for most tubes.   This nomenclature choice extends to problems involving multigrid tubes, and involving electron guns in cathode-ray tubes.

5.12   Interrelations between Tube Constants.   The interrelation between μ, g_m, and r_p is important.   The plate characteristic curves, Fig. 1.3b and equation (5–35), show that i_b is a function of both e_c and e_b.   Suppose that a small change de_c occurs in grid voltage, the plate voltage remaining constant; then

$$di_b = \frac{\partial i_b}{\partial e_c} de_c = g_m\, de_c \qquad (5\text{--}43)$$

Now suppose that a subsequent change de_b in plate voltage occurs, grid voltage remaining constant at its new value; a second change $\overline{di_b'}$ in current results.   Mathematically,

$$\overline{di_b'} = \frac{\partial i_b}{\partial e_b} de_b = \frac{de_b}{r_p} \qquad (5\text{--}44)$$

Only if $di_b + \overline{di_b'} = 0$ does the current return to its original value.

Therefore, *for constant current*

$$g_m \, de_c + \frac{de_b}{r_p} = 0 \tag{5-45}$$

or, after rearrangement,

$$-\left(\frac{\partial e_b}{\partial e_c}\right)_{i_b \text{ constant}} = g_m r_p \tag{5-46}$$

Comparison of this with (5–18) shows that

$$\mu = g_m r_p \tag{5-47}$$

This result is in accordance with the general mathematical principle illustrated by the following equation:

$$\frac{\partial i_b}{\partial e_c} \times \frac{\partial e_b}{\partial i_b} = -\frac{\partial e_b}{\partial e_c} \tag{5-48}$$

This seems fairly obvious except for the minus sign; the reason for giving the derivation in the preceding paragraph is to demonstrate the necessity for the minus sign.

5.13   UHF Triode Figure of Merit.   At very high frequencies there is a tendency for the capacitance C_k' to act more or less as a short circuit, thus introducing a severe capacitive loading on the input source.   In order to minimize this difficulty it is desirable to maximize the ratio of transconductance to capacitance; a ratio of this nature is sometimes employed as a "figure of merit" for uhf operation.

The term in brackets in the denominator of (5–37b) for g_m is only moderately different from unity, because for most tubes $\mu \gg 1$.   Therefore, from that equation and (5–14) for C_k', and in relation to the effect of variations in grid-plate spacing a,

$$g_m \cong \frac{\text{Constant}}{a^2} \times \sqrt{e_c + \frac{e_b}{\mu}} \qquad C_k' \cong \frac{\text{Constant}}{a} \tag{5-49}$$

Therefore

$$\frac{g_m}{C_k'} \cong \frac{\text{Constant}}{a} \times \sqrt{e_c + \frac{e_b}{\mu}} \tag{5-50}$$

Thus in order to achieve good operation at as high a frequency as possible and with modest voltages, the cathode-to-grid spacing a is made as small as possible.   In the triodes known as "lighthouse tubes" [11a] this spacing is of the order of 0.003 inch (3 mils); in the Western Electric 416–A 4000-megacycle triode amplifier [11b] it is 0.0005 inch (½ mil).

In stating the uhf figure of merit for a particular tube, the input capacitance to the grid (see Sections 4.14, 4.16), rather than C_k, is usually employed; however, it is C_k that basically establishes the design limits to input capacitance.

5.14   Complete-Space-Charge Relations; Cylindrical Geometry.[5p, 15b] For radial space-charge flow between concentric cylinders, the three basic equations are:

$$\frac{1}{r}\frac{d}{dr}\left(r\frac{dE}{dr}\right) = -\frac{\rho}{\epsilon_0} \quad \text{[Poisson's equation]} \qquad (5\text{-}51)$$

$$\tfrac{1}{2}m_e v^2 = E q_e \quad \text{[the energy equation]} \qquad (5\text{-}52)$$

$$\frac{I}{l} = 2\pi r \rho v = 2\pi r J \quad \text{[the equation of flow]} \qquad (5\text{-}53)$$

where E, ρ, and v are potential, space-charge density, and radial electron velocity; I/l is the current per unit axial length l of the cylinders, and J is current density. The form of this last equation arises from the fact that the current per unit length is $2\pi r$ times the current density ρv. These three equations combine to give

$$\frac{1}{r}\frac{d}{dr}\left(r\frac{dE}{dr}\right) = -\frac{1}{2\pi\epsilon_0}\frac{I}{l}\sqrt{\frac{m_e}{2q_e}}\frac{1}{r\sqrt{E}} \qquad (5\text{-}54)$$

Boundary conditions for the complete-space-charge solutions of this differential equation are, as in the planar case, that the potential and the potential gradient must be zero at the cathode. The method of solution [5p, 15b] is described in the next section.

The solution is expressible in the form

$$-J = \frac{4\epsilon_0}{9}\sqrt{\frac{2q_e}{m_e}}\frac{E^{3/2}}{r^2\beta^2} \qquad (5\text{-}55)$$

also as

$$-J = 2.33 \times 10^{-6}\frac{E^{3/2}}{r^2\beta^2} \qquad (5\text{-}56)$$

where β^2 is a known function of r/r_k, the cathode radius being r_k. The dependence of β^2 on r/r_k is charted in Fig. 5.6 for an internal cathode $(r > r_k)$ and tabulated in Table III for both internal and external cathodes. The potential distribution is obtained by solving (5-56) for

E and using (5–53) to replace J by I. Useful forms are

$$E = \left(-\frac{1}{2\pi\epsilon_0} \frac{9}{4} \sqrt{\frac{m_e}{2q_e}} \frac{Ir_k}{l} \right)^{2/3} \left(\frac{r}{r_k} \beta^2 \right)^{2/3} \tag{5–57}$$

and

$$E = \left(-\frac{1}{2\pi \times 2.33 \times 10^{-6}} \frac{Ir_k}{l} \right)^{2/3} \left(\frac{r}{r_k} \beta^2 \right)^{2/3} \tag{5–58}$$

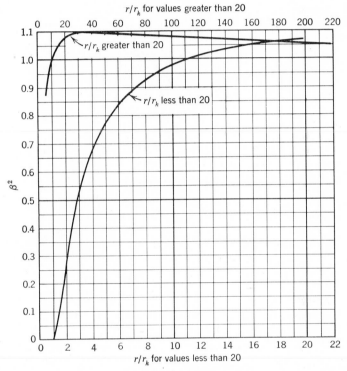

FIG. 5.6 Variation of β^2 with r/r_k in the space-charge-limited equations for cylindrical geometry, when the anode is outside the cathode. See Table III.

Figure 5.7 illustrates the details of the potential distribution for an internal cathode. For an internal cathode, β^2 is nearly unity for values of r/r_k exceeding about 10; therefore the potential distribution is asymptotic to a $\frac{2}{3}$ power function of r/r_k at large values of r/r_k. Note that the potential curve is shown as rising slightly *above* the $\frac{2}{3}$ power curve as r/r_k rises through a value of 11 or so.

The potential and the radius of an outer cylinder may be symbolized as E_s and r_s; then $\beta_s{}^2$ is β^2 evaluated for $r = r_s$. This outer cylinder

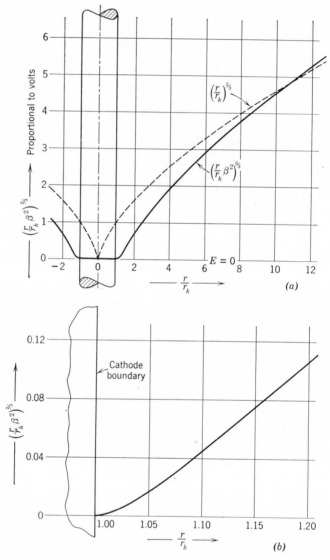

FIG. 5.7   (a) Form of the complete-space-charge potential distribution curve, concentric cylinders. See (5–58). (b) Detail of the potential distribution curve in the vicinity of the cathode.

might be the equivalent grid sheet of a space-charge control tube, or the anode of a diode. Using these $r = r_s$ values in (5–56) gives current density J_s at $r = r_s$ as

$$-J_s = 2.33 \times 10^{-6} \frac{E_s^{3/2}}{r_s^2 \beta_s^2} \tag{5–59}$$

where of course

$$J_s = \frac{I}{2\pi l r_s} \tag{5–60}$$

The similarity between (5–59) and (5–12) is interesting, but deceptive, as r_s is *not* cathode-to-anode diode spacing.

Another very useful form, obtained by multiplying (5–59) by $2\pi r_s$, is

$$-\frac{I}{l} = 2\pi \times 2.33 \times 10^{-6} \frac{E_s^{3/2}}{r_s \beta_s^2} \tag{5–61}$$

Since β_s^2 is approximately unity if $r_s > 10 r_k$, approximate numerical answers for large values of r_s/r_k come very directly from this equation.

5.15   Space-Charge Control of Current in Cylindrical Tubes. The application of the above equations to the space-charge control of current in a rigorously symmetrical cylindrical triode is straightforward, employing (5–22) and (5–61), and identifying E_s and r_s with the potential and the inner radius of the grid sheet cylinder; C_k' must be determined properly for concentric geometry, from (5–63). Contact differences of potential must be considered, as discussed in Section 8.25. The equation obtained for cathode current, comparable with (5–36), is

$$\frac{i_a}{l} = \frac{2\pi \times 2.33 \times 10^{-6}}{r_s \beta_s^2} \frac{\left(e_c + \dfrac{e_b}{\mu}\right)^{3/2}}{\left(1 + \dfrac{1}{\mu} + \dfrac{1}{\mu} \dfrac{C_k'}{C_p}\right)^{3/2}} \tag{5–62}$$

See (4–92) and (4–74) or (4–89) and (5–63), to determine μ, C_p, and C_k'. Rarely will a commercial "cylindrical" tube be found sufficiently symmetrical to make these relations represent its behavior very closely.

It is left as an exercise for the student to derive expressions for perveance and transconductance of a cylindrical triode, comparable with (5–42) and (5–37).

To determine C_k', it is first necessary to find the charge per unit length on a cylindrical surface at radius r_s, under complete-space-charge conditions. This is done by multiplying the potential gradient at this surface by ϵ_0 and by the circumference. This gradient is the r derivative of (5–58), evaluated at $r = r_s$. The capacitance per unit length is then the charge per unit length divided by E_s. The complete expression is

$$C_k{}' = \frac{4\pi\epsilon_0}{3}\left\{1 + \frac{r_s}{r_k}\frac{1}{\beta_s{}^2}\left[\frac{d\beta^2}{d(r/r_k)}\right]_{r=r_s}\right\} \qquad (5\text{–}63a)$$

For large values of r/r_k the slope of the β^2 versus r/r_k curve of Fig. 5.6 approaches zero rapidly, and $\beta_s{}^2 \cong 1$. Therefore, to a first approximation, for large values of r_s/r_k

$$C_k{}' \cong \frac{4\pi\epsilon_0}{3} \qquad \text{[farads per meter of length, if } r_s \gg r_k\text{]} \qquad (5\text{–}63b)$$

This is about the same as the capacitance between two space-charge-free concentric cylinders for which the outer cylinder has 4.5 times the radius of the inner one.

Note that, as r_s/r_k becomes very large, the first term in (5–63a) is the important one. In contrast, as r_s/r_k approaches unity, $\beta_s{}^2$ approaches zero; the second term then predominates and causes the entire expression to approach the (5–14a) planar value.

5.16   Derivation of the Complete-Space-Charge Equations for Concentric Cylindrical and Spherical Geometries.[5p, 15b] There are certain important circumstances, particularly in relation to microwave-tube beam establishment, in which the complete-space-charge relationships for concentric spheres are important. The three basic equations comparable with (5–51, 5–52, 5–53) are:

$$\frac{1}{r^2}\frac{d}{dr}\left(r^2\frac{dE}{dr}\right) = -\frac{\rho}{\epsilon_0} \qquad (5\text{–}64)$$

$$\tfrac{1}{2}m_e v^2 = E q_e \qquad (5\text{–}65)$$

$$I = 4\pi r^2 \rho v = 4\pi r^2 J \qquad (5\text{–}66)$$

where E, ρ, and v describe values on a spherical surface of radius r, and I is the total current over the entire spherical solid angle.

The differential equation similar to (5–54) is

$$\frac{1}{r^2}\frac{d}{dr}\left(r^2\frac{dE}{dr}\right) = -\frac{I}{4\pi\epsilon_0}\sqrt{\frac{m_e}{2q_e}}\frac{1}{r^2\sqrt{E}} \qquad (5\text{–}67)$$

It is convenient, by using (1–26), to express (5–54) and (5–67) as a single relation, as follows:

$$\frac{d^2E}{dr^2} + \frac{k}{r}\frac{dE}{dr} = -\frac{J}{\epsilon_0}\sqrt{\frac{m_e}{2q_e}}\frac{1}{\sqrt{E}} \qquad (5\text{–}68)$$

Here k takes on the values 1 and 2 respectively for cylindrical and spherical geometries.[15b] Eliminate J and r from (5–68) by the introduction of variables u and β. u is defined by the equation

$$u = \ln\frac{r}{r_k}, \text{ that is, } \qquad r = r_k \exp u \qquad (5\text{–}69)$$

and β is defined by

$$E^{3/2} = -\frac{9}{4}\frac{J}{\epsilon_0}\sqrt{\frac{m_e}{2q_e}}r^2\beta^2 \qquad (5\text{–}70)$$

which is the same as (5–55). Equation (5–68) then becomes

$$\frac{d^2E}{du^2} + (k-1)\frac{dE}{du} = \frac{4}{9}\frac{E}{\beta^2} \qquad (5\text{–}71)$$

Differentiate (5–53) and (5–66) relative to r, noting that I is a constant; the results are respectively

$$r\,dJ + J\,dr = 0 \qquad \text{[cylindrical geometry]} \qquad (5\text{–}72)$$

$$r\,dJ + 2J\,dr = 0 \qquad \text{[spherical geometry]} \qquad (5\text{–}73)$$

Therefore a general relationship is

$$r\frac{dJ}{dr} = -kJ \qquad (5\text{–}74)$$

expressible as

$$\frac{dJ}{du} = -kJ \qquad (5\text{–}75)$$

Introduction of (5–70) into both sides of (5–75), with subsequent differentiations and reduction, gives

$$\frac{dE}{du} = \frac{2}{3}(2-k)E + \frac{4}{3}\frac{E}{\beta}\frac{d\beta}{du} \qquad (5\text{–}76)$$

Substitution of this relation and its u derivative into (5–71) eliminates E by cancellation and results in [5p, 15b]

$$3\beta\frac{d^2\beta}{du^2} + \left(\frac{d\beta}{du}\right)^2 + (5-k)\beta\frac{d\beta}{du} + \frac{1}{2}\beta^2(2+k-k^2) = 1 \qquad (5\text{–}77)$$

The boundary conditions for the solution of this differential equation are stated fundamentally in terms of the potential and potential gradient at $r = r_k$. Therefore it is necessary to relate β and its derivative, evaluated at $r = r_k$, to E and its derivative. Thus (5–70) gives rise to

$$E_a^{3/2} = -\frac{9}{4}\frac{J_a}{\epsilon_0}\sqrt{\frac{m_e}{2q_e}}\,r_k^2\beta_k^2 \qquad (5\text{–}78)$$

where

$$E_a,\, J_a,\, \beta_k \text{ are } E, J, \beta \text{ at } r = r_k \qquad (5\text{–}79)$$

For the space-charge-limited situation of present interest, both the potential and the potential gradient are zero at the cathode surface, $r = r_k$. It follows from (5–78) that for this simple case $\beta_k = 0$. If now (5–77) is expressed for $r = r_k$, using $\beta_k = 0$, one obtains

$$\left(\frac{d\beta}{du}\right)_{r=r_k} = \pm 1 \qquad \text{when } \beta_k = 0 \qquad (5\text{–}80)$$

(5–82) and (5–84) below show that this makes $dE/dr = 0$ at $r = r_k$. The solution for β is initiated by assuming a power series for β, thus:

$$\beta = A_0 + A_1 u + A_2 u^2 + A_3 u^3 + \cdots \qquad (5\text{–}81)$$

$d\beta/du$ and $d^2\beta/du^2$ are then expressed as the derivatives of this equation. These expressions for β and its derivatives are then entered in (5–77), and the coefficients of each power of u are equated to zero. Each equation so obtained leads to the determination of one of the A's.

For the space-charge-limited problem, A_0 will be zero, and A_1 will be ± 1, because of (5–80). All other coefficients are obtainable in sequence, given these two. The $A_1 = +1$ condition corresponds to electrons flowing from a central cathode to an outer concentric anode or grid, the $A_1 = -1$ condition to electrons flowing inward from an external cathode.

To confirm the cathode boundary conditions, use (5–78) in (5–76) to give, at $r = r_k$,

$$\left(\frac{dE}{du}\right)_{r=r_k} = \frac{2}{3}\left(-\frac{9}{4}\frac{J_a}{\epsilon_0}\sqrt{\frac{m_e}{2q_e}}\,r_k^2\right)^{2/3}\left[(2-k)\beta_k^{4/3} + 2\beta_k^{1/3}\left(\frac{d\beta}{du}\right)_{r=r_k}\right] \qquad (5\text{–}82)$$

Note from (5–69) that

$$du = \frac{dr}{r} \qquad \text{so that } \frac{dE}{du} = r\frac{dE}{dr} \qquad (5\text{–}83)$$

Therefore from (5–82)

$$\left(\frac{dE}{du}\right)_{r=r_k} = r_k\left(\frac{dE}{dr}\right)_{r=r_k} = 0; \text{ if } \beta_k = 0, \left(\frac{d\beta}{du}\right)_{r=r_k} = \pm 1 \quad (5\text{–}84)$$

5.17   Complete-Space-Charge Equations; Cylindrical and Spherical Geometries.[5p, 15b] For the cylindrical case, $k = 1$ in (5–77), giving

$$3\beta\frac{d^2\beta}{du^2} + \left(\frac{d\beta}{du}\right)^2 + 4\beta\frac{d\beta}{du} + \beta^2 - 1 = 0 \qquad (5\text{–}85)$$

Use of the inner cathode form of the (5–80) boundary condition indicates that $A_0 = 0$ and $A_1 = +1$ in (5–81); the series as then evaluated, by the method outlined below (5–81), takes the following form given by Langmuir and Blodgett: [5p]

$$\beta = u - \frac{2}{5}u^2 + \frac{11}{120}u^3 - \frac{47}{33,000}u^4 + 0.00168u^5 + \cdots \quad (5\text{–}86)$$

Numerical values of β^2 for both the inner and outer cathode case appear in Table III. (See bibliography reference 15b for complete β^2 curves.) The current density at radius r is of course given, from (5–56), by

$$-J = 2.33 \times 10^{-6}\frac{E^{3/2}}{r^2\beta^2} \qquad (5\text{–}87)$$

For the spherical case, $k = 2$ in (5–77), and it is convenient, in employing (5–87), to replace β by α for the sake of clarity; the differential equation for α becomes [5p, 15b]

$$3\alpha\frac{d^2\alpha}{du^2} + \left(\frac{d\alpha}{du}\right)^2 + 3\alpha\frac{d\alpha}{du} = 1 \qquad (5\text{–}88)$$

The series solution for the inner cathode case begins as

$$\alpha = u - 0.3u^2 + 0.075u^3 - 0.01432u^4 + 0.00216u^5 - \cdots \quad (5\text{–}89)$$

Table IV gives values of α^2 for both the internal and external cathode situations. The current density is of course given by (5–87), with α^2 used in place of β^2.

In the spherical case, usually only a portion of the spherical solid angle is used; to get the total current, $-J_s$ is multiplied by the area of the receiving anode surface. J_s is J at $r = r_s$, obtained from (5–87) by using α in place of β.

To obtain the spherical-case potential distribution equation, first replace β^2 by α^2 in (5–87), and then multiply through by 4π, giving

$$-4\pi J = 4\pi \times 2.33 \times 10^{-6} \frac{E^{\frac{3}{2}}}{r^2\alpha^2} \tag{5–90}$$

Now recognize that $4\pi J = I$ (invariant with r), and solve for E; the result is

$$E = \left(\frac{-I}{4\pi \times 2.33 \times 10^{-6}}\right)^{\frac{2}{3}} (\alpha^2)^{\frac{2}{3}} \tag{5–91}$$

This is the counterpart of (5–58); it has no simple asymptote. The corresponding capacitance, obtained in the same general manner as (5–63a), is

$$C_k' = \frac{8\pi\epsilon_0}{3} \frac{r_s^2}{r_k} \frac{1}{\alpha_s^2} \left[\frac{d\alpha^2}{d(r/r_k)}\right]_{r=r_s} \qquad \begin{bmatrix} \text{for the entire} \\ \text{spherical} \\ \text{solid angle} \end{bmatrix} \tag{5–92}$$

5.18   Space-Charge-Limited Current from a Filamentary Cathode between Plane Anodes.   A single-filament cathode and two parallel-plane-surfaced anodes, as illustrated in Fig. 5.8, represent an intermediate circumstance between planar and cylindrical geometry.

It is evident that in Fig. 5.8 some definite flux line from the cathode terminates at the point A' on the lower plate, that some definite complete-space-charge electron trajectory terminates at A', and that some definite radial straight line from the cathode center terminates at A'. These three lines all start normal to the cathode surface, and at three different points on the cathode surface. Thus in this geometry the flux lines, the electron trajectories, and the lines of geometrical symmetry are not coincident, as they are for planar, cylindrical, and spherical geometries. It is nevertheless possible to set up for this geometry a set of simultaneous partial differential equations that correspond to (5–6) and (5–54), but the set has not been solved, even formally.

An approximate current determination can be made, which applies (5–59), in a manner that makes the radius a function of the angle; this will be outlined in this section, and an entirely different alternative method given in the next section.

Refer to locality A on the upper plate of Fig. 5.8, and imagine the sector $d\phi$ to be a small portion of a pair of concentric cylinders having complete space charge. This pair has inner and outer radii r_k and r respectively. The distance from the cathode surface to the anode surface element dy has one value if measured along a radial straight line terminating at A, another value if measured along a flux line terminating at A, and still another value if measured along an electron trajectory terminating at A.

No one of these distances is precisely correct for employment as a radius in incremental use of (5–59). If $s \gg r_k$ they differ very little from one another for most areas receiving substantial current; therefore, it is reasonable in applying (5–59) to the sector $d\phi$ to employ the radial line, as that is the easiest to use. Thus the space-charge-limited current reaching the element dy per unit axial distance is, to a first approximation,

$$-\frac{dI}{l} = 2.33 \times 10^{-6} \frac{E_s^{\,\frac{3}{2}}}{r^2 \beta^2} r \, d\phi \qquad (5–93)$$

Here $r \, d\phi$ describes the anode area, included in $d\phi$, of a cylindrical arrangement having an outer cylinder of radius r. The value of β^2 is that corresponding to r/r_k. Introduction of $\cos \phi = s/r$ into (5–93) gives

$$-\frac{dI}{l} = 2.33 \times 10^{-6} \frac{E_s^{\,\frac{3}{2}}}{s} \frac{\cos \phi \, d\phi}{\beta^2} \qquad (5–94)$$

The total current I is twice that to either plate; the current to either plate is obtained by integration from $\phi = -\pi/2$ to $\phi = +\pi/2$. For most filamentary cathode devices $s/r_k > 10$, so that β^2 is approximately unity. In this case the integration is straightforward and yields

$$-\frac{I}{l} \cong 4 \times 2.33 \times 10^{-6} \frac{E_s^{\,\frac{3}{2}}}{s} \qquad [\text{if } s > 10 r_k] \qquad (5–95)$$

This relation is in good agreement with experiment. It was presented by Kusunose [5r] on the basis of considerations very different from those used in the present derivation. His experiments, performed on triodes, gave results essentially in agreement with the form taken by (5–95) when adapted for such use, as described in Section 5.20, and illustrated by Fig. 5.11.

It is of course possible to integrate (5–94) for cases in which s/r_k is not large enough to permit calling β^2 unity. In such cases β^2 is expressed as a function of ϕ by using $s/r_k \cos \phi$ for r/r_k, in obtaining values of β^2 from Table III. The integration is then carried out numerically or graphically. However, the approximation introduced, which amounts to identifying with one another the three lines to A' in Fig. 5.8, is difficult to justify when s is only two or three times as large as r_k. The author has used the integration of (5–94), employing

β^2, to study a few irregular geometries of very modest s/r_k ratio; in those cases tried the agreement with experiment was not good, the equations indicating a current considerably less than that observed experimentally.

However, as applied to the large s/r_k ratio cases, the agreement with experiment is excellent, the nature of the approximation is such as to

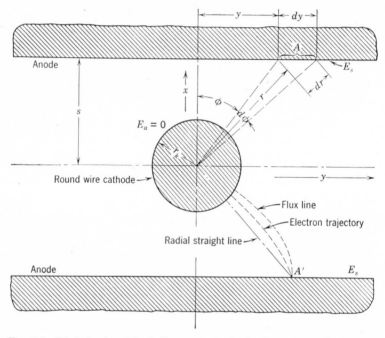

FIG. 5.8   Diode having a single filamentary cathode wire and two planar anodes. Cathode potential is $E_a = 0$; both anodes are at potential E_s. For application of the associated analysis to a triode, place the grid plane where anode surfaces appear in this figure; E_s then becomes the equivalent grid sheet potential.

suggest that agreement should be good, the method of derivation is a rational and satisfying one, and the result, (5–95), is very simple in form and easy to use.

5.19   Equivalent Capacitance Derivation of Space-Charge-Limited Current from a Filamentary Cathode.[5q]   To approach the second method of approximating the solution for complete-space-charge current in a filamentary cathode device, the conformal transformation of Section 4.2, Figs. 4.5 and 4.6, will be employed to determine the space-charge-free capacitance between the flat plates and the round cathode wire of Fig. 5.8.   It will then be presumed as a first approximation that two concentric cylinders whose capacitance per unit length has this same value will draw the same space-charge-limited current as the geometry of Fig. 5.8.*, [5q]

In carrying out the transformation, which gives a Z-plane diagram as in Fig. 5.9, representing the transformation of Fig. 5.8 as a W-plane diagram, the quantity $1/n$ in the transformation is chosen to have the

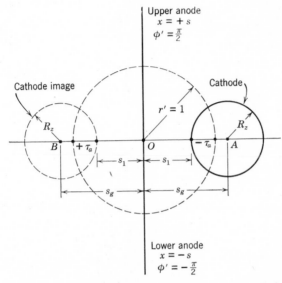

Fig. 5.9 Z-plane representation of the single-filament planar diode of Fig. 5.8. Note that charges $\pm\tau_a$ are located at kernel positions, radius $r' = 1$.

value $4s$, and the W-plane origin is at the cathode-wire center.   Thus the transformation relations are

$$y + jx = \frac{2s}{\pi} \ln \left(r' \exp j\phi' \right) \tag{5-96}$$

$$r' = \exp \frac{\pi y}{2s} \tag{5-97}$$

$$\phi' = \frac{\pi x}{2s} \tag{5-98}$$

Along the upper anode surface, $x = +s$, so $\phi' = \pi/2$; along the lower anode surface, $\phi' = -\pi/2$.   Thus the two anodes together form the

* This method is essentially that used by G. D. O'Neill, reference 5q.

vertical line through the origin of the Z-plane figure. The cathode transforms to a figure that is essentially circular if

$$\frac{r_k}{2s} \text{ is less than about } \frac{1}{5} \qquad (5\text{-}99)$$

that is, if the cathode diameter is less than about 40 per cent of the anode-to-anode spacing. There may also be drawn on the Z-plane figure an "image" of the cathode in the vertical dividing plane.

Employment of the relations governing the location of a line charge and its image shows that the Z-plane cathode cylinder and its image, also the vertical Z-plane anode plane, will be equipotentials if equal and opposite line charges $\pm\tau_a$ are located at radius $r' = 1$, as shown in Fig. 5.9. To demonstrate this, note that:

$$\text{Distance from } +\tau_a \text{ to } A \text{ is } s_g + 1$$
$$\text{Distance from } -\tau_a \text{ to } A \text{ is } s_g - 1 \qquad (5\text{-}100)$$

and that, with respect to the (4-39) type of relation,

$$(s_g + 1)(s_g - 1) = s_g{}^2 - 1 = R_z{}^2 \qquad (5\text{-}101)$$

because

$$s_g{}^2 = \cosh^2 \frac{\pi r_k}{2s} \qquad R_z{}^2 = \sinh^2 \frac{\pi r_k}{2s} \qquad (5\text{-}102)$$

The potential difference between the cathode and the anode plane in the field of the *two* charges will be

$$E_s - E_a = -\frac{-\tau_a}{2\pi\epsilon_0} \ln \frac{1}{1 - (s_g - R_z)} - \frac{+\tau_a}{2\pi\epsilon_0} \ln \frac{1}{1 + (s_g - R_z)} \qquad (5\text{-}103a)$$

$$= +\frac{+\tau_a}{2\pi\epsilon_0} \ln \frac{1 + (s_g - R_z)}{1 - (s_g - R_z)} \qquad (5\text{-}103b)$$

$$= +\frac{\tau_a}{2\pi\epsilon_0} \ln \coth \frac{\pi r_k}{4s} \qquad (5\text{-}103c)$$

The capacitance per meter of length, between anode and cathode, will then be

$$C_{pk} = \frac{2\pi\epsilon_0}{\ln \coth (\pi r_k/4s)} \qquad \text{[farads per meter]} \qquad (5\text{-}104)$$

Thus the space-charge-free capacitance between the cathode and the two anodes will be just the same as that between two concentric cylinders, having

Inner radius: r_k [an arbitrary choice]   (5–105a)

Outer radius: $r_s = r_k \coth \dfrac{\pi r_k}{4s}$ (5–105b)

This expression's accuracy is subject only to (5–99). Furthermore, if the cathode wire size is such that (5–99) is satisfied:

The outer radius r_s approaches $\dfrac{4s}{\pi}$, that is, $1.275s$ (5–106)

because, as $\pi r_k/4s$ becomes modest relative to unity,

$$\coth \frac{\pi r_k}{4s} \text{ approaches } \frac{4s}{\pi r_k}$$ (5–107)

The capacitance becomes

$$C_{pk} \cong \frac{2\pi\epsilon_0}{\ln (4s/\pi r_k)} \qquad \text{[if } s/r_k > 5/2]$$ (5–108)

Thus the space-charge-free capacitance between a fairly large cathode wire centrally located between two parallel-plane anodes of spacing $2s$ is very nearly that which would exist between the cathode wire and a fictitious cylinder around it, of radius $4s/\pi$. Note particularly that the radius of this fictitious outer cylinder is independent of the diameter of the cathode, if that diameter is modest enough relative to s.

It might seem not unreasonable to suppose as a first approximation that the space-charge-limited current from a hot filament will be the same between the two anode plates as inside a cylindrical anode to which it has the same capacitance. The space-charge-limited current for the geometry of Fig. 5.8 might therefore be approximated by determining the space-charge-limited current between the two cylinders of (5–105a), (5–106). From (5–61), this is, in amperes per meter of filament length,

$$-\frac{I}{l} \cong 2\pi \times 2.33 \times 10^{-6} \frac{E_s^{3/2}}{1.275s\beta_s^2}$$ (5–109)

The value $r_s/r_k \cong 1.275s/r_k$ is used in determining β_s^2.

By using the analytical method of this section, O'Neill [5q] has obtained very good agreement with experiment even for values of s/r_k as low as $5/2$, β_s^2 being much less than unity. The method of Section

5.18 does not check well with experiment for such cases. Both methods agree acceptably with experiment when $s \gg r_k$, leading to $\beta_s{}^2 \cong 1$.

As the filament becomes small, $\beta_s{}^2$ can be called unity; then the preceding equation reduces to

$$-\frac{I}{l} = 2\pi \times 2.33 \times 10^{-6} \frac{E_s{}^{3/2}}{1.275s} \qquad [\text{if } s \gg r_k] \qquad (5\text{-}110)$$

$$= 4.93 \times 2.33 \times 10^{-6} \frac{E_s{}^{3/2}}{s} \qquad (5\text{-}111)$$

The difference between this and (5–95) is not sufficient to permit an easy determination as to which is in best agreement with experiment, and no precise analytical solution has been made. Either expression is satisfactory for usual design purposes.

In subsequent sections in this text (5–95) will be used, if $s \gg r_k$, not because (5–95) is believed to be more nearly correct than (5–111), but because it is believed to be about equally good as an approximation and is more easily derived and more simply expressed.

Note that neither of the two derivations given for I/l is seriously affected in principle if the filament wires have rectangular, ribbon-like, or other noncircular sections, as long as every dimension of the filament is small relative to s.

5.20 Planar Triodes with Multiple-Filament Cathodes. In order to adapt the treatment of Section 5.18 to the study of a planar triode having a filamentary cathode, as illustrated by Fig. 1.2, the first step in concept is to identify the plates of Fig. 5.8 with the equivalent grid sheet of the triode. Then the total cathode current should be determinable by multiplying (5–95), which gives current per unit length, by the total length of the filament wire exposed to the planar grid-and-plate structure.

Suppose that there are many parallel filament wires spaced a distance $1/n_k$ apart. If the between-cathode-wire spacing $1/n_k$ is large relative to the cathode-plane-to-grid-plane spacing s, that is, if

$$n_k s \ll 1 \qquad (5\text{-}112)$$

the individual wires will deliver current independently of one another. To determine the current density at the grid sheet by (5–95), note that:

(a) Half the current goes laterally to each grid, thus calling for the use of a factor of $\frac{1}{2}$ to give the current density on one side; and

(b) There are n_k meters of filament length per square meter of structure. Therefore the average current density J_s on each of the two opposite sides is obtained by multiplying (5–95) by n_k, after applying the ½ factor from (a); thus

$$J_s = 2 \times 2.33 \times 10^{-6} \frac{E_s^{3/2}}{s} n_k \quad \begin{bmatrix} \text{filamentary cathode,} \\ \text{remotely spaced} \\ \text{cathode wires} \end{bmatrix} \quad (5\text{–}113)$$

Curve GTB in Fig. 5.10 represents this relationship.

It is impossible for the space-charge-limited current on each side to exceed the value given by (5–12) for a flat-surfaced cathode; this value is shown as $J_{s\ max}$ in Fig. 5.10. For example, if the cathode wires were placed so close together as to make the cathode appear to be a

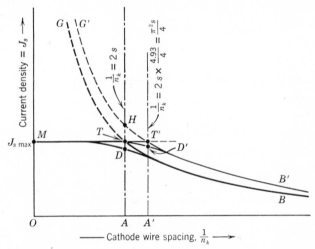

FIG. 5.10 Dependence of current density J_s at grid sheet on spacing between cathode wires, for a filamentary-cathode planar device. MTB represents (5–114) and (5–113), based on (5–95). $MT'B'$ represents (5–114) and a relation like (5–113) but based on (5–111). $J_{s\ max}$ is given by (5–114).

plane surface, the current density would not be that along GT, but rather that along MT, in Fig. 5.10. Thus from (5–12)

$$J_{s\ max} = 2.33 \times 10^{-6} \frac{E_s^{3/2}}{s^2} \quad (5\text{–}114)$$

Comparison of the last two equations shows that they give the same value when $1/n_k = 2s$. Thus:

As the cathode wires are moved closer together, the maximum theoretical value of grid sheet current density occurs when $\left.\begin{matrix} \\ \\ \\ \end{matrix}\right\} \dfrac{1}{n_k} = 2s \quad (5\text{–}115)$

Therefore in a filamentary cathode planar triode nothing is gained as to increase of perveance or of transconductance by using a spacing less than 2s between cathode wires. It is therefore quite common practice to use the spacing 2s.

The obvious implication of the intersection of the straight line MT with the curve GTB, in Fig. 5.10, is that when the cathode wires are closer together than 2s the space charge from each one has an important effect in limiting the current that its neighbors would otherwise provide. It is reasonable to expect that this mutual space-charge-limiting effect should appear gradually rather than abruptly. Therefore one might anticipate that an overall curve would have some such shape as MDB in Fig. 5.10, representing a merging into the two limiting conditions each way.

If the (5–111) relation, based on the equal-current-for-equal-capacitance concept is employed, rather than (5–95), the curve $G'T'B'$ is obtained for the relation corresponding to (5–113), and the maximum theoretical value of grid sheet current density should be reached when $1/n_k = \pi^2 s/4$ rather than when $1/n_k = 2s$. An expected merging-in curve would then be $MD'B'$.

It is frequently desirable to apply (5–95) to estimate the space-charge-limited current for a planar triode having an M-shaped filament, as illustrated in Fig. 1.2, and in more detail in Fig. 5.11. For application to such a geometry it is convenient to recognize that (5–95) can be written as follows:

$$I \cong 2 \times \left(2.33 \times \frac{E_s^{\frac{3}{2}}}{s^2} \right) \times (\text{Width } 2s) \times (\text{Length } l) \quad (5\text{–}116)$$

which is the same as

$$I \cong 2J_{s \text{ max}} \times (\text{Width } 2s) \times (\text{Length } l) \quad (5\text{–}117)$$

where $J_{s \text{ max}}$ is as in (5–114). This implies that the space-charge-limited current from a single cathode filament is the same as that which would appear in a section of flat-cathode planar triode for which the grid sheet area has the width 2s and the length l and has two faces, one each way from the flat cathode. The distinguishing characteristic of such an area is that it comprises all the grid sheet region that is distant not more than s from the projection of the filament wire on the grid sheet. Figure 5.11 illustrates the application to the determination of current from an M-shaped filament. The line $MMMM$ represents the filament location, that is, the projection on the grid plane of the filament, and the area $AAAAAAA$ includes all the area, within the extent of the grid structure, that lies not farther than s from the filament location line $MMMM$. The total cathode current is then obtained by multiplying this area by $J_{s\ \max}$ as given by (5–114). This method checks back in principle to (5–95), by way of (5–116).

Kusunose [5r] introduced this type of approach to the determination of space-charge-limited current from filamentary cathodes, although his basis for using his very similar method was entirely different from

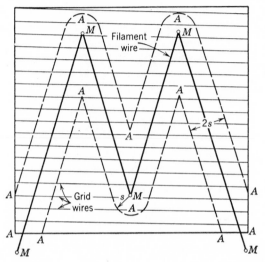

Fig. 5.11   Determination of effective grid sheet area to use in finding space-charge-limited current from a filamentary cathode in a planar electrode structure. Obtain the cathode current by multiplying area outlined as $AAAA$, etc., by $J_{s\ \max}$, given by (5–114).

the (5–95) derivation given here. The author's experience verifies Kusunose's findings that this method may be expected to check very well with experimental measurements.

Perhaps it should be pointed out that this method corresponds to the (5–113) equation, that is, the GTB curve in Fig. 5.10, without the inclusion of any downward adjustment, as from point T to point D along a merging curve. An almost identical result could be obtained by employing (5–111) properly, that is, curve $G'T'B'$, and at the same time including a downward adjustment, as for example from H to T. Thus the agreement of the Fig. 5.11 method with experiment gives no strong reason for choice between the (5–95) and (5–111) approximations, as applied to small-diameter filaments, for which $r_k \ll s$.

5.21   Evaluation of Triode Grid Sheet Potential for Filamentary Cathodes.   In order to employ the methods outlined in connection with Fig. 5.11 to find the current from a filamentary cathode in a planar triode, it is necessary to be able to determine e_s by a proper adaptation of (5–22). Note that the cathode location and geometry affect only C_k' in that equation, and also that changes in C_k' have relatively little effect on e_s, because ordinarily $\mu \gg 1$. Therefore no great precision is needed in the evaluation of C_k'.

First consider a design within the MT range in Fig. 5.10, that is, one in which the cathode wire separation is not greater than $2s$. The space-charge-limited current is then very nearly the same as if the cathode were a flat surface located in the plane of the filament wires. This implies that *in the neighborhood of the grid* the potential distribution must be about the same as in the flat-cathode triode potential diagram, Fig. 5.3. Therefore charge distributions on grid and plate surfaces are about the same as in Fig. 5.3.

With electrode charges and potentials about the same as in the flat-cathode geometry, the capacitances must also be about the same, so that (5–14a) is a good approximation to C_k'. Therefore, as in (5–23), equation (5–22) becomes, approximately,

$$e_s \cong \frac{e_c + \dfrac{e_b}{\mu}}{1 + \dfrac{1}{\mu} + \dfrac{1}{\mu}\left(\dfrac{4}{3}\dfrac{b}{a}\right)} \qquad \begin{bmatrix} \text{planar triode with} \\ \text{filamentary cathode,} \\ \text{if } 1/n \leqq 2s \end{bmatrix} \qquad (5\text{–}118)$$

(Contact difference of potential must of course be considered; see Section 8.25.) Thus if the cathode wires are not too far apart, e_s is determined in the same way as for the flat cathode. The use of (5–118) for e_s, and of a for s, in (5–95), results in a triode current expression similar in nature and use to (5–36).

In some tubes, as illustrated in Fig. 5.11, there are fairly extensive regions in which the cathode wire spacing is greater than $2s$. This puts the problem into the TB region of Fig. 5.10, and (5–14a) for C_k' will no longer apply, because it is no longer true that the potential distribution in the neighborhood of the grid is closely similar to that in the flat-cathode case. The analytical approach is now to treat e_s as being a function of position in the direction parallel to the grid wires, in Fig. 5.11, because the charge distribution on the grid, and therefore C_k', will so vary.

An analysis of this kind, not presented here, indicates that for the extreme case of a lone filament wire an approximate and suitably averaged value of e_s is obtained by using $\frac{4}{9}$ rather than $\frac{4}{3}$ in the third denominator term in (5–118). This brackets the problem; in Fig. 5.10, for designs beyond B, $\frac{4}{9}$ should be used, whereas for designs within the MT range, $\frac{4}{3}$ should be used. For intermediate conditions, an estimated interpolation should be satisfactory. In any case, no great precision is needed, because of the relatively minor part played by the third denominator term as a whole.

5.22   Effect on Space-Charge-Limited Current of Potential Variation along the Cathode.[5r] It has been shown that for various geometries the space-charge-limited cathode current density is proportional to the $\frac{3}{2}$ power of a voltage. This can be summarized by writing

$$I_a = P_s E_s^{\frac{3}{2}} \tag{5–119}$$

where E_s is the plate voltage of a diode or the equivalent grid sheet potential of a space-charge-control tube. I_a is the cathode current; P_s is the perveance, defined in terms of equivalent grid sheet potential if the treatment is to apply to a space-charge-control tube; see (5–40) and (5–41). P_s depends on geometry and always contains the factor 2.33×10^{-6}.

The derivations leading to the various forms of (5–119) are based on the assumption that the cathode is an equipotential surface, as in a heater-type tube. In many real devices the cathode is heated by the passage of an electric current, which causes a potential drop between its two extremes. Since this drop may be several volts, hence comparable in magnitude with the grid sheet potential, it often produces marked variations in current density along the cathode surface. This results in a distinct modification of the volt-ampere relationship; the modification will be derived here as applied to a space-charge-control tube.

The nature of the modification can be analyzed by assuming that (5–119) holds for each incremental length of cathode surface but that the voltage to be used varies from point to point. This assumption is satisfactorily near to the truth as long as the spacing between electrodes is considerably less than the extent of the cathode.

Suppose the voltage E_s to be measured from the more negative end of the cathode; also let

    l = length of cathode (also of plate).

    z = distance along cathode from negative toward positive end; z varies from 0 to l.

    w = width of grid sheet surface ($= 2\pi r_s$ if cylindrical).

    $-F_z$ = potential gradient along cathode due to heating current.

E_f = potential drop between $z = 0$ and $z = l$ due to heating current; of course $E_f = -F_z l$.

S = area of grid sheet surface ($= wl$).

I_a = total current from cathode.

Now apply (5–119) to an increment of length dz, width w, current dI_a. Then

$$dI_a = wG_s[E_s - (-F_z z)]^{3/2} dz \qquad (5\text{–}120)$$

where G_s = perveance per unit area of grid sheet surface; that is,

$$P_s = SG_s \qquad (5\text{–}121)$$

Two cases must be considered in the integration:

Case A: $E_s > E_f$. The integration extends between $z = 0$ and $z = l$, as follows:

$$I_a = wG_s \int_{z=0}^{z=l} (E_s + F_z z)^{3/2} dz \qquad (5\text{–}122)$$

$$= \frac{2}{5} \frac{wG_s}{F_z} [(E_s + F_z l)^{5/2} - E_s^{5/2}] \qquad (5\text{–}123)$$

When numerator and denominator are multiplied by l, then rearranged, using $E_f = -F_z l$ and $S = wl$, this becomes

$$I_a = \frac{2SG_s}{5} E_f^{3/2} \left[\left(\frac{E_s}{E_f}\right)^{5/2} - \left(\frac{E_s}{E_f} - 1\right)^{5/2} \right] \qquad (5\text{–}124)$$

The quantity $[(E_s/E_f) - 1]^{5/2}$ may be expanded by the binomial theorem; the rapidity of the convergence of the series so obtained is such that, when E_s is twice or more as large as E_f, the following expression, containing only two terms, is a satisfactory approximation:

$$I_a = SG_s E_s^{3/2} \left(1 - \frac{3}{4} \frac{E_f}{E_s} \right) \qquad (5\text{–}125)$$

Case B: $E_s < E_f$. The integration extends only to the point along the cathode at which $E_s + F_z z = 0$. Beyond this point the cathode potential is greater than E_s, and therefore no current will flow.

The integration yields

$$I_a = \frac{2}{5} SG_s E_f^{3/2} \left(\frac{E_s}{E_f}\right)^{5/2} \qquad (5\text{–}126)$$

The following general relationship includes cases A and B:

$$I_a = \frac{2}{5} SG_s E_f^{3/2} f\left(\frac{E_s}{E_f}\right) \qquad (5\text{–}127)$$

The function $f(E_s/E_f)$ has the numerical values given in Table V, which are in accord with (5–124) and (5–126) for the appropriate circumstances.   The effect on I_a of contact difference of potential is accounted for by including in E_s an added contact potential term as described in Section 8.25.

The above relations indicate a $\frac{5}{2}$ power dependence of I_a on E_s when $E_s < E_f$, and a $\frac{3}{2}$ power variation when $E_s \gg E_f$.   Actual filamentary cathode triode characteristic curves usually extend through a case B into a case A range, and when plotted logarithmically are often found to follow approximately and over a considerable range a power curve whose exponent lies between $\frac{3}{2}$ and $\frac{5}{2}$.   Thus Fig. 6.1b shows that the Western Electric 101–F triode average characteristics follow a 2.2 power curve fairly closely.

5.23   Microphonics in Space-Charge-Control Tubes.[5s, t]   By suitable modifications of (5–95) it is possible to analyze the effects on plate current to be expected as a result of small lateral oscillatory motions of the filament wires in a planar triode having a filamentary cathode. Because of the minor part played by $C_k'/\mu C_p$, and therefore by C_k', in (5–22) it may be assumed to a good first approximation that the equivalent grid sheet potential e_s will be unaffected by an oscillation of the filament wires.   The important *microphonic* effect on plate current results from the presence of the cathode-to-grid spacing distance $s \cong a$ in the denominator of (5–95).

In the derivation of (5–95) from (5–94), the integration was taken from $-\pi/2$ to $+\pi/2$ for each anode, then the answer doubled to obtain the total for both anodes.   For the present purpose the result of the integration must be expressed separately for each anode.   Suppose that before any oscillations occur the cathode plane is unsymmetrically located, at a distance $a_0 - a_1$ from the lower grid, $a_0 + a_1$ from the upper grid, as in Fig. 5.12.   Then the total cathode current per unit length of filament (i_a/l) will be

$$-\frac{i_a}{l} = 2 \times 2.33 \times 10^{-6} e_s{}^{\frac{3}{2}} \left(\frac{1}{a_0 - a_1} + \frac{1}{a_0 + a_1} \right) \quad (5\text{–}128)$$

that is,

$$-\frac{i_a}{l} = 4 \times 2.33 \times 10^{-6} e_s{}^{\frac{3}{2}} \frac{a_0}{a_0{}^2 - a_1{}^2} \quad (5\text{–}129)$$

Note that this is slightly more current than if the cathode wires were centered accurately.

When oscillatory motion of amplitude a_m occurs,

$$a_1 \text{ is replaced by } a_1 + a_m \cos \omega t \quad (5\text{–}130)$$

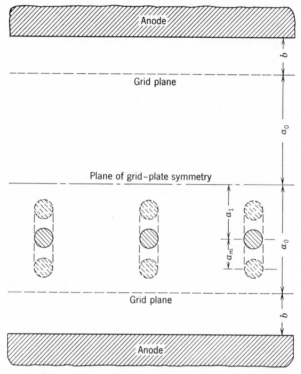

FIG. 5.12 Multiple-filament cathode vibrating with amplitude a_m, in a planar triode structure. Mean position of cathode wires is offset a distance a_1 from the plane of symmetry for the grid-plate assembly.

Equation (5–128) then becomes

$$-\frac{i_a}{l} = 2 \times 2.33 \times 10^{-6} e_s{}^{3\!/\!2} \left(\frac{1}{a_0 - a_1 - a_m \cos \omega t} \right.$$

$$\left. + \frac{1}{a_0 + a_1 + a_m \cos \omega t} \right) \quad (5\text{--}131)$$

that is,

$$-\frac{i_a}{l} = 2 \times 2.33 \times 10^{-6} e_s{}^{3\!/\!2} \left[\frac{1}{(a_0 - a_1)\left(1 - \dfrac{a_m \cos \omega t}{a_0 - a_1}\right)} \right.$$

$$\left. + \frac{1}{(a_0 + a_1)\left(1 + \dfrac{a_m \cos \omega t}{a_0 + a_1}\right)} \right] \quad (5\text{--}132)$$

where $a_m/(a_0 \pm a_1) \ll 1$. Expand each term by the binomial theorem, retaining only the first three terms of the expansion, giving

$$-\frac{i_a}{l} \cong 2 \times 2.33 \times 10^{-6} e_s{}^{3/2} \left\{ \frac{1}{a_0 - a_1} \left[1 + \frac{a_m \cos \omega t}{a_0 - a_1} + \frac{a_m{}^2 \cos^2 \omega t}{(a_0 - a_1)^2} \right] \right.$$

$$\left. + \frac{1}{a_0 + a_1} \left[1 - \frac{a_m \cos \omega t}{a_0 + a_1} + \frac{a_m{}^2 \cos^2 \omega t}{(a_0 + a_1)^2} \right] \right\} \quad (5\text{-}133)$$

Now use $\cos^2 \omega t = \frac{1}{2} + \frac{1}{2} \cos 2\omega t$, and define a_{01} by

$$a_0{}^2 - a_1{}^2 = a_{01}{}^2 \quad (5\text{-}134)$$

Then, after considerable manipulation, (5-133) becomes

$$-\frac{i_a}{l} \cong 4 \times 2.33 \times 10^{-6} e_s{}^{3/2} \frac{a_0}{a_{01}{}^2} \left[1 + \left(1 + \frac{4a_1{}^2}{a_{01}{}^2} \right) \frac{a_m{}^2}{2a_{01}{}^2} \right.$$

$$\left. + \frac{2a_1 a_m \cos \omega t}{a_{01}{}^2} + \left(1 + \frac{4a_1{}^2}{a_{01}{}^2} \right) \frac{a_m{}^2 \cos 2\omega t}{2a_{01}{}^2} \right] \quad (5\text{-}135)$$

For practical purposes, this expression describes the d-c, fundamental-frequency, and second-harmonic currents produced in the cathode (and plate) circuit by the microphonic action of the oscillating filament wire.

The important properties of this microphonic current effect are: [5s]

(a) If the cathode plane is symmetrically located, so that $a_1 = 0$, only the second harmonic of the oscillation appears in the circuit; the fundamental-frequency component is zero.

(b) When asymmetry exists, and $a_1 \ll a_0$, the fundamental-frequency component of current is directly proportional to a_1 and to a_m. Note, however, that the derivation permits a_1 to be a very substantial fraction of a_0, and that a_1 contributes to the value of a_{01}.

(c) As long as a_1 is a modest fraction of a_0, the amplitude of the second harmonic is affected only very slightly by the asymmetry.

(d) There exists a small increment in the d-c component of current; this increment has the same magnitude as the amplitude of the second-harmonic voltage.

The above discussion refers only to microphonics caused by vibration of the filament, which is the tube element most likely to be shock-excited into oscillation. If the grid oscillates, there is superposed on the effects just described a fundamental-frequency periodic variation in the amplification factor, because of the variation in grid-to-plate spacing b.

The presence of microphonics is usually distinctly objectionable. However, tubes have been built in which the microphonic properties are used to advantage for instrumentation purposes, as sensing elements for measurements of motion.[5t]

PROBLEMS

1. (a) Assume the potential distribution between two parallel plates, spacing s, to be given by $E = Ax^2$; A is a constant. Find the ratio of ρv at $x = 3s/4$ to ρv at $x = s/4$. Is this an equilibrium potential distribution?

(b) Same as (a), except that the potential equation is $E = Ax^{4/3}$.

2. Planar diode: potential distribution between the flat cathode and the parallel flat anode is $E = Ax^{4/3}$. At the cathode $x = 0$; at the anode $x = 0.3$ mm, and $E = E_b = 7$ volts. Evaluate A numerically. Then express, as functions of x: (a) electron velocity; (b) space-charge density; (c) the product of velocity by space-charge density; this is convection current density.

3. Planar diode: cathode, anode, each 4 sq cm area, 1 mm apart. Cathode thermionic emission, at its operating temperature, cannot exceed 250 ma per sq cm. (a) Find the actual current flow when plate voltage E_b is 100; (b) when E_b = 150.

4. A tungsten wire filament, 0.02 cm diameter, 5 cm long, is the cathode of a diode. The plate is a cylinder concentric with the filament.

(a) Select the plate radius so that the space-charge-limited current will be 40 ma per cm axial length when $E_b = 30$.

(b) Conditions as in (a); find the potential, electron velocity, potential gradient, and space-charge density at twice the cathode radius; using these results show that $2\pi r \rho v$ is the given current per unit length.

5. Cylindrical diode: outer cylinder the cathode, inner one the anode; radii 0.2, 0.01 cm; $E_b = 1000$. Find space-charge-limited current per centimeter length; calculate points for and draw space-charge-free and space-charge-limited potential distribution curves.

6. Prove that in Fig. 5.3 the plane $k'k'$ is at $\frac{1}{4}$ of the distance from the cathode to the near face of the grid sheet.

7. Planar triode: flat cathode 1 sq cm area, $\mu = 20$; spacings (mm): cathode to grid, 0.1; grid to anode, 0.3. Shadow fraction 0.10.

(a) Find: C_k', C_g, C_p ($\mu\mu$f); also find grid wires per centimeter.

(b) If $E_c = -5$, $E_b = +180$, find E_s, I_b, g_m, r_p.

(c) Sketch carefully and approximately to scale the potential distribution diagram, with particular attention to the cathode-grid region and to fillets.

(d) State input, output, and grid-plate capacitances.

(e) Find the ratio: [g_m/(input capacitance)], a "figure of merit."

(f) Find the cathode-to-grid and grid-to-plate transit times.

8. Planar triode: flat cathode, area 1 sq cm. Grid 0.2 mm (about 8 mils) from cathode; space-charge-limited current of 0.10 amp flowing. $E_c = -4$. (a) Find E_s, C_k'. (b) Find space-charge density ρ at the grid plane, also at a distance 0.01 mm from the cathode. (c) If plate is 1 mm from grid plane, and $\mu = 10$, find C_g, E_b.

9. In Fig. 4.5, given that $2nR = 0.10$, $na = 2$, $nb = 3$, $a + b = 3$ mm, active area 2 sq cm, $E_c = -10$, $E_b = 100$, current is space-charge limited.

(a) Find n, C_k', C_g, C_p, μ, E_s, I_b, g_m, r_p.

(b) Using construction lines, and carefully sketched fillets, draw a potential distribution diagram, for *space-charge-limited conditions*.

(c) State input, output, and grid-plate capacitances when space-charge-limited current is flowing, making appropriate use of (5–14b) for C_k''; also state the "figure of merit" (Section 5.13).

10. Similar to Prob. 9, for geometry and voltages of Prob. 2, Chapter IV.

11. Planar triode: flat cathode of area 1 sq cm; grid 0.23 mm from cathode, 0.70 mm from plate; grid mesh 6 wires per mm; $e_c = -25$, $e_b = +250$, $i_b = 0.180$ (space-charge-limited). Find e_s, C_g, grid-wire diameter, μ.

12. For the triode and voltages of Prob. 7 sketch diagrams similar to Figs. 5.4 and 5.5, with $k'k'$ and the q plane carefully located; from it determine E_s without evaluating any of the C's of the equivalent electrostatic circuit.

13. In relation to Fig. 5.5, demonstrate algebraically that the quantity

$$\frac{1 + \left(\dfrac{q}{a}\right)}{1 + \dfrac{1}{\mu} + \dfrac{1}{\mu}\dfrac{b}{a}} \text{ [is independent of } a, \text{ if] } \rightarrow q = \frac{b}{\mu + 1}$$

14. For a cylindrical triode express the radius r_q of a q cylinder between grid and plate, that corresponds to the q plane in a parallel-plane triode. Radii of cathode, grid cylinder, plate cylinder are given; μ is known.

15. For the cylindrical triode of Prob. 8, Chapter IV, suppose that $E_s = +9$, $E_c = -7$. Determine: I_b, E_b, μ, g_m, r_p, the figure of merit.

16. Determine the cathode-to-grid and grid-to-plate transit times for Prob. 15. This requires a numerical integration.

17. Derive the complete equations, in terms of dimensions and potentials, for amplification factor and transconductance of a cylindrical triode.

18. Planar triode: filamentary cathode; grid plane 0.8 mm from cathode, 2 mm from plate; 4 parallel filament strands each 1 cm long, 1.6 mm apart, diameter 0.3 mm. Grid shadow fraction 0.10, $\mu = 10$, current space-charge-limited. $E_s = +9$, $E_c = -7$; find I_b, E_b, g_m, figure of merit, current density at cathode-wire surface. Ignore voltage drop along the filament.

19. Cylindrical diode: $r_k = 0.2$ mm, $r_p = 1.0$ mm, length 3 cm. Voltage drop along cathode 10 volts, current space-charge-limited. Find plate current when plate voltage relative to negative end of cathode is (a) 5 volts, (b) 10 volts, (c) 20 volts.

20. In Prob. 18, find I_b with a 6-volt d-c drop along the filament; E_c, E_s, E_b are measured from the negative end of the filament.

CHAPTER VI

TRIODES, TETRODES, PENTODES *

6.1 Negative Grid Provides Electrostatic Control of Space-Charge-Limited Current. In most vacuum tubes the electron current is space-charge-limited; its magnitude is determined by geometry and potentials within the tube, according to the space-charge-control principles of Chapter V.

By modifying the grid potential of a triode, the voltage $e_c + (e_b/\mu)$ in (5–35) can be changed, and so the plate current changed. Since the grid is usually maintained, by means of a *bias* voltage, at a potential negative relative to the cathode, electrons do not reach it; the grid is not an emitter and so cannot release electrons. Carrying no electron current in either direction, its potential, and therefore the tube current, can be controlled with the expenditure of little or no power in the controlling circuit. The space-charge control of current so provided in a negative-grid triode is *electrostatic* in nature, in that it is accomplished by modifying the electrostatic field within the tube. The only current demanded of the controlling circuit is that drawn by the interelectrode capacitances.

6.2 Volt-Ampere Relations for Triodes.[6b] For reasons described in Section 5.22, the plate current of a triode should be expected to vary as the $\frac{3}{2}$ power, or the $\frac{5}{2}$ power, of the voltage $e_c + (e_b/\mu)$, or according to some intermediate relationship. A heater-type tube, having a uniform-potential cathode, may be expected to obey a $\frac{3}{2}$ power law. The effect of contact differences of potential is discussed in Section 8.25.

It is found *experimentally* that for many triodes the plate current can be satisfactorily expressed over the useful range of e_c and e_b by an empirical expression of the following form: [4B, 6b]

$$i_b = G \left(e_c + \frac{e_b}{\mu} \right)^n \tag{6–1}$$

If this can be done, the current is a function of $e_c + (e_b/\mu)$, rather than having some other type of dependence on e_c and e_b. The value of μ in such empirical equations usually agrees reasonably closely with the

* See also bibliography references 4B, C, E, 6A, B, 5o, 6a to 6j.

174

value obtained from the dimensions by the methods of Chapters IV and V, especially with planar geometry. The exponent for a particular device is determinable from the logarithmic form of (6–1), as follows:

$$\log_{10} i_b = \log_{10} G + n \log_{10}\left(e_c + \frac{e_b}{\mu}\right) \qquad (6\text{–}2)$$

This has the general form

$$y = b + nx \qquad (6\text{–}3)$$

Here n and $\log_{10} G$ are respectively the slope and i_b axis intercept of a logarithmic graph like that illustrated in Fig. 6.1b.

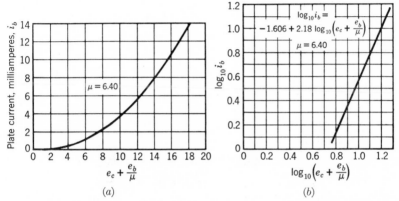

FIG. 6.1   Dependence of plate current on the composite voltage $e_c + (e_b/\mu)$, for a Western Electric type 101-F triode. The curve in (a) and the straight line in (b) represent any one of the characteristic curves in Fig. 1.3. (a) Plate current vs. the composite voltage. (b) A logarithmic representation of (a).

To the extent that the different *plate characteristic curves*, illustrated in Figs. 6.2b and 1.3, are parallel to one another, that is, identical except for a horizontal shift, the plate current is a function of the voltage $e_c + (e_b/\mu)$. To the extent that they are not so identical, the plate current is not a function of $e_c + (e_b/\mu)$ but has a more complex dependence on e_c, e_b. Figure 6.2b illustrates a kind of deviation, from the simple dependence on $e_c + (e_b/\mu)$, that is typical of most commercial triodes: the high-plate-voltage characteristics show progressively gentler slopes, particularly near cut-off. One important cause of this is a variation in μ from point to point along the cathode.

Chaffee [4B, 6b] gives interesting discussions of other types of variations of actual tube characteristic curves from the simple shapes predicted by the analyses of Chapters IV and V.

The analysis of electric circuits containing tubes is commonly based on a graphical representation of the tube characteristics. Figures 6.2a

176   TRIODES, TETRODES, PENTODES

and 6.2*b* are such graphical representations for a 6C5G power-amplifier triode. The curves of Fig. 6.2*b*, called *plate characteristics*, show the variation of plate current with plate voltage for a variety of values of the grid voltage parameter; those of Fig. 6.2*a*, called *mutual characteristics*, show the variation in plate current in response to grid voltage changes, plate voltage being the parameter.

The prediction of electronic circuit behavior is aided by a knowledge of transconductance g_m, amplification factor μ, and plate resistance

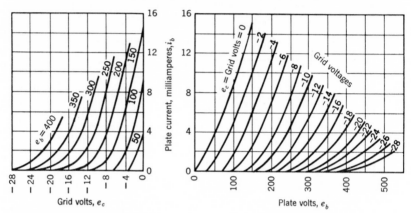

(*a*) Mutual characteristics, sometimes called transfer characteristics.

(*b*) Plate characteristics.

Fig. 6.2   Average characteristic curves, for the type 6C5G cylindrical-geometry triode. Note that, *for any type of vacuum tube*, the characteristic curves for any one individual tube may be expected to differ appreciably from the published average characteristics applying to that tube type. Circuit designs must be such as to provide satisfactory operation with any individual tube of a given type, in spite of the variation in characteristics from tube to tube.

r_p, defined in (5–18), (5–19), (5–20), in terms of the slopes of characteristic curves. In triodes g_m and r_p are dependent on i_b, but their product is reasonably constant and equal to the amplification factor μ; see (5–47).

The lower end or *cut-off point* of each of the characteristic curves of Fig. 6.2 is associated with the condition $e_b = -\mu e_c$ in (6–1). Actually the various space-charge-control equations do not represent accurately the manner of decrease to the zero axis at *very* small current values, because of the effects of initial electron velocities; see Sections 8.18 through 8.21.

6.3   Grid Current.[6A, 6c]   Equation (6–1), from the nature of its analytical development, describes the variations in current from the cathode, whereas the curves of Fig. 6.2 relate to plate current only. As long as the grid voltage is negative, which is the normal condition

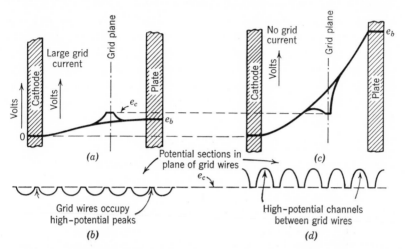

(a)

Potential sections in plane of grid wires

(c)

Grid wires occupy high-potential peaks

High-potential channels between grid wires

(b)

(d)

FIG. 6.3 Space-charge-flow potential distribution in a triode with the grid positive, showing diversion of current from positive grid to plate at high plate voltages. See also Fig. 6.4.

for many tube applications, there is no grid current. For positive grid voltages and low or negative plate voltages a substantial portion of the cathode current may pass to the grid. The dotted curves in the lower left portion of Fig. 1.3b indicate the magnitude of the current from the cathode there; although in this range the cathode current for the most part follows the space-charge-limited type of variation, it is divided between grid and plate. At slightly negative plate voltages, the grid current in some tubes exhibits an irregular dip below the smooth (6–1) type of curve; this is caused by an oscillating space-charge effect similar to that described in Section 6.6, dealing with pentodes.

Figure 6.3 illustrates the general form taken by the potential distribution in a triode when the grid voltage is positive and the plate

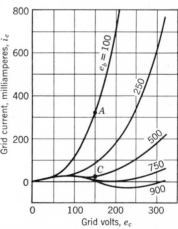

FIG. 6.4 Typical grid current curves for a triode. See Fig. 6.3 for potential diagrams, for conditions similar to those at points A and C.

voltage is relatively low. The grid wires occupy potential peaks, into which the streaming electrons "fall," so that most of them fail to reach the plate. Figure 6.3*b* is a potential section through the grid wires in a plane parallel to plate and to cathode. Because the grid wires occupy potential peaks in both directions, there is considerable grid current. This corresponds to conditions as at *A*, Fig. 6.4.

In contrast with this, the high plate voltage of Fig. 6.3*c* results in the existence of high-potential "channels" between grid wires, illustrated in Fig. 6.3*d*. The electrons tend to follow these channels in much the way that water follows channels down a steep hillside; thus the electrons tend to pass by on either side of each grid wire. However, electrons whose acceleration due to the field has aimed them almost directly at the grid will strike and enter it; furthermore, they arrive with energy enough to knock other electrons out of the grid. The field near the grid is such as to remove these *secondary electrons* at once to the plate, for the potential line slopes upward away from the grid wires on all sides. Thus the grid current is small, because (*a*) most of the electrons pass along the high-potential channels, and (*b*) those that do enter the grid knock others out, producing a *secondary emission* current.[6d, e] This corresponds to conditions as at point *C*, Fig. 6.4.

Certain voltage combinations in Fig. 6.4 make the grid current negative. This happens when each electron that strikes and enters the grid releases on the average more than one secondary electron. With a field like that illustrated in Fig. 6.3*a* there can be no secondary emission current, for secondary electrons appear in a field that returns them to the grid; see also Section 6.5.

6.4 Tetrodes. The plate of a *triode* serves two functions: (*a*) in combination with the grid, it determines the electric field configuration within the tube, and therefore the magnitude of the space-charge-limited cathode current; (*b*) it receives the electrons at the end of their travel and starts them along a return circuit to the cathode.

When a triode is used in an amplifier circuit, the plate's two functions partly conflict with one another. Thus in the simple triode amplifier circuit of Fig. 1.1, an increase of grid potential causes an increase in plate current; the flow through the load resistance of the additional plate current causes a downward change in plate voltage, which tends to reduce the plate current, because of the dependence of plate current on $e_c + (e_b/\mu)$. This behavior is treated analytically in terms of the "load line" circuit concept of Figs. 9.4 and 9.5.

The use of a second grid at a relatively high d-c potential makes possible a separation of the electron-receiving and current-controlling functions of the plate as used in a triode, with resulting very substantial increase in the voltage gain obtainable from a single tube; see Chapter IX. This is one of the important reasons for the use of tetrodes and pentodes, having two and three grids respectively, in amplifier circuits. Another important reason for their use is the minimizing of the interelectrode capacitance C_{g_1p}, as discussed in Section 4.16.

The historical approach to the initial description of an engineering device, or even of a physical principle, is usually confusing and waste-

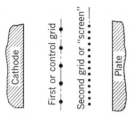

(a) Geometrical arrangement

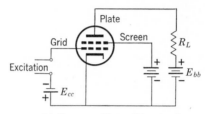

(c) Screen–grid amplifier circuit

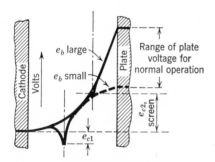

(b) Space–charge–free potential distribution, normal operating voltages

Fig. 6.5   Tetrode of the screen-grid type.

ful of attention. However, here there is distinct merit in discussing first the "screen-grid" type of tetrode, now infrequently used, as an introduction to the treatment of pentodes.

The geometry of a screen-grid type of tetrode is illustrated in Fig. 6.5a. The plate is normally operated at a higher potential than that of the screen. The dotted potential line in Fig. 6.5b terminates at about the lower end, the solid one at about the upper end, of the normal range of plate voltage variations; within this range the plate current is relatively constant. As long as the plate voltage is within this range, the few electrons that make direct hits on and therefore immediately enter the screen wires constitute the screen current.

The others pass to the plate, because the gradient beyond the screen is positive. Thus the ratio of screen current to cathode current is approximately the rather small shadow fraction of the second grid; most of the electrons pass to the plate. Thus, as in a triode, the plate receives the electrons.

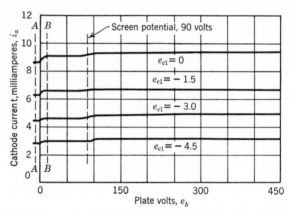

Fig. 6.6   Cathode current vs. plate voltage curves, for a type 24 tetrode, a screen-grid tube; for the plate characteristic curves, see Fig. 6.7.

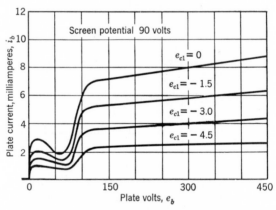

Fig. 6.7   Plate characteristic curves for a type 24 tetrode, a screen-grid tube. This tube employs a unipotential (heater-type) cathode.

The screen-grid potential takes over the part played by a triode's plate potential in determining the cathode current, so that the controlling voltage is essentially $e_{c1} + \dfrac{e_{\text{screen}}}{\mu_{\text{screen}}}$. The second grid shields the cathode from the plate effectively enough so that changes in plate voltage modify only very slightly, if at all, the equivalent grid sheet potential of the first grid.

This *lack* of control of plate voltage over cathode current is indicated by the essentially horizontal nature of the cathode-current curves in Fig. 6.6.

Within the normal operating range of plate voltages the screen current is small, so that the plate current is nearly equal to the cathode current and, like it, is very little affected by plate voltage variations. Figure 6.7 is a set of plate characteristic curves that correspond to the cathode-current curves of Fig. 6.6, all being taken with the screen at 90 volts. The useful part of this diagram is that above about 100 volts; in that region the curves have only very gentle slopes.

6.5   Tetrode Characteristics; Secondary Emission.[6A, C, d, e]   Variations in plate voltage have very little effect on the cathode current of a tetrode, but they do affect very strikingly the division of the cathode current between screen and plate.   Figures 6.9a, b, c, d, e, and f illustrate the potential structure for various positions marked AA, BB, CC, etc., on the one plate characteristic curve of Fig. 6.8.   This curve corresponds to a slightly negative grid voltage, in a tube with properties a little different from that used for Figs. 6.6 and 6.7; in particular it has a directly heated cathode, with a drop of several volts along the filament.   The screen- and control-grid voltages are the same for all conditions illustrated in Figs. 6.8 and 6.9, all variations in potential structure and in current being due to changes in plate voltage.

At AA the plate voltage is very slightly negative, so that no electrons can have energy enough to reach it; the plate current is zero. Electrons are emerging from the cathode in considerable volume; most of them travel through the holes in the second grid, for by the time they reach the second grid their velocity is such as to carry them successfully through the considerable side-pulling field that draws them toward individual wires.   But none can reach the plate, for an electron cannot reach a lower potential than that from which it started.

Each electron's situation may be compared to that of a ball rolling down the smooth sloping side of a trough with a rounded bottom; it cannot acquire kinetic energy enough on the way down to carry it up the opposite slope to a point higher than that from which it started. A ball started down one side of such a trough at the bottom of which there are regularly spaced holes presents a more nearly complete analogy.   If the top of the opposite side of the trough is higher than the starting point, the ball may roll back and forth several times, first down one side, then up and down the other, and so on, before it happens to drop into one of the holes.   Similarly at AA most of the elec-

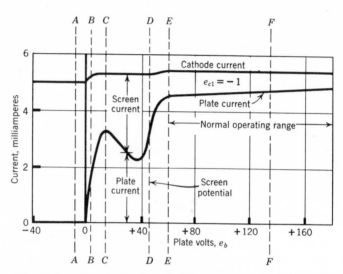

FIG. 6.8 Plate and cathode characteristic curves for a screen-grid type of tetrode; see also Fig. 6.9. Directly heated filamentary cathode having several volts drop along the filament. Screen potential 45 volts, control grid potential −1 volt.

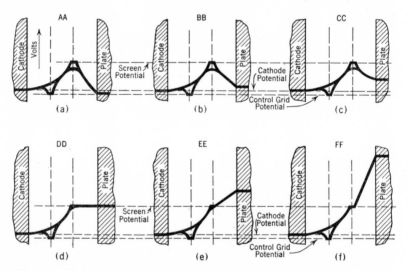

FIG. 6.9 Space-charge-free potential distributions in the Fig. 6.8 tetrode, corresponding to potentials as at AA, BB, etc., in that figure.

trons oscillate back and forth between the two sides of the screen many times before finally entering the screen wires, as all must eventually do.

At *BB* the plate current is rapidly rising. There are two distinct reasons why in this portion of the curve a small increase in plate voltage produces a large rise in plate current, as follows:

(*a*) There may be a potential drop of several volts along the filament of the tube; when as at *BB* the plate potential is near that of the midpoint of the filament, the electrons that start from a filament section that is more positive than the plate cannot possibly reach the plate. Each increment of plate voltage increases the length of the filament section that is lower in potential than the plate and so able to supply electrons that can reach it. This effect is not present in tubes with cathodes that are equipotential surfaces.

(*b*) Dispersion in passing the neighborhood of the second grid makes it impossible for all electrons that start from a potential lower than that of the plate to reach it. All such have energy enough, if properly directed, to bring them to the plate, but many are deflected in passing between wires of the second grid, as described in connection with Fig. 2.2. This occurs to an extent that makes it impossible for many of them to get to a plate that is at a potential even several volts above that of the point on the cathode from which they start. Each increase in plate potential overcomes the lateral-deflection limitation of an additional group of electrons. This effect is present whether the cathode is an equipotential surface or not.

Before the plate voltage has risen far enough to permit the plate current to approach at all closely to its maximum share of the total current, an entirely different effect begins to distort the shape of the curve, as at *CC*. Here the plate voltage has just become high enough for some of the electrons that strike and enter the plate to arrive with energy sufficient to "splash" one or more electrons out of the plate surface. As soon as the plate potential is from 4 to 6 volts higher than that of the starting point, incoming electrons begin in this way to produce *secondary emission from the plate*.[6A, C, d, e] Because the ejected electrons appear in a field which draws them toward the screen, the plate current becomes less, the screen current greater, by the amount of secondary emission current. This accounts for the pronounced dip in plate current just beyond *CC*. In general the secondary emission current at first increases linearly with the energy possessed by the "primary" electrons (those arriving at the plate), so that the initial tendency is toward a straight-line decrease of plate current in this region.

Evidence of secondary emission disappears rather abruptly as the plate potential approaches and rises above screen potential, as beyond *DD*. Although incoming electrons at the plate may continue to be increasingly capable of ejecting secondaries, the plate potential is higher than that of the screen, so that the electric field adjacent to the plate prevents any ejected electrons from leaving the neighborhood of the plate; they promptly reenter it.

EE is about the beginning of the normal operating voltage range of the tube used for Fig. 6.8; FF is about the normal operating value of plate voltage, that is, the plate potential may ordinarily be expected to swing about equally above and below FF.

The plate characteristic curves of Fig. 6.7 are not quite horizontal in the operating range; the gentle rise of plate current in this range is due to increasing secondary emission from the screen, the secondary electrons going to the plate. As this change is in the nature of an increase in the *ratio* of plate current to total current, the actual change should be and is greater along the upper plate characteristic curves of Fig. 6.7 than along the lower ones.

It is rather generally true, as for the variation just described, that each ordinate of any one of a screen-grid tube's plate characteristic curves is a definite fraction, dependent on plate voltage, of a cathode current which is controlled by grid and screen voltages.

6.6 Lowering of Cathode Current by Oscillating Space Charge. The curves of Fig. 6.6 bear out for the most part the statement that cathode current is independent of plate voltage. However, there is in these and in similar pentode curves a small but sharp rise in cathode current just above zero plate voltage. This section describes the change in space-charge distribution that causes this rise.

The potential lines in Fig. 6.10a apply to a tetrode when the plate is slightly positive, and the plate current substantial, as at CC in Fig. 6.8. The space-charge density is greatest in the low-potential region between cathode and control grid, as indicated by the convex-downward flexion of the potential line there. The potential lines in Fig. 6.10b apply when the plate is slightly negative, so that all the current is flowing to the screen, as at AA in Fig. 6.8. All the electrons enter the second grid, but only after oscillating back and forth through it a number of times. Just before, during, and just after an oscillating electron's reversal of motion, its velocity will be slow, therefore its contribution to space charge substantial, because of the relation $J = \rho v$. This reversal occurs at low potentials, as between cathode and grid. Thus there is more space charge between cathode and control grid than that corresponding to the normal $\frac{2}{3}$ power potential distribution curve. This makes (5–12) no longer correct; the cathode current becomes distinctly less than that given by (5–12), for any given value of e_{s1}.

Furthermore, there is a multiple-stream type of space-charge flow *between the two grids*, with resulting substantial space charge in spite of the relatively high velocity of electron movement. The oscillating electrons' contribution to space charge between the two grids, also between cathode and control grid, tends toward downward convexity of the potential distribution, therefore toward a lowering of the equivalent grid sheet potential of the control grid. Thus e_{s1} is lower, also the

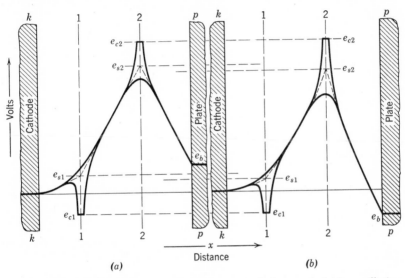

(a)   Distance   (b)

Fig. 6.10   Reduction of cathode current in a tetrode (or a pentode) by oscillating space charge. (a) Conditions as at CC, Fig. 6.8, the plate being slightly positive. (b) Conditions as at AA, Fig. 6.8, the plate being slightly negative. Oscillating space charge lowers e_s and also results in there being less current for any given e_s.

ratio of cathode current to e_{s1} is lower, therefore the cathode current is less, for the AA than for the CC condition.

At the current minimum just to the left of DD, Fig. 6.8, there is again considerable screen current, especially when the total current is large. However, this current is due to secondary electrons that start from the plate, at a potential only slightly less than that of the screen. Their energy on approaching the screen is moderate; so that only a few (and rather low-amplitude) oscillations occur; the space-charge effect is moderate. Its disappearance accounts for the slight rise in total current as the plate rises above screen potential and thereby eliminates secondary emission from the plate.

6.7   Secondary Emission Ratio; "Dynodes." [6A, B, C, d, e, f, 10b, 14f]   Secondary emission can be of considerable value, for example in photomultiplier tubes [14f] (Section 14.9), in television pick-up tubes, and in trigger and storage tubes.[6f]   In devices usefully employing secondary emission the electrodes from which the secondaries originate are often called "dynodes."   Figure 6.11 can be used to illustrate the dependence of secondary emission on plate (dynode) voltage, that is, on the energy with which the incoming or *primary* electrons strike the secondary emitting surface.   Plate (dynode) current curves appear for

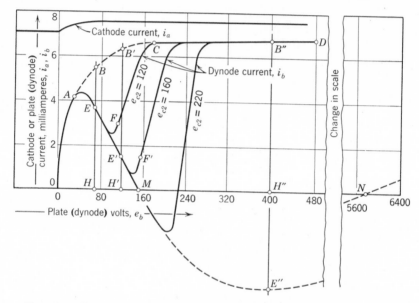

Fig. 6.11 Dependence of secondary emission on plate (dynode) potential, as indicated by plate characteristic curves for a tetrode at different screen voltages, for constant cathode current. Cathode current is maintained constant by adjusting control grid potential to compensate for changes in screen voltage. Thus the equivalent grid sheet potential for the control grid is held essentially constant for all values of screen voltage.

three different values of the second-grid voltage e_{c2}, but the control-grid voltage has been adjusted simultaneously with changes in the second-grid voltage, so that the cathode-current curve is the same for the three different values of e_{c2}.

The solid line *OAEFCD* describes the dynode current variation when $e_{c2} \cong 120$ volts. The line *OABB'CD* describes approximately the primary electron current to the dynode; that is, what the current might be if there were no secondary emission. Because there is no convenient way of measuring the primary electron current in the *ABB'C* range, the detail position of the *ABB'C* curve is estimated by interpolation, determined so as to make $OABB'CD$ appear smoothly continuous.

Thus, for the plate voltage as at HEB, the current HB represents primary electron current; EB represents secondary emission current. The ratio of secondary emission current to primary current [6C, d] is therefore

$$\left.\begin{array}{r}\text{Secondary emission ratio,}\\ \text{for voltage as at } HEB\end{array}\right\} = \frac{EB}{HB} \qquad (6\text{--}4)$$

This ratio is independent of the magnitude of the primary current; it depends on the energies of the primary electrons, and on the material and processing of the secondary emitting surface, in this case the plate (dynode) surface.

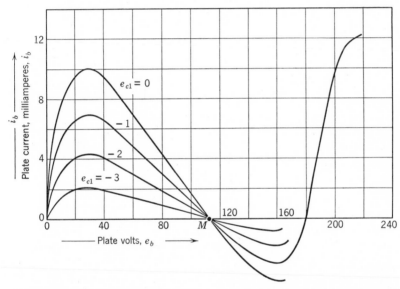

Fig. 6.12   Plate (dynode) characteristic curves of a tetrode subject to pronounced secondary emission. Current goes to zero at the same plate potential for all values of control grid potential. Zero-current plate potential at M corresponds to a secondary emission ratio of unity.

Suppose that the second-grid potential becomes 160 volts, the control grid potential being simultaneously lowered so as to maintain the total current curve unchanged. The primary electron current is $OABB'CD$ as before. However, secondary emission persists until the plate potential approaches that of the new second-grid potential, so that the new plate current curve $OAEE'F'D$ follows the straight line $EE'M$ farther than the old one did.

If e_{c2} is still further increased with cathode current still held constant, the plate current curve passes through zero at M to negative values, then rises to the CD value. At point M the secondary emission ratio is unity. Figure 6.12 illustrates the form tetrode plate characteristics possessing negative plate currents have if the control grid potential is changed, second-grid potential remaining constant; the similar-

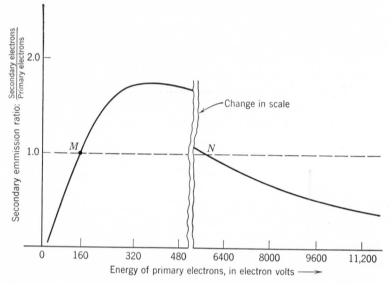

Fig. 6.13 Illustrative dependence of the secondary emission ratio on primary electron energy, for a metal surface. Much higher values of the ratio at the maximum of the curve than shown here can be obtained by special surface processing and materials selection. This curve is drawn to be consistent with Fig. 6.11 and is not intended to describe the properties of any particular surface. Note that the secondary emission ratio declines through 1 at a voltage much higher than that at the maximum.

ity of the several curves indicates that the secondary emission ratio is independent of the primary current.

In Fig. 6.11, the secondary emission ratio for plate voltage at H is EB/HB; for plate voltage at H' it is $E'B'/H'B'$; for plate voltage at M it is unity. Thus the curve $EE'M$ is a locus from which the secondary emission ratio can be determined, since the primary current is held constant along CD. For a still higher second-grid voltage, this locus should be expected to have the general shape $EE'ME''N$, because the secondary emission ratio eventually reaches a maximum, then declines to less than unity again. Thus the maximum value of the secondary emission ratio would be $E''B''/H''B''$. Usually the maximum value of the secondary emission ratio is between 2 and 7, and occurs at a primary electron energy of several hundred electron volts.

Figure 6.13 illustrates the general nature of the dependence of secondary emission ratio on primary electron energy, for metal dynodes; it is drawn to be consistent with Fig. 6.11. Special vacuum processing techniques [6d] are employed to produce the larger values of secondary emission ratio; it is very difficult to control the materials and processing precisely enough to make the secondary emission curves closely reproducible from tube to tube, for high-ratio surfaces. Also, a given dynode may exhibit changes in its secondary emission curve from time to time, depending on the temperature, the short-time and long-time history of currents used, and various other factors. [6d] Note that the decline from the maximum occurs slowly. The decline through unity secondary emission ratio will in general take place in excess of 2500 volts, and for some substances at as much as 15,000 volts.

Dynodes having secondary emission ratios in excess of unity can provide *current amplification*, as in photomultiplier tubes [14f] (Section 14.9), cathode-ray television camera ("pick-up") tubes, [3i] and shaped-wave-form dynatron oscillators (Giacolleto, [10b] also Section 10.13). The crossing of the Fig. 6.13 type of curve from below to above unity permits designing circuits having two stable states, transfer from either to the other being caused by a transient pulse voltage. This feature is made use of in fast switching or "trigger" circuits and in cathode-ray tubes used for digital computer memory devices.

6.8 Pentodes; the Constant-Current Property. Pentodes rather than tetrodes are commonly employed when the advantages accruing from a second grid are to be employed. Pentode plate characteristics are essentially constant-current curves; see Fig. 6.15b. The Chapter IX circuit analyses show that the constant-current property permits amplifier voltage gain per stage to be of the order of a hundred or so, as compared with voltage gains of the order of 10 or 20 obtainable with triodes.

As ordinarily used, the term *pentode* is applied to devices, otherwise similar in arrangement and principle to screen-grid tubes, in which a third grid *at cathode potential* is introduced between the second grid and the plate to "suppress" secondary emission; see Fig. 6.14b. As illustrated in Fig. 6.14a, the important result of the suppressor grid's presence is to produce a potential valley between second grid and plate. This makes the gradient just outside the plate such as to drive back into the plate any secondary emission electrons. It also makes the gradient adjacent to the second grid such as to drive back into it any secondary emission electrons that might appear there. As no secondary emission from the plate occurs, the dip in plate current at modest plate voltages that is characteristic of a screen-grid tube is eliminated. As no secondary emission from the screen occurs, the

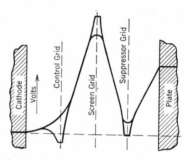

Fig. 6.14a Potential diagram for a pentode showing at the plate a positive gradient which prevents secondary emission.

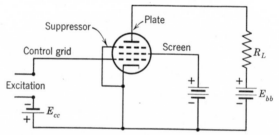

Fig. 6.14b Pentode amplifier circuit diagram showing suppressor grid connected to the cathode.

gradual rise of plate current to and above cathode current, at high plate voltages, is also eliminated.

Figures 6.15a and 6.15b are typical mutual and plate characteristic curves for a voltage amplifier pentode. The detail shapes of such curves at low plate voltages are, as in screen-grid tubes, jointly dependent on (a) electron dispersion in passing through the grids, and on (b) the fact that the electrons may not all start from the same potential. At higher plate voltages the division of current between screen and plate depends chiefly on (c) the shadow fraction of the screen, which measures the probability of direct hits on it in the absence of electron deviation by the field, and on (d) the effects of first and third grid and plate potentials in establishing a potential configuration near the second grid which tends to divert electrons into

the second grid.   In screen-grid tubes, but not in pentodes, there are
two additional effects: (e) the flow of secondary electrons from plate
to screen, and (f) the flow of secondary electrons from screen to plate.
   All these influences are alike in that they act to modify the *fraction*
of the cathode current that reaches the plate.   This fraction is approximately the same for a given plate voltage, regardless of the magnitude

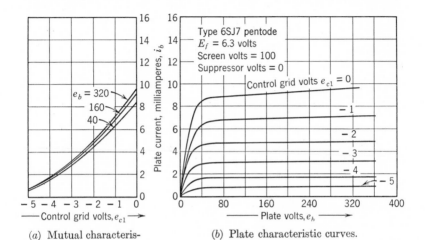

(a) Mutual characteris-   (b) Plate characteristic curves.
tic curves.

Fig. 6.15   Average characteristic curves, type 6SJ7 tube, pentode connection,
with second grid potential 100 volts.   This shows the essential constancy of plate
current over a wide range of values of plate voltage.

   Note that, for any type of vacuum tube, the characteristic curves for any one
individual tube may be expected to differ appreciably from the published average
characteristics applying to that tube type.   Circuit designs must be such as to
provide satisfactory operation with any individual tube of a given type, in spite of
the variation in characteristics from tube to tube.

of the cathode current, until the cathode current becomes large enough
to make space charge effects important, as in beam power tetrodes.
   In summary, for pentodes and screen-grid tubes, (1) control-grid and
screen-grid potentials determine the magnitude of the space-charge-
limited cathode current just the way control-grid and plate voltages
do in a triode, and (2) the plate voltage, in relation to grid potentials
beyond the first, determines what percentage of the cathode current
shall reach the plate.
   Hence all plate characteristics for a given pentode or screen-grid
tetrode may be expected to be alike in shape, their ordinates being related by constant ratios.   In contrast to this, plate characteristics for
a triode are alike except for a horizontal shift.

6.9   Energy Dissipation at the Plate and at Grids.[6A, B, g]   A space-charge-limited current consists of electrons which fall freely from their point of origin at the cathode to the point of entry into the plate, or into a grid if there is present a grid at a positive potential. Each one arrives with an amount of energy measured, in electron volts, by the potential difference between the electrodes. Upon striking, this entire amount of energy is converted into heat, just as the kinetic energy of a falling pebble is converted into heat when it strikes the ground.

The total rate of energy conversion into heat at the plate, called *plate dissipation*, is the product of the energy brought in per electron by the number of electrons arriving per second. The rate of electron arrival at the plate is measured by the current i_b to the plate, and the energy of each by the potential difference e_b through which the electrons have fallen, so that the rate of heat generation at the plate surface is $e_b i_b$ watts. Note that this is an *instantaneous* rate; as e_b and i_b change with time, the average plate dissipation is the time average of the product $e_b i_b$. If secondary emission from the plate is important, the current employed in determining plate dissipation must be the *primary* electron current.

The temperature of the plate must rise; as it is located in a vacuum, radiation accounts for most of the heat removal. Heat radiation from the plate increases as the fourth power of the temperature, so that in general only a moderate temperature rise is enough to produce equilibrium between electrical power input and radiant heat output. Because graphite is a better radiator of heat than most metals, graphite plates are often used to permit operation at high current densities and high voltages. It is of course desirable to arrange the geometry so as to permit direct outward heat radiation from the plate to surrounding objects. Tubes with water-cooled anodes, or with air-blast-cooled radiating fins, are commonly used in radio broadcasting transmitters.

If there is present a grid at a positive potential, its instantaneous *grid dissipation* is the product of the grid potential by the current carried by *primary* electrons originating at the cathode and entering the grid. Thus in Fig. 6.4, along the curve for $e_b = 900$ volts, the grid current at $e_c = 200$ volts is *negative*, yet there will be at those voltages substantial grid dissipation.

6.10   Beam Power Tetrodes.[6h, i]   In beam power tetrodes (e.g., the 6L6 tube) potential distributions which suppress secondary emission from the plate are obtained without the use of a third grid. The negative space charge of the electron stream is employed to produce the potential minimum between screen and plate that the suppressor grid provides in a pentode; see Fig. 6.16. As long as such a minimum exists, no secondary electrons pass from plate to the second grid, or vice versa. The potential minimum in case of "space-charge suppression" of secondary emission may or may not drop to zero voltage. Plate characteristic curves of beam power tubes are qualitatively similar to those for pentodes.

The essential requirements for space-charge suppression of secondary emission, of the type employed in beam power tubes, are:

(a) Between screen and plate, electron flow must take place in a beam of high enough concentration so that space charge makes an appreciable contribution to the convex-downward flexion of the potential distribution curve.

(b) The plate must be located far enough beyond the screen to permit the convex-downward flexion to produce a minimum in the potential distribution curve between screen and plate.

A detailed analysis [6h] requires solving (5-6) with new boundary conditions; see Chapter III, in *Fundamentals of Physical Electronics*.

It is also a characteristic of beam power tubes that each wire of the second or screen grid is located in the shadow, so to speak, of a wire of the first grid. The electron optical focusing action of the control grid then tends to pass flat electron beams between the wires of the second grid. This keeps the primary electron current to the screen substantially below the shadow-fraction share of cathode current, and therefore the screen dissipation is modest even at high screen voltages.

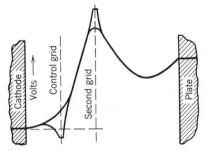

FIG. 6.16 Potential diagram for a beam power tetrode, showing the potential dip, between second grid and plate, that provides space-charge suppression of secondary emission. Compare with Fig. 6.14a.

6.11   Pentagrid Tubes.[6i]   Figure 6.17 illustrates the potential distribution in a space-charge-control tube employing five grids, called a pentagrid mixer because of the nature of its use in radio circuits. Grids 1–1 and 3–3 are called the first control grid and the second control grid.

The cathode current is determined primarily by grids 1–1 and 2–2, as in a pentode. Most of the cathode current passes through 2–2 unhindered. If the potential e_{c3} of grid 3–3 is only slightly negative, the potential distribution in the 3–3 plane resembles Fig. 6.18. The shaded area indicates qualitatively the effect of space charge. Space charge can be important in the 3–3 neighborhood, because the electrons are traveling slowly. Capacitances C_{23}' and C_{34}', greater than C_{23} and C_{34} by the factor $\frac{4}{3}$, should be used in a quantitative analysis.

Under conditions as in Figs. 6.17 and 6.18, nearly all the electrons that pass the 2–2 grid will reach and pass through the 4–4 grid; only

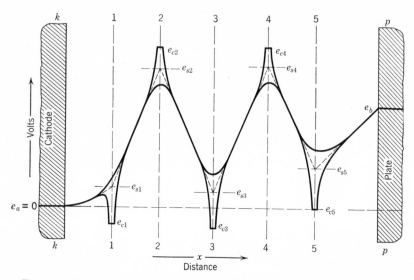

FIG. 6.17 Potential distribution diagram for a pentagrid mixer, for example, the type 6L7 tube.

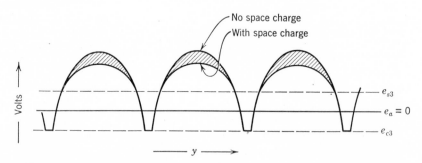

FIG. 6.18 Potential distribution in the plane 3–3 of the third grid of Fig. 6.17.

a few will be turned back, by an electron rejection process similar to that described in Section 2.4. Thus, an increase in e_{c3} above its value in Fig. 6.18 will not appreciably increase the plate current. This condition is that at AA in the third-grid control characteristic curve set of Fig. 6.19; the shapes of these curves correspond to the assumption of constant values of e_{c2} and e_{c4}. The grid 5–5 serves the same purpose as a suppressor grid in a pentode. At normal plate voltages, the plate potential has negligible effect on the plate current.

If e_{c3} is made more negative than its value at AA, the maximum potential in the 3–3 plane drops. A sorting process similar to that described in Section 2.4 results in many of the electrons' being sent back to the 2–2 grid. Thus the second control grid 3–3 is used to determine what fraction reaches the plate, among the electrons that pass 2–2.

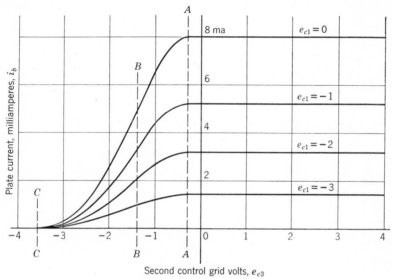

Fig. 6.19 Mutual or transfer characteristic curves, i_b vs. e_{c3}, illustrating the control of plate current exercised by e_{c1} and e_{c3} in a pentagrid mixer, Fig. 6.17.

A pentagrid mixer may be used as a small-signal multiplying device. To show this, note that small variations of e_{c3} about a bias value, as at BB, Fig. 6.19, will result in corresponding variations in plate current, as determined by the suitable transconductance. That is,

$$\frac{\partial i_b}{\partial e_{c3}}\bigg|_{\text{all voltages constant except } e_{c3}} = g_{p3} \qquad (6\text{–}5)$$

is the slope of a plate characteristic curve at such a point as BB. This slope, and therefore the transconductance g_{p3}, are *proportional to the plate current that flows after e_{c3} has risen to a value such that it ceases to control the current.* Thus, for small a-c variations e_{g3}, i_p, e_{g1} of the quantities e_{c3}, i_b, e_{c1}

$$i_p = \text{Constant} \times e_{g1}e_{g3} \qquad (6\text{–}6)$$

As usefully employed, a small high-frequency (radio-frequency) signal e_{g1} is applied to the first control grid, and a small lower-frequency signal e_{g3} to the second control grid. Thus the plate circuit carries a signal at radio frequency f_1 *modulated* at a lower frequency rate f_2. The important component in the modulated signal is that having the difference frequency $f_1 - f_2$; filtering action of the output circuit selects this component from among the others.

Unfortunately, there is in most pentagrid mixers only a very limited range of values of e_{c3} over which the curves of Fig. 6.19 are essentially straight slant lines, so that strictly *linear* modulation results only if a very small signal voltage appears on each of the control grids.

In a *pentagrid converter*,[6j] for example the 6A8 tube, grids 3, 4, and 5 function much as grids 2, 3, and 4 do in the pentagrid mixer. No suppressor is employed. The second "grid" consists merely of a pair of small round rods or posts located between the first and third grids, and opposite one another diametrically. These posts and grid 1 are normally connected to serve as the amplifying element of an r-f oscillator. The oscillator action swings the voltage of grid 1 rather widely, causing a large-signal variation in the electron stream passing through grid 3. As this tube is commonly used, the multiplying action of grid 4 is used to convert a signal at an input frequency f_1 at grid 4 to a plate circuit output frequency $f_3 = f_1 - f_2$, where f_2 is the frequency generated in the oscillator circuit employing grids 1 and 2. Thus the circuit in which the tube is used is called a frequency converter circuit, giving rise to the name pentagrid converter for the tube itself.

PROBLEMS

1. Using equation (6–1) and the definition of r_p, show that $r_p = (\mu e_c + e_b)/ni_b$.

2. Plot values of e_b vs. e_c necessary to keep i_b constant at 8 ma, as e_c varies, for the triode of Fig. 6.2. From this graph of e_b vs. e_c at constant plate current, determine μ at 8 ma, as defined by (5–18). Repeat for 2 ma, and for zero current (cut-off points). Which of these values of μ is most useful?

3. Triode of Fig. 1.5: $E_c = +30$, $E_b = +50$; current space-charge-limited, $a = 0.8$ mm, cathode area 1 sq cm.

(a) By Chapter V methods, find μ, E_s; construct the potential distribution diagram, using appropriate construction lines; sketch fillets carefully.

(b) Estimate what percentage of the total tube current will be grid current, not considering the possibility of secondary emission from the grid.

(c) Determine plate current and grid current, proportioning them in accordance with (b).

4. Determine, from the Fig. 6.15 plate characteristics, four points on the $E_b = 100$ mutual characteristic curve; draw this curve on graph paper. From its slope at $E_c = -3$, determine g_m. Similarly for the Fig. 1.3 tube find g_m at $E_c = -8$, $E_b = 130$; for Fig. 6.2, at $E_c = -8$, $E_b = 200$; for Fig. 6.7, at $E_c = -3$, $E_b = 300$. Determine r_p at these same points, from the slopes of the plate characteristic curves; determine corresponding μ's from $\mu = g_m r_p$. Compare μ's so obtained with μ's obtained for the same points as $\mu = -\Delta E_b / \Delta E_c$, where ΔE_b, ΔE_c are differences in plate and grid voltage values measured at constant current between adjacent plate characteristic curves.

5. Sketch carefully, approximately to scale, the potential distribution diagram for a planar tetrode, current space-charge-limited. Dimensions and potentials are: first grid 0.5 mm from cathode, 1.0 mm from second grid, 2 mm from plate; $E_{s1} = +8$, $E_{s2} = +100$, $E_{c1} = -6$, $E_{c2} = +115$, $E_b = +70$. Find C_1 and C_2, if flat cathode area is 4 sq cm.

6. Tube and voltages as in Prob. 5. I_a (cathode current) is 21 ma per sq cm; 1 ma out of the 21 enters the screen as screen current. For each electron that strikes the plate, one electron leaves the plate by secondary emission; thus $I_b = 0$. Secondary electrons are assumed to be emitted with negligible initial velocities and to flow directly to and into the screen. Find the space-charge density half-way between screen and plate.

7. Tetrode voltages and dimensions as in Prob. 5, except that the plate is moved back to provide 4-mm spacing between second grid and plate, in order to permit the beam power tube type of space-charge suppression of secondary emission, described in Section 6.10. Sketch the new potential distribution diagram, showing a potential minimum at 60 volts between second grid and plate, the location of this minimum being estimated during the sketching process. From your sketched curve, determine graphically the flexion of the potential distribution curve at the potential minimum, thus determining the space-charge density there. Using this and the potential at the minimum, find the plate current density. To find whether your curve is self-consistent, determine similarly the space-charge density and the current density at two other points, respectively, toward the second grid and toward the plate from the minimum. For a self-consistent curve, the current will be the same at all three points.

8. Tetrode: equivalent electrostatic circuit C's are: $C_k = 4$, $C_{12} = 2$, $C_p = 2$; $C_1 = 18$, $C_2 = 25$ (micromicrofarads). The second grid is connected directly to the cathode; then, with the cathode unheated, 14 rms volts a-c are applied between plate and cathode. What is the a-c voltage between the first grid and the cathode?

9. Tetrode: plate and cathode current curves as in Fig. 6.20; $e_{c1} = -2$.

(a) About what is the screen voltage e_{c2}, in Fig. 6.20?

(b) Estimate secondary emission current and primary current to the plate, for e_b at AA.

(c) Sketch plate current curve for $e_{c2} = 280$, with e_{c1} changed to whatever new value will keep the cathode current essentially as before.

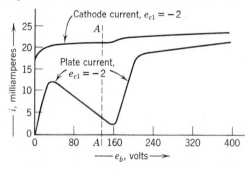

FIG. 6.20 Tetrode plate and cathode currents.

(d) Sketch plate current curve with e_{c2} unchanged, but e_{c1} made sufficiently more negative to reduce cathode current to $\frac{1}{3}$ its value in Fig. 6.20.

(e) Explain the slight rise in cathode current just to the right of AA.

10. Planar pentode: potentials are $E_{c1} = -10$, $E_{c2} = 100$, $E_{c3} = 0$, $E_b = 70$, $E_{s1} = 9$, $E_{s2} = 90$, $E_{s3} = 20$.

(a) Sketch carefully, to scale, the potential distribution diagram. Electrodes equally spaced.

(b) Assuming $C_{12} = C_{23}$, determine the ratio C_2/C_{23}.

(c) Grid is 0.3 mm from cathode; find cathode current density.

(d) Find grid-plate transconductance g_m, for voltages stated, if the second grid intercepts $\frac{1}{8}$ of the cathode current, using the fairly good assumption that the behavior is similar to that in a triode, with E_{c2} playing about the same part in current determination that E_b does in a triode.

11. Cylindrical pentode: current space-charge-limited; length 10 cm; radial dimensions: $r_k = 1$, $r_{g1} = 4$, $r_{g2} = 6$, $r_{g3} = 9$, $r_p = 11$ (millimeters). Potentials: $E_{s1} = +25$, $E_{s2} = +400$, $E_{s3} = +50$, $E_{c3} = 0$, $E_b = 200$. Shadow fractions 0.1 for all grids; $n_1 = n_2$, $C_1 = 10C_{12}$.

(a) Find: C_k', C_{12}, C_{23}, C_p, C_1, C_2, C_3, E_{c1}, E_{c2}, n_1, n_2, n_3, R_1, R_2, R_3.

(b) Find cathode current; find grid-plate transconductance g_m by an approximate method that assumes E_{s2} constant as E_{c1} changes; assume second-grid electron intercept fraction is the shadow fraction.

(c) Find transconductance without using this approximation. To do this, assume an incremental change in E_{s1}, then find corresponding changes in E_{s2}, E_{s3}, E_{c1}, and cathode current. This can be done by using either a numerical increment or an algebraically expressed increment that is allowed to approach zero as a limit.

(d) Find potentials at points midway between grid wires, all grids.

(e) Draw to scale the potential distribution diagram, using appropriate construction lines, and sketching fillets in accordance with (d) potentials. Construction lines are of course logarithmic except between cathode and first grid, where β^2 must be employed.

12. For a planar tetrode, derive expressions for location and potential of a q_2 plane between second grid and plate, properties similar to the triode q plane.

13. Planar tetrode spacings as in Prob. 5: shadow fractions 0.1; 20 wires per cm, for both grids; $E_{c1} = -6$, $E_{c2} = +115$, $E_b = +70$.

(a) Using a q_2 plane, as in Prob. 12, reduce this tetrode to an equivalent triode, in which the q_2 plane is the plate, E_{q2} the plate voltage. This will involve a μ-factor C_2/C_p which should be evaluated without determining either C_2 or C_p.

(b) By the method associated with Figs. 5.4 and 5.5, reduce the triode of (a) to an equivalent diode, and in this way find E_{s1}.

(c) Work backward to find E_{s2}.

14. Using principles illustrated by Prob. 13, derive a general expression for E_{s1} in a tetrode, of the form:

$$E_{s1} = \frac{E_{c1} + \dfrac{E_{c2}}{A_2} + \dfrac{E_b}{A_b}}{1 + \dfrac{1}{A_2} + \dfrac{1}{A_b} + \dfrac{1}{A_1}}$$

where the A's are combinations of C_k', C_1, C_{12}, etc., in general similar to μ-factors. (The forms of the A's in terms of the C's should be found.)

15. Extend the Prob. 14 treatment to apply to a pentode.

CHAPTER VII

THERMIONIC CATHODES *

7.1 Electron-Emitting Efficiency of a Cathode Surface. The cathode surfaces of thermionic devices are made of special materials which when heated to high temperatures release electrons (thermionic emission) in much the way that hot water releases water molecules (evapo-

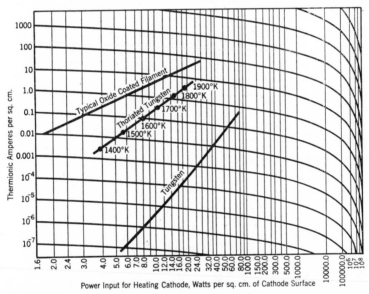

FIG. 7.1 Power-emission chart, coordinate warping based on Dushman's equation (7–2) for thermionic current density.

ration). The current in most high-vacuum apparatus is space-charge-limited, so that the basic requirement for a cathode is that it must be able to provide by thermionic emission at least the maximum space-charge-limited current demanded by the normal electrode potentials.[7A, B, C, D, a]

* The design and processing of thermionic cathodes is at least as much an art as it is a science, and much of the existing knowledge is of a factual, empirical nature. See the Chapter VII bibliographical references for details.

Cathodes are heated electrically; it is important to use materials and arrangements of parts that make the requisite thermionic current available with a minimum of heating power consumption. The more efficient cathode surfaces are somewhat fragile, having a limited life, and many of them are more or less easily damaged by the presence of small amounts of gas in the tube. Hence the element of judgment is important in selecting the proper type of cathode for a given service; power consumption and life requirements must be properly balanced.

The electron-emitting efficiency of a cathode is measured by the ratio:

$$\frac{\text{Thermionic amperes available}}{\text{Power for heating, in watts}} \tag{7-1}$$

Both numerator and denominator may be expressed per unit area of cathode surface. Figure 7.1 illustrates the variation of thermionic current with power input for three different types of cathode surface, plotted on a special set of coordinates which makes all the curves substantially straight lines. These curves represent graphically the combination of two basic relationships, one between thermionic current density and temperature, the other between temperature and power consumption.

7.2 Dushman's Equation Relating Thermionic Current Density and Temperature. The mathematical expression of the first of the two relations just referred to will be called Dushman's equation, expressible as follows: [7A, B, D, a, b]

$$J_{th} = A_0 T^2 \exp\left(-\frac{E_W q_e}{kT}\right) \tag{7-2a}$$

$$J_{th} = A_0 T^2 \exp\left(-\frac{E_W}{E_T}\right) \tag{7-2b}$$

$$J_{th} = A_0 T^2 \exp\left(-\frac{b_0}{T}\right) \tag{7-2c}$$

in which J_{th} = thermionic current density in amperes per unit area.

A_0 = a semiempirical constant; its units are:

$$\frac{\text{Amperes per unit area}}{(\text{Degrees Kelvin})^2}$$

T = temperature of the cathode in degrees Kelvin (degrees centigrade + 273).

k = Boltzmann's universal gas constant; its value is 1.380 $\times 10^{-23}$ joule per degree Kelvin.[1b]

q_e = the electronic charge, 1.602×10^{-19} coulomb per electron.

E_W = an empirical constant of the emitting surface, called its *work function*, measured in electron volts.

b_0 = work function measured in temperature units; $b_0 = E_W q_e / k$.

E_T = the *voltage equivalent of temperature*, defined by the relation

$$E_T q_e = kT \tag{7-3a}$$

which reduces numerically to

$$E_T = \frac{T}{11,610} \tag{7-3b}$$

A_0 is called semiempirical because theoretical considerations indicate it should have the same value for all homogeneous metal surfaces, a prediction reasonably well substantiated by experiment.[7A, B, 7a, b] Theory also correctly predicts its order of magnitude. By a homogeneous metal surface is meant one whose behavior is not complicated by the presence of surface layers of different composition from that of the underlying metal.

In (7-2a) the numerator of the exponent, $E_W q_e$, describes in joules per electron the kinetic energy which must be given to a most favorably situated electron within the metal to enable it to escape through the metal surface to outside space. This energy is roughly analogous to the latent heat of evaporation, per molecule, of a liquid at some temperature below the boiling point. For example, the equation relating the vapor pressure of the mercury vapor inside a mercury rectifier to the temperature of the pool of mercury in the base of the tube (see Table XVII) has an exponential factor similar in form to that appearing in (7-2).

The *work function* E_W is a measure of the required energy of escape in electron volts; its value is usually between 1 and 6 or 7 volts, varying with the material and processing of the surface. Tables of emission constants sometimes give values of E_W, sometimes of b_0; see Table VI.

7.3 The Voltage Equivalent of Temperature. The electrons, while within the metal and immediately after emerging from it, behave considerably like the particles of a gas heated to cathode temperature, in that they have randomly directed velocities of various magnitudes, the average velocity depending on the temperature. The quantity kT in the exponent of (7-2a) is a definite amount of kinetic energy, in joules per gas particle or per electron, which is characteristic of the temperature T in a very fundamental way (see Chapter XII). The corresponding characteristic random velocity will be called ζ (zeta), defined by the relation

$$\tfrac{1}{2}m\zeta^2 = kT \tag{7-4}$$

m being the mass of one particle. The voltage equivalent of temperature, E_T, is as used here *the characteristic energy kT measured in electron volts*, as indicated in (7–3). This meaning applies equally well whether the particles are charged or neutral. The extent to which the energy kT, or E_T, characterizes the temperature cannot be fully appreciated without a study of theoretical thermodynamics,[II, J, K, 12A, B, D] but it is possible to illustrate its importance in several specific ways, as follows:

(a) kT is the kinetic energy, in joules, associated with the *most probable* total translational velocity of any particle in an ordinary gas at temperature T.[12A, B, C] This statement means that, if one were to make a record of the magnitudes of the velocities, regardless of direction, of all the gas particles within a given volume at a given instant (a "snapshot observation throughout a volume"), more particles would be found to have velocities near ζ than similarly near any other value. It also means that, if a random selection of one particle were made from the interior of the volume and its velocity noted, the chance of the velocity's being near ζ would be greater than for any other velocity.

(b) The familiar ideal gas law, $PV = RT$, can be written

$$PV = NkT \tag{7-5}$$

where P = pressure, newtons per square meter.
 V = volume, cubic meters.
 N = total number of gas particles in the volume.
 kT = as above, the characteristic particle energy for temperature T.

(c) If the translational thermal motions of the particles of an ordinary gas are segregated into x-directed, y-directed, and z-directed components, the average energy associated with each of these three "degrees of freedom" of motion is $\tfrac{1}{2}kT$ joules, or $\tfrac{1}{2}E_T$ electron volts. Hence the average total kinetic energy of each gas particle in monatomic gases, such as helium, neon, argon, mercury vapor, and sodium vapor, is $\tfrac{3}{2}E_T$, three times the value for each of the 3 degrees of freedom. Molecules of a diatomic gas are dumbbell-like and have 2 additional degrees of freedom of motion, one vibrational, one rotational, so that the average kinetic energy per particle is $\tfrac{5}{2}E_T$ volts. Thus at 40° C the average air-particle energy is $\dfrac{273 + 40}{11610} \times \dfrac{5}{2} = \dfrac{1}{15}$ electron volt.

(d) If an observer were to record the velocities with which each gas particle that arrives hits the wall of an enclosure for a definite area and period of time ("time exposure over a surface"; see Section 12.9), the average normal-to-the-surface energy at impact would be found to be just E_T electron volts. This is greater than the overall average energy of normal-to-the-surface motion ($\tfrac{1}{2}E_T$) because the high-velocity particles move faster than the low-velocity ones, therefore hit more often, and are counted more times in a second.

(e) If the time-exposure-over-a-surface observer in (d) above were to analyze his records of y- and z-directed impact velocities, both being parallel to the surface, their average energies would be just $\frac{1}{2}E_T$ each, for rapid y- or z-directed motion has no tendency to increase the number of impacts against a y, z surface. Hence the average *total* energy at impact on a surface is

$$E_T + \tfrac{1}{2}E_T + \tfrac{1}{2}E_T = 2E_T \tag{7-6}$$

All the relations just described can be shown to be true by means of the Maxwellian velocity distribution equations given in Chapter XII.

7.4 Energies of Escaping Electrons. It has been experimentally demonstrated that as electrons emerge from a hot emitting surface their *random velocity distribution* is that of the particles of a perfect gas. The average energy of emergence, that is,

$$\frac{\text{Total energy brought through the surface per second}}{\text{Number of electrons emerging per second}}$$

has been found to be $2E_T$ and is divided between the three components in accordance with (7-6). For example, the electrons emerging from a cathode whose temperature is 2320° K have on the average an *outwardly directed* kinetic energy of 0.2 electron volt. Ordinarily only the outwardly directed energies, of average value E_T, are of interest.

Thus the energies of escaping electrons are in all ordinary devices *small relative to those acquired later from the electric fields*. Cathode temperatures usually range between 1000° and 2500° K, corresponding to energies between about 0.1 and 0.2 volt, whereas potentials inducing flight between electrodes are many volts, and often many hundreds of volts. Thus initial velocities of emission are ordinarily of little or no consequence; circumstances do exist, however, that give them importance. They have been entirely neglected in the discussions of space-charge-limited currents in previous chapters.

7.5 Graphical Evaluation of Emission Constants. Dushman's equation can be written:

$$\ln J_{th} + 2\ln\left(\frac{1}{T}\right) = \ln A_0 - b_0\left(\frac{1}{T}\right) \tag{7-7}$$

and experimental data relating temperature to thermionic current density represented by plotting $1/T$ horizontally and $\ln J_{th} + 2\ln(1/T)$ vertically. This results in straight-line relationships, of the type illustrated in Fig. 7.2, for a variety of substances.

Figure 7.3 is a somewhat more easily readable representation of the set of facts that appear in Fig. 7.2. The straight lines that represent the thermionic properties of individual types of surfaces are exactly the same in the two figures, but Fig. 7.3 has a direct-reading coordinate

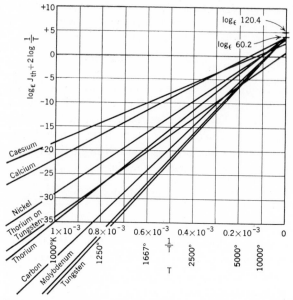

Fig. 7.2 Logarithmic temperature-emission chart, illustrating method of determining thermionic emission constants. For each line the slope is b_0, and the infinite-temperature intercept is $\ln A_0$. Plotted according to (7–7), except that here J_{th} and A_0 are in amperes per square centimeter rather than per square meter.

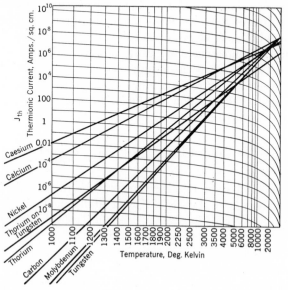

Fig. 7.3 Direct-reading temperature-emission chart with warped coordinate lines (compare with Fig. 7.2).

system. Each line corresponds to the graph, on the coordinates of Fig. 7.2, of an equation of the form

$$\left[\ln J_{th} + 2 \ln \left(\frac{1}{T} \right) \right] = \text{Constant} + 2 \ln \left(\frac{1}{T} \right) \qquad (7\text{--}8)$$

where the constant is a selected value of $\ln J_{th}$. The tendency of the various straight lines to focus at a common point suggests the universal nature of the constant A_0, for $\ln A_0$ for any line is the intercept at $1/T = 0$, or $T = \infty$.

An early alternative for Dushman's equation is known as Richardson's equation; [7B-22, 7C] its form, explained later, in Section 12.15, is

$$J_{th} = aT^{\frac{1}{2}} \exp \left(-\frac{b}{T} \right) \qquad (7\text{--}9)$$

a and b being empirical constants. The exponent has the same general significance as in Dushman's equation, and b is, like b_0, the work function measured in temperature units. A graphical representation of Richardson's equation, similar to Fig. 7.2, would employ along the vertical scale the quantity $\ln J_{th} + \frac{1}{2} \ln (1/T)$.

Experimental data give equally satisfactory straight lines on either type of graph, or for that matter on one in which the vertical scale is simply $\ln J_{th}$, because the effect of the exponential factor completely overshadows that of T^2 or $T^{\frac{1}{2}}$. The thermionic properties of an emitter can therefore be described by a set of empirical constants corresponding to Dushman's equation, as in Table VI, or by a corresponding set based on Richardson's equation, or by a set based on any reasonable value of the exponent of the T factor, including the zero exponent.

The preference for Dushman's equation is based on theoretical indications that it is the correct form,[7A, B] strongly supported by the convergence of the various straight lines of Fig. 7.2 toward a common point whose location is reasonably well predicted by the theory. Theory predicts a value of 1.201×10^6 for A_0, but experimental data favor a value of 0.60×10^6.*

7.6 Cathode Power Dissipation. The second of the two physical laws that contribute to the power-emission relationship described by Fig. 7.1 is that between temperature and cathode power dissipation.[7D, F-XIV] The temperature of an electron-emitting cathode is of course that at which equilibrium exists between rates of heat removal

---

* This agreement of theory and experiment to within a factor of 2 appears as a rather remarkable confirmation of the theory, when it is realized that the theory contains no adjustable empirical constants. See Chapter IV in *Fundamentals of Physical Electronics* for details of the theory.

and of heat input. The heat input is the heat power provided by the flow of electric current through the filamentary cathode or the heater coil.

In most vacuum tubes the major portion of the cathode heating power is removed by radiation from the cathode, so that the relation between heat power input required and the temperature attained is controlled almost entirely by the heat-radiating properties of the cathode. A cathode that is a poor radiator of heat energy will require less heating power to maintain it at any given temperature than will a cathode that is a good radiator. Convection cooling is entirely absent, and the heat removal by conduction through the supports and terminals, though measurable, is usually small relative to the power radiated.

The power directly expended in causing electron emission is the product of emission current in amperes by the work function in volts. This amount of power describes the rate of removal of heat by the cooling action of electron emission. The mechanism is the same as that of cooling by evaporation; the particles that leave are high-energy ones, so that after the departure of any one of them the average kinetic energy of the body as a whole is less than it was before.

Although the heat input requirement necessary to make up this "electron evaporation" heat loss is measurable with refined apparatus, and measurements of it have been made for determining work function, it is in most high-vacuum thermionic devices negligible by comparison with the radiant heat loss. In an ideal emitter it would be a major part of the total heat power input, yet would itself be small. Most present-day devices are far from the ideal, which can, however, be much more closely approached in gaseous-conducting than in high-vacuum devices.

Corresponding to the cooling action of electron departure from the cathode there is a heating action on entrance to the plate. Each electron delivers to the plate, when it strikes, energy corresponding to the plate voltage plus the plate-surface work function.

7.7   Heat Transfer by Radiation; Emissivity Coefficients. The rate of radiant heat dissipation from a cathode is the difference between the radiation rate from the cathode to its surroundings and that from surroundings to the cathode; the latter is usually very small. The quantitative relation between the temperature of a radiating body and the power radiated away from it is, for a "gray" surface [1J, K, 7F-106]

$$P_R = 5.73 \times 10^{-8} \gamma T^4 = 57{,}300\gamma \left(\frac{T}{1000}\right)^4 \qquad (7\text{--}10)$$

in watts per square meter, T being temperature in degrees Kelvin. The quantity 5.73×10^{-8} is a universal radiation constant (the Stefan-

Boltzmann constant), and γ is the *emissivity coefficient* of the surface. This coefficient has a double significance; it is (a) the ratio of power *radiated* by a given gray surface to that radiated by a perfectly black surface at the same temperature, and (b) the fraction of incident radiation that is *absorbed* by a gray surface, this fraction being unity for a perfectly black surface.   For a given temperature a truly black surface radiates more heat than any other kind, and absorbs all the radiation incident to it.   Lampblack (soot) is the blackest substance known; its emissivity coefficient is about 0.98.

Heat radiation takes place at a variety of wavelengths.   The solid line in Fig. 7.4 illustrates the distribution of the energy radiated by a

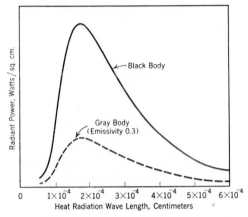

FIG. 7.4   Spectral distribution of black and gray body radiation, at 1600° K.

perfectly black body at one particular temperature.[1J]   This distribution curve has the same shape for all temperatures, but the wavelength corresponding to the crest varies inversely as the temperature.

The dotted line is the corresponding radiation distribution curve, at the same temperature, for a *gray body* whose emissivity coefficient is 0.3. Its ordinates are at every point 0.3 of the height of those for the black body.   If the dotted curve were at the left 0.1, and at the right 0.3, of the height of the solid one, the surface whose properties it described could not be called gray.   It is reasonable to assume that all vacuum-tube electrodes have gray surfaces, but such an assumption in regard to the enclosing glass would be open to question.

Figure 7.5 illustrates graphically the variation of P_R with temperature, for several different surfaces.[7D]   The fact that the various lines are not all parallel to the straight black-body line indicates that the emissivity coefficients vary slightly with the temperature.   The value of the emissivity coefficient γ corresponding to any point on these curves is the ratio of P_R at that point to P_R for the black-body line at the same temperature.

As applied to the study of the incidence of radiant energy on a surface, the emissivity coefficient describes the fraction of such energy

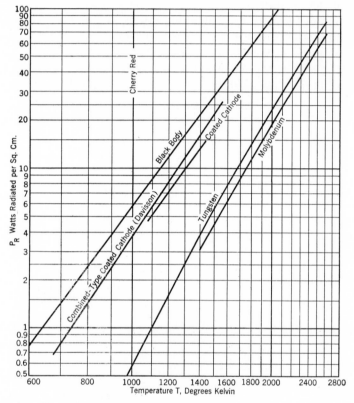

Fig. 7.5 Radiation from thermionic surfaces.[7D] Curves for platinum and tantalum would lie for the most part between those for tungsten and molybdenum. For Davisson's combined-type coated cathode, square centimeter area units,

$$P_R = 5.735 \times 10^{-12} (0.4 + 2.5 \times 10^{-4}\, T)\, T^4$$

For tungsten (Worthing and Forsythe),

$$\log_{10} P_R = 3.680 (\log_{10} T - 3.3) - (1040/T) + 1.900$$

that is not reflected; that is, $(1 - \gamma)$ may be called a *reflectivity* coefficient.

In many electron tubes the distances to the heat-receiving surfaces are large relative to the dimensions of the radiating cathode. Under such circumstances successive reflections between radiator and receiver make the overall radiant energy transfer P follow the general law that is known to apply for concentric spheres or cylinders if the radius of the hot inner cylinder is much smaller than that of the outer one. This relation is [7F, 6g]

$$P = 5.73 \times 10^{-8}\, S\gamma(T_k{}^4 - T_p{}^4) \qquad (7\text{--}11)$$

where S, γ, and T_k are respectively the radiator's area in square meters, the emissivity coefficient of both radiator and receiver, and the temperature of the radiator. T_p is the temperature of the receiver. This can usually be simplified, for $T_p{}^4$ is ordinarily very much smaller than $T_k{}^4$, even when the receiving surface is at a moderately high temperature. Ordinarily the expression

$$P = 5.73 \times 10^{-8}\, S\gamma T_k{}^4 \qquad (7\text{--}12)$$

gives a satisfactory approximation to the true radiant power dissipation from the cathode.

If the cathode dimensions are not small relative to distances to the receiving surfaces, the analysis of the rate of radiant heat transfer from the cathode requires a study of multiple reflections for the particular geometry involved. The approach to such problems is described by Moore.[7F–XIV]

7.8   Temperature Measurements; Lead Losses.   Basic measurements of the temperatures of hot filaments are made by means of optical pyrometers, which compare the optical brilliance of the surface to be measured with that of a standard one.

In any attempt to use (7–12) for accurate calculations, the rather pronounced effect of "lead losses," that is, the cooling of the ends of the filament by conduction to the supports or lead-in wires, must be taken into account. Within this limitation, and subject to accurate knowledge of cathode dimensions and of the emissivity coefficient, (7–12) can be used for the estimation of cathode temperature at a given power input. The emissivity coefficients of oxide-coated surfaces vary somewhat with the details of surface preparation, but that for thoriated tungsten is the same as for ordinary tungsten. Numerical values of emissivity coefficients can be estimated from Fig. 7.5. A very smooth surface has a definitely lower emissivity than one that is slightly roughened.

Temperature can be determined, if the resistance properties of the filament are known, by measurement of the ratio of hot to cold resistance; see Table VII. Koller [7D] gives a good general discussion of methods of temperature measurement, and of the handling of lead losses.

7.9 Overall Relationship between Thermionic Current and Heating Power. Since nearly all the heat supplied to the cathode of a high-vacuum thermionic device is removed by radiation, it is permissible, if lead losses are small, to equate electrical power input to cathode radiation, either total or per unit area. If E_f and I_f are rms values of heating voltage and current, and S the total heat-radiating surface, P_R, the radiant power dissipation *per square meter* of radiating surface is, in watts:

$$P_R = \frac{E_f I_f}{S} \qquad (7\text{–}13)$$

This permits evaluation of P_R from experimental data.

Equation (7–12) can be written

$$\frac{1}{T_k} = 1.55 \times 10^{-2} \gamma^{\frac{1}{4}} \left(\frac{S}{E_f I_f} \right)^{\frac{1}{4}} \qquad (7\text{–}14)$$

If thermionic current I_{th} is expressed as

$$I_{th} = S J_{th} \qquad (7\text{–}15)$$

and this expression, (7–3b), and (7–14) are used to eliminate T and J_{th} from the logarithmic form of (7–2b), the thermionic current can be expressed as a function of $E_f I_f$. A convenient form is

$$\ln I_{th} + 2 \ln \left(\frac{1}{E_f I_f} \right)^{\frac{1}{4}} = \ln \frac{10^4 A_0}{2.4} \sqrt{\frac{S}{\gamma}} - 180 (S\gamma)^{\frac{1}{4}} E_W \left(\frac{1}{E_f I_f} \right)^{\frac{1}{4}}$$

$$(7\text{–}16)$$

Experimental observations give $(E_f I_f)^{\frac{1}{4}}$ and I_{th}, permitting a plot of experimental points on a graph for which

$$\left(\frac{1}{E_f I_f} \right)^{\frac{1}{4}} \text{ is the abscissa (plotted with maximum} \qquad (7\text{–}17a)$$
$$\text{power points on the right)}$$

$$\ln I_{th} + 2 \ln \left(\frac{1}{E_f I_f} \right)^{\frac{1}{4}} \text{ is the ordinate} \qquad (7\text{–}17b)$$

Such points lie on a line that is very nearly straight, because γ varies only very slightly with temperature. Warped coordinate lines of constant I_{th} and constant $E_f I_f$ can then be drawn, much as the warped lines for Fig. 7.3 were drawn. Figure 7.1 is the result of such a treatment of experimental data, for $S = 1$ square centimeter.

The warping in Fig. 7.1 is based on Dushman's equation, which was used in building up to (7–16). A useful kind of special graph paper, called "power emission paper" with coordinates similar to those of Fig. 7.1 but based instead on Richardson's $T^{1/2}$ equation (Section 12.15), has been designed by the engineers of the Western Electric Company [7c] and can be purchased from the Keuffel and Esser Company.

7.10 Inward-Radiating Cathodes. High emission efficiency is favored by a small rate of heat radiation from the cathode, for this permits the maintenance of a high cathode temperature with small energy consumption. The emissivity coefficient depends on the material and smoothness of the cathode; total heat radiation is dependent, not only on emissivity, but also on the geometrical shape of the cathode.

A cathode so shaped as to have some similarity to a furnace, with electron-emitting interior walls radiating heat toward one another, and having the nonemitting outer surfaces heat-insulated by two or three reflecting baffles, can be made many times more efficient than the ordinary outward-radiating kind.[7D] The radiation from each part of the inner surface helps to maintain the temperature of the other parts, and very little radiation escapes to the outside.

Such heat-conserving cathodes can be used in gas-filled electronic devices in which the space charge in the interior region is neutralized by positive ions of the gas. Electric field effects in this interior region are much the same as those inside a metallic conductor, and the electrons can be drawn out through an open end of the cathode enclosure. The radiating and emitting areas are not the same for this type of cathode, so that power-emission charts lose their significance. Considerable time (often minutes) must be allowed, after filament power is turned on, for them to reach temperature equilibrium before plate current is allowed to flow.

In any *high-vacuum* space-charge-limited current device the electrons in general travel in approximately parallel or diverging paths toward the receiving electrode. If the receiving electrode is placed so as to be a satisfactory target for these electrons, it is obviously likely also to be a good target for heat radiation. Consequently the inward-radiating heat-conserving cathode construction has not been applied successfully to high-vacuum thermionic devices.

7.11 Low-Work-Function Surfaces.* High emission efficiency is favored by low work function; see Table VI. A great deal of ingenuity, scientific thought, and expense has been devoted to the search for materials and for processing methods which will produce very low work

* See bibliography references 4B, C, 6A, B, 7A, B, D, E, *a, d, f, g, h, i, j, k, l.*

functions, with considerable success. Most commercial electron tubes are equipped with *oxide-coated* or *thoriated* cathodes prepared in accordance with the results of these investigations; see the next two sections. For some purposes cathodes of pure or nearly pure refractory metals, such as tungsten or molybdenum, are used.

Thoria (thorium oxide) cathodes are also coming into use, in uhf devices. Thoria is a ceramic material.[7i]

In the recently developed dispenser cathode [7l] a reservoir of barium exists under some pressure beneath a thin layer of tungsten. The barium diffuses through the tungsten to maintain a very thin layer of barium (perhaps monatomic) as the emitting surface.

Also, a lanthanum boride cathode with interesting properties has recently been reported.[7k]

Structural stability, including resistance to damage by bombardment of ions of residual gas, and other considerations (such as evaporation of surface material) that relate to useful life must be considered along with work function and emissivity in comparing merits of various materials and processes. Of course the melting point must be higher than the temperature at which appreciable emission takes place; hence the higher the work function, the more refractory a material must be to serve at all, regardless of efficiency. This rules out copper, nickel, aluminum, iron, and similar metals entirely, as having fairly high work functions but not correspondingly high melting points. Unfortunately, materials such as cesium, rubidium, barium, strontium, etc., that have low work functions, melt, and in some cases boil, at temperatures lower than those required for appreciable thermionic emission.

Special methods of preparation make it possible, however, to provide stable thin layers of low-work-function substances on filaments of tungsten, nickel, platinum, or various alloys. These *base metals* maintain structural stability at temperatures high enough to produce substantial emission from outer layers of low-work-function materials.

7.12   Thoriated Tungsten Cathodes.[4B, 6A, B, 7B, D, E, a, d, h]   Cathodes consisting of tungsten filaments with surfaces covered by a single layer of thorium atoms are rather widely used commercially. The major steps in the preparation of such a *thoriated tungsten* filamentary cathode are as follows:

(*a*) The filament is drawn from tungsten which contains a small percentage of thorium oxide, called *thoria*.

(*b*) The filament is "carburized" by heating in the presence of a hydrocarbon vapor at a modest vacuum. The depth of carburization is important; if there is too much carbide the filament will be brittle, and if too little the emission will be low. A typical compromise is to carburize the outer 25 per cent of the filament radius, corresponding to 44 per cent of the cross section. This increases the filament resistance by 10 to 11 per cent; the resistance change is used as a measurement control of the depth of carburization. The filament is sometimes "flashed" [see (c) below] in dry hydrogen and then in a vacuum, perhaps several times, *before* carburization, as well as afterward.

(c) It is "flashed" in a high vacuum; this means that it is heated for a short time to a temperature of about 2800° K. Flashing reduces some of the thoria within the tungsten to metallic thorium.

(d) The filament is "activated" by being held for some time in a high vacuum at a temperature in the neighborhood of 2100° K. It seems probable that during this process a monatomic surface layer of thorium is formed, as a result of the following circumstances:

(1) The thorium atoms formed during flashing diffuse from the interior of the tungsten to its surface. Tungsten, like all metals, has a granular structure; the thorium atoms are believed to diffuse along boundary surfaces between grains, so that fine grain structure aids diffusion. This movement toward the surface takes place more rapidly at high than at low temperatures.

(2) At the activation temperature the first thorium atoms to arrive at the surface evaporate from it very much *less* rapidly than new ones arrive from the interior, because of the strong attachment energy that exists between a thorium atom and the tungsten surface; hence thorium atoms accumulate on the surface.

(3) As soon as any small portion of the surface becomes covered with a monatomic layer of thorium atoms, any additional ones that arrive from the interior must form a second layer. But the attachment energy between thorium atoms of the second layer and those of the first layer is very small. At the activation temperature evaporation of the second layer occurs much *more* rapidly than arrival of additional thorium atoms from the interior. Only the atoms of the first layer remain on the surface for any considerable length of time.

(e) The filament with its monatomic thorium layer is now ready for use at a temperature several hundred degrees lower than that used for activation, at which neither diffusion of thorium atoms to the surface nor evaporation of them from it are appreciable. Such filaments have low work functions and are satisfactory as thermionic emitters for many purposes. They require an extremely good vacuum.

The monatomic layer of thorium on such a filament can be destroyed by contact with gases, or by heating to above the activation temperature. There is some evaporation of thorium atoms even at the operating temperature, so that a thoriated surface has a limited life even if properly used. It can, however, be rejuvenated by "reactivation," providing previous activations or misuse have not driven all the thorium atoms to the surface. In that case more thorium atoms may be produced internally by flashing again, for at each flashing operation only a small fraction of the available thoria is reduced to thorium.

7.13   Oxide-Coated Cathodes.[4B, 6A, B, 7B, D, E, a, d, e, f, g]   An oxide-coated cathode has an emitting surface layer of mixed barium and strontium oxides over a base metal, which is usually nickel or a nickel alloy. The thickness of the layer is usually measurable in thousandths or ten-thousandths of an inch. Each tube manufacturer has preferred formulas for the preparation and processing of oxide-coated cathodes for specific purposes, selected as a result of laboratory studies and manufacturing expediency. In general the barium and strontium are applied to the base metal of the cathode in the form of mixed carbonates. Subsequent progressive heating in a vacuum causes a conversion to the oxides, with evolution of carbon dioxide which passes out through the exhaust system. During and after this conversion the cathode is "activated" by drawing an electron emission current to the anode. In the final stages of activation the cathode temperature is considerably higher than the normal operating temperature subsequently used.

The various emission properties of an oxide-coated surface depend on the base metal, on the proportions of the contributing oxides, on the composition of the residual gas in the tube, *and on the material, location, processing, and potential of the anode.* An oxide-coated cathode is especially sensitive to "poisoning" by certain kinds of impurities in the residual gas, or gas evolved from the electrodes during use. Only by painstaking control of manufacturing operations can any given set of thermionic emitter properties be produced with even a reasonably acceptable degree of uniformity from tube to tube.

In all cases emission is markedly affected by relatively weak external fields. In this respect the behavior of oxide-coated cathodes exhibits a sharp contrast with that of homogeneous surfaces; see Section 7.14. Also, oxide-coated surfaces are sometimes found to give many times higher thermionic emission current densities for "pulse" currents, each pulse lasting a few microseconds, than for steady ("continuous-wave") operation. This high pulsed emission density has made oxide-coated cathodes very valuable in radar magnetrons.

As yet no generally accepted theory of the behavior of oxide-coated cathodes exists. However, they are, on the whole, more efficient thermionically, and at the same time more generally satisfactory as to most other important properties, than any other type of commercial emitting surface, in spite of their relatively high radiation emissivity coefficients.

7.14.   "Saturation"; Failure of Composite Surfaces to Saturate. When a *temperature-limited current* is flowing through a tube the potential gradient just outside the cathode is definitely positive; every escaping electron emerges into an electric field that drives it toward the anode. For homogeneous metal surfaces such as possessed by essentially pure metallic filaments—tungsten, tantalum, molybdenum, etc.—the emission as given by Dushman's equation (7–2) is not affected by variations in the strength of the potential gradient adjacent to the surface (except for very unusual extreme values of the gradient as discussed in Section 8.22).

Figure 7.6a shows the customary *saturation* of the plate characteristic curves of a triode having a pure refractory metal filament. All the curves ultimately level off at a definite temperature-limited or saturation value of plate current. The saturation current is independent of

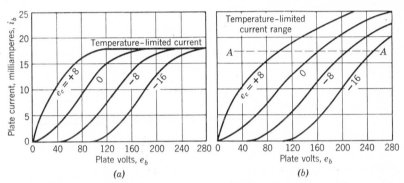

(a)

"Saturation" with a refractory metal cathode, as for example tungsten, molybdenum, or tantalum.

(b)

Failure to saturate with an oxide-coated cathode.

FIG. 7.6   Temperature limitation of triode plate currents.

plate and grid voltages, because it is for all practical purposes independent of the gradient just outside the cathode.

Tubes containing oxide-coated and some other types of composite cathode surfaces exhibit a marked failure to saturate with increasing plate voltage, as illustrated by Fig. 7.6b.[7B] Above values of plate current indicated by the line AA the current is truly *temperature-limited*, in that the gradient at the cathode surface is definitely positive, and the effect of space charge on the determination of current magnitude insignificant. Yet the different plate characteristic curves do not level off at all, and it is obviously possible, even in the temperature-limited range, to affect the magnitude of the current by variations in grid voltage. This has not proved to be a useful method of current control, because there is an important time dependence in the response of current to grid voltage changes, and the individual curves are not in general reproducible. Prolonged passage of a temperature-limited current at a high off-cathode gradient permanently modifies the thermionic properties of a composite emitting surface.

This failure to saturate indicates, of course, that one or both of the constants A_0 and E_W in Dushman's equation have, for oxide-coated and some other composite surfaces, different values for different off-cathode gradients.

PROBLEMS

1. Find E_T, the voltage equivalent of temperature (Section 7.3) for 0° C, 100° C, 2500° K.

2. (a) Use Dushman's equation to find the *temperature-limited* current of the diode of Prob. 4, Chapter V; cathode (filament) temperature 2500° K. (Use Table VI.)

(b) Above what plate voltage will this diode's current be temperature-limited, plate radius being 30 times cathode radius, cathode 2500° K?

(c) Sketch to scale the i_b vs. e_b curve, cathode 2500° K; also 2000° K.

(d) Estimate the power that must be supplied to this filament to maintain its temperature at 2500° K; also at 2000° K.

(e) Cathode at 2500° K, e_b as in (b): what power must the plate radiate?

3. Consider a cylindrical triode, cathode temperature such that the temperature-limited current density J_{th} is 60 ma per sq cm. The actual space-charge-limited current density J_b is one-third of this. Cathode radius 0.05 cm, plate radius 0.5 cm. Axial length 4.0 cm. $E_b = 130$, $E_c = -10$. The average *total* energy of the electrons as they leave the cathode surface is 0.2 electron volt. Cathode work function 2.10 volt. Find: (a) the average *outwardly directed* energy of the escaping electrons; (b) cathode temperature; (c) the value of A_0 in Dushman's equation, for this cathode; (d) the power required to heat the cathode, emissivity 0.4 (assume that all the heating power input to the cathode is radiated to the plate); (e) the rate (watts) at which *electron emission* removes heat from the cathode, as evaporation cools water [relative to (d), this is insignificant]; (f) the power, in total watts and watts per sq cm, that must be radiated by the plate (this includes power radiated to it by the cathode); (g) the temperature reached by the plate, emissivity 0.9 (graphite).

4. Consider a planar triode: cathode material, cathode temperature, ratio J_b/J_{th}, plate and grid voltages, are as in Prob. 3. The cathode radiates heat only from the side facing the plate. Answer questions (d), (f), and (g) of Prob. 3, dealing now entirely in watts per sq cm. What does comparison of the results with those of Prob. 3 indicate?

5. Planar diode, 5 mm spacing; cathode, of tungsten, 10 sq cm area, at 2500° K; anode voltage $E_b = 200$. (a) Is the current space-charge-limited or temperature-limited? (b) As the plate voltage e_b rises from zero, at what value of e_b does the current first become temperature-limited?

6. Figure 7.7 contains curves taken on a tungsten-filament diode. Points A and B are at the same filament current but different plate voltages. (a) Is the current at A temperature-limited or space-charge-limited? *Give a clear explanation justifying your answer.* (b) Same as (a), applied to point B.

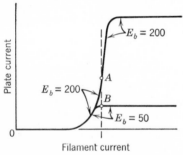

FIG. 7.7 Plate current vs. filament current in a tungsten-filament diode.

CHAPTER VIII

ELECTRONS IN METALS AND SEMICONDUCTORS

8.1 Ionizing Potentials of Atoms. An atom of any element consists of a central positively charged nucleus surrounded by a cloud or "atmosphere" of electrons, normally of just the right number to neutralize the positive nuclear charge.[12C, 1J, K] These electrons place themselves systematically in a series of "shells" located progressively farther from the nucleus. Each shell can accommodate no more than a definite number of electrons, though it may contain less than the maximum, even when a more remote shell is partially occupied. The maximum number of electrons in each shell is $2n^2$ for the nth shell; [1J] see Section 13.15.

Large atomic weight is usually associated with large nuclear charge, so that the electronic atmospheres extend into more remote shells for the heavy than for the light elements. None of the elements completely fills either the fifth or sixth shells, but some radioactive elements have one or two seventh-shell electrons. Table II gives the distribution of electrons among the shells for the various elements. The *atomic number* is the nuclear charge, in electron-charge units, hence also the normal number of electrons in an atom's atmosphere.

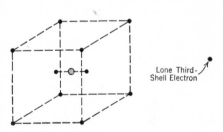

Fig. 8.1 Locations of the eleven electrons of a sodium atom's "atmosphere."

Figure 8.1 illustrates in a general way how the electrons in a sodium atom's atmosphere are distributed. There are two in the first shell, eight in the second, and a lone one in the third. The placement, in the figure, of the eight second-shell electrons at the corners of a cube is merely suggestive of symmetry in their average positions.

An atom from which one of the outer-shell electrons has been removed is said to be *ionized*. The restraining force that tends to prevent such removal is the electrostatic attraction between the electron about to leave and the remainder of the atom. Such attraction exists because, as an electron starts away, its departure leaves the atom positively charged by an amount equal to the electron's own negative charge. A definite minimum amount of energy, usually measured in electron volts and called the *ionizing potential*, must be given to an outer-shell electron to enable it to escape in spite of the loss of kinetic energy experienced in overcoming this electric restraining force. Thus the ionizing potential is a measure of the strength of attachment of an outer-shell electron to the atom of which it is a part.

For a given type of electron arrangement, the attachment of a remote-shell outer electron is less than that of a close-in one. Thus the ionizing potential of sodium is 5.12 volts, of rubidium 4.16 volts, and of cesium only 3.87 volts, although in all three elements the last shell contains one, the next-to-the-last eight, electrons; see Table II.

8.2 Free Electrons in Metals. An electron that, like the eleventh one of sodium, has the entire outer shell to itself, is in general much less strongly attached to its atom than one, like a third-shell argon electron, that has many companions in its own shell. Thus although the outermost electrons of both sodium and argon are in the third shell, the ionizing potential of sodium is 5.12 volts, that of argon 15.69 volts. Good electrical conductors are made from the elements, scattered through the periodic table, in which the farthest-out shell occupied contains only one, two, or—in a few elements—three electrons.

Atoms of these elements are located so close together when in solid metallic assembly that the outer-shell electrons are no more closely associated with one atom than with another. The electron attachment to individual atoms is weak to begin with and vanishes altogether in this very close spacing. At least one, sometimes two, in a few cases three, electrons per atom are not bound at all to any *one* atom but are free to rove throughout the interior of the metal. They can therefore move very rapidly in response to electric fields that result from the introduction of the metal into electric circuits; they are called *free electrons.* *

Since these roving electrons continually interchange their kinetic energies of motion with vibrational kinetic energies of the atoms of the metal, the freedom of electron motion aids in the transfer of heat energy from one point to another; hence good electrical conductors are also good heat conductors.

8.3 Work Function. The free electrons possess varying amounts of kinetic energy, which for reasons detailed in later sections range upward from zero to a definite normal maximum, usually several electron volts. There are always more electrons with energies near the normal maximum than with lesser amounts. The highest-energy free electrons in a metal are situated somewhat as are the outer-shell electrons in a

---

* See bibliographical references 1J, K, 7A, B, 8A through 8K, 8a, b.

single atom, in that they are more nearly in position to escape than are any of the others.

Although there is no attachment of consequence between the free electrons and individual atoms in a metal, there is a strong attachment between the free electrons and the metal as a whole. An electron escaping from the surface of a conductor, like one on the way out from a single atom, leaves on the parent body a positive charge, called the *image* charge, which exerts an electric *image force* tending to prevent departure.

A definite minimum amount of energy, usually measured in electron volts and called the *work function*, made use of in Chapter VII, must be given to any one of the highest-energy free electrons to enable it to escape in spite of the loss of kinetic energy experienced in overcoming the image force. The addition to low-energy free electrons of an amount of energy equivalent to the work function cannot release them, for it is an electron's total energy to which the possibility of escape is primarily related. Work functions of metals range between 1.5 and 7 volts (see Table VI) as compared with a range of 3.5 to 25 volts for the ionizing potentials of atoms and molecules in gases and vapors.

8.4 Energy-Level Diagrams; Gross Work Function. As an escaping electron moves away from the metal, its kinetic energy is reduced to the extent that its *potential energy* is increased. The electric-force barrier offered to an electron's outward flight may be represented diagrammatically in an *energy-level diagram*, Fig. 8.2, in which vertical distances describe energies.[8A, D, G, a, b] It is convenient to use

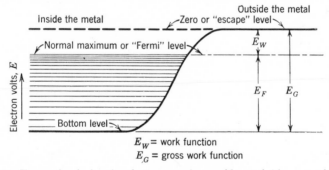

E_W = work function
E_G = gross work function

Fig. 8.2   Energy levels for the electron gas in a cold metal (the normal state).

the *electron volt* as a unit of energy in such diagrams, both potential energy and kinetic energy being convertible between joules and electron volts E by the familiar relation

$$E q_e = \text{joules} \qquad (8\text{–}1)$$

The upward reverse curve in the heavy solid line in Fig. 8.2 represents the change in an outwardly moving electron's potential energy from a "bottom-level" value inside the metal at the left to a uniform "zero-level" value everywhere outside at the right. Thus the *potential energy* is *zero outside, negative inside.* The difference between these two extreme zero and bottom *energy levels* is the increase in potential energy, hence also the loss in kinetic energy, experienced by an escaping electron during its outward flight. This difference describes the kinetic energy that must be imparted to a *stationary* electron inside the metal in order to permit escape and will be called the *gross work function* in this text. It is considerably larger than the quantity called work function.

Since the electrons in the metal are not stationary, the addition of a considerably smaller amount of energy than the gross work function may result in one's escape. The many horizontal lines in the left, interior-of-the-metal, part of Fig. 8.2 represent *kinetic-energy levels.* They symbolize the fact that the free electrons in the metal possess a great variety of kinetic energies ranging from none at all (for the "bottom-level electrons") up to that described by the normal maximum or "Fermi" level. The quantity described in the preceding section and in Chapter VII as work function, and universally referred to in that way, is the additional kinetic energy that must be given to an electron *already in the Fermi level* to enable it to escape. This is of course the difference between gross work function and the kinetic energy of the electrons in the Fermi level.

The height of the Fermi or normal maximum level is dependent entirely on the concentration of free electrons within the metal, as discussed in Section 8.10. Available evidence indicates that it ranges from about 2 volts in some of the lighter metals to 10 or more in some of the heavier ones. Note that the *average kinetic energy* of the "gas" made up of the free electrons in a metal is several volts ($\frac{3}{5}$ of the Fermi-level energy) even at very low temperatures. This is in sharp contrast to the average molecular kinetic energy in ordinary gases, which rarely exceeds $\frac{1}{2}$ to $\frac{2}{3}$ of a volt, even at extremely high temperatures.

8.5 Normal (Low-Temperature) Distribution of Kinetic Energy. The many horizontal lines in the left, interior-of-the-metal, part of Fig. 8.2 suggest the many different values of kinetic energy possessed by the free electrons. The actual number of electrons that have a given amount of kinetic energy is controlled, for reasons outlined in a later section, by the following two general sets of facts: [7A, B, 8B, D, E, G, a, b]

(a) The values of kinetic energy that it is possible for an electron to have differ from one another by finite though extremely small amounts. Each permissible value can be represented diagrammatically as a *kinetic-energy level;* hence the use of discrete horizontal lines in the diagram.

(b) Each kinetic-energy level can accommodate only a limited number of electrons, the number increasing approximately as the square root of the energy. This is true for the same kind of reason that limits to a definite maximum the number of electrons in any one shell of an atom's electronic atmosphere. Each kinetic-energy level may be empty, partly filled, or completely filled, just as each of the shells around an atomic nucleus may be empty, partly filled, or completely filled.

Absolute zero (0° K) is the temperature at which all particles, including the free electrons, have the least possible energy. The electrons cannot all have bottom-level kinetic energy, however, for at that level there is no to-and-fro motion, and it happens that there can be only two such electrons. The levels immediately above the bottom can accommodate only a few electrons each, and the number available per level grows rather slowly. *Most of the electrons must "occupy" levels that are several volts above the bottom.*

Least-possible energy does require, however, that no electron shall be able to find a vacancy in a level lower than the one it occupies. This means that at absolute zero all levels must be completely filled as far up as is necessary to accommodate all the electrons, and that all levels above that height must be completely empty. The Fermi level in Fig. 8.2 is the level so described; all the electrons, but no more, can be accommodated below it.

The discussion just given has been based on conditions at absolute zero temperature. It happens, however, that because of the very small mass and very high concentrations of the free electrons, very few of them indeed occupy levels above the Fermi level in metals heated even considerably above ordinary room temperature. Hence at room temperatures the distribution of electrons among the levels is practically the same as that at absolute zero, and the adjective "normal" is appropriate for absolute zero conditions. To the electron gas in a metal the change from 0° K to 300° K appears a trifling variation.

8.6 Thermionic Emission. It is sometimes helpful to think of the bottom level in Fig. 8.2 as the bed of a lake, the Fermi level indicating the normal water level, and the zero or escape level the height of the land around the lake.[7B-22] As long as there is no wind, all the space below the normal water level is full of water, and that above it empty, for exactly the same reason that at absolute zero all the kinetic-energy levels below the Fermi level are filled and those above it empty: that is, in the absence of agitation the water must be so distributed that no water particle shall be able to find a vacant space at an elevation lower than the one it now occupies.

Heating the metal has an effect similar to that of agitating the water. Wind or some other disturbing factor may produce waves or spray; but waves or spray can exist only if some of the normally filled space is vacated in order to provide water for the spray drops or wave crests. If the agitation is severe enough some of the spray rises above the escape level and passes out over the land (thermionic emission) and can be drawn away to other lakes (other electrodes) if there is a slope (electric field) in the terrain. If there is no slope in the terrain, the water carried out onto the perfectly level shore piles up there (space charge) with the result that a water-surface gradient (electric field set up in accordance with Poisson's equation) makes some of the water flow back into the lake. This analogy is imperfect and must not be carried too far, but it can be very helpful.

Thermionic emission takes place only when thermal agitation throws an appreciable proportion of the high-kinetic-energy free electrons up into normally vacant levels that are *above the escape level*. It is evident from this requirement why the important energy element in thermionic emission is the net rather than the gross work function. Dushman's equation grows out of a mathematical statement of the relation between temperature and the number of electrons that occupy high-up normally vacant levels.

Figure 8.4 illustrates the distribution of free electrons among the kinetic-energy levels in tungsten, assuming that each tungsten atom contributes two free electrons, for (a) 0° K ("normal") and (b) 2500° K, the temperature at which pure tungsten filaments are commonly operated. Ordinates describe the relative number of free electrons occupying levels located according to the various kinetic-energy values. The zero-temperature curve is a true horizontal-axis parabola that terminates abruptly at the Fermi energy value. It will be noted that the *average energy* of the free electrons changes very little between 0° and 2500°.

8.7   The Quantum of Action. It is desirable to show why the available kinetic-energy levels within a metal are separated by finite amounts of energy and can each accommodate only a limited number of free electrons.

Electric charge occurs only as integral multiples of q_e, and mass also as integral multiples of minute units. Similarly another physical quantity called "action" occurs (for periodic motions of ultimate particles) only as integral multiples of a definite small amount.

The *action* of a particle in periodic motion is the line integral of the momentum taken over one cycle of movement. Thus the action associated with the periodicity of a particle of mass m moving with uniform velocity v in a circular path of radius a is [1J, K, 12C]

$$\int_{s=0}^{s=2\pi a} mv \, ds = 2\pi mav \qquad (8\text{--}2)$$

The symbol h will, in accordance with universal practice, be used to represent the indivisible unit of action. $h = 6.624 \times 10^{-34}$ joule-second; h is called "Planck's constant," or sometimes "Planck's quantum of action."

Action is described in joule-second units because its dimensional formula (ML^2T^{-1}), happens to be obtainable by multiplying that for energy (ML^2T^{-2}) by a time factor T. It is, however, more often desirable to think of action as the product of momentum by distance traveled in the direction of the momentum, rather than as the product of energy by time.

The requirement that the action of a circularly moving particle must be an integral multiple of h is expressed by the relation

$$2\pi mav = nh \qquad (8\text{--}3)$$

n being any whole number.

An entirely different type of periodic motion in which the action must be "quantized" is that of a particle shuttling back and forth between two parallel-faced walls of an enclosing rectangular box, from whose inside surfaces the particle rebounds without loss of energy. For the sake of simplicity the box may be supposed to be a hollow cube. The particle might be one of the free electrons within, and the walls the work-function barrier around, a piece of metal or a metallic crystal. Such a particle's velocity component parallel to one edge of the cube is constant in magnitude but reverses periodically. The action limitation requires that the momentum times cyclic length of path must be an integral multiple of h, thus

$$mu \cdot 2a = n_u h \qquad (8\text{--}4)$$

where u is the velocity parallel to one edge of the cube, m is the mass of the particle, a the length of one edge of the cube, and n_u any whole number.

With a cube of given size *this limits the velocities to integral multiples of h/2ma.* There are of course three relations like (8–4), expressible as follows:

$$u = n_u \frac{h}{2ma} \tag{8–5a}$$

$$v = n_v \frac{h}{2ma} \tag{8–5b}$$

$$w = n_w \frac{h}{2ma} \tag{8–5c}$$

v and w being velocities in the two directions normal to the u motion and to each other. Thus three distinct *quantum numbers, n_u, n_v, n_w,* are required to specify any particular type of motion within the cube. The total or resultant velocity c of course satisfies the relation

$$c^2 = u^2 + v^2 + w^2 \tag{8–6}$$

This suggests the use of a quantity n, here called the *resultant quantum number,* related as follows:

$$c = n \frac{h}{2ma} \tag{8–7}$$

and

$$n^2 = n_u{}^2 + n_v{}^2 + n_w{}^2 \tag{8–8}$$

The total translational kinetic energy is of course $\frac{1}{2}mc^2$; this can also be expressed as follows in terms of n^2:

$$\frac{h^2}{8ma^2} n^2 = \text{Total translational kinetic energy of the particle} \quad \text{[joules]} \tag{8–9}$$

Since n_u, n_v, n_w must be whole numbers, $n_u{}^2$, $n_v{}^2$, $n_w{}^2$, and their sum n^2 must also be whole numbers. One or more sets of values of n_u, n_v, n_w can be found to fit most whole-number values of n^2. Free electrons within a metal may therefore possess kinetic-energy values corresponding to almost any whole-number multiple of the quantity $h^2/8ma^2$; this amount of energy expressed in electron volts is the "finite though small" difference, referred to in (*a*), Section 8.5, between the heights of adjacent kinetic-energy levels of Fig. 8.2.

8.8 The Exclusion Principle. It was stated in Section 8.5 that each kinetic-energy level can accommodate only a limited number of electrons. It has just been pointed out that the movements of the particles in the cube, or of electrons in the metal, must be "quantized," so indicating discrete, separate values of translational kinetic energy. In addition, the "exclusion principle" must be accepted; [1J, K, 7A, B, 8D, E, G, a, b] this requires that *no two particles within the cube can have an identical set of quantum numbers.* The exclusion principle and the limitation of cyclic action to whole-number multiples of h are adopted, not as outgrowths of any abstruse philosophical concepts of matter, but *because if consistently used they give solutions, that are verifiable by experiment, to an immense number of complicated problems in remotely scattered fields of scientific work.*

The energy corresponding to any given type of motion depends on n^2, according to (8–9); and the number of different particles that can

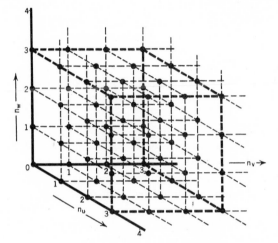

FIG. 8.3   Quantum-number lattice.

be accommodated in a given kinetic-energy level depends, according to the exclusion principle just stated, only on the number of different ways in which n_u, n_v, n_w can combine to give a particular value of n^2, as listed in the column entitled "number of possible arrangements" in Table VIII. For example, $n^2 = 2$ can correspond to (a) $n_u = 1$, $n_v = 1$, $n_w = 0$, (b) $n_u = 1$, $n_v = 0$, $n_w = 1$, and (c) $n_u = 0$, $n_v = 1$, $n_w = 1$. Thus the kinetic-energy level corresponding to $n^2 = 2$ can accommodate just three different kinds of translational motion simultaneously.

Figure 8.3 is a three-dimensional diagram of the various possible quantum-number combinations. There is a scale of n_u values along the forward axis, of n_v values along the horizontal axis to the right, and of n_w values upward along the vertical axis. The octant bounded by the positive portions of these three axes contains a set of many points, one point being located at each possible combination of values of n_u, n_v, n_w. These quantum numbers have all possible whole-number values, and the points represent a "cubical lattice." Each point corresponds to a particular kind of motion; the energy for each kind is measured by the square of the resultant quantum number n, which is the radius vector from the origin to the lattice point that identifies that particular motion; see (8–8) and (8–9). The sixth column in Table VIII states how many lattice points are located at the radius n given in the fifth column.

The exclusion principle is a statement of this fundamental fact of nature: It is as impossible for any two of these particles in a box to have simultaneously identical velocities as for them to have identical positions. Human sense perceptions make the positional restriction obvious enough but do not permit a ready, off-hand grasp of the velocity restriction.

8.9   Electron Spin.   As indicated by the last column in Table VIII, there can in fact be *two* electrons in the cube, not just one, having each possible type of translational motion. Each electron has *four* types of periodic motion, as follows: (a) x-directed shuttling, (b) y-directed shuttling, (c) z-directed shuttling, and (d) an *electron spin*,[1J, K, 12C] similar to the spin of the earth on its own polar axis. Only two kinds of spin motion are possible; each electron may spin clockwise, or it may spin counterclockwise. The angular velocity of either type of spin is such that a change to the other results in a change of one action unit h. The spin quantum number is always $\frac{1}{2}$, thus

$$\frac{1}{2}h \text{ clockwise} + h = \frac{1}{2}h \text{ counterclockwise}$$
and   (8–10)
$$\frac{1}{2}h \text{ counterclockwise} + h = \frac{1}{2}h \text{ clockwise}$$

Since there are two possible spin quantum numbers, $\frac{1}{2}$ clockwise, and $\frac{1}{2}$ counterclockwise, two electrons, one with each kind of spin, can have each possible type of translational motion without violating the requirement that no two particles can have an identical set of quantum numbers. The number of electrons that can be accommodated in each kinetic-energy level is therefore just twice the number of lattice points at the corresponding radius in Fig. 8.3.

It is probable that the mental picture of a box full of shuttling, spinning particles is as remote from the true mechanism inside a metal or metallic crystal as is the picture of individual flux lines threading through a coil from the true nature of a magnetic field. Yet both concepts are useful because, if properly employed, they point the way to correct solutions of scientific and engineering problems.

8.10   The Fermi-Level Energy in a Metallic Conductor.[7A, B, 8A, D, E, G, H, a, b]

Because the lattice points of Fig. 8.3 are everywhere spaced one n unit apart, each one is located at the center of a cube whose volume is one cubical n unit; hence the number of lattice points within any restricted part of the figure is the volume of that region in cubical n units.

Invariably the values of n considered in any specific problem are tremendously large, and the energy-unit spacing $h^2/8ma^2$ between individual kinetic-energy levels extremely small, relative to the total range of energy values. Therefore it is convenient and permissible to ignore the discontinuity between levels in a mathematical analysis.

The symbol E_F will be used to describe the Fermi energy in electron volts, and n_F to describe the corresponding resultant quantum number; they are related in accordance with (8–9), that is:

$$\frac{h^2}{8m_e a^2} n_F{}^2 = E_F q_e \tag{8–11}$$

This expression is made valid for *any* values of E and n by dropping the subscripts.

n_F is invariably a tremendously large number. The absolute zero or "normal" condition of the free electrons within a metal conductor is that at which all kinetic-energy levels below the Fermi level are completely filled. As applied to the lattice-point picture, Fig. 8.3, this means that all the lattice points, out to a very large radius n_F, are "occupied" by their full quota of electrons, that is, two for each lattice point. The number of points within the n-space octant that is thus completely filled is one-eighth of the volume, in cubical n units, of a sphere of radius n_F.

Let N symbolize the number of free electrons per cubic meter of real volume of the metal; the real volume of the cubical piece of metal or metallic crystal being considered is a^3. Hence the total number of electrons to be accommodated below the Fermi level, so within the n-space spherical octant of radius n_F, is Na^3. Therefore

$$Na^3 = 2\frac{1}{8}\left(\frac{4}{3}\pi n_F{}^3\right) = \frac{2\pi n_F{}^3}{6} \tag{8–12}$$

The electron spin accounts for the factor 2. This relation may also be stated as

$$n_F = a\left(\frac{6N}{2\pi}\right)^{\frac{1}{3}} \tag{8–13}$$

If this expression for n_F is introduced into (8–11), a solution for the Fermi-level energy E_F is obtained, as follows:

$$E_F = \frac{h^2}{8 q_e m_e} \left(\frac{6N}{2\pi} \right)^{2/3} = 5.73 \times 10^{-19} \left(\frac{N}{2} \right)^{2/3} \qquad (8\text{–}14)$$

The factor 2 under the N represents the effect of electron spin.

Thus the Fermi-level energy is found to depend only on N, the number of free electrons per cubic meter, aside from the universal constants h, q_e, m_e, π. For tungsten, E_F is 9.17 electron volts, assuming that tungsten has two outer-shell, therefore free, electrons per atom (see Table II). For cesium, with one free electron per atom, E_F is 1.51 volts. The number of atoms per cubic meter is found by dividing the density, in kilograms per cubic meter, by the mass per atom, as determined from the atomic weight. See Chapter V in *Fundamentals of Physical Electronics* for a discussion of magnitudes of E_F and E_W for the alkali metals.

8.11   Normal-State Fermi Energy Distribution.   Figure 8.4a illustrates the *distribution of energy* among the various levels in the normal

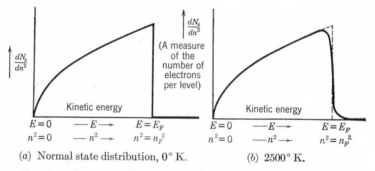

(a) Normal state distribution, 0° K.   (b) 2500° K.

Fig. 8.4   Energy distribution curves for the electrons within a metal.

(absolute zero) state.[7A, B, 8D, E, G, a, b]   To determine the shape of this curve, first imagine in the quantum-number lattice space of Fig. 8.3 a hollow spherical shell of thickness dn at radius n. This shell contains $a^3 \, dN_s$ electrons, dN_s being the number *per unit volume* whose resultant quantum numbers lie between n and $n + dn$. In the normal state, $a^3 \, dN_s$ is twice the number of lattice points in one octant (twice because of electron spin); thus

$$a^3 \, dN_s = 2 \times \frac{1}{8} \times 4\pi n^2 \, dn = \pi n \cdot n \, dn = \frac{\pi}{2} \sqrt{n^2} \, dn^2 \qquad (8\text{–}15a)$$

The energy is measured by n^2, and the differential increment of energy by dn^2; the equation of the distribution curve of Fig. 8.4a is therefore

$$\frac{dN_s}{dn^2} = \frac{\pi}{2a^3} \sqrt{n^2} \qquad (8\text{--}15b)$$

This describes a parabola with a horizontal axis, vertex at the origin. This energy distribution curve drops abruptly to zero at $n^2 = n_F{}^2$, for the shells beyond $n = n_F$ are all vacant.

A curve of *distribution of velocities* describes the variation, with *velocity*, of the ratio of the number of electrons in a shell to the corresponding differential increment of velocity. The equation for a velocity distribution curve, using n as the measure of total velocity, is obtainable from (8–15a); it is

$$\frac{dN_s}{dn} = \frac{\pi n^2}{a^3} \qquad (8\text{--}16)$$

The unit of measurement along the horizontal axis is in this case n; the distribution curve is a parabola with vertex at the origin, but with the axis *vertical;* that is, at right angles to the velocity scale.

The energy distribution curve, Fig. 8.4a, can be charted in terms of dN_s/dE and E. To do this, eliminate n^2 in (8–15b) in favor of E by using the form of (8–11) obtained by dropping the subscripts from E and n. The resulting expression is

$$\frac{dN_s}{dE} = \frac{4\pi(2m_e q_e)^{3/2}\sqrt{E}}{h^3} \qquad (8\text{--}17)$$

Note that the volume a^3 has disappeared from the expression; this distribution of energy is thus *independent of the volume.*

dN_s may be thought of as the number of electrons within a shell whose energies lie between E and $E + dE$. The energy content in any shell is therefore $E\,dN_s$ electron volts. The average energy is then

$$\frac{\text{Sum of the energies in all the shells}}{\text{Sum of the number of electrons in all the shells}}$$

This is stated mathematically as

$$\bar{E} = \frac{\displaystyle\int_{E=0}^{E=E_F} E\,dN_s}{\displaystyle\int_{E=0}^{E=E_F} dN_s} \qquad (8\text{--}18a)$$

where $\bar{E}$ is the average energy. E_F is employed as the upper limit because shells at energies greater than E_F contribute nothing either to the total energy or to the total electron content, at the absolute zero condition being considered. With dN_s expressed as in (8–17), this reduces to

$$\bar{E} = \frac{\int_{E=0}^{E=E_F} E\sqrt{E}\,dE}{\int_{E=0}^{E=E_F} \sqrt{E}\,dE} = \frac{3}{5}\frac{E_F^{5/2}}{E_F^{3/2}} = \frac{3}{5}E_F \qquad (8\text{–}18b)$$

Thus the normal-state average energy is $3/5$ of the Fermi-level energy.

For temperatures greater than absolute zero the shells below the Fermi level are not completely filled, nor are those above the Fermi level completely vacant. The fractional occupancy for any shell is given by the *Fermi distribution function*,[7A, B, 8A, B, D, E, G, I, J, a, b] a function of particle energy whose specific form depends on density of particles and on temperature. For the very high particle density represented by the electrons in a metal or semiconductor, at all temperatures attainable in engineering devices, the form of the function is as follows, applying to a shell of thickness dn at radius n, energy E, energy increment dE:

Ratio of: The number of *occupied* lattice points in the shell⎫
   to: The total number of lattice points in the shell⎬

$$= \frac{1}{1 + \exp\left[(E - E_F)/E_T\right]} \qquad \begin{bmatrix} \text{The Fermi} \\ \text{distribution} \\ \text{function} \end{bmatrix} \quad (8\text{–}19)$$

Thus the energy distribution curve at temperatures above absolute zero, as illustrated in Fig. 8.4b for 2500° K, is the product of (8–17) by (8–19),

$$\frac{dN_s}{dE} = \frac{4\pi(2m_e q_e)^{3/2}}{h^3} \frac{\sqrt{E}}{1 + \exp\left[(E - E_F)/E_T\right]} \qquad \begin{bmatrix} \text{The distribution of en-} \\ \text{ergies for the electrons in} \\ \text{a metal, at the tempera-} \\ \text{ture corresponding to } E_T \end{bmatrix}$$

$$(8\text{–}20a)$$

that is

$$\frac{dN_s}{dE} = 6.82 \times 10^{27} \frac{\sqrt{E}}{1 + \exp\left[(E - E_F)/E_T\right]} \qquad \begin{bmatrix} \text{units are reciprocal} \\ \text{of (volts} \times \text{volume)} \end{bmatrix}$$

$$(8\text{–}20b)$$

At $0°$ K the exponential term in the denominator is either zero or infinity, depending on whether $E < E_F$ or $E > E_F$. Thus (8–20) reduces to Fig. 8.4a at absolute zero temperature. E_F is given by (8–14).

Equation (8–19) may be said to express the probability that any given set of quantum numbers (including the spin) for which the total translational energy is E will correspond to some one electron's motion, when the temperature is as specified by E_T.

Note that when the temperature has a value other than absolute zero, the Fermi distribution function has the value ½ at the Fermi level $(E = E_F)$.

8.12 Semiconductor Energy Levels.[8A, D, E, F, G, I, J, b, e, i]   Figure 8.5 is a typical energy-level diagram for a semiconductor. Representative

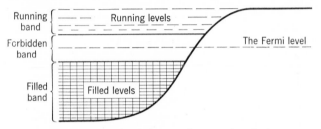

FIG. 8.5   Energy-level diagram for a semiconductor.

semiconductors [8A, F, I, J, e, g, h, i] are germanium, silicon, selenium, the oxides of copper, of barium, and of strontium, and partially reduced titanium dioxide.

Within a *metal* at ordinary room temperatures the electrons in all levels, as in Fig. 8.2, whether below or above the Fermi level, are able to move about freely; thus all the levels indicated may be called "running levels." In an insulator almost all the electrons are firmly bound to individual atoms; there are extremely few free electrons, and thus extremely few electrons occupy "running levels."

In Fig. 8.5 the semiconductor's "running levels" in the "running band" are in general similar in nature to the levels of Fig. 8.2. However, for the most part the running levels of a semiconductor are very sparsely populated; they may in this respect be thought of as resembling the running levels above the Fermi level in a metal. The "filled levels" of Fig. 8.5 are populated by electrons that are more or less permanently attached to individual atoms, as in an insulator. The vertical lines in the filled-level area symbolize the lack of freedom of movement of electrons in these levels. Because these electrons are not free to move, they do not provide electron-borne conduction current in the ordinary sense. However, by giving a few electron volts of energy to an electron in the filled band, it may be shifted up into the running-level band. Thus external effects, as heat or light, can cause such a shift and increase the electrical conductivity, by increasing the population of the running levels. In a completely pure semiconductor there can be no electrons possessing energies corresponding to the forbidden band, which lies above the top of the filled band but below the bottom of the running band, because no levels exist in the forbidden band.

Thus the forbidden band may be thought of as ordering an absence of levels within a certain energy range. As always, the Fermi distribution function, (8–19), describes, as a function of temperature, the fractional occupancy among the levels that do exist. The Fermi level is located at an intermediate height within the forbidden band. At ordinary temperatures some few electrons will lie in the running band, and there will be an equal number of vacancies in the "filled" band, in proportions ordered by the Fermi distribution function.

If a few electrons have been moved from the filled levels up into the running levels, there exist "holes" among the filled levels. A hole is merely a normal semiconductor atom that has been "ionized," in that it has lost one of its outer-shell electrons. Because of the low density of holes and free electrons, "recombination" to fill the hole is unlikely; even if recombination were to occur, the requirement of thermal equilibrium would demand an off-setting reappearance of a new hole and electron pair elsewhere. But it appears relatively easy in some substances for any hole to transfer from one atom to an adjacent one, giving rise to "hole conductivity." This implies merely a strictly local, atom-to-adjacent-atom transfer of an individual electron, thus shifting the electron deficiency without moving an electron into a running level. Experimentally, hole conductivity exhibits all the attributes of conductivity due to the drift of *positive* charges. The transfer of holes may be moderately rapid and occur in a steady direction under the influence of an electric gradient; the hole conductivity is usually less than, but of the same order of magnitude as, the electron conductivity. There exist methods of measurement which distinguish experimentally between electron conductivity and hole conductivity.

To explain certain properties of semiconductors it is usually assumed that the presence of extremely small proportions of impurities may provide a few relatively widely spaced levels *within the forbidden band*. If these are above the Fermi level they resemble running levels in some respects; the term "acceptor" is applied, as these levels can *accept* electrons, thus producing conductivity due to motion of electrons. If these impurity levels lie below the Fermi level, the term "donor" is applied, for such levels are normally filled and can *donate* electrons, leaving holes. Donor impurity levels produce hole conductivity in the forbidden band. Thus impurity levels may provide either or both kinds of conductivity.

Thus four distinct kinds of electrical conductivity may exist within a semiconductor, as follows:

(1) Electron conductivity due to electrons in the running band.
(2) Hole conductivity due to vacancies in the filled band.
(3) Electron conductivity due to forbidden-band impurity levels of the acceptor type.
(4) Hole conductivity due to forbidden-band impurity levels of the donor type.

The difference in energy between the uppermost of the filled levels and the lowest running level may be thought of as a sort of within-the-solid-state ionizing potential for the semiconductor; it describes the minimum energy necessary to detach an electron from an atom, so creating a hole and electron pair, both being reasonably free to move about. Within a metallic conductor zero energy is required to detach the outermost electron from an atom.

8.13   Semiconductor Electron Devices: * **Crystal Rectifiers, Transistors, Thermistors, Varistors, Metal Plate Rectifiers, Photosensitive Devices.** Semiconductors form the important substances in crystal rectifiers used in radio and radar detectors. A typical crystal rectifier consists of an extremely fine tungsten wire ("cat-whisker") whose point bears on a polished and specially treated surface of a semiconductor (silicon and germanium are used).[8C, J, h, i] In an *n-type* rectifier the low-resistance direction of current flow corresponds to emission of holes by the cat-whisker into the semiconductor, whereas a high resistance is offered to flow in the reverse direction. Thus an *n*-type crystal rectifier has the same polarity behavior as a high-vacuum diode; the anode easily collects electrons but refuses to emit them. A *p-type* crystal rectifier has polarity properties opposite to those of the *n* type.

The *point contact transistor*,[8c, d, e] used as a semiconductor amplifier [8A, J, c, d, e] is similar to a crystal rectifier in general form, except that two (*n*-type) rectifying elements, employing two cat-whiskers, are used instead of one, the spacing between the two active (welded-on) tungsten tips being one or two thousandths an inch. The crystal material is germanium. In this type of device the inverse-voltage resistance of one of the tips is markedly modified by the strength of the forward-voltage current in the other one. This produces a set of

* See bibliographical references 8A, C, D, E, F, G, I, J, 8b through 8i, 14a, h, i, j.

characteristic curves resembling in general form the plate characteristic curves of a triode, therefore permitting use as an amplifier.

A *junction transistor* [8c] of the *n-p-n* type consists of an *n*-type crystal of germanium within which there is produced a very thin transversely oriented *p*-type layer, forming, so to speak, a *p*-type door across an *n*-type region. A *p-n-p* junction transistor has conversely a thin *n*-type layer transverse to the length of a *p*-type crystal. The three points of electrical connection to a junction transistor are respectively to the thin layer and to the two portions of the crystal separated from each other by the layer.

Transistor semiconductor amplifiers respond to changes in "input" *current* rather than "input" *voltage*. They are members of the general family of low-impedance circuit devices. In contrast, space-charge-control tubes belong to the family of high-impedance circuit devices. Thus, optimum circuits for transistor amplifier use will differ greatly from optimum triode amplifier circuits as to accessory components, d-c elements, etc. The comparative analysis may sometimes involve a shift in mental concept from Thévenin's theorem to Norton's theorem; see Sections 9.11 and 9.12.

In the point contact transistor the input element acts as an emitter of holes into the semiconductor, whereas the output electrode acts as a collector of holes. The sensitive region is that in the immediate neighborhood of the output electrode, that is, the hole collector.

Point contact and junction transistors should be thought of as the forerunners of a very large and important family of semiconductor amplifying devices. It appears reasonably certain that stable, reproducible, and relatively noise-free members of this family ultimately will be developed and will become extremely useful for engineering purposes.

Thermistors [8f] are thermally sensitive resistors made of suitably processed semiconductor materials, and used extensively for control and instrumentation purposes.

Varistors [8f] are nonlinear resistors, that is, resistors in which the current does not vary linearly with applied voltage, also useful for control and instrumentation purposes.

Section 14.17 introduces briefly some of the properties of conductor-to-semiconductor flat surface boundaries that are useful both for preparing metal plate rectifier units, and in semiconductor photocells.[14h] Photoconducting cells, of semiconductor materials, are discussed in Section 14.18.[14i, j]

8.14   The Image Force. The atoms of a metal will in this section be referred to as ions, for each one has contributed one or more electrons to the make-up of the gas of free electrons. The structural properties of a metal are due to attachments between the ions, which are arranged according to some regular crystalline pattern. The bottom energy level in Fig. 8.2 is made horizontal in order to indicate the equipotential nature of the interior, as far as the gross potential structure is concerned.

On its way out from the interior of a metal an escaping electron passes through three more or less distinct regions, distinguished by the nature of the predominant force action in each, as follows: [15a]

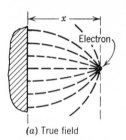

(a) True field

(a) It must pass between the adjacent members of a last layer of ions. While passing through this layer, and for a very short distance beyond it, the important forces are those due to the near-by ions.

(b) At a distance from the last layer that is not much greater than the spacing between the ions of the metal, the forces due to individual particles become indistinguishable; the metal takes on the aspect of an equipotential surface. The electric field between an equipotential surface and an electron at a distance x in front of it is, as illustrated in Fig. 8.6, exactly the same as that in the front half of the region between an electron in free space and an equal and opposite image charge distant $2x$ from the electron. For this reason the retarding force on the outward-moving electron is often called the *image force*. It has the value

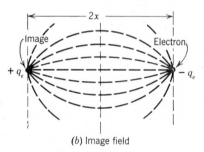

(b) Image field

FIG. 8.6 The electric field around an escaping electron.

$$\text{Image force on the electron, in newtons} = -\frac{q_e}{4\pi\epsilon_0 \cdot 4x^2} \qquad (8\text{--}21)$$

within this second region in which the electron reacts to the metal as to an equipotential surface. The negative sign indicates that the force tends toward a decrease in x.

(c) There may be an external electric field aiding escape, that is, tending to draw electrons away from the metal to other electrodes (anodes). Such a field, of strength F volts per meter, exerts an outwardly directed force $q_e F$ newtons. At a definite value of x, which will be called x_m, this withdrawal force is equal and opposite to the restraining force, the net force being zero. Therefore if F is uniform, the "escape distance" x_m is determinable from the force equation:

$$\frac{q_e^2}{16\pi\epsilon_0 x_m^2} = q_e F \qquad (8\text{--}22)$$

Any electron whose kinetic energy of outwardly directed motion vanishes before it reaches the distance x_m from the surface must fall back into it. Any electron that still possesses some outwardly directed velocity after coming that far enters the third region, in which the external field force predominates, and is accelerated toward a more positive electrode. If the external field force is zero or negative, electrons that escape do so without passing through such a third region.

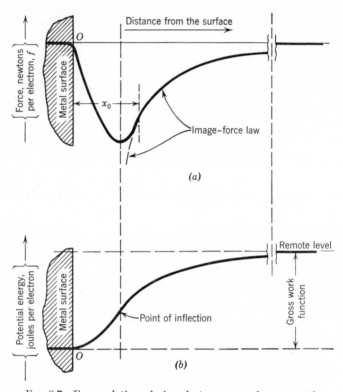

FIG. 8.7   Force relations during electron escape from a metal.

(a) Retarding force f on an escaping electron.

(b) Potential energy barrier at a metal surface, given by (8–23) in joules per electron.

Note that the force curve is shown as becoming zero at a very few atomic layers within the crystal lattice of the metal.

Figure 8.7a illustrates the relation between the retarding force in newtons and the distance from the surface, in the absence of an external field (no third region present).

It has been experimentally demonstrated that the force curve follows the image-force law within the second region; see Section 8.22. The shape of the force curve in the first region near the surface, where force actions of individual ions predominate, can only be estimated; see, however, the analysis given by Langmuir,[15a] and the treatment in Chapter V of *Fundamentals of Physical Electronics.*

8.15 Potential-Energy Curves and Force Curves. Figure 8.7b is a diagram very similar to Fig. 8.2; however, it indicates measurement of energy in joules rather than in electron volts. In both figures the gross work function is measured by the difference in height between the inside (left) and outside (right) levels of the potential-energy curve. The gross work function in joules is the total work done against the retarding force of the previous section, during an electron's escape. This is the total area, considered positive, between the retarding-force curve, Fig. 8.7a, and the x axis. Therefore

$$\left.\begin{matrix}\text{Total change in joules of poten-}\\ \text{tial energy during escape}\end{matrix}\right\} = -\int_{x=0}^{x=\infty} f\,dx \qquad (8\text{--}23)$$

This integral is the area between the force curve and the x axis, if the force is in newtons.

Since the force and the ordinates of the force curve are negative, the integral and the corresponding area are also negative. The minus sign in (8-23) thus indicates that the change in potential energy is positive. Because ordinates of the potential-energy curve represent, negatively, *areas* under the force curve, ordinates of the force curve must conversely represent, also negatively, *slopes* along the potential-energy curve.

The symbol x_m (escape distance) was used in the preceding section to describe the distance at which the external field exerts a force equal and opposite to the image force, so that at x_m the actual force on an escaping electron is zero. The force being zero, the slope of the potential-energy curve is also zero; therefore the escape distance describes the position of a maximum in the potential-energy curve. Two potential-energy curves that have such maxima are illustrated in Fig. 8.10. Any electron that starts outward but comes to a stop before reaching the crest must fall back into the metal surface. Any electron that reaches the crest with ever so little velocity passes over it and "falls" down the other side of the hill to the opposite electrode. The other side of the hill is the third type of region described in Section 8.14.

8.16 Potential-Energy vs. Potential Distribution Diagrams. The relation described above between potential energy and restraining force is exactly the same as that between electric potential and electric field intensity. Up to this point the only apparent difference between potential distribution diagrams, and potential-energy diagrams that employ the electron volt as the unit of energy, is that of being upside down relative to one another. That is, as an electron moves to the right, in a region like that of Fig. 1.7 or Fig. 5.3, its potential rises, yet its potential energy *becomes smaller*, for it moves in the direction of the electric force. The reason for this reversal is that electric potential is defined in terms of positive charges, whereas the particles for which the potential-energy diagrams are needed (electrons) carry negative charges.

There exists a temptation to jump to the false conclusion that graphical inversion is the only distinction of consequence between

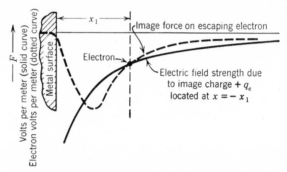

FIG. 8.8   Contrast between the dashed-line curve of electric force and the solid-line curve of electric field strength due to the image charge, in the continually changing field set up by an escaping electron.

potential distribution curves and potential-energy curves in energy-level diagrams. The nature of a much more fundamental distinction can be clarified by a study of conditions in the image-force region of Fig. 8.7, as detailed in Fig. 8.8.

Imagine the electron to be momentarily at some specified distance x_1 from the metal surface. The *solid* line in Fig. 8.8 is a curve of the negative of the *electric field intensity* due to the image charge, which is, for the particular moment represented, located at $-x_1$. The equation for the solid line is, in volts per meter,

$$F = -\frac{q_e^2}{4\pi\epsilon_0(x_1 + x)^2} \tag{8-24}$$

The *dotted* line in Fig. 8.8 is the *retarding-force curve*, which near x_1 follows the image-force law, equation (8-21). The contrast is apparent. The two curves must have a common value at $x = x_1$, for the image force is always just that due to the electric field; *but the electric field is continually changing as a result of the electron's motion.*

The situation is very different in the first region described in Section 8.14. Here the important forces on an escaping electron are those due to near-by ions, whose locations are permanently fixed. Hence in this region, as in Fig. 1.7, the movement of the electron does not affect the locations of the charges that produce the field, and a single electric intensity curve satisfactorily describes both the field and the retarding force.

When well out in the third (escape) region, the electron is so remote from the metal that the image-force field is ignorably small, and the electric field is as ordered by electrode potentials and Poisson's space equation. Therefore, in this region as in Fig. 1.7, potential-energy and potential curves are identical except for a graphical inversion.

8.17   Valve Action When Current Is Space-Charge-Limited. Dushman's equation (7–2) describes the maximum electron current density that can ordinarily flow from a heated thermionic cathode at a given temperature; multiplication by the cathode surface area gives the *temperature-limited current*.

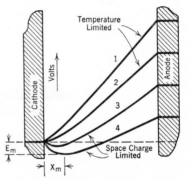

When electrode geometry and potentials limit the actual current density to a *space-charge-limited* value less than the temperature-limited value, some mechanism must exist for turning back into the cathode the electrons representing the excess of temperature-limited over space-charge-limited current. This mechanism is illustrated in Fig. 8.9, which represents an evac-

Fig. 8.9 Potential distribution curves illustrating valve action at emitter surface when current is space-charge-limited.

uated region between two parallel-plane electrodes, the cathode being an emitter obeying Dushman's equation. The four curves represent different potential distributions that may exist between the electrodes, all corresponding to the same cathode temperature but to different plate potentials.

Curves 1 and 2 represent potential distributions when the plate potential is high enough for the possible space-charge-limited current to be greater than the temperature-limited current of the cathode at the existing temperature; the actual current flowing has, therefore, the temperature-limited value. All electrons emitted enter an electric field that causes acceleration toward the anode, for the slope of the potential line at $x = 0$ is definitely positive. All of them of course reach the plate.

Curves 3 and 4 represent a much more usual type of potential distribution, corresponding to plate potential (or grid sheet potential in a triode) low enough so that the space-charge-limited current allowed to flow is less than the available thermionic current. Under these conditions electrons are emitted from the cathode more rapidly than geometry and potentials permit their passage to the anode, so that negative space charge accumulates just outside the cathode. This produces a "negative dip" in the potential line as it leaves the cathode, with consequent negative electric gradient at the cathode surface. All the electrons emitted thermionically under these typical conditions enter a field that tends to send them back into the cathode. Only those escape whose x-directed kinetic energies *after overcoming the work-function barrier* are sufficient to permit them to overcome the additional obstacle presented by the negative dip of E_m volts.[7B, 8I, J, K, j, 15b]

Equilibrium exists when the negative dip is just low enough to send back to the cathode all the electrons that represent the excess of the temperature-limited over the space-charge-limited current that is permitted by geometry and potentials. If the negative dip is momentarily too low, more than the proper fraction of emitted electrons are sent back to the cathode, so that the space charge causing the negative dip becomes less, and the bottom of the dip rises. If it rises too high, more electrons emerge from the cathode than can pass to the anode, more space charge accumulates, and the bottom of the dip drops back down again. Thus a local mechanism exists which automatically maintains the equilibrium condition.

8.18   Conditions in a Triode near Cut-Off.[7B, 8j, 15b]*   The potential distribution curves of Fig. 8.9 take no account of work-function details at the cathode surface. Figure 8.10 illustrates the two potential-energy curves, similar to that of Fig. 8.7b, that correspond to curves 1 and 3 of Fig. 8.9.

The extreme right-hand part of Fig. 8.10 is, in accordance with the principles outlined in Section 8.16, simply a large-scale potential distribution diagram inverted. Although electrons move rapidly through the interelectrode region, the average space-charge density in each locality remains constant; consequently the flow of electrons does not result in changes in the distribution of potential.

The left-hand part of Fig. 8.10 resembles Figs. 8.2 and 8.7b, in that it represents variations in the potential energy of each individual electron on the way out from the metal. The distance scale at the left of Fig. 8.10 is greatly exaggerated relative to that at the right. The *zero*

* See also Sections 8.20, 8.21, and the detailed analysis in Chapter VI of *Fundamentals of Physical Electronics*.

level E_0 in Fig. 8.10 is the top of the gross-work-function barrier and corresponds to the horizontal cathode-potential line in Fig. 8.9.

At the crest or escape point on temperature-limited curve 1, Fig. 8.10, the image force and the electric force due to the external field gradient are equal and opposite, as discussed in Sections 8.14 and 8.15. The escape distance under such conditions is very small indeed, as can be determined by a numerical solution of (8–22) for x_m, using for F any reasonable value of electric gradient. Just as curve 1, Fig. 8.9,

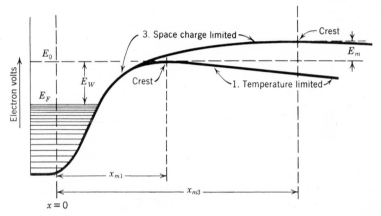

FIG. 8.10 Valve action at an emitter surface. Potential energy curves 1 and 3 correspond to potential distribution curves 1 and 3 in Fig. 8.9. The distance scale at the left is greatly exaggerated relative to that at the right.

reaches but does not drop below cathode potential, so curve 1, Fig. 8.10, may for all ordinary external gradients be assumed to reach but not rise above the zero level. Only when the external gradient is extremely large does the crest of such a curve drop appreciably below the zero level, as described later in Section 8.22.

Just as the accumulation of space charge outside the cathode drops the bottom point on potential curve 3, Fig. 8.9, to E_m volts below cathode potential, so it raises the crest of the corresponding potential-energy curve 3, Fig. 8.10, to E_m electron volts above the zero level. Thus the crest of the potential-energy curve with current space-charge-limited is E_m electron volts higher than it is with current temperature-limited.

The effect of this rise in the crest on the rate of escape of electrons is exactly the same that would result from an increase of work function by the amount E_m. Hence Dushman's equation can be used to express J_a, the actual space-charge-limited current density, by using $E_W + E_m$

instead of E_W in the exponent, as follows:

$$J_a = A_0 T^2 \exp\left(-\frac{E_W + E_m}{E_T}\right) \qquad (8\text{–}25a)$$

$$= A_0 T^2 \left(\exp\frac{-E_W}{E_T}\right)\left(\exp\frac{-E_m}{E_T}\right) \qquad (8\text{–}25b)$$

or, calling the temperature-limited current density J_{th}, as in (7–2),

$$J_a = J_{th} \exp\frac{-E_m}{E_T} \qquad (8\text{–}26)$$

This should be thought of as an equation for the determination of E_m, because J_{th} is determined by cathode material and temperature, E_T by cathode temperature, and J_a by electrode geometry and potentials (because it is space-charge-limited).

A negative dip of less than a volt is sufficient to reduce the plate current to a small fraction of the thermionic emission, because the exponential factor shrinks very rapidly as E_m grows. For example, with a filament temperature of 2500° K, customary for tungsten filaments, a negative dip of ½ volt makes the plate current about 10 per cent, and of 1 volt about 1 per cent, of the emission. At 1000° K, which is in the temperature range used for coated filaments, the corresponding negative-dip voltages are 0.2 and 0.4. The distance x_m to the bottom of the negative dip is usually a minute fraction of a millimeter. Thus in most useful devices at normal operating plate currents E_m and x_m are very small; see Sections 8.20 and 8.21.

The normal ³⁄₂ power dependence of plate current on equivalent grid sheet potential e_s would indicate that plate current should go to zero (cut-off) when e_s goes to zero. However, as the plate current approaches zero, J_a becomes very much less than J_{th}. From (8–26) and the principles outlined in the preceding section, a decrease in J_a/J_{th} requires that E_m, and more particularly x_m, increase substantially. Eventually x_m becomes about equal to the grid-cathode spacing and will never exceed that value, because of the field beyond the grid established by the plate potential. As soon as x_m is about the same as the cathode-to-grid spacing, E_m can be approximately identified with the grid sheet potential e_s, so that there sets in an exponential dependence of plate current on e_s. The general form of this dependence is indicated by using e_s in place of E_m in (8–26).[15b, 8j, m]

Thus, *in the neighborhood of cut-off*, the dependence of current on equivalent grid sheet potential is exponential in nature.

8.19   An Upper Limit to Transconductance per Ampere; Electrometer Tubes.   Equation (8–26) permits the statement of a theoretically determined upper limit to the transconductance per ampere of a space-charge-control tube.[8j, m, n, o]

Referring to Fig. 8.9, imagine the anode to be replaced by the equivalent grid sheet of a triode (Fig. 5.3); the potential curves of Fig. 8.9 then represent potential variations between cathode and grid sheet.   Thus the right-hand terminations of these curves are now thought of as values of e_s.   Obviously, in a shift from curve 3 to curve 4, the change in E_m is less than that in e_s.   If the potential minimum had been farther from the cathode and closer to the grid, the change in E_m would have more nearly approached that in e_s.   Thus the condition for maximum response of E_m to changes in e_s is *that the potential minimum occur at the grid location*, for then the change in E_m equals the change in e_s.

The most nearly perfect grid imaginable would be one having grid wires infinitely close together and infinitely small.   Equation (4–63) shows that for such a grid C_g in Fig. 4.10c would be infinite, and the grid sheet potential e_s would equal the grid potential e_c.

Thus the theoretical condition for the maximum effect of grid potential on the potential minimum value E_m, therefore also from (8–26) the maximum effect on J_a, is one for which

$$e_c = e_s = -E_m \qquad \begin{bmatrix} \text{for maximum transcon-} \\ \text{ductance per ampere} \end{bmatrix} \qquad (8\text{–}27)$$

Note that e_c will be numerically negative in this condition.   Transconductance is of course

$$g_m = \text{Cathode area} \times \frac{\partial J_a}{\partial e_c} \qquad (8\text{–}28)$$

On substituting $e_c = -E_m$ in (8–26), and using the result in (8–28), g_m becomes

$$g_m = \text{Cathode area} \times J_{th}\left(\exp\frac{e_c}{E_T}\right)\left(\frac{1}{E_T}\right) \qquad (8\text{–}29)$$

that is,

$$g_m = \text{Cathode area} \times \frac{J_a}{E_T} \qquad (8\text{–}30)$$

The total cathode current I_a is cathode area $\times J_a$, so that this becomes

$$\left.\frac{g_m}{I_a}\right]_{\text{max}} = \frac{1}{E_T} \qquad \begin{bmatrix} \text{this is the theoretical maximum} \\ \text{transconductance per ampere,} \\ \text{in mhos per ampere} \end{bmatrix} \qquad (8\text{–}31)$$

As a numerical illustration, consider a cathode temperature of 1160° K, near the usual range of oxide-coated cathode operation and corresponding to $E_T = 0.1$ electron volt. The theoretical maximum is then [8m]

$$\left.\frac{g_m}{I_a}\right]_{max} \cong 10 \times 10^6 \quad \left[\begin{array}{l}\text{theoretical maximum, in}\\ \text{micromhos per ampere,}\\ \text{cathode at 1160° K}\end{array}\right] \quad (8\text{–}32)$$

Corresponding values for commercial tubes in their normal working ranges are included in the following table:

Tube Type	Rated Plate Current (amperes) I_b	Trans-conduc-tance (micro-mhos) g_m	Trans-conduc-tance per Ampere g_m/I_b	Input Capaci-tance (micro-micro-farads) C	Figure of Merit $\left(\dfrac{\text{micromhos}}{\text{micromicrofarads}}\right)$ $\dfrac{g_m}{C}$
6AC7	0.01	9,000	900,000	11	800
6AK5	0.0077	5,100	660,000	4.0	1,300
2C43 (lighthouse tube [11a])	0.02	8,000	400,000	4.5	1,800
416A (Western Electric [11b])	0.033	50,000	1,500,000	7.5	6,700
Theoretical maximum at 1160° K			10,000,000		

For all these tubes an important design objective was to obtain a maximum "figure of merit" (ratio of transconductance to input capacitance, see Section 5.13) in order to aid operation at very high frequencies. The last three are useful at ultra-high frequencies. To make e_s differ as little as possible from e_c, fine-meshed grids were employed, giving a large value of C_g.

Note that these commercially available triodes approach reasonably closely the theoretical upper limit of transconductance per ampere, for available cathode temperatures. Therefore it is not to be expected that future research discoveries will lead to spectacular improvements in the transconductance per ampere of space-charge-control tubes, unless distinctly new principles are introduced.

Electrometer tubes, usually tetrodes,[80] are designed to amplify minute currents, of the order of 10^{-12} ampere. An electrometer tube of conventional planar *triode* design would achieve maximum transconductance per ampere by being operated very close to cut-off, where the potential minimum automatically approximates the grid location.

8.20   Effects of Initial Velocities on Space-Charge-Limited Current, Planar Geometry.[15b]   The derivation, in Section 5.4, of the fundamental space-charge-limited current equations was based on the assumptions that the potential gradient into which the electrons emerge is zero at the cathode surface, and that the electrons emerge with negligible initial velocities.   Actually the point of zero potential gradient is at the bottom of a negative dip, illustrated in Fig. 8.9, and the electrons that succeed in passing the bottom of the dip do so with velocities distributed in accordance with the Maxwellian velocity distributions presented in Chapter XII.

The bottom of the negative dip may be thought of as a virtual cathode, located at a distance x_m from the true cathode, and below the potential of the true cathode by E_m, as in curve 4, Fig. 8.9.   Langmuir and Frye [15b] developed a complete planar-geometry mathematical solution for the potential distribution and space-charge-limited current as affected by this dip and the initial electron velocities; this solution appears in Chapter VI of *Fundamentals of Physical Electronics*. In addition, Langmuir [15b] has given the following approximate equation for space-charge-limited current in planar geometry, which has the merit of indicating the nature of the effects of the initial velocities:

$$J_a \cong 2.33 \times 10^{-6} \frac{(E_s - E_m)^{\frac{3}{2}}}{(s - x_m)^2} \left[1 + 2.66 \left(\frac{E_T}{E_s - E_m} \right)^{\frac{1}{2}} \right] \quad (8\text{–}33)$$

This is reasonably valid if E_s and s are substantially larger numerically than E_m and x_m respectively.

In these and the following equations, J_a, J_{th}, and E_T have the same meanings as in Section 8.18; x and E are distance and potential measured from the cathode.   In Langmuir's equations, and here, E_m is numerically negative.   Thus E_m in (8–33) is the negative of the E_m in Section 8.18; the change is only in the meaning of the symbol.   In (8–33), s is the distance between cathode and equivalent grid sheet of a triode, or between cathode and plate of a diode. E_s is the equivalent grid sheet potential for a triode, or the plate potential for a diode, all for planar geometry.

A comparison of (8–33) with the earlier corresponding equation, (5–12), suggests the three distinct effects that initial electron velocities have on the space-charge-limited current density, all tending to make the actual current larger than (5–12) predicts, as follows:

(a) The virtual cathode is closer to the plate than is the true cathode; correspondingly $(s - x_m)^2$ in the denominator of (8–33) is numerically less than s^2 occurring similarly in (5–12).

(b) The potential difference between virtual cathode and plate is greater than that between true cathode and plate; correspondingly $(E_s - E_m)^{3/2}$ in the numerator of (8–33) is numerically greater than $E_s^{3/2}$ occurring similarly in the earlier equation, for E_m is negative as used here.

(c) The electrons that pass the virtual cathode do so with velocities whose average is proportional to ζ defined by (7–4), so to $\sqrt{E_T}$. The expression for current density should therefore include an additive term containing the factor $\sqrt{E_T}$. Equation (8–33) has such a term.

The form of (8–33) shows that all three effects become progressively less important as the plate potential and spacing distance are increased relative to E_m and x_m.

Equation (8–33) is not satisfactory for numerical computation because values of E_m and x_m must be determined before the expression can be used; the complete solution in Chapter VI, in *Fundamentals of Physical Electronics* leads to results reasonably convenient for numerical use.

8.21   Effects of Initial Velocities on Space-Charge-Limited Current Flow from a Cylindrical Cathode.[15b]

No complete mathematical analysis has been made of the effect of initial velocities on the space-charge-limited current from a cylindrical cathode. Exact analysis is difficult because of the nonradial motions due to sideways components of initial velocities. The urge to obtain an exact solution is lessened by the fact that the initial velocities are relatively less effective in cylindrical than in parallel-plane geometry.

The electrons that pass the virtual cathode do so with average energies proportional to the temperature. The average energy due to initial *radial* motion is E_T; that due to initial *sideways* motion, perpendicular to a radius and to the axis, is $E_T/2$. Both radial and sideways motion carry an electron nearer to a receiving electrode. Energy due to motion parallel to the axis has no effect on the current, because it does not affect the rate of travel toward an outer point. Hence, in his analysis of this problem, Langmuir considers only the radial and lateral energies, totaling $\frac{3}{2}E_T$.

Thus Langmuir considers that an electron at radius r, potential E relative to the true cathode, has on the average a radial energy component $E - E_m + \frac{3}{2}E_T$ electron volts. He then uses this average radial energy in place of E in the denominator radical of (5–54). An approximate solution, valid only when $\frac{3}{2}E_T \ll E_s - E_m$, is then obtained by the general method of Section 5.16. The result is [15b–253]

$$\frac{I_a}{l} = 2\pi \times 2.33 \times 10^{-6} \frac{1}{r_s \beta^2} \left[E_s - E_m + \frac{3}{8} E_T \left(\ln \frac{2E_s}{3\lambda E_T} \right)^2 \right]^{3/2} \quad (8\text{–}34)$$

Here β^2 depends on r_s/r_m according to Fig. 5.6. I_a/l is cathode current per unit length, and E_s is potential (relative to the cathode) at radius r_s. λ is a numerical constant whose value probably lies between 1 and 2 and cannot be definitely determined except by experiment. This treatment is not valid near cut-off in a triode, for then E_s is very small, and in some cases negative.

Comparison of the earlier (5–61) with (8–34) indicates that (8–34), like (8–33), takes the three modifying effects of initial velocities into account separately, as follows:

(a) The effect of the outward shift of the cathode from the true to the virtual position appears in the value of β^2. This is more a formal than a real accounting, because the condition that $\frac{3}{2}E_T$ must be small relative to $E_s - E_m$ is usually satisfied only when r_s is so large relative to both r_k and r_m that β^2 is nearly constant at a value near 1.

(b) The use of $E_s - E_m$ rather than E_s takes account of the dip to virtual cathode potential.

(c) The term containing E_T accounts for the effects of the random energies possessed by the electrons as they pass the virtual cathode.

Even without knowing definitely the proper value to use for λ, it is possible to estimate how much larger the current specified by (8–34) is than that given by (5–61). Langmuir's calculations show that the percentage of increase is in general only about one-fourth or one-fifth of that in the corresponding plane cathode comparison.

In contrast with (8–33), equation (8–34) *can* be used rather easily for numerical calculations, although a trial-and-error process is necessary. Suppose that I_{th}/l, E_T, E_s, r_s, and r_k are all given, and that 1 is to be used for β^2 and for λ. Equation (8–26) takes the form

$$\frac{I_a}{I_{th}} = \exp \frac{E_m}{E_T} \qquad (8\text{–}35)$$

and permits determination of E_m (negative) corresponding to an arbitrarily chosen preliminary value of I_a/l. This value of E_m used in (8–34) either will or will not give the assumed value of I_a/l. If it does, the preliminary choice is the correct one; if not, another trial must be made. This handling is possible because the radius of the virtual cathode does not appear in (8–34).

8.22 Reduction of Work Function by Strong External Fields.[7A, B, 8H, p, 15a] A cathode supplying temperature-limited current is exposed to a positive external field, as in curves 1 and 2, Fig. 8.9. In an ordinary electron tube any such field is so small that its effect on the height of the crest of the potential-energy curve is negligible, as for curve 1, Fig. 8.10, provided the cathode surface is a homogeneous one, like that of a tungsten filament. However, very large but experimentally obtainable fields lower the crest enough to affect the current measurably.

Figure 8.11 is a detail of the potential-energy curve in the presence of a very strong external field. The curve is, at every point, below its usual (dotted) position by just the amount of encouragement to escape contributed by the external field. This is the product of field

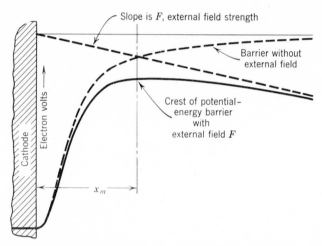

FIG. 8.11   Reduction in work function due to presence of strong external field; the amount of change is $\sqrt{q_e F / 4\pi \epsilon_0}$; homogeneous metal surface.

force by distance traveled, that is, $q_e F x$ joules or $F x$ electron volts. Hence the potential energy is represented at remote points by a straight line with slope $-F$.

The solid-line curve of potential energy, in the presence of the field F, has a maximum at the escape distance x_m, where the image force and external force are equal. Solution of (8–22) for x_m gives

$$x_m = \sqrt{\frac{q_e}{16\pi \epsilon_0 F}} \qquad (8\text{–}36)$$

The magnitude of the reduction in work function due to the external field is the amount by which the crest lies below the zero level; the zero level is the escape level in the absence of the field.

It is apparent from Fig. 8.11 that there are two contributions to the distance downward from the zero level to the crest.

(a) The normal potential-energy curve is, at the distance x_m, below the zero level by an amount obtained by integration of the image force, (8–21), from $x = x_m$ to infinity, as follows:

$$\int_{x=x_m}^{x=\infty} \frac{q_e^2}{16\pi\epsilon_0 x^2}\, dx = \frac{q_e^2}{16\pi\epsilon_0 x_m} \quad \text{[joules]} \tag{8–37}$$

By substituting for x_m from (8–36), and dividing by q_e to convert to electron volts, this contribution to the reduction in work function is found to be $\sqrt{q_e F/16\pi\epsilon_0}$.

(b) The crest is below the normal potential-energy curve at x_m by an additional amount Fx_m. Again substituting for x_m from (8–36), this second contribution is found to be exactly the same as the first.

Thus the total change ΔE_W in work function due to the external field is, in electron volts,

$$\Delta E_W = 2\sqrt{\frac{q_e F}{16\pi\epsilon_0}} = 3.78 \times 10^{-5}\sqrt{F} \tag{8–38}$$

This can be checked experimentally by varying F to very large values and measuring the resultant thermionic current; in general, using Dushman's equation in logarithmic form:

$$\ln J_{th} = \ln\left(A_0 T^2 \exp\frac{-E_W}{E_T}\right) + \sqrt{\frac{q_e}{4\pi\epsilon_0}}\frac{\sqrt{F}}{E_T} \tag{8–39}$$

A plot of $\ln J_{th}$ against $\sqrt{F}$ should then give a straight "Schottky" line of slope

$$2\sqrt{\frac{q_e}{16\pi\epsilon_0 E_T^2}} = \frac{3.78 \times 10^{-5}}{E_T} = \text{Slope of Schottky line} \tag{8–40}$$

This expectation has been confirmed experimentally,[7B, 8p, 15a] thus demonstrating the validity of the image-force law for points not too close to the surface. Figure 8.12 illustrates the type of curve obtained from such experiments. The experimental points taken at low field strengths depart markedly from the Schottky line, because of space-charge limitation of current.

It was stated in Section 7.14 that cathodes made of composite surfaces do not exhibit the definite temperature-limited "saturation" of homogeneous metal surfaces. This corresponds to a change in the nature of the experimental curve in the Schottky-line region. The curved solid line in Fig. 8.13 is the same kind of curve for an oxide-coated surface that the straight slant line in Fig. 8.12 is for a homogeneous one.[7B, 8p, 15a] At values of field strength toward the low end of the temperature-limited range the available emission current is immensely more sensitive to variations in the field strength than is to be expected from the analysis presented above, as indicated by the steepness of the solid line in Fig. 8.13 to the right of point A. At very large

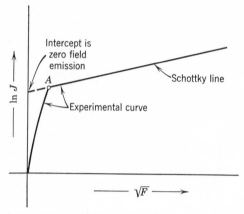

FIG. 8.12   Variation of thermionic emission due to external field, homogeneous metal surface, showing the Schottky line.   Below A the shape of the experimental (solid-line) curve is governed by space-charge limitations.   "Zero field emission" is at the intercept of the dashed extrapolation of the Schottky line.   The slope of the Schottky line is given by (8–40).

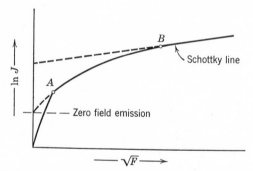

FIG. 8.13   Variation of thermionic emission due to an external field, oxide-coated and other composite surfaces.   Below A the shape of the experimental (solid-line) curve is governed by space-charge limitations.   "Zero field emission" is the intercept of the dashed extrapolation from A.   To the right of B the experimental curve follows a Schottky line, with slope given by (8–40).   Note the radical departure from the Schottky line in the portion of the temperature-limited range that lies between A and B.

field strengths, as beyond B, the emission approaches a Schottky line, the dotted line with slope given by (8–40).

For comparing different surfaces and the results of different experimenters it is customary to use the values of A_0 and E_W corresponding to zero field emission. This is the emission current corresponding to the vertical-axis intercept obtained by extrapolation toward the axis from A, Figs. 8.12 and 8.13. The purpose of the extrapolation is to eliminate the effect of space charge in interpreting the data.

The reasons for the marked variations of the emission from composite surfaces caused by small and moderate values of off-cathode gradient are not well understood. There is frequently an important time dependence of temperature-limited current in relation to field strength; the available emission for 1-microsecond pulses may be many times that for pulses of a thousand microseconds' duration. Also, the d-c temperature-limited current frequently shows slow time variations (it may either rise or fall), having time constants measured in minutes.

8.23   Field Emission.[7A, B, a, d, 8H, l] It has been experimentally shown that when extreme fields of the order of 10^{10} volts per meter are applied to a metal surface, an electron emission occurs which is essentially independent of temperature but varies rapidly with electric field strength F, according to a relation similar to Dushman's equation but with F replacing temperature; thus *field emission* current density J_{field} is given by

$$J_{field} = f(F) \exp \frac{-F_0}{F} \qquad (8\text{--}41)$$

where the function $f(F)$ of F is mathematically analogous to the $A_0 T^2$ factor, and F_0 to the work function, of Dushman's equation (7–2) for thermionic emission.

To explain field emission in terms of Fig. 8.11 it is desirable to modify the representation to indicate a greater external field strength, as suggested by the steepness of the potential distribution line external to the metal in Fig. 8.14. Note that the rapid descent of this potential distribution line at the right results in there being *a relatively thin potential barrier at the Fermi level.* According to quantum-mechanical theory [7A, B, 8B, D, E, G, H, l] there is an appreciable probability of the passage of an electron *through* such a potential barrier, if the barrier is sufficiently thin. This concept of a small but finite probability of "passage through" implies that a small percentage of the electrons that arrive at the barrier from the inside *with energies at or less than the Fermi-level energy* may move from the left of the barrier to the right of it. Thus there may be some "field emission" even though the metal is cold enough so that no electrons escape over the top of the barrier (i.e., there is no thermionic emission).

At and for many levels below the Fermi level the electron population per level within the metal is extremely large, and even a very small probability of transmission through the barrier can provide substantial current. The theory predicts that such field emission current should have an inverse exponential type of dependence on barrier thickness and therefore on field strength; this agrees with the experimental relationship (8–41). Also, this implies that most of the field emission current will come from levels only moderately below the Fermi level, because the inverse exponential dependence on barrier thickness will rapidly reduce the contributions from progressively lower levels.

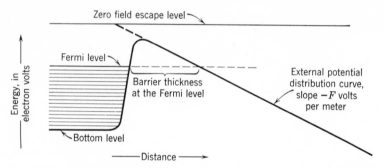

Fig. 8.14 Energy-level diagram for a metal from which "field emission" of electrons is occurring because of the very strong external electric field at the surface. A small percentage of the electrons reaching the potential barrier from the inside, and possessing kinetic energies at or a little below the Fermi level, will pass through the barrier *because it is thin,* and are thereafter drawn away by the external field; see (8–41).

Such through-the-hump emission should not depend on temperature, because the electron population in levels at and below the Fermi level is essentially independent of temperature, as indicated by the very little change, for such energy values, of the distribution curves, Fig. 8.4, between the very wide range of temperatures encompassed by the two curves in that figure.

Field emission theory plays an important part in the explanations sometimes advanced for the very large emission current densities observed at the cathode spot of an electric arc between metallic electrodes at atmospheric pressure.

8.24 Contact Difference of Potential. [8A, D, F, G, I, J, k, 14a, 15a]   The significance of the term "contact difference of potential" may be understood by reference to Fig. 8.15. If pieces of two different metals are moderately close to one another but not touching, both being electrically uncharged, there is, of course, no electric field between them. The potential-energy curve between them is, as illustrated in Fig. 8.15a, horizontal except very near each surface.

If these two pieces of metal are brought very close together, still, however, not touching, the two image-force regions overlap. Calculation of the force in the narrow gap between the surfaces would require imaging in both conductors, and there would in general be some force

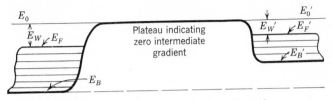

(a) Remote unlike surfaces both uncharged.

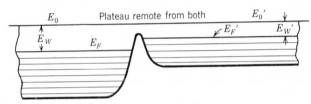

(b) Same surfaces approaching closely, but not touching. No charge interchange; no shift of bottom levels.

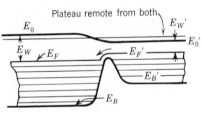

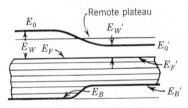

(c) Electrical contact just made, transferring electrons to the left; E_B, E_F, E_0 all raised; E_B', E_F', E_0' all lowered.

(d) Complete electrical contact; Fermi levels coincide. Contact difference of potential is $E_0 - E_0' = E_W - E_W'$.

FIG. 8.15 Potential energy diagrams, relative to contact difference of potential. Note that the low-work function metal has in (d) acquired a potential *higher* than the other metal, because its zero of potential energy is lower than for the other metal. As these are energy diagrams, not potential diagrams, electrons "fall" toward lower levels.

each way. The crest of the potential-energy curve through the gap is then below the zero level, as illustrated in Fig. 8.15b. As yet there has been no charge transfer; both pieces of metal are uncharged. A potential-energy line drawn between two *nonadjacent* (perhaps backside) boundaries of these two metals must still be flat-topped, and the vertical positions of the top and bottom energy levels are unchanged.

As soon as the potential-energy barrier in the narrowing gap becomes thin enough so that a substantial number of electrons can penetrate it, or as soon as the crest of the barrier drops low enough so that electrons can spill over it, there will be electron flow from the low-work-function metal to the high-work-function metal. Thus electrons move away from the right-hand piece, giving it a positive charge and the left-hand piece a negative charge. Therefore the right-hand one acquires a more positive potential and the left-hand one a more negative potential than before; the two zero levels shift relative to one another, the right-hand one moving downward, the left-hand one upward, as illustrated in Fig. 8.15c. This shift continues until the two Fermi levels line up horizontally, as in Fig. 8.15d. Then there is no further tendency for electrons to flow either way, because no electron in either metal can by crossing the boundary find a vacant level lower than its present one. This is an equilibrium condition.

The two zero levels are now displaced vertically by just the difference between the two work functions. This displacement is measurable and is called the *contact difference of potential;* thus *the contact difference of potential between two metals is the difference between their work functions.*[8G, k, 14a, 15a] Low-work-function metals are called electropositive because they become positively charged, and therefore acquire positive potentials, when in contact with high-work-function metals.

Two pieces of metal are in contact only along one surface of each, and there are other sides to both. A potential or potential-energy curve between noncontacting sides must, of course, have a slope, to accommodate the change in height in passing from one zero level to the other, and this slope corresponds to an external electric field. Measurements of contact differences of potential are basically measurements of this electric field and are always made by electrostatic voltage-measuring devices.

Ordinary electromagnetic meters respond only to continuous current flow. The vertical shift of energy levels that sets up the external field between metals in contact establishes an equilibrium in which there is no tendency toward transfer of electrons from one metal to another; therefore electromagnetic meters cannot be used to measure contact differences of potential. Also, all the contact differences of potential around a closed completely metallic circuit must add up to zero, as consideration of their origin will make evident; this again indicates that no current flow can result from them in such a circuit.

8.25 Effect of Contact Differences of Potential on Triode Plate Current. The various electrodes of a triode, tetrode, pentode, etc., are connected to one another through external circuits and may be of unlike metals, so that the electrodes expose within the tube just such noncontacting surfaces as are referred to in the previous paragraph. Hence the space-charge-free potential gradients within such tubes must include contributions due to contact differences of potential. Heating the cathode so that electrons are emitted does not change the situation in principle; it merely adds space charge to the list of items controlling the potential distribution.

In determinations of equivalent grid sheet potential values, as for example by means of (5–22), contact differences of potential may be taken into account by adding with proper algebraic sign, and to plate and grid voltages respectively, the corresponding contact differences of potential relative to the cathode.

As the cathode-to-grid and cathode-to-plate contact differences of potential, E_c'' and E_b'', are within any given tube independent of the voltages applied, it is possible to combine them into a constant term

$$E'' = E_c'' + \frac{E_b''}{\mu} \qquad (8\text{–}42)$$

If as usual the work function of the cathode is less than that of either grid or plate, E_c'' and E_b'' will both be numerically negative, as will E''. The constant term E'' can be incorporated into (4–71), (5–22), (5–23), and similar expressions. Thus for a triode E_s, to be used in finding space-charge-limited current, becomes

$$E_s = \frac{E'' + E_c + \dfrac{E_b}{\mu}}{1 + \dfrac{1}{\mu} + \dfrac{1}{\mu}\dfrac{C_k'}{C_p}} \qquad (8\text{–}43)$$

If it is found experimentally that heating the cathode affects the value of E'' (possibly by changing the cathode work function), of course the hot value of E'' must be used.

PROBLEMS

1. For how many free electrons within a rectangular enclosure can n^2 have the value 7? the value 8? (See Table VIII.)

2. Aluminum has a specific gravity of 2.70, atomic weight as in Table II. Find E_F (kinetic energy at the Fermi level). (The shell distribution of electrons, Table II, suggests how many free electrons per atom may be expected.)

3. A rectangular enclosure, volume 10^{-27} cubic meter, contains an electron gas having 30 electrons. Find the Fermi-level energy (a) by use of Table VIII and equation (8–11), also (b) by use of equation (8–14). Which answer is correct and why? (c) Find the least possible average energy, in electron volts.

4. (a) Find the Fermi-level energy (electron volts) for argon at $0°$ C and 760-mm pressure, and (b) for helium at 10 atmospheres pressure and $10°$ K, assuming the helium still monatomic.

5. Derive an expression for the gross work function of a homogeneous metal surface, if the retarding-force curve starts as a straight line through zero force at the surface, intersecting the image force at distance b from the surface. If the gross work function is 12 volts, what value has b?

6. Consider a cathode surface capable of thermionically emitting 200 ma per sq cm at $1160°$ K. Find the voltage equivalent of temperature, the work function (assuming A_0 in Dushman's equation is 60×10^4), the value of ζ (the electron velocity characteristic of this temperature). If the potential dip (Fig. 8.9) drops to $3E_T$ volts below the cathode, what is the space-charge-limited current density? How far below the cathode does the potential dip drop when the space-charge-limited current is 0.1 per cent of the temperature-limited value?

7. Consider a cathode whose temperature-limited current is 50 ma at $1700°$ K, 0.5 ma at $1400°$ K. Find the work function, using Dushman's equation.

8. The Prob. 7 cathode has a circular cross section, 0.008-cm radius, and is 2 cm long. An outer concentric anode has a 0.032-cm radius. Cathode temperature $1700°$ K. Neglecting contact potential difference, find the current when E_b is (a) 30 volts, (b) 5 volts. In (b), how many volts below the cathode potential is the bottom of the potential dip?

9. Electrodes as in Probs. 7 and 8, temperature $1400°$ K, current therefore so small that the effect of space charge on potential distribution can be neglected. E_b = 1200 volts. What is the temperature-limited current? (See Section 8.22.)

10. Solve (b), Prob. 8, by the method outlined in Section 8.21, using $\lambda = 1$, then $\lambda = 2$. Comparison with the solution of Section 5.14 will illustrate the effects of initial velocities.

11. The work function of a surface might conceivably depend on the temperature. Find what function E_W must be of E_T and of a constant E_W' to convert Dushman's equation into the following: $J_{th} = A_0'T \exp(-E_W'/E_T)$.

12. Cylindrical diode: $r_k = 3$ mm, $r_p = 5$ mm, length 80 mm. Plate potential zero (same as cathode). Cathode at $1040°$ K. Potential minimum between cathode and plate at -0.08 volt. Plate current $I_b = 0.85$ amp. (a) Find I_{th}, thermionic current from cathode. (b) If $A_0 = 60 \times 10^4$ in Dushman's equation, find cathode work function. (c) Find the anode dissipation.

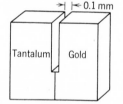

13. A piece of tantalum and a piece of gold are shaped and placed in contact along one surface, as in Fig. 8.16. (a) What is the electrostatic potential gradient in the slot between their adjacent noncontacting surfaces? (b) Toward which metal would an electron in this slot be accelerated?

Fig. 8.16 Tantalum and gold in contact.

14. In a certain triode, the work function of the cathode surface is 2 volts; the grid is nickel, the plate graphite (a form of carbon). Write an expression for the equivalent grid sheet potential, accounting for contact differences of potential between the various electrodes, assuming that μ, C_p, and C_k' are known.

15. To what value must the work function of a tungsten surface be reduced, by an external field, to make the current density 20,000 amp per sq cm at $2500°$ K? How strong must the field be? How near must the adjacent plane anode be if its potential is 10 volts above that of the tungsten?

CHAPTER IX

AMPLIFIER CIRCUIT PRINCIPLES *

9.1 Plate Resistance, Transconductance, Amplification Factor.
The current-voltage relationships for high-vacuum thermionic tubes
are easily measureable and reproducible. They can be satisfactorily
represented by families of characteristic curves as discussed in Chapter
VI. The most important families
of curves are sets of *mutual characteristics* and *plate characteristics*,
illustrated by Figs. 6.2a and
6.2b.

Any thermionic vacuum tube
is an example of a *nonlinear*
circuit element. An ordinary
resistance which follows Ohm's
law is called a *linear* circuit element, because the current is
directly proportional to the voltage. Figure 9.1 contrasts the current-voltage relationship for an

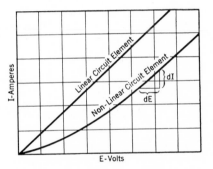

Fig. 9.1 Contrast between linear and
nonlinear circuit elements.

ordinary linear resistance (the straight line through the origin) with
that for an illustrative *nonlinear* circuit element.

The term "resistance," as applied to a nonlinear circuit element,
may have a variety of meanings. e/i (volts divided by amperes) may
have one value, watts/i^2 another, and de/di still another, although for
an ordinary resistance all three have the same value. In many nonlinear circuit elements, and especially in vacuum tubes, the currents
and voltages are usually pulsating, consisting of a-c components superposed on d-c ones. When the a-c components of voltage and current
are relatively small, the ratio between them is de/di, which can therefore be called the a-c resistance of the element.

In triodes, tetrodes, pentodes, etc., the a-c resistance to flow of
plate current, relating the a-c components of plate current and plate

* See bibliography references 9A through 9O for more extensive treatments.

voltage, is called the *plate resistance* r_p. As discussed in Section 5.7, it is defined mathematically as

$$r_p = \frac{\partial e_b}{\partial i_b}, \text{ that is, } r_p = \left(\frac{de_b}{di_b}\right)_{e_c \text{ constant}} \tag{9-1}$$

where e_b, i_b, and e_c signify respectively plate voltage, plate current, and grid voltage.

It is evident that r_p is the reciprocal of the slope of a plate characteristic curve. As this slope is by no means the same for all values of

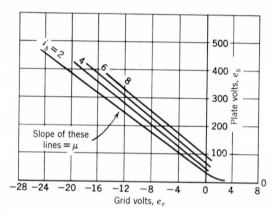

Fɪɢ. 9.2 Plate voltage-grid voltage curves corresponding to Fig. 6.2. Slope of these curves is the amplification factor μ.

plate and grid voltages, the value of r_p is markedly dependent on the circuit in which the tube is used.

The equation

$$g_m = \frac{\partial i_b}{\partial e_c}, \text{ that is, } g_m = \left(\frac{di_b}{de_c}\right)_{e_b \text{ constant}} \tag{9-2}$$

defines the *grid-plate transconductance* g_m, which is obviously the slope of a mutual characteristic curve and, like r_p, varies with circuit voltages. Transconductance is usually stated in *micromhos*.

The *amplification factor* μ is defined as

$$\mu = -\frac{\partial e_b}{\partial e_c}, \text{ that is, } \mu = -\left(\frac{de_b}{de_c}\right)_{i_b \text{ constant}} \tag{9-3}$$

μ is therefore the slope of the various parallel straight slant lines in Fig. 9.2, for along each straight line the plate current is constant. The relationships of μ, r_p, and g_m to geometry and potentials are discussed in and following Section 5.7.   Equation (5–46) is the final step in the proof that

$$\mu = g_m r_p \qquad (9\text{–}4)$$

The plate characteristic curves of Fig. 6.2b are essentially parallel to one another; that is, each one is like its neighbor except for a horizontal shift.   This means that any change Δe_c in grid voltage can be compensated for by a change Δe_b in plate voltage, provided that $\Delta e_c + (\Delta e_b/\mu) = 0$, μ being assumed constant, that is, independent of the magnitude of Δe_c.   Under these circumstances i_b is some function of the quantity $e_c + (e_b/\mu)$.

Adjacent curves are not parallel to one another in families of tetrode and pentode plate characteristics, for in such devices the plate current is not even approximately a function of $e_c + (e_b/\mu)$; see Figs. 6.7 and 6.15.   When used in connection with multigrid tubes the quantity μ, as defined by (9–3), loses the simple significance relative to interelectrode geometry that it has in connection with triode characteristics. It becomes, like r_p and g_m, simply a quantitative measure of a certain decidedly variable property of a family of curves.

9.2   Evaluation of Tube "Constants."   The quantities μ, r_p, and g_m are sometimes called "tube constants" in spite of the fact that only one of them, μ, is constant, and that one so only for triodes.   The values of these "constants" can be obtained by direct measurement, using a vacuum-tube bridge, or graphically from the characteristic curves.

The value of r_p at any point on a set of plate characteristics can be obtained by measuring the slope at that point.   It can be obtained from a set of mutual characteristics by determining from the graph the increments Δe_b and Δi_b along a line of constant grid voltage (vertical in this case).   Then

$$r_p = \left(\frac{\Delta e_b}{\Delta i_b}\right)_{e_c \text{ constant}} \qquad (9\text{–}5)$$

The quantity g_m is similarly obtainable as the slope of a mutual characteristic curve, or as $\Delta i_b/\Delta e_c$ in a vertical section of a set of plate characteristic curves.

μ is the slope in a set of curves like Fig. 9.2, or it is $\Delta e_b/\Delta e_c$ along a horizontal (constant i_b) section of mutual or plate characteristic curves.

9.3   Simple Amplifier Circuits; the Load Line.   Triodes and pentodes are used extensively in amplifier circuits.   The time variations of the voltage between the output terminals of a perfect amplifier follow the pattern set by the input voltage, but are of greater magnitude by a constant factor called the *voltage amplification* or *voltage gain*

of the amplifier. Most actual amplifiers introduce some distortion of
the voltage pattern, and the kind and magnitude of the distortion is
a controlling factor in the selection of the type of amplifier to be used
for a particular purpose.

There is in general use a classification of electron tube amplifiers
into Class A, Class B, and Class C types, the distinction between them
having to do with the bias voltage, as stated in the last paragraph of
Section 9.5. Class B and C amplifiers are easily understood, once the
essentials of Class A operation are grasped. A discussion of Class B
amplifiers appears in Sections 9.22, 9.23, and 9.24. Class C amplifier
operation is discussed briefly in Section 11.3, and in detail in various
texts devoted primarily to electronic circuit studies.*

Figure 9.3a is a diagram of a simple Class A amplifier circuit. The
cathode of the tube is heated by current from a filament transformer,

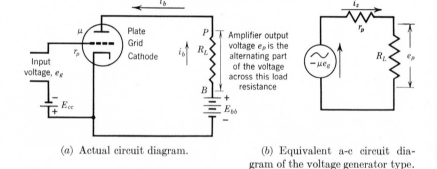

(a) Actual circuit diagram.

(b) Equivalent a-c circuit diagram of the voltage generator type.

Fig. 9.3   Amplifier circuit with resistance load.

or from a battery (called the A battery). The plate and grid circuits
contain respectively a B battery, or rectifier power supply, of voltage
E_{bb}, and a C bias battery of voltage E_{cc}. The plate circuit contains
also an *output resistance* or *load resistance* R_L. The a-c input voltage,
of rms value E_g, instantaneous value e_g, is introduced into the grid
circuit in series with the bias battery. The useful output voltage, of
rms value E_p, instantaneous value e_p, is the a-c component of the voltage across R_L. The voltage amplification or voltage gain of this
amplifier is the ratio

$$\frac{E_p}{E_g} = \text{Voltage gain} \tag{9-6}$$

The input voltage is sometimes called the *excitation voltage*.

* See especially Terman,[9M] Argimbau,[9A] and the books by the staffs of Cruft
Laboratory at Harvard [9C] and of the Electrical Engineering Department at M.I.T.[9H]

In accord with standards established by the Institute of Radio Engineers [9a] the following symbolism will be used, potentials usually (but not always) being measured relative to a zero value at the cathode.

e_b, e_c, i_b, i_c symbolize respectively instantaneous values of plate and grid voltages and of plate and grid currents.   (9–7a)

E_b, E_c, I_b, I_c symbolize similarly the d-c values of plate and grid voltages and of plate and grid currents.   (9–7b)

e_p, e_g, i_p, i_g symbolize the instantaneous values of the varying (or a-c) components of plate and grid voltages and of plate and grid currents.   (9–7c)

E_p, E_g, I_p, I_g symbolize the rms values of the a-c components of plate and grid voltages and of plate and grid currents.   (9–7d)

E_{bb}, E_{cc} symbolize the battery voltages in the plate and grid circuits. In a great many circuits $E_c = E_{cc}$.   (9–7e)

Also, in this text:

i_a, i_k symbolize respectively the instantaneous total value, and the instantaneous value of the varying component, of the cathode current.   (9–8a)

I_a, I_k symbolize respectively the d-c value, and the rms value of the varying component, of the cathode current.   (9–8b)

In the circuit analysis of this and the following chapter the cathode potential will be considered to be zero.

It is evident from the above definitions that

$$e_b = E_b + e_p \qquad (9–9a)$$

$$i_b = I_b + i_p \qquad (9–9b)$$

$$e_c = E_c + e_g \qquad (9–9c)$$

$$i_c = I_c + i_g \qquad (9–9d)$$

The grid potential is usually negative relative to the cathode, so that e_c, E_c, and E_{cc} usually have negative numerical values.

In a circuit like that of Fig. 9.3a the instantaneous plate voltage e_b is less than the plate battery voltage E_{bb} by the voltage drop in R_L, that is

$$e_b = E_{bb} - i_b R_L \qquad (9–10)$$

This equation describes the plate voltage in terms of the circuit external to the tube. Its graphical representation on a set of e_b, i_b coordinates is called the *load line* and is drawn, on Fig. 9.4, for $R_L = 2500$ ohms and $E_{bb} = 400$ volts. The location of the load line for a given external circuit is entirely independent of the kind of tube used. To emphasize this fact no plate characteristic curves are shown in Fig. 9.4. Actual placement of the load line for a given set of circuit constants is most easily accomplished by locating the two extreme points.

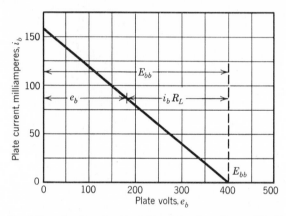

FIG. 9.4   Load line, for the circuit of Fig. 9.3, when $E_{bb} = 400$, $R_L = 2500$.

Thus in this figure, when $i_b = 0$, $e_b = E_{bb} = 400$ volts; when $e_b = 0$, $i_b = E_{bb}/R_L = 160$ milliamperes. The load line describes graphically the concept that the plate voltage must fall as the plate current rises, and vice versa.

9.4   Point Q of Zero Excitation; Current-Voltage Locus, Dynamic Characteristic. Figure 9.5 represents the load line of Fig. 9.4 combined with a particular set of plate characteristic curves. Suppose that the input voltage E_g for the moment is zero. Then $e_c = E_{cc}$; both e_b and i_b are constant at values corresponding to the intersection of the $e_c = E_{cc}$ plate characteristic curve with the load line. This intersection will be called the "point of zero excitation" and identified by the letter Q ("quiescence"). Corresponding plate current and plate voltage values for this point are symbolized as I_b and E_b; the grid voltage at Q is of course E_{cc}.

Suppose that there is introduced into the grid circuit, in series with the grid bias voltage E_{cc}, an a-c voltage of instantaneous value e_g. Then

$$e_c = E_{cc} + e_g \qquad (9\text{–}11)$$

If e_g varies sinusoidally, with rms value E_g and frequency f, this becomes

$$e_c = E_{cc} + \sqrt{2}\, E_g \cos 2\pi f t \qquad (9\text{–}12)$$

Each successive momentary value of grid voltage now corresponds to a new plate characteristic curve, with a new intersection point on the load line. The point describing instantaneous values of e_b and i_b oscillates along the load line with the frequency f. The range of the

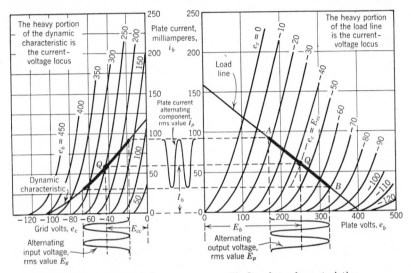

(a) On mutual characteristics.   (b) On plate characteristics.

Fig. 9.5 Current and voltage variations in a Class A amplifier with resistance load. At the point Q of zero excitation: $e_c = E_c = E_{cc}$, $e_b = E_b$, $i_b = I_b$.

oscillation for a given value of E_g is illustrated in Fig. 9.5b by the heavy portion AB of the load line, extending from $e_c = E_{cc} - \sqrt{2}\, E_g$ to $e_c = E_{cc} + \sqrt{2}\, E_g$. This portion of the load line is the *current-voltage locus* for this particular circuit and excitation voltage.

According to Fig. 9.4 and equation (9–10), any variation in e_b must be accompanied by an equally large variation in the voltage $i_b R_L$ across the load resistance, for E_{bb} cannot change. Hence, as indicated in Fig. 9.5b, the peak value of the a-c output voltage (rms value E_p) is half the total extent of the e_b variations of the locus. Similarly the peak value of the plate current's a-c part (rms value I_p) is half the total extent of the i_b variations of the locus.

Graphical representation of this behavior on a set of mutual characteristics is often more useful than that on the plate characteristic graph. The load line can be transferred to the e_c, i_b graph by plotting thereon the values of e_c and i_b that correspond to the intersections of the various plate characteristic curves with the load line. The curve resulting from such a process is called the *dynamic characteristic;* it is shown in Fig. 9.5a.

The dynamic characteristic differs from the load line in that the dynamic characteristic is not in general straight and depends for its placement on properties both of the tube and the external circuit. Its flexion results from the flexion of the tube characteristic curves, as is evident from the manner of spotting points along it. If the tube characteristic curves are straight or nearly straight within a given range of plate currents, the dynamic characteristic is likewise straight or nearly so within the same current range. The load line and the dynamic characteristic represent the response of the circuit both to d-c and a-c variations in the grid voltage.

The heavy portion of the dynamic characteristic in Fig. 9.5a is the current-voltage locus that corresponds to the similar heavy portion of the load line in Fig. 9.5b. The value of e_c at the point Q of zero excitation is of course E_{cc}. Therefore Q lies half-way between the extreme points of the "swing" of the grid voltage on Fig. 9.5a.

9.5 Relations between A-C and D-C Components of Voltage and Current. Suppose that, as in the preceding section, a sinusoidal excitation voltage of rms value E_g is used in the circuit illustrated in Fig. 9.3a. Equations (9–11) and (9–12) then describe the relations between the d-c and a-c components of grid voltage; see the (9–9) set and the definitions preceding it. These grid voltage relations are illustrated graphically in Fig. 9.6, in which T is any point along the current-voltage locus. The following plate current relations correspond to (9–11) and (9–12):

$$i_b = I_b + i_p \tag{9–13}$$

$$i_b = I_b + \sqrt{2}\, I_p \cos 2\pi f t \tag{9–14}$$

An inspection of Fig. 9.6 indicates that as the grid voltage swings in the positive direction (toward zero) the plate current increases (i.e., moves to the left and *upward* along the load line). Thus e_g and i_p rise and fall together and reach maximum positive values at the same instant. They may be said to be in phase with one another. The t's in (9–12) and (9–14) are therefore identical; that is, they are measured from a common zero instant. In relation to plate voltage, the counterpart of (9–13) is, for Fig. 9.6,

$$e_b = E_b + e_p \tag{9–15}$$

The total load voltage e_{BP} (see Figs. 9.3a and 9.7) is of course the voltage drop in R_L due to the flow of plate current.   Figure 9.7 illustrates the fact that e_{BP}, measured from B to P, Fig. 9.3a, is negative; that is, the potential of P is below that of B.

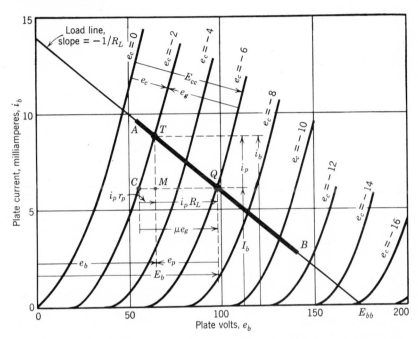

FIG. 9.6   Relations between d-c and a-c components of plate voltage and plate current in a Class A amplifier with resistance load.   At the point T on the figure:

E_{cc}, e_c are negative, e_g positive.
I_b, i_b, i_p are positive.
E_b, e_b, μe_g are positive, e_p negative.

These quantities are related as follows [see (9–9)]:

$$e_c = E_{cc} + e_g \qquad i_b = I_b + i_p$$
$$e_b = E_b + e_p \qquad e_p = -i_p R_L$$

Figure 9.7 also illustrates the fact that, as e_b increases, e_{BP} becomes less negative by an equal amount; that is, e_{BP} and e_p experience identical positive increments simultaneously.   Therefore e_p in (9–15) is the a-c component of load voltage as well as of plate voltage.   Thus e_p is in fact the useful output voltage of the amplifier illustrated in Fig. 9.3a. The point T in Fig. 9.6 is chosen so as to make e_p negative, whereas P in Fig. 9.7 corresponds to a positive value of e_p.

266   AMPLIFIER CIRCUIT PRINCIPLES

It is evident from Fig. 9.6 that:

$$\text{Slope of the load line} = \frac{i_b - I_b}{e_b - E_b} = \frac{i_p}{e_p} \qquad (9\text{--}16)$$

But this slope is $-1/R_L$; therefore

$$e_p = -i_p R_L \qquad (9\text{--}17)$$

An inspection of Fig. 9.6 shows that along the load line i_p increases in a positive sense as e_p swings negative, as is to be expected from (9–17).

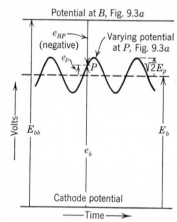

A relation similar to (9–17) exists between the corresponding rms values, that is

$$E_p = -I_p R_L \qquad (9\text{--}18)$$

The negative signs in (9–17) and (9–18) are of importance only when phase angles are being considered.

The counterpart, for plate voltage variations, of (9–14) is

$$e_b = E_b + \sqrt{2}\,E_p \cos 2\pi ft \qquad (9\text{--}19)$$

The effect of the negative sign in (9–18) is made evident by a comparison between (9–14) and the following, obtained by using (9–18) in (9–19):

$$e_b = E_b - \sqrt{2}\,I_p R_L \cos 2\pi ft \qquad (9\text{--}20)$$

Fig. 9.7 Voltage relations in the plate circuit of a Class A amplifier employing the Fig. 9.3a circuit. The plate potential is always lower than the plate battery potential, because of the d-c voltage drop in the load resistance.

Thus as i_b and i_p *increase*, e_b and e_p *decrease*; i_p and e_p are 180° out of phase with one another.

In summary:

$$e_g \text{ and } i_p \text{ rise and fall together} \qquad (9\text{--}21a)$$

$$e_p \text{ falls when } i_p \text{ rises} \qquad (9\text{--}21b)$$

Therefore, necessarily,

$$e_p \text{ falls when } e_g \text{ rises} \qquad (9\text{--}21c)$$

This summarizes the reasons why e_p and e_g are said to be 180° out of phase with one another in an amplifier that has a purely resistive load.

The distinctive feature of a Class A amplifier is that the current-voltage locus, Fig. 9.6, lies entirely *above* cut-off (does not extend to zero i_b) and entirely *below* the plate characteristic curve for which e_c = 0. Thus the grid bias voltage E_{cc} for a Class A amplifier is very much less in value than would be necessary to produce cut-off along the load line. In contrast, a Class B amplifier (Section 9.22) is biased approximately to cut-off, and a Class C amplifier (Section 11.3) is biased to much below cut-off.

9.6 Elliptical Current-Voltage Locus with Reactive Load. Often the load is reactive; for example, it may contain an inductance of L henrys, having reactance X_L ohms, as illustrated in Fig. 9.8a. If the

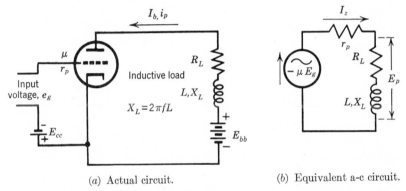

(a) Actual circuit.   (b) Equivalent a-c circuit.

Fig. 9.8   Class A amplifier circuit with inductive load, having resistance R_L, reactance X_L, impedance $Z_L = \sqrt{R_L{}^2 + X_L{}^2}$.

plate current is a sine wave of a single frequency, uncomplicated by the presence of harmonics, the corresponding current-voltage locus on a set of plate characteristics is a true ellipse, of the type illustrated in Fig. 9.9b. Furthermore, the shape of the ellipse is, for sine wave i_p, not at all dependent on the shapes of the tube characteristic curves. The plate battery voltage is fixed when the battery is chosen, and the voltage drop between the plate battery and the plate depends only on the amplitude of the sine-wave current variation and on the R_L, X_L of the load.

Current and voltage variations in the plate circuit of Fig. 9.8a must obey the following circuit equation:

$$e_b = E_{bb} - i_b R_L - L \frac{di_b}{dt} \qquad (9\text{--}22)$$

Certain general features of the ellipse in Fig. 9.9b can be determined by a study of this equation.

The upper and lower extremes of the ellipse, points A and B, correspond to the positive and negative peak values of the a-c component

i_p. At both points the rate of change of i_p, so also of i_b, is zero. Therefore, $L(di_b/dt)$ is zero in (9–22), and the expression for plate voltage
reduces to $e_b = E_{bb} - i_b R_L$. But according to (9–10) any point whose
coordinates are i_b and $E_{bb} - i_b R_L$ lies on a load line drawn for load
resistance R_L and plate battery voltage E_{bb}. Therefore the upper and

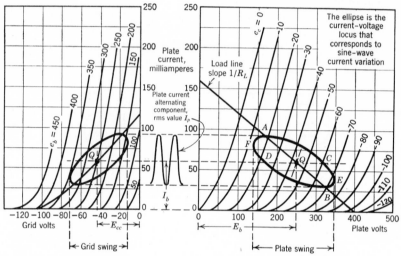

(a) On mutual character-
istics.

(b) On plate characteristics.

Fig. 9.9 Current and voltage variations in a Class A amplifier having an inductive load, sine-wave plate current variation.

lower extremes of the ellipse must lie on such a load line. This is
equivalent to saying that *the ellipse must have horizontal tangents at both
intersections with the load line.*

Introduce (9–13) into (9–22), and then recognize that $dI_b/dt = 0$
and $E_{bb} - I_b R_L = E_b$; the following expression results:

$$e_b = E_b - i_p R_L - L \frac{di_p}{dt} \qquad (9\text{–}23)$$

The two points C and D, at which the current is I_b, correspond to
passage of i_p through zero. When i_p is zero, di_p/dt in (9–23) is a
maximum. The inductive voltage in the load is therefore at its maximum value, which is $\sqrt{2}\,I_p X_L$. At this moment $i_p R_L$ is zero. Thus
at C and D the plate voltage is respectively just $\sqrt{2}\,I_p X_L$ volts less
and greater than E_b. These two points are of course horizontally in
line with Q.

Comparison of (9–15) and (9–23) shows that in this circuit (Fig. 9.8a)

$$e_p = -\left(i_p R_L + L\frac{di_p}{dt}\right) \tag{9–24}$$

If i_p is sinusoidal it can be expressed as

$$i_p = \sqrt{2}\, I_p \cos 2\pi ft \tag{9–25}$$

This may be introduced into (9–24) and the resulting expression handled as in elementary a-c circuit theory. Such treatment leads to a sinusoidal expression for e_p of the form

$$e_p = -\sqrt{2}\, I_p \sqrt{R_L{}^2 + X_L{}^2} \cos (2\pi ft + \theta) \tag{9–26}$$

E_p is the rms value of e_p, so that

$$E_p = -I_p \sqrt{R_L{}^2 + X_L{}^2} = -I_p Z_L \tag{9–27}$$

The angle θ is that between E_p and I_p; obviously

$$\cos \theta = \frac{R_L}{\sqrt{R_L{}^2 + X_L{}^2}} \tag{9–28}$$

The extreme right and left points, E and F in Fig. 9.9b, correspond to peak values of the a-c component of load voltage, so that they must be $\sqrt{2}\, E_p$ volts to the right and left respectively of Q, and above and below it by an amount depending on the value of θ.

The parametric equations for the ellipse can be written by using (9–25) in (9–13), and (9–26) in (9–15). They are

$$i_b = I_b + \sqrt{2}\, I_p \cos 2\pi ft \tag{9–29}$$

$$e_b = E_b - \sqrt{2}\, I_p Z_L \cos (2\pi ft + \theta) \tag{9–30}$$

By assuming arbitrary values for $2\pi ft$ (in radians or degrees), corresponding values of i_b and e_b can be determined from these parametric equations, if E_b, I_b, R_L, X_L, and I_p are known. Points around the ellipse can then be spotted.

The elliptical current-voltage locus of Fig. 9.9b transfers to a similar figure on the mutual characteristic graph, Fig. 9.9a, in exactly the way that the load line of Fig. 9.5b transfers to the dynamic characteristic of Fig. 9.5a. If the plate characteristic curves are parallel, straight, and uniformly spaced within the area enclosed by the ellipse on Fig.

9.9b, the locus of Fig. 9.9a derived from it is also a true ellipse, and the grid excitation necessary to produce a sine-wave current is itself sinusoidal.

The vector diagram of Fig. 9.10 applies to the situation just described.

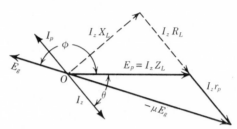

Fig. 9.10 Vector diagram for equivalent circuit of an amplifier having an inductive load, Figs. 9.8 and 9.9. Dotted vectors indicate components of E_p. Note that E_g is opposite in phase to $-\mu E_g$, and that $I_z \equiv -I_p$.

9.7 The Voltage Generator A-C Equivalent Circuit.

It is convenient to be able to express the gain of an amplifier quickly and easily in terms of tube constants evaluated at Q. This is accomplished by the aid of an imaginary equivalent a-c circuit. For example, the equivalent circuit shown in Fig. 9.3b is one that may be used in predicting the behavior of the actual circuit diagrammed in Fig. 9.3a. This equivalent circuit consists in general of the load in series with an imaginary resistance of value r_p and an imaginary a-c voltage generator generating a voltage $-\mu E_g$. The negative sign in $-\mu E_g$ is a reminder of the phase shift introduced by an amplifier, besides being mathematically correct.

The instantaneous and rms values of current in the equivalent circuit are i_z and I_z, where

$$i_z \equiv -i_p \qquad (9\text{–}31a)$$

$$I_z \equiv -I_p \qquad (9\text{–}31b)$$

i_p and I_p have the meanings assigned in (9–7). The quantities μ and r_p have the values that exist at Q in the actual circuit. The use of this voltage generator equivalent circuit is justified in the following paragraphs.

Horizontal distances in Fig. 9.6 can be measured in both plate voltage and grid voltage units. The conversion ratio between results of the two kinds of measurement is $-\mu$; see (9–3). For example, the difference between the plate voltage at C and that at Q is $-\mu$ times the corresponding difference in grid voltage.

The grid voltage, therefore also e_g, is obviously the same at T as at C. Using this fact, and measuring distances in plate voltage units:

$\overline{CQ} = \mu e_g$ (positive at C, for $\overline{CQ}$ is a positive distance;
furthermore μ, also e_g at T, is positive)   (9–32a)

$\overline{CM} = i_p r_p$ (for r_p is the reciprocal of the slope of the plate
characteristic curve)   (9–32b)

$$\overline{MQ} = i_p R_L \tag{9–32c}$$

But of course

$$\overline{CQ} = \overline{CM} + \overline{MQ} \tag{9–33}$$

Therefore

$$\mu e_g = i_p r_p + i_p R_L \tag{9–34}$$

The following form of this is also useful:

$$i_p = \frac{\mu}{r_p + R_L} e_g \tag{9–35}$$

As e_g and i_p rise and fall together, that is, are in phase with one another, no negative signs appear in (9–34) or (9–35).

The most useful relation involving the a-c components is that between e_p and e_g, obtained by multiplying (9–35) through by R_L, then using (9–17), with the following result:

$$e_p = -\mu e_g \frac{R_L}{r_p + R_L} \tag{9–36}$$

Voltages in a series resistive circuit divide in proportion to the resistances. Therefore *in the equivalent circuit*, Fig. 9.3b, the relation between E_p and $-\mu E_g$ is in accordance with (9–36). That is, according to both the real and equivalent circuits, the voltage gain of the amplifier is

$$\frac{E_p}{E_g} = -\mu \frac{R_L}{r_p + R_L} \tag{9–37}$$

It is not convenient in equivalent circuit calculations to deal with a current I_p that is negatively related to E_p, as in (9–18). It is convenient instead to define and use a current i_z, of rms value I_z, such that, with a resistive load,

$$E_p = I_z R_L \qquad e_p = i_z R_L \tag{9–38}$$

It is evident that $I_z \equiv -I_p$ as stated earlier, in (9–31).

On using $-i_z$ instead of i_p in (9–35), it appears that

$$i_z = \frac{-\mu e_g}{r_p + R_L} \tag{9–39a}$$

also that

$$I_z = \frac{-\mu E_g}{r_p + R_L} \tag{9–39b}$$

These expressions are of course in agreement with the equivalent circuit, Fig. 9.3b.

If the load contains an inductance, the point used (in the way T, Fig. 9.6, has been used) for graphical analysis of instantaneous relations, will lie along an elliptical locus, of the type illustrated in Fig. 9.9. It will therefore in general lie to the right or left of the load line by an amount $L(di_p/dt)$, as indicated by (9–23). Then for a point M that is still, as in Fig. 9.6, directly below T,

$$\overline{MQ} = i_p R_L + L \frac{di_p}{dt} \tag{9–40}$$

giving

$$\mu e_g = i_p (R_L + r_p) + L \frac{di_p}{dt} \tag{9–41}$$

Use of the relation $i_p = -i_z$ converts to

$$-\mu e_g = i_z (r_p + R_L) + L \frac{di_z}{dt} \tag{9–42}$$

This is the circuit equation for an equivalent circuit having an inductance L in series with the load resistance (Fig. 9.8b). The method used in obtaining it can be generalized to satisfy any complicated assembly of resistances and reactances in the load. The general vector relation

$$-\mu E_g = I_z r_p \oplus I_z Z_L \tag{9–43}$$

involving a generalized load impedance Z_L, follows directly, once the instantaneous relation is established. Figure 9.10 illustrates this vector relation.

Analysis of amplifier circuit behavior by means of the equivalent circuit is justifiable only if both μ and r_p are reasonably constant throughout the range of the current-voltage locus; see Section 9.13. Values of μ and r_p at Q are used because such values are presumably most nearly representative of true values throughout the range of the locus.

9.8   Demonstration of the Equivalent Circuit by Expansion of the Plate Current Equation. Equation (9–42) can be derived entirely analytically, as applied to any portion of a plate characteristic curve set in which the "curves" are parallel, straight, equally spaced lines. Within such a range the dependence of current on $e_c + (e_b/\mu)$ is *linear*, and μ is a constant. Therefore one may write

$$i_b = I_0 + g_m\left(e_c + \frac{e_b}{\mu}\right) \tag{9–44}$$

Here I_0 is an empirical constant. To substantiate this use of g_m, apply (9–2) to (9–44).

At the point Q, (9–44) becomes

$$I_b = I_0 + g_m\left(E_c + \frac{E_b}{\mu}\right) \tag{9–45}$$

Subtraction of this from (9–44), with subsequent use of (9–11), (9–13), and (9–15), leads to

$$i_p = g_m\left(e_g + \frac{e_p}{\mu}\right) \tag{9–46}$$

Use of $\mu = g_m r_p$ from (9–4) and rearrangement, after letting $i_p = -i_z$, gives

$$-\mu e_g = i_z r_p + e_p \tag{9–47}$$

But of course with the R and L load

$$e_p = i_z R_L + L\frac{di_z}{dt} \tag{9–48}$$

Combination with (9–47) gives (9–42), with subsequent generalization to (9–43). Thus the validity of an equivalent circuit chosen to obey (9–43) has been verified without recourse to graphical study.

This method can, in principle, be extended to large-signal and therefore nonlinear situations, as for example when

$$i_b = G\left(e_c + \frac{e_b}{\mu}\right)^n \tag{9–49}$$

by use of the "plate circuit expansion theorem," employing a Mac-Laurin series.[9A, E, L]

9.9   The Current Generator Equivalent Circuit. Figure 9.11*b* is a diagram of an equivalent circuit employing a *current generator*, which is in every detail rigorously applicable wherever the *voltage generator* circuit, Fig. 9.11*a*, is valid.

A *current* generator is a device that (a) orders a specified current to flow through the external circuit, and (b) stands ready to produce whatever voltage is necessary to compel that current to flow. Usually a current generator incorporates an internal *shunt* resistance, just as a voltage generator usually incorporates an internal *series* resistance. r_p plays both parts, in Fig. 9.11. The voltage across a current generator is zero at short circuit, just as the current in a voltage generator is zero at open circuit. The voltage across a physically real current

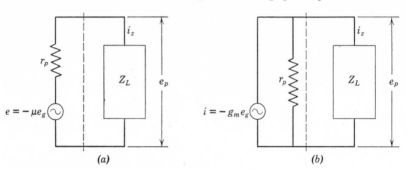

(a)   (b)

FIG. 9.11 Contrasting equivalent circuits.
(a) Voltage generator equivalent circuit, based on Thévenin's theorem.
(b) Current generator equivalent circuit, based on Norton's theorem.

generator may become destructively high at open circuit, if the internal shunt impedance is very large. Similarly the current in a voltage generator may become destructively large at short circuit, if the internal series impedance is very small.

To demonstrate the mutual equivalence of Figs. 9.11a and 9.11b, use $\mu = g_m r_p$ in (9–47), then divide through by r_p. This gives

$$-g_m e_g = \frac{e_p}{r_p} + i_z \tag{9–50}$$

This is obviously the circuit equation for Fig. 9.11b, for the current in r_p is e_p/r_p. In vector form

$$-g_m E_g = E_p \left(\frac{1}{r_p} \oplus \frac{1}{Z_L} \right) \tag{9–51}$$

For a simple resistive load circuit, as Fig. 9.3a, the gain equation is found by letting $Z_L = R_L$ in (9–51) and rearranging to give

$$\frac{E_p}{E_g} = -g_m \frac{1}{\dfrac{1}{r_p} + \dfrac{1}{R_L}} \tag{9–52}$$

that is

$$\frac{E_p}{E_g} = -g_m \frac{r_p R_L}{r_p + R_L} \qquad (9\text{-}53)$$

By using $g_m r_p = \mu$, this is made identical with (9–37), the gain equation for the voltage generator equivalent circuit with resistive load.

The generalized form of (9–53) is of course

$$\frac{E_p}{E_g} = -g_m \frac{1}{\dfrac{1}{r_p} \oplus \dfrac{1}{Z_L}} \qquad (9\text{-}54)$$

for the current generator circuit, corresponding to

$$\frac{E_p}{E_g} = -\mu \frac{Z_L}{r_p \oplus Z_L} \qquad (9\text{-}55)$$

for the voltage generator circuit.

The equivalent circuit concepts apply just as well for the pentode amplifier circuit, Fig. 6.14b, as for the triode circuit, Fig. 9.3. However, for a pentode, tube characteristics as in Fig. 6.15, μ and r_p are likely to be indeterminately large, so that (9–55) becomes meaningless. The voltage generator equivalent circuit is then a useless concept. However, g_m always has a magnitude easy to work with, and in (9–54) uncertainties in magnitude of a large r_p are not important, because $1/r_p$ is then insignificant relative to $1/Z_L$. Therefore (9–54), based on the current generator equivalent circuit, is somewhat more generally applicable than (9–55), based on the voltage generator circuit.

A very commonly used and often excellent first approximation to the voltage gain of a pentode amplifier is obtained by assuming that $r_p \to \infty$ in (9–54). Then for a resistive load, $Z_L = R_L$, so that

An approximate gain expression for pentode amplifiers with resistive loads $\biggr\}$ is $\dfrac{E_p}{E_g} \cong -g_m R_L$ $\qquad (9\text{-}56)$

It is left as an exercise for the reader to devise the graphical demonstration for the current generator equivalent circuit paralleling in principle the demonstration in Section 9.7; it is actually a little simpler than the voltage generator demonstration. A useful first step is to draw a diagram similar to Fig. 9.6 but enlarged to encompass the high-up intersection, of the plate characteristic curve through C and T, with a vertical line through Q (see Fig. 9.15). The process is one of adding currents along the vertical line through Q, rather than adding voltages along a horizontal line through Q as in (9–33).

9.10   Slope of the Dynamic Characteristic.   The *slope* of the dynamic characteristic is of course uniform within the range of parallel, straight-line, equally spaced characteristic curves. Its value is di_b/de_c, therefore also di_p/de_g. Thus, differentiating (9–35):

$$\left.\begin{array}{c}\text{Slope of the dynamic}\\ \text{characteristic at } Q\end{array}\right\} = \frac{di_p}{de_g} = \frac{\mu}{r_p + R_L} = g_m \frac{1}{1 + \dfrac{R_L}{r_p}} \quad (9\text{–}57)$$

As Q can be chosen, quite arbitrarily, to lie at any point along the dynamic characteristic, this relation expresses the slope at *any* point along a curved dynamic characteristic, in terms of the values of μ, r_p, and g_m, at that point.

Note that di_p/de_g differs markedly from $\partial i_p/\partial e_g$, which is the slope of a mutual characteristic curve.

9.11   Use of Thévenin's Theorem in Amplifier Circuit Analysis.   It is frequently desirable to employ Thévenin's theorem (see Argimbau [9A]) in amplifier circuit studies.   Figure 9.12 shows how the voltage across any load resistance, applied to a given amplifier circuit, may be obtained by means of Thévenin's theorem; the figure is in effect an illustrative statement, in circuit diagram form, of Thévenin's theorem. Any combination of linear resistances and reactances may be used inside the dotted box.   The application of the usual a-c circuit techniques in the obtaining of E_{th} and Z_{th} is straightforward.

Thévenin's theorem may also be used in case the source within the box is a current generator with a shunting r_p rather than a voltage generator.   In that case the current generator is replaced by an open circuit in step c; the end form still contains the E_{th} voltage generator.

Note that the elementary voltage generator equivalent circuit of Fig. 9.11a is already in Thévenin's theorem form; E_{th} would be $-\mu E_g$, and Z_{th} would be r_p.

9.12   Use of Norton's Theorem in Amplifier Circuit Analysis. Figure 9.13 is a diagrammatic representation of the employment of Norton's theorem [9A] to determine the voltage across a given amplifier's load when the current generator equivalent circuit is employed.   In the particular example illustrated, it turns out that I_{no} is just I_g, because the various impedance elements all appear in parallel branches. Because this situation exists in many amplifiers, the Norton theorem method of study is often extremely useful.

Note that the elementary current generator equivalent circuit of Fig. 9.11b is in Norton's theorem form: I_{no} would be $-g_m E_g$, and Z_{no} would be r_p.

Norton's theorem may also be applied when the source is a voltage generator with a series resistance; in that case the voltage generator is replaced by a short circuit, in step c.

9.13 Limitations of the A-C Equivalent Circuits; Harmonic and Frequency Distortion. It is apparent from the preceding sections that the equivalent circuits must be thought of in terms of a-c quantities exclusively. The current in and voltage across the load are I_z and E_p, respectively the negative of the a-c part of the actual plate current and the a-c part of the plate voltage. Batteries or power supplies are d-c devices and therefore do not appear in the equivalent circuit, except that their internal resistances should be included, if appreciable.

For a Class A amplifier with resistive load, Fig. 9.3a, the equivalent circuits give

$$I_z = \frac{-\mu E_g}{r_p + R_L} = \frac{-g_m E_g}{1 + \dfrac{R_L}{r_p}} \tag{9-58}$$

$$\frac{E_p}{E_g} = -\mu \frac{R_L}{r_p + R_L} = -g_m \frac{1}{\dfrac{1}{r_p} + \dfrac{1}{R_L}} \tag{9-59}$$

These expressions and other similar ones for more complex loads are valid to the extent that the plate characteristic curves are *straight, parallel, equally spaced lines throughout the area encompassed by the current-voltage locus*. Of course, strictly speaking, the characteristic curves satisfy this requirement only for infinitesimal current variations. Practically, however, it is reasonably well satisfied within the operating range of many useful amplifiers including nearly all Class A amplifiers.

The usual practical criterion, for resistive loads, of the range within which the equivalent circuit calculations are valid is the uniformity of slope of the dynamic characteristics (see Section 9.10). The dynamic characteristic is often nearly straight over a considerably wider range than are the mutual characteristic curves.

If the tube characteristic curves are not straight, parallel, equally spaced lines throughout the extent of the current-voltage locus, *harmonics* appear in the load circuit. Harmonics are a-c currents and voltages whose frequencies are twice, three times, four times, etc., that of the *fundamental* or excitation voltage frequency. Operation under such conditions is said to result in *harmonic distortion*. The magnitudes of the various harmonic voltages and currents depend partly on the flexion of the tube characteristics, and partly on any reactive properties of the load circuit.

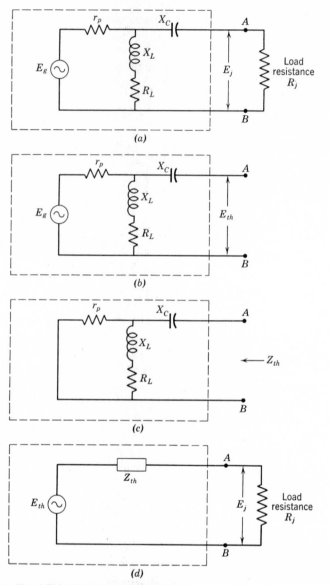

FIG. 9.12 Use of Thévenin's theorem to determine the output voltage E_j across an amplifier's load resistance R_j, using a voltage generator equivalent circuit. The (a) representation is converted to the (d) representation, from which E_j is determined.

(a) This is the voltage generator amplifier equivalent circuit, with terminals at A and B, load R_j, to which Thévenin's theorem is to be applied.

(b) The load resistance R_j is replaced by an open circuit, and the voltage between A and B determined; this voltage is E_{th}.

(c) The generator E_g is replaced by a short circuit, and the impedance looking into the circuit at its terminals A and B is determined. This impedance is Z_{th}.

(d) The circuit in the dashed-line box is replaced by Z_{th} in series with E_{th}, and the load resistance R_j again connected between A and B. The voltage across R_j is now E_j, just as in (a); as far as R_j is concerned, (a) and (d) are completely equivalent.

278

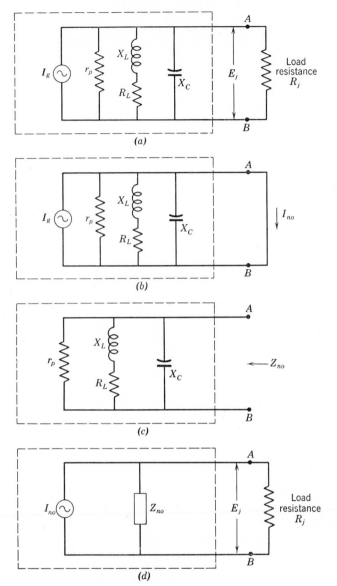

Fig. 9.13 Use of Norton's theorem to determine the output voltage E_j across an amplifier's load resistance R_j, using a current generator equivalent circuit. The (a) representation is converted to the (d) representation, from which E_j is determined.

(a) This is the current-generator amplifier equivalent circuit, with terminals at A and B, load R_j, to which Norton's theorem is to be applied.

(b) The load resistance is replaced by a short circuit, and the current between A and B determined; this current is I_{no}. (Note that, with this purely parallel-branch network in the dashed-line box, no series circuit elements between r_p and AB, I_{no} is equal to I_g.)

(c) The generator I_g is replaced by an open circuit, and the impedance looking into the circuit at its terminals A, B, is determined. This impedance is Z_{no}.

(d) The circuit in the dashed-line box is replaced by Z_{no} in parallel with I_{no}, and the load resistance again connected between A and B. The voltage across R_j is now E_j, just as in (a). The environment provided by (d) looks to R_j just the same as that provided by (a).

Harmonic distortion is described quantitatively by stating percentages. Thus there may be a 15 per cent second harmonic and an 8 per cent third harmonic; the rms second- and third-harmonic voltages in the output are then respectively 15 per cent and 8 per cent of the fundamental-frequency voltage. The total harmonic distortion in such a case would be $\sqrt{15^2 + 8^2} = 17$ per cent. See Sections 9.19, 9.20, and 9.21 for further discussions of harmonic distortion.

The a-c equivalent circuits are especially useful in the study of *frequency distortion*, that is, nonuniformity of gain at different excitation frequencies. In many cases the gain will be reasonably constant over a definite range of frequencies but will drop off rapidly outside that range. This is illustrated in Fig. 10.8. Speech or music contains many frequencies. If some lie within the range of uniform gain of an amplifier used for voice reproduction, and some outside it, not all are amplified alike; frequency distortion then exists.

9.14 Choice of Tube and Load Resistance. There are *voltage amplifiers*, designed to increase the signal voltage level without regard

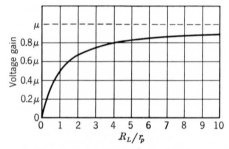

Fig. 9.14 Dependence of voltage gain on the ratio of load resistance R_L to plate resistance r_p in a Class A triode amplifier.

to power, which is then very small, and *power amplifiers*, for which the obtaining of useful power output at the signal frequency is the prime objective, the voltage gain being modest. There may also be *current amplifiers*. To achieve satisfactory performance for any of such design objectives, it is important that tube and load resistances be properly chosen relative to one another.

General principles for this selection can be illustrated by reference to the triode amplifier circuit of Fig. 9.3. First, note that according to (9–59) the greatest possible voltage gain for such an amplifier is μ. That value cannot be approached closely except by making R_L extremely large, which is undesirable because it would require an extremely high plate battery voltage, to supply the d-c part of the plate current.   Practically, a compromise must be reached between the desirability of high voltage gain and the equipment expense and power waste inherent in using a high plate battery voltage.   Figure 9.14 illustrates the fact that the gain increases rapidly with rising load resistance until R_L is several times r_p, but that a continued increase to tens or hundreds of times r_p gives very little further improvement. Hence there arises a general working principle, for a Class A triode amplifier, that R_L should be large enough to make the gain between two-thirds and nine-tenths of μ, if the primary function of the amplifier is to provide voltage amplification.

In a pentode voltage amplifier g_m in (9–59) is the controlling quantity; often both μ and r_p are indeterminately large; in general, R_L is chosen as large as is possible without requiring an excessive plate battery voltage.

In a power amplifier triode the proper ratio of tube to load resistance depends on which one of the three following sets of circumstances exists:

(a) The excitation voltage is small, and it is desired to choose a load resistance that will make power delivered to the load as great as possible for a specified tube. In this case μ and r_p are fixed.   This problem is identical with that of determining the load resistance into which a separately excited generator delivers maximum power.   The power delivered to the load of the equivalent circuit, Fig. 9.3b, is of course $I_z{}^2 R_L$; using (9–58),

$$\text{A-c power delivered to load} = (\mu E_g)^2 \frac{R_L}{(r_p + R_L)^2} \qquad (9\text{–}60)$$

The value of R_L needed to maximize this power is obtained by differentiating the expression with respect to R_L and equating the result to zero.   The required condition is met when

$$R_L = r_p \qquad (9\text{–}61)$$

(b) The excitation voltage is small, and it is desired to deliver maximum power to a load of fixed resistance R_L.   The power delivered to the load is as before given by (9–60), but now r_p is the variable.   It is apparent from an inspection of this relation that with all other quantities fixed the power is greatest when r_p is least. However, very little can be gained by reduction of r_p below one-fourth or one-fifth of R_L.   This requirement is therefore satisfied in a practical sense when r_p is a moderately small fraction of R_L.   This analysis explains the occasional need for tubes of very low plate resistance.

(c) The excitation voltage may be made as large as desired, but the tube and its properties are specified.   It is desired to choose a load resistance that will give maximum undistorted power output.   A graphical study of this problem, carried out in the next section, shows that the stated requirement is met when

$$R_L = 2r_p \qquad (9\text{–}62)$$

9.15   Maximum Undistorted Power Output.   Figure 9.15 is a diagram of the plate characteristic curves of a tube that is to be used for power amplification in a circuit like that of Fig. 9.3a. Preliminary estimates and manufacturers' data suggest that the operating point Q might well lie along a vertical line at E_b plate volts. It is desired to select the values of load resistance and excitation voltage that will result in maximum undistorted power output.

In order to avoid distortion, (a) the current-voltage locus must remain above a horizontal line FT, Fig. 9.15, placed so that above it the plate characteristic curves are practically straight, and (b) the current-voltage locus must remain below the $e_c = 0$ plate characteristic curve. If the grid swings positive, grid current flows (usually through a grid resistor) during part of each cycle, with resulting distortion of the *excitation* voltage wave form, and so of the output.

In order to make maximum use of the region available, the current-voltage locus should extend from some point B on the line FT to some point A on FG, the $e_c = 0$ plate characteristic. Furthermore, points A and B must lie equally to the right and left of the vertical line for which $e_b = E_b$, in order to locate Q properly. They must also lie equally above and below Q.

Let $I_{b\,max}$, $I_{b\,min}$, $E_{b\,max}$, and $E_{b\,min}$ symbolize the respective maximum and minumum values of plate current and plate voltage. These are evidently related to rms a-c values as follows:

$$E_p = \frac{E_{b\,max} - E_{b\,min}}{2\sqrt{2}} \qquad (9\text{--}63)$$

$$I_z = \frac{I_{b\,max} - I_{b\,min}}{2\sqrt{2}} \qquad (9\text{--}64)$$

The a-c power P_L in the load is

$$P_L = E_p I_z = \tfrac{1}{8}(E_{b\,max} - E_{b\,min})(I_{b\,max} - I_{b\,min}) \qquad (9\text{--}65)$$

Graphically, in Fig. 9.15,

$$\overline{AH} = \tfrac{1}{2}(E_{b\,max} - E_{b\,min}) \qquad (9\text{--}66)$$

also

$$\frac{\overline{AH}}{\overline{HG}} = r_p \qquad (9\text{--}67)$$

Therefore

$$E_{b\,max} - E_{b\,min} = 2r_p \cdot \overline{HG} \qquad (9\text{--}68)$$

Also

$$I_{b\,max} - I_{b\,min} = \overline{SH} \qquad (9\text{--}69)$$

Therefore power can be expressed as

$$P_L = \tfrac{1}{4}r_p \cdot \overline{HG} \cdot \overline{SH} \qquad (9\text{--}70)$$

As r_p is constant above $\overline{FT}$, power must be a maximum when the product $\overline{HG} \cdot \overline{SH}$ in this equation is greatest. Now the lines FG, FT, and GS, and hence the intersection G and S, are located by imposed conditions, so that the value of $\overline{SH} + \overline{HG}$ is fixed. Thus for maximum power:

$$(a) \qquad \overline{SH} + \overline{HG} \text{ must be constant} \qquad (9\text{–}71a)$$

$$(b) \qquad \overline{SH} \cdot \overline{HG} \text{ must be a maximum} \qquad (9\text{–}71b)$$

It is left as an exercise for the reader to show that these conditions are satisfied only when

$$\overline{SH} = \overline{HG} \qquad (9\text{–}72)$$

If $\overline{SH}$ and $\overline{HG}$ are equal, Q must be located at one-fourth of the distance from S to G. Now $R_L = \overline{AH}/\overline{QH}$, but $\overline{QH} = \tfrac{1}{2}\overline{SH} = \tfrac{1}{2}\overline{HG}$; therefore, using (9–67),

$$R_L = \frac{\overline{AH}}{\tfrac{1}{2}\overline{HG}} = 2\frac{\overline{AH}}{\overline{HG}} = 2r_p \qquad (9\text{–}73)$$

This result is independent of E_b. Therefore *for maximum undistorted power output $R_L = 2r_p$ for any value of E_b*. The excitation voltage and grid bias required do depend on the choice of operating voltage and

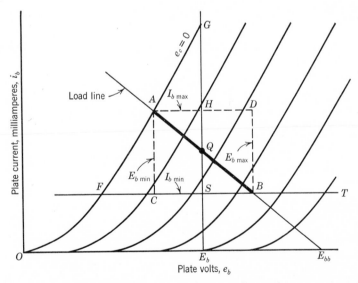

Fig. 9.15 Current-voltage locus for maximum undistorted power output, in a Class A triode amplifier. $R_L = 2r_p$.

can be read directly from a diagram like Fig. 9.15, drawn for the tube used.

9.16   Plate Circuit Efficiency and Plate Dissipation.   Figure 9.16 illustrates graphically the various power relationships associated with the operation of a circuit like that of Fig. 9.3a.   Two sets of conditions will be contrasted: (a) that when the excitation voltage is zero, and

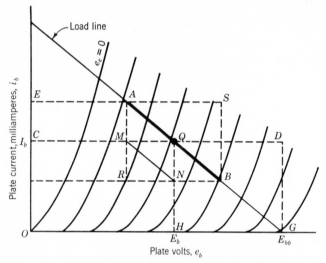

Fig. 9.16   Power relationships in a Class A amplifier with resistance load.

(b) that when there is an excitation voltage, but the current-voltage locus AB does not extend beyond the range in which the plate characteristic curves are straight or nearly so.   With this limitation the effect of harmonics need not be considered.   Thus:

(a) When the excitation voltage is zero, the plate current is I_b, plate voltage E_b, and plate battery voltage E_{bb}, all perfectly steady.   Areas in Fig. 9.16 measure power in watts, as follows:

$OCDG$ = Power introduced into the circuit by the plate
       battery.   (9–74)

$HQDG$ = Power dissipated as heat in the load resistance,
       owing to the passage of the direct current I_b.   (9–75)

$OCQH$ = Power brought to the plate of the tube by the raining
       on it of electrons which have been accelerated
       through the plate voltage field.   This power must
       be removed from the plate (by heat radiation) and
       is called the *plate dissipation*.   (9–76)

(b) When there is an excitation voltage, giving rise to the current-voltage locus AB, the tube and the load resistance carry both direct current and alternating current. The *average value* of plate current is still I_b, and the *average value* of the voltage across the load resistance is still $E_{bb} - E_b$. As before,

$OCDG$ = Power introduced into the circuit by the plate battery. (9–77)

$HQDG$ = Power introduced into the load resistance *owing to the passage of direct current*. (9–78)

However, there is an additional input of power to the load resistance because of the a-c component of current. As pointed out in the previous section, its value is $\frac{1}{8}(E_{b\,max} - E_{b\,min})(I_{b\,max} - I_{b\,min})$. This quantity is one-eighth of the area $ASBR$ and can be conveniently indicated by the area QMN. Thus

QMN = Power introduced into the load resistance *by the passage of alternating current*. (9–79)

Plate dissipation is the remainder, that is,

$$OCMNH = \text{Plate dissipation} \qquad (9\text{–}80)$$

The interesting feature of this comparison is the indication that the plate dissipation decreases to just the extent that the power output increases. The greater the useful output, the less severe is the dissipation burden on the plate of the tube.

The plate circuit efficiency is of course

$$\frac{\text{A-c power in the load}}{\text{Power input from the plate battery}} = \frac{QMN}{OCDG} \qquad (9\text{–}81)$$

It is apparent that ordinary Class A power amplifiers are not highly efficient devices. They are nevertheless satisfactory for many purposes, because of compensating merits of simplicity and freedom from distortion.

It is desirable to know how much heat power must be dissipated in the load resistance itself, in order to determine what its rating in watts must be. In R_L of Fig. 9.3a there are two currents, I_b and I_z, one of zero frequency, the other of excitation voltage frequency. Therefore

$$\text{RMS value of total current in load resistance} = \sqrt{I_b{}^2 + I_z{}^2} \qquad (9\text{–}82)$$

Therefore also

$$\left.\begin{array}{l}\text{Total power in}\\ \text{load resistance}\end{array}\right\} = (\sqrt{I_b{}^2 + I_z{}^2})^2 R_L = I_b{}^2 R_L + I_z{}^2 R_L \qquad (9\text{–}83)$$

9.17   Use of a Choke and a Condenser to Provide "Parallel Feed" of D-C Power to the Plate.   The discussion in the preceding section indicates a low efficiency for the type of amplifier illustrated in Fig. 9.3a.   The efficiency can be somewhat increased, and the investment in batteries or equivalent power source reduced, by introducing in the plate circuit a *blocking* condenser and a large inductance, called a *choke*.   This circuit arrangement is indicated in Fig. 9.17a.

It is helpful to think of the choke as primarily a device that "chokes off" a-c current but offers no obstruction to d-c current.   Conversely the condenser blocks the passage of d-c current but offers little or no obstruction to the passage of a-c current.   The inductance of the choke and the capacitance of the blocking condenser must be chosen large enough to prevent and permit, respectively, passage of currents of the frequency range within which the excitation voltage is to lie.

The complete equivalent circuit for a parallel-feed amplifier is shown in Fig. 9.17b.   However, within the frequency range for which the choke and condenser are designed their reactances approach respectively infinity and zero, so that they may be omitted from the equivalent circuit diagram.   It then becomes identical with that of a "series-feed" amplifier, Fig. 9.3b.   This section contains a discussion of conditions existing *when the excitation frequency is within this range*.

In the actual circuit the d-c part of the plate current passes through the choke, with negligible voltage drop, so that *the plate battery voltage E_{bb} need only be the desired operating-point voltage, E_b*.   The power introduced by the plate battery becomes $E_b I_b$, indicated by the area $OCQH$ in Fig. 9.16.   The power required to operate the amplifier is therefore less than for the similar series-feed circuit, Fig. 9.3a, by the amount of the area $QDGH$.   This area represents the power loss in the load resistor due to the passage of direct current; no such power loss takes place in a parallel-feed amplifier.

The a-c part of the plate current passes through the resistance-condenser path.   The reactance of the condenser is made small enough so that the $I_z X_C$ across it is insignificant.   Therefore $E_j = E_p$.   That is, the a-c voltage across the resistance-condenser path as a whole is just the load voltage E_j.   This same a-c voltage must of course exist across the parallel choke-and-battery path.   The choke permits this a-c voltage to be established by an extremely small a-c current.   Thus *the total instantaneous plate voltage is the algebraic sum of the steady plate battery voltage and the instantaneous a-c load voltage*, the latter appearing across the choke.

It has just been pointed out that the a-c component of voltage appears across the load resistance in one path and across the choke in the other.   Similarly the d-c potential difference established by the battery in one path exists across the condenser in the other path. The overall voltage for both paths is the algebraic sum of $E_b(= E_{bb})$ and the a-c load voltage.

As in the series-feed circuit, an *increase of plate current above* I_b results in a *decrease of plate voltage below* E_b. Therefore the summation of a-c and d-c plate circuit quantities is properly described by (9–14) and (9–20), for the parallel-feed as well as for the series-feed circuit.

This shows that *the load line for a parallel-feed amplifier is the same as that for a similar series-feed amplifier, provided the point Q of zero excitation* and the load resistance are the same. The a-c component of the plate current passes through the load resistance in both cases, and in both cases the a-c voltage so produced is algebraically added to the d-c part, E_b, of plate voltage.

Note that the zero current and zero voltage intercepts of the load line of a parallel-feed amplifier have no particular significance. The load line is located by passing a line of slope $-1/R_L$ through Q. And of course $E_{bb} = E_b$.

9.18 Frequency Limitations of Parallel-Feed Amplifiers. The frequency of the excitation voltage of a parallel-feed amplifier may fall below the range for which the choke and condenser are designed. The variation of voltage across the output resistance must then be calculated by means of a complete equivalent circuit, Fig. 9.17*b*. For very small frequencies the reactance of the inductance is so small as practically to short-circuit the condenser-resistance circuit, so that as the frequency approaches zero the gain vanishes. A series-feed amplifier is not subject to this limitation; its output voltage follows the pattern of the excitation voltage faithfully no matter how low the frequency.

X_L and X_C are the reactances of choke and condenser respectively in Fig. 9.17. In order to make the circuit separate the d-c from the a-c current effectively, the ratios r_p/X_L and X_C/R_L must be small. Hence the lower the frequency at which effective action is desired, the larger must be the physical dimensions and hence cost of both choke and condenser. Equations (9–88) and (9–89) below show that chokes and condensers large enough to result in satisfactory response as far as the magnitude of the output voltage is concerned may yet be small enough to introduce considerable deviation from the 180° phase shift of the series feed circuit. This is important in television circuits.

Figure 9.17*c* is a vector diagram for the complete voltage generator parallel-feed amplifier equivalent circuit. The current I_z divides into I_L in the choke and I_C in the resistance-condenser path. These two paths are in parallel; therefore

$$I_L X_L = I_C \sqrt{R_L^2 + X_C^2} \qquad (9\text{--}84)$$

In the vector diagram:

$$I_{LH}(\text{part of } I_L \text{ in phase with } I_C) = I_C \frac{X_C}{X_L} \qquad (9\text{--}85)$$

$$I_{LV}(\text{part of } I_L \text{ at right angles with } I_C) = I_C \frac{R_L}{X_L} \qquad (9\text{--}86)$$

$$(\mu E_g)^2 = \left(I_C R_L + I_C r_p - I_C r_p \frac{X_C}{X_L}\right)^2 + \left(I_C X_C + I_C r_p \frac{R_L}{X_L}\right)^2 \quad (9\text{--}87)$$

This rearranges into the following expression for gain:

$$\text{Gain} = \frac{E_j}{E_g} = \frac{\mu}{\sqrt{\left(1 + \dfrac{r_p}{R_L} - \dfrac{r_p}{X_L}\dfrac{X_C}{R_L}\right)^2 + \left(\dfrac{X_C}{R_L} + \dfrac{r_p}{X_L}\right)^2}} \qquad (9\text{--}88)$$

This reduces to (9–59) when r_p/X_L and X_C/R_L vanish.

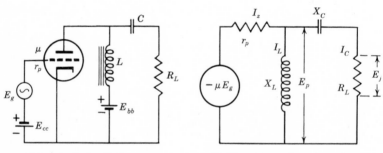

(a) Actual circuit diagram.

(b) Complete voltage generator a-c circuit diagram.

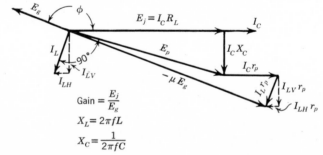

(c) Vector diagram for the complete equivalent circuit. Within normal frequency ranges the vectors E_p, E_j, $-\mu E_g$, E_g all lie along a continuous line, and $E_j = E_p$. Then $\phi = 180°$.

Fig. 9.17 Parallel-feed Class A amplifier with resistance load.

The phase angle ϕ between the output voltage E_j and the input voltage E_g can be calculated from its sine, which is expressible as follows:

$$\sin \phi = \sin (180° - \phi) = \frac{\dfrac{X_C}{R_L} + \dfrac{r_p}{X_L}}{\sqrt{\left(1 + \dfrac{r_p}{R_L} - \dfrac{r_p}{X_L}\dfrac{X_C}{R_L}\right)^2 + \left(\dfrac{X_C}{R_L} + \dfrac{r_p}{X_L}\right)^2}}$$

(9–89)

The ratios r_p/X_L and X_C/R_L need be only moderately small in order to make the gain approach closely to the high-frequency value given by (9–59). For example, if both ratios are 0.2, and $R_L = 2r_p$, the actual gain is 0.661μ, as compared with a value 0.667μ if both ratios are zero. This is a difference of three-fourths of 1 per cent. There is, however, a phase shift of 15.3° in this case; that is, E_j makes an angle of 164.7° with E_g.

It is left as an exercise for the reader to draw the current generator equivalent circuit corresponding to Fig. 9.17b and construct the corresponding vector diagram permitting determination of the $-g_m E_g$ vector, thereby leading to a gain equation similar to (9–88) but with μ eliminated in favor of g_m.

9.19 Straightness of the Dynamic Characteristic a Criterion of Freedom from Harmonic Distortion. Harmonic distortion was briefly mentioned in Section 9.13. The requirements for freedom from it are illustrated in Fig. 9.18.

The grid swing in Fig. 9.18 does not extend beyond the straight-line portion of the dynamic characteristic. The graphical construction used shows that, because the dynamic characteristic is straight, the sine-wave excitation voltage produces a true sine-wave plate current. As the dynamic characteristic is straight, its slope, (9–57), must be uniform; therefore, introduction of the sine-wave relation $e_g = \sqrt{2}\,E_g$ cos $2\pi f t$ into (9–35) leads to a single-frequency sine-wave expression for i_p. Thus an amplifier is free from harmonic distortion if the current-voltage locus remains on and within the straight portion of the dynamic characteristic.

The manner in which harmonics are introduced into the output by flexion of the dynamic characteristic is illustrated in Figs. 9.19 and 9.20. and described in associated discussions. For the present the important fact is that such flexion does produce harmonics.

The mutual characteristic curves in Fig. 9.5a are by no means free from flexion within the range of plate current swing. Yet the dynamic characteristic is nearly straight within that range, and the harmonic distortion is correspondingly small. Straightness of the dynamic characteristic is evidently a better criterion of freedom from harmonic distortion than is straightness of the tube characteristics.

To see why this is true, note that the slope of the dynamic characteristic is $\mu/(r_p + R_L)$; that of a mutual characteristic is μ/r_p. In a

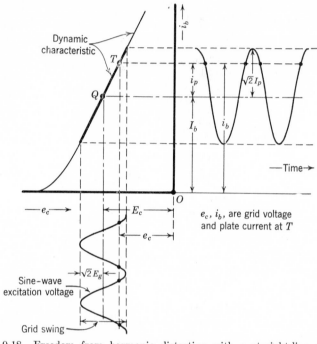

Fig. 9.18 Freedom from harmonic distortion with a straight-line dynamic characteristic. A sine-wave excitation voltage produces a true single-frequency sine-wave plate current variation.

triode μ is practically constant, but r_p changes, as indicated by the changing slopes of the tube characteristic curves. If, as is usually true, R_L is considerably larger than r_p, the latter may change substantially without producing a marked change in the slope of the dynamic characteristic. Thus in circuits employing triodes harmonic distortion can be minimized by the use of a load resistance large relative to r_p.

If an amplifier's load circuit contains an inductance, the current-voltage locus opens up into a loop, as illustrated in Fig. 9.9. Perfect freedom from harmonic distortion would require the mutual characteristics to be parallel, straight, equally spaced lines throughout the extent of the loop.   This would correspond to uniformity of both μ and r_p throughout the loop.   However, just as when there is no loop, a reasonably valid criterion of freedom from distortion is the degree of uniformity of the quantity $\mu(r_p + R_L)$ within the locus.

9.20   Curved Dynamic Characteristic Introduces a Second Harmonic.   Figure 9.19 illustrates the response to sinusoidal excitation

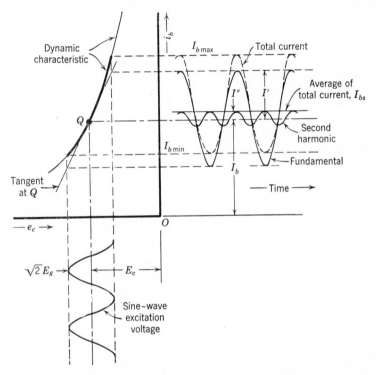

Fig. 9.19   Production of second harmonic, and upward shift in average current, when the dynamic characteristic is adequately approximated by a parabola.   The no-signal value (at Q) of average current is I_b; the average current in the presence of the signal is I_{bs}.

when the dynamic characteristic is to some modest extent convex downward, and the load purely resistive.   This is the usual condition in a Class A amplifier circuit employing a triode.

A curve of this type can be represented with reasonable accuracy over a considerable range by a parabola (second-degree curve).   If the point Q is taken as the origin of reference, the equation of the parabola is

$$i_p = Ae_g + Be_g^2 \qquad (9\text{--}90)$$

The slope of this parabola at Q is

$$\frac{di_p}{de_g}\bigg|_{i_p=0} = A \tag{9-91}$$

But the parabola is the dynamic characteristic. Therefore, according to (9–57),

$$A = \frac{\mu}{r_p + R_L} \tag{9-92}$$

in which μ and r_p are evaluated at Q. Thus the first term in (9–90) corresponds exactly to the equivalent circuit prediction as stated by (9–35).

The second term in (9–90) is proportional to B. Differentiation shows that the flexion $d^2 i_p/de_g{}^2$ of the parabolic characteristic is constant and equal to $2B$. This gives graphical significance to B.

To determine the pattern of the total current when both terms are taken into account, the excitation voltage must be expressed as

$$e_g = \sqrt{2}\, E_g \cos \omega t \tag{9-93}$$

Here, as usual, at frequency f,

$$\omega = 2\pi f \tag{9-94}$$

On entering the sinusoidal expression for e_g into (9–90), the following equation for i_p is obtained:

$$i_p = \sqrt{2}\, A E_g \cos \omega t + 2B E_g{}^2 \cos^2 \omega t \tag{9-95}$$

If now the relation

$$\cos^2 \omega t = \tfrac{1}{2} + \tfrac{1}{2} \cos 2\omega t \tag{9-96}$$

is used, the cosine-squared term in (9–95) expands into a constant (d-c) term plus a second-harmonic (double-frequency) cosine term. The quantity A can be expressed in terms of tube and circuit constants. These operations convert (9–95) to:

$$i_p = \sqrt{2}\, \frac{\mu E_g}{r_p + R_L} \cos \omega t + B E_g{}^2 + B E_g{}^2 \cos 2\omega t \tag{9-97}$$

Thus the overall results of the use of a sinusoidal excitation voltage with a parabolic dynamic characteristic are:

(a) To produce in the load a fundamental-frequency current that is exactly in accordance with the prediction of the equivalent circuit.

(b) To increase the d-c current in tube and load from I_b to $I_b + BE_g{}^2$. This is of course the new average value of the total current, called I_{bs}.

(c) To introduce a second-harmonic a-c current whose *crest* value is just the same as the increase in the direct current, that is, $BE_g{}^2$.

The various current components are shown in correct phase relationship in Fig. 9.19. The dotted curve represents the total current. The zero axis for all components is at $i_b = I_b$.

Let $I_{b\,max}$ and $I_{b\,min}$ represent the maximum and minimum instantaneous values of total plate current. These can be determined graphically from a diagram like Fig. 9.19. Let I' and I'' represent the amplitudes (crest values) of the fundamental and second-harmonic currents respectively. Then, from the figure,

$$I_{b\,max} = I_b + I' + I'' + I'' \qquad (9\text{-}98)$$

$$I_{b\,min} = I_b - I' + I'' + I'' \qquad (9\text{-}99)$$

I'' occurs once for the second harmonic and once for the d-c increment, in each equation. Subtraction of these equations gives

$$I' = \frac{I_{b\,max} - I_{b\,min}}{2} \qquad (9\text{-}100)$$

Addition of them gives

$$I'' = \frac{I_{b\,max} + I_{b\,min} - 2I_b}{4} \qquad (9\text{-}101)$$

The percentage of second-harmonic distortion is of course $100 \times (I''/I')$.

9.21 Third Harmonic Introduced by Dynamic Characteristic of Cubic Form. When a power amplifier pentode is used in a Class A amplifier, the dynamic characteristic may have a point of inflection in the working range. It cannot then be represented, even approximately, by a parabola. In such a case the true shape can often be reasonably well approximated by a cubic equation; see Fig. 9.20. The equation of a dynamic characteristic of this type, with the origin taken at Q, is

$$i_p = Ae_g + Be_g{}^2 + Ce_g{}^3 \qquad (9\text{-}102)$$

As with the second-degree curve, A is the slope at Q and is related to tube and circuit constants according to (9-92). A is acceptably evaluated in any particular case as the slope of a tangent, at Q, to the dynamic characteristic.

When the sinusoidal expression for the excitation voltage is introduced, the first two terms of (9-102) produce exactly the three terms that appear in (9–97). The term in $e_g{}^3$ becomes $2\sqrt{2}\,CE_g{}^3\cos^3 \omega t$. This can be expanded by the relation

$$\cos^3 \omega t = \tfrac{3}{4}\cos \omega t + \tfrac{1}{4}\cos 3\omega t \qquad (9\text{–}103)$$

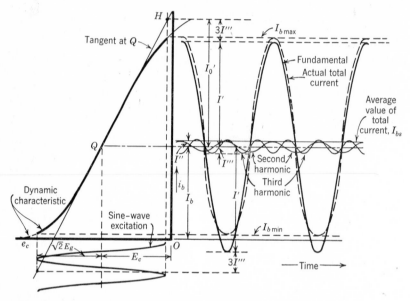

Fig. 9.20 Production of second and third harmonics, also shift of average current, when the dynamic characteristic is of cubic form.

I_0' is amplitude of the equivalent circuit fundamental-frequency prediction. I' is the actual fundamental-frequency amplitude. The average current shifts from a no-signal value I_b (at Q) to a larger value I_{bs} when the signal is present.

If, as in Fig. 9.20, C is negative, the third-degree term contributes a subtraction from the fundamental, also a third-harmonic term, thus:

$$\text{Term in } e_g{}^3 \text{ contributes}\bigg\} \; \frac{3}{\sqrt{2}}CE_g{}^3\cos \omega t + \frac{1}{\sqrt{2}}CE_g{}^3\cos 3\omega t \qquad (9\text{–}104)$$

Thus the overall results of the use of a sinusoidal excitation voltage with a dynamic characteristic of cubic form, with C negative, are:

(a) To produce a fundamental-frequency current in the load that is less than that predicted by the equivalent circuit, by three times the value of the third harmonic; see (9–104). Therefore

$$\text{RMS value of fundamental-frequency component}\atop\text{of load current}\bigg\} = \frac{\mu E_g}{r_p + R_L} + \frac{3}{2}CE_g{}^3 \qquad (9\text{–}105)$$

(b) To increase the d-c current from I_b to a new value $I_b + BE_g{}^2$, called I_{bs}.

(c) To introduce a second-harmonic current component whose crest value is the same as the increase in d-c current, that is $BE_g{}^2$. If the dynamic characteristic is symmetrical with respect to Q, $B = 0$, and there is no second-harmonic component.

(d) To introduce a third-harmonic current component whose crest value is $CE_g{}^3/\sqrt{2}$, rms value $CE_g{}^3/2$.

The fundamental-frequency component, both harmonic components, the increase in d-c current, and the total current (dotted) are all illustrated in Fig. 9.20. The zero axis for all components is at $i_b = I_b$.

At the maximum value of plate current the fundamental, the d-c increment, and the second harmonic are all positive, the third harmonic negative, so that

$$I_{b\,\text{max}} = I_b + I' + I'' + I'' - I''' \qquad (9\text{--}106)$$

At the minimum value of plate current only the fundamental is negative, the d-c increment and both harmonics being positive, so that

$$I_{b\,\text{min}} = I_b - I' + I'' + I'' + I''' \qquad (9\text{--}107)$$

Addition of these two equations leads to

$$I'' = \frac{I_{b\,\text{max}} + I_{b\,\text{min}} - 2I_b}{4} \qquad (9\text{--}108)$$

Thus the second harmonic and the d-c increment are evaluated exactly as in the previous section. Subtraction of the same equations gives

$$I_{b\,\text{max}} - I_{b\,\text{min}} = 2I' - 2I''' \qquad (9\text{--}109)$$

This rearranges into

$$I' = \frac{I_{b\,\text{max}} - I_{b\,\text{min}}}{2} + I''' \qquad (9\text{--}110)$$

This last equation shows that the fundamental-frequency component of the load current has an amplitude differing from half the plate current swing by just the amplitude of the third harmonic.

The third harmonic can be evaluated, and the true crest value of the fundamental then obtained, by use of a tangent drawn to the dynamic characteristic at Q. At the point H in Fig. 9.20 this tangent reaches the extreme positive value of grid voltage. The current I_0', *measurable graphically*, is the crest value of the fundamental that is predicted by the equivalent circuit. That is, $I_0' = \sqrt{2}\,AE_g$. From (9–105), the actual fundamental is less than the equivalent circuit prediction, by three times the third-harmonic amplitude. Therefore

$$I' = I_0' - 3I''' \qquad (9\text{--}111)$$

This can be introduced into (9–109), and a solution for I''' obtained in the form

$$I''' = \frac{2I_0' - (I_{b\max} - I_{b\min})}{8} \qquad (9\text{–}112)$$

On using this in (9–110), it appears that

$$I' = \frac{3(I_{b\max} - I_{b\min}) + 2I_0'}{8} \qquad (9\text{–}113)$$

It has just been shown how to determine, entirely by graphical means, the amplitudes of the fundamental, the d-c increment, and the second and third harmonics for a dynamic characteristic that is best approximated by a cubic curve. Ordinarily the existence of the third harmonic is of more consequence than the modification in value of fundamental that goes along with it. Considerable reverse curvature is required to produce an appreciable third harmonic; thus the very pronounced inflection in the curve of Fig. 9.20 produces only a $6\frac{1}{4}$ per cent third harmonic.

It is sometimes useful to express the combined effects of the various harmonics as follows:

$$\left.\begin{array}{r}\text{Per cent total har-}\\ \text{monic distortion}\end{array}\right\} = \frac{\sqrt{I''^2 + I'''^2 + I''''^2 + \cdots}}{I'} \times 100 \quad (9\text{–}114)$$

Ordinarily harmonics higher than the second and third are so small as to escape attention, except in *frequency multiplying devices*, which are designed to maximize certain harmonics.

9.22   Class B Amplifiers. Up to this point in the text attention has been confined to Class A amplifier operation. As pointed out in Section 9.16, this type of operation results in low plate circuit efficiency, whereas a Class B amplifier can be designed to operate at a reasonably high plate circuit efficiency. The essential distinguishing feature of a Class B amplifier is that it is *biased to cut-off*, or approximately so. The meaning of this phrase is illustrated by Fig. 9.21. The grid bias E_{cc} in this figure extends approximately to the lower end or cut-off point of the dynamic characteristic.

In typical Class B operation, illustrated by Fig. 9.21:

(a) The plate current consists of half-wave impulses. To the extent that the dynamic characteristic approaches a straight line with a sharp turn at cut-off, the plate current impulses approach true half sine waves, sometimes called *sine loops*.

(b) Grid current is to be expected during a part of each positive grid swing. For this reason the source of grid excitation must have an internal impedance low relative to that between cathode and positive grid. If the source of excitation voltage has a high internal impedance, the flow of grid current causes an internal voltage drop which flattens the positive wave crests of the excitation voltage. This distortion of excitation voltage is of course amplified and appears in the output.

(c) The crest values, also the rms and average values, of the plate current loops are proportional to the excitation voltage if the dynamic characteristic is a straight line. Because of this *linear* relation between the excitation voltage and the plate current, such an amplifier is sometimes called a *linear* Class B amplifier.

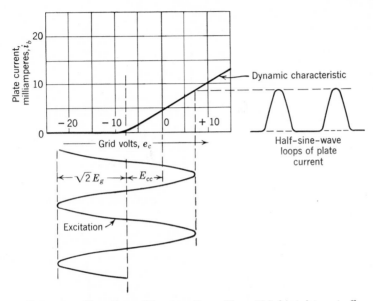

FIG. 9.21. Class B amplifier operation. The grid is biased to cut-off.

(d) The variations in plate current are much larger in proportion to its average steady value than is true for Class A amplifiers. Because these variations provide the useful output, and the average current measures the plate circuit power demand, the plate circuit efficiency is much higher than for Class A amplifiers. Furthermore, the existence of a large a-c component of plate current tends to *reduce* the plate dissipation (see Section 9.16).

(e) Plate current variations of the type indicated in Fig. 9.21, though possessing the merit of linearity, are not directly serviceable because they are very far from being full-sine-wave variations. The sine-loop type of plate current contains very pronounced harmonics.

These sine-loop impulses can be made useful either (a) by employing a *push-pull* circuit which matches each half sine wave with its mate of opposite polarity, thus producing a full sine wave reasonably free from harmonics, or (b) by using a tuned plate circuit which eliminates the harmonics. The push-pull type is usually employed with audio-frequency excitation, the tuned type with modulated radio-frequency excitation. The push-pull type is discussed in the next section. Discussions of Class B tuned ("linear") amplifiers are given in various texts.[9A, C, D, E, H, L, M, b]

9.23 Class B Push-Pull Amplifiers. Figure 9.22 is a circuit diagram and Fig. 9.23 a plate current-grid voltage diagram for a push-

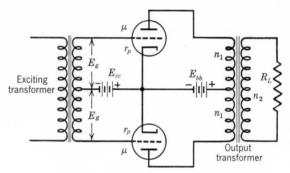

FIG. 9.22 Push-pull amplifier circuit.

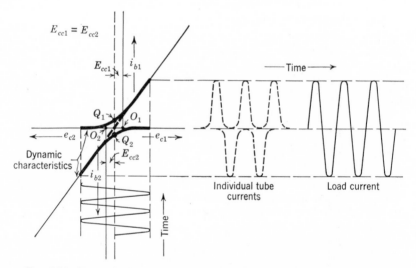

FIG. 9.23 Dynamic characteristics for Class B push-pull amplifier operation.

pull Class B amplifier. The plate circuits are coupled to the load by means of a transformer. An analysis of transformer-coupling principles appears later, in Sections 10.5 and 10.6. For the present it is necessary only to bear in mind that a transformer's voltage ratio is the same as its turns ratio, and that primary ampere turns must equal secondary ampere turns.

The excitation voltage is introduced through a center-tapped transformer, so that one grid swings positive while the other swings negative. In Fig. 9.23 grid voltages for one tube are plotted positively toward the right, those for the other positively toward the left, so that a common sine wave can be used for illustrating grid excitations. The plate current coordinate directions are similarly reversed. The grid bias is the same for the two tubes.

The pronounced fillets in the dynamic characteristics near cut-off make each tube produce current loops that are decidedly widened out at the bottom. However, the transformer coupling into the load gives the two tube currents opposite effects on current in the load, so that the fillet currents cancel one another. A resultant or composite dynamic characteristic, whose plate current is everywhere the algebraic sum of the plate currents in the two tubes, can be used to predict the load-current wave form. In Fig. 9.23 this composite characteristic consists of the straight slant portions of the two individual characteristics, plus a short dotted extension across the gap between them. If the composite dynamic characteristic is a straight line, the current in the load is free from harmonics.

In Figs. 9.18, 9.19, and 9.20 the zero reference axis for the various a-c components of load current is a horizontal line through Q. The origin of the equations used for approximating the shapes of the dynamic characteristics in these figures was taken at Q. In Fig. 9.23 the reference axis is the common zero-plate-current axis. The origin of an approximating equation is therefore taken along this axis, at a point midway between Q_1 and Q_2. The composite dynamic characteristic, whether straight or curved, is necessarily symmetrical about that point. Therefore it can be approximated by a cubic equation that has no second-degree term and so introduces no second-harmonic current term. Thus the output of a symmetrical push-pull amplifier is free from second-harmonic distortion; *all* even harmonics are eliminated by such a circuit. Only odd harmonics can appear.

9.24 Dynamic Characteristics and Equivalent Circuits for Push-Pull Amplifiers.[9b, A, C, D, E, H, L, M] The push-pull circuit illustrated in Fig. 9.22 can be used for either Class A or Class B operation, or for intermediate Class AB operation. For each type of operation even harmonics are eliminated, and the steady components of plate current oppose each other magnetically in the transformer core, eliminating any tendency toward core saturation.

A plate current-grid voltage diagram for a Class A push-pull amplifier appears in Fig. 9.24. Class A operation is indicated in that the tubes are not biased to cut-off, and the grids do not swing positive. The composite dynamic characteristic represents, as before, the algebraic sum of the two plate currents for a given grid voltage, and its symmetry permits only odd harmonics. In this case the individual-tube plate current variations do not extend downward to the zero current axis.

Class A push-pull amplifier operation can be analyzed by means of the equivalent circuit diagram in Fig. 9.25a. The load resistance R_L is

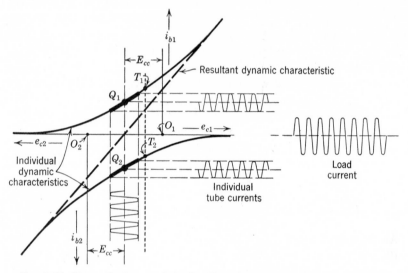

Fig. 9.24 Dynamic characteristics for Class A push-pull amplifier operation.

just that used in the actual circuit. However, the two tubes feed through a common transformer core into a common load resistance, so that a little study is necessary to determine what value of load resistance should be used in (9–57) to determine the slope of the dynamic characteristics at the Q's.[9b]

In a Class A push-pull amplifier neither tube's current-voltage locus extends appreciably beyond the region in which the tube characteristic curves are approximately straight. Therefore the plate resistances of the two tubes are equal and approximately uniform throughout each cycle. The primary circuit in Fig. 9.25a therefore has identical values of r_p in its upper and lower halves.

The middle connection in this diagram is shown dotted because the tubes produce equal and opposite fundamental-frequency currents through it; hence its net fundamental-frequency current is zero. It may therefore be omitted in the analysis of fundamental-frequency Class A operation.

With the middle (dotted-line) connection omitted, and the two excitation voltages, as well as values of μ and r_p, alike, it is evident that

$$-2\mu E_g = 2I_z r_p + 2E_p \qquad (9\text{-}115)$$

The usual simple transformer relations require that

$$2E_p = \frac{2n_1}{n_2} I_j R_L \qquad \text{and} \qquad n_2 I_j = 2n_1 I_z \qquad (9\text{-}116)$$

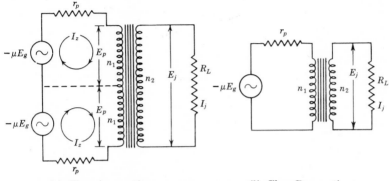

(a) Class A operation.   (b) Class B operation.

FIG. 9.25   Equivalent circuit diagrams for push-pull operation.

An expression for the gain E_j/E_g is easily derived by using these in (9-115). To determine how the load affects tube operation, equations (9-116) are combined to give an expression for E_p, as follows:

$$2E_p = I_z \left(\frac{2n_1}{n_2}\right)^2 R_L \qquad (9\text{-}117)$$

The use of this equation converts (9-115) to

$$-2\mu E_g = 2I_z r_p + I_z \left(\frac{2n_1}{n_2}\right)^2 R_L \qquad (9\text{-}118)$$

After substituting $-I_p$ for I_z, this can be written

$$\frac{I_p}{E_g} = \frac{\mu}{r_p + 2R_L(n_1/n_2)^2} \qquad (9\text{-}119)$$

Since both dynamic characteristics are straight or nearly so within the range of grid swing, their slopes are uniform and equal to i_p/e_g, so to I_p/E_g. Therefore

$$\frac{di_b}{de_c} = \frac{\mu}{r_p + 2R_L(n_1/n_2)^2} \qquad [\text{at the } Q\text{'s}] \qquad (9\text{-}120)$$

Comparison with (9–57) shows that the dynamic characteristics must have at the Q's the same slope as though each tube were in a single-tube Class A amplifier, with a load resistance of $2R_L(n_1/n_2)^2$ ohms. Thus in push-pull *Class A operation* each tube may be said to be "working into" a resistance of the magnitude just stated, whereas the "plate-to-plate" resistance is twice this value, that is, $4R_L(n_1/n_2)^2$ ohms.

In a *Class B* push-pull amplifier the current flows through the two tubes alternately, each one being an open circuit while the other carries current. The two circuit halves in Fig. 9.25a then carry current in alternate half-cycles, the middle dotted connection completing the circuit for both. Because the two halves are identical and work alternately, they can be satisfactorily represented by either one working alone continuously, as in the Class B push-pull equivalent circuit diagram of Fig. 9.25b. Calculations based on this circuit can be used to predict the gain.

The use in connection with Fig. 9.25b of relations similar to (9–116) shows that in Class B operation each tube is "working into" a resistance of $R_L(n_1/n_2)^2$ ohms, half the value found for Class A operation. The "plate-to-plate" resistance is still $4R_L(n_1/n_2)^2$.

The major (straight-slant) parts of the individual dynamic character-istics in Fig. 9.23 have slopes that are described by using $R_L(n_1/n_2)^2$ for the load resistance in (9–57). Neither the load lines nor the dynamic characteristics are, over these major straight portions, directly in line with the points Q on their respective diagrams.*

Figure 9.24 may be thought of as a detail, to an enlarged scale, of a small portion of Fig. 9.23; thus in the immediate neighborhood of the Q's the two diagrams are identical in nature.

PROBLEMS

In order to work properly many of the problems for Chapters IX and X, it is desirable to have reproduced for class use sets of plate characteristic curves of the following standard tubes: 6C5G, 6SN7, 6SJ7, 6L6.

1. A 6C5G triode is used in the Fig. 9.3 circuit. Grid bias E_C is -8 volts, plate battery voltage 350, $R_L = 20{,}000.$

---

* The load line in Thompson's useful method of graphical analysis of push-pull operation [9b] is drawn with a slope corresponding to $R_L(n_1/n_2)^2$, the resistance that each tube works into in Class B operation. His curve descriptive of effective operating conditions for one tube has the slope $1/2R_L(n_1/n_2)^2$ at passage through the Class A operating point and is asymptotic to the straight Class B load line of slope $1/R_L(n_1/n_2)^2$.

(a) On a set of 6C5G plate characteristics draw the load line; determine from it plate voltage and current at the point Q of zero excitation, and on a separate sheet plot the corresponding dynamic characteristic.

(b) Locate the ends of the current-voltage locus on both load line and dynamic characteristic, for an excitation of 3 volts (rms); determine voltage gain by inspection of the current-voltage loci.

(c) Determine r_p and μ graphically from the plate characteristic curves; then calculate gain from equation (9–37). Compare with (b).

(d) Plot the mutual characteristic, for plate voltage as at Q, on the graph that contains the dynamic characteristic. Measure its slope at Q, which is g_m at Q; see how nearly this checks the result obtained by using r_p and μ from (c) in $\mu = g_m r_p$.

2. Circuit similar to Prob. 1, tube the same; the load now contains a 15,000-ohm inductive reactance in series with the 20,000-ohm resistance.

(a) On the plate characteristic set for this tube, spot the following six points of the elliptical e_b, i_b current-voltage locus: the upper and lower extreme values of i_b, two points for which i_b has the same value as at Q, two points for which e_b has the same value as at Q. Also draw vertical lines to which the two ends of the ellipse must be tangent. Sketch the ellipse.

(b) Transfer (point-by-point) this ellipse to an i_b, e_c diagram, in just the way a load line is transferred to become a dynamic characteristic.

3. Plate current for a certain triode is approximated by the relation $i_b = 17 \times 10^{-5} [e_c + (e_b/8)]^{1.7}$ amp.

(a) Find i_b when $e_c = -15$, $e_b = 200$; find r_p and g_m at this point.

(b) If a load resistance of 10,000 ohms is provided, and grid bias is -15, what plate battery voltage will make i_b at Q have the (a) value?

(c) Determine voltage gain for conditions as in (b).

4. Find approximate values of μ, r_p, g_m, at the point $e_b = 180$, $e_c = 12.5$, if: $i_b = 7.5$ (ma) when $e_b = 180$, $e_c = -12.5$; $i_b = 7.5$ when $e_b = 160$, $e_c = -10$; $i_b = 7.84$ when $e_b = 180$, $e_c = -12.3$.

5. A 6SN7 triode is used in a Class A amplifier; $E_{cc} = -8$ volts; i_b at Q is 6 ma.

(a) State e_b at Q, and determine graphically μ and r_p at Q.

(b) What output resistance R_L should be used to give maximum a-c power in R_L, if the grid excitation is 2 volts rms?

(c) Using this R_L, determine the voltage gain, output power, and plate circuit efficiency.

6. A 6C5G triode (Fig. 6.2) is used in a series-feed Class A amplifier, Fig. 9.3. $R_L = 25,000$; e_c and e_b at Q are -8 and $+250$.

(a) On a set of 6C5G plate characteristics, draw the load line. Locate the point of Q of zero excitation; state i_b at Q, and E_{bb}.

(b) Grid excitation 5 volts rms. Find plate circuit efficiency, plate dissipation.

(c) The circuit is changed to parallel feed, Fig. 9.17. The frequency is high enough so that all the alternating current may be assumed to pass through R_L. What new plate battery voltage E_{bb} will produce operation along the same load line as in (a), grid bias unchanged?

(d) Determine the new plate circuit efficiency and plate dissipation.

7. Parallel-feed amplifier as in (c), Prob. 6. At 25 cycles, what values of L and C will make the gain 70.7 per cent of its high-frequency value, and also make $X_C/R_L = r_p/X_L$? State input-to-output phase angle at 25 cycles, for these values of L and C.

8. A 6SJ7 tube (Fig. 6.15) is used in a Class A amplifier; series feed, as shown in Fig. 6.14b. Grid excitation 1 volt rms.

(a) On a set of 6SJ7 plate characteristics, draw a load line intersecting the $e_c = 0$ curve a little to the right of the knee, and going to cut-off ($i_b = 0$) at $e_b = 300$. Point Q is at $e_c = -1.5$ volts. Mark on a circuit diagram d-c grid, plate, and screen voltages, and value of R_L.

(c) Identify on the load line the extremes of the current-voltage locus. Find the voltage gain, by inspection of your diagram.

(d) Determine r_p and g_m graphically, at Q, from the plate characteristics; employ them in the current-generator gain equation to determine voltage gain. Note that a reasonably accurate gain determination is possible this way, even though only a rough approximation to r_p can be obtained.

(e) How much error would result here from use of the rather common pentode gain approximation: gain = $g_m R_L$?

9. A 6SN7 triode is used in a parallel-feed amplifier (the frequency being high enough to make X_L very large and X_C very small) under the following conditions, selected to minimize distortion and maximize power output, without excessive dissipation: i_b is not to fall below 1.5 ma; e_b is not to exceed 300 volts; $R_L = 21,600$; e_c is not to swing above zero. (For a 2A3 triode, i_b and e_b limits might be 15 ma and 300 volts, with $R_L = 1600$.)

(a) On a set of plate characteristic curves, draw the load line, identify the point Q of zero excitation, and state the grid bias voltage, plate battery voltage, and *plate current under zero excitation conditions*.

(b) State the rms grid excitation voltage necessary for maximum power output, subject to the limitations stated above.

(c) State rms values of load resistance current and voltage, with the (b) excitation.

(d) State the power output and plate dissipation.

(e) Determine the per cent second harmonic distortion.

10. A 6L6 beam power tube (a tetrode) is operated with the point Q of zero excitation at $E_c = -10$, $E_b = +300$, $R_L = 6000$, parallel feed. $E_{b\,max} = 400$, $E_{b\,min} = 200$. (a) Draw the circuit diagram, showing connections between the various electrodes and other circuit components. (b) Draw the load line, on a set of 6L6 plate characteristics. (c) State the plate battery voltage. (d) Determine by simple graphical means the grid excitation voltage. (e) State power output, plate dissipation, and plate circuit efficiency. (f) Determine the harmonic distortion, quantitatively.

11. Derive an equation, using Thévenin's theorem, for the ratio of the output voltage E_j to the generator voltage E_g, for the Fig. 9.26 circuit.

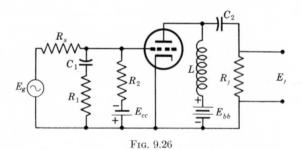

FIG. 9.26

12. Same as Prob. 11, but using Norton's theorem.

13. The voltage generator equivalent circuit of an amplifier is as in Fig. 9.27.

(a) Draw the vector diagram showing the relations between $-E_g$, E_j, E_p, I_2, I_1, and I_z.

(b) Derive from this diagram expressions for voltage gain (E_j/E_g) and for phase angle between E_j, E_g, in terms of μ, r_p, R_j, X_1, and X_2.

(c) Draw the corresponding *current generator* equivalent circuit; identify on it r_p, X_1, X_2, R_j; indicate where current I_z flows, and where E_p exists.

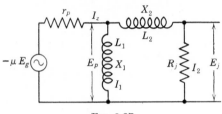

Fig. 9.27

14. A tuned amplifier has a current generator equivalent circuit as in Fig. 9.28.

(a) Draw the vector diagram relating E_p, I_z, I_{gen}, and E_g (showing all contributory vectors) for the nonresonant condition, that is, $X_L \neq X_C$. To make the diagram convenient to study, make X_L about twice X_C.

(b) Using this current generator vector diagram, derive the equations for voltage gain and for phase angle between input and output voltages. Output voltage is that across the capacitance.

(c) Reduce these to the resonant-frequency gain equations by letting $X_L = X_C$.

(d) For $X_L = X_C$, express, in terms of R, L, and C only, the ratio I_C/I_{RL}.

(e) State the input-to-output phase angle for the frequency that makes the algebraic sum of I_L and I_C numerically equal to the sum of I_{RL} and I_{rp}.

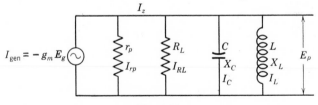

Fig. 9.28

15. The load circuit of a certain tuned amplifier is a capacitance C in parallel with a series combination of inductance L and resistance R. Output voltage is that across the capacitance. Using the current generator equivalent circuit:

(a), (b), (c), (d): As in Prob. 14, except in (c) add the requirement that $R^2 \ll X_L^2$.

(e) If, in (c), $X_L = X_C = 1000$, and $R = 100$, what is the impedance of the L, R, C combination (the "tank circuit"), considered as a unit?

16. Work parts (a), (b), and (c) of Prob. 15, except that the output voltage (E_0) is now that across the resistance R; *use E_0 as the reference vector in the (a) diagram.*

17. A 6C5G tube is used in a Class A amplifier circuit; the point of zero excitation is at $I_b = 5$ ma, $E_c = -6$; $R_L = 30,000$.

(a) What rms value of excitation will just cause grid current to flow? What value will just cause i_b to become zero at one point in each cycle?

(b) The excitation exceeds the last-stated value by 3 volts. Sketch, approximately to scale, the plate current wave form, assuming a large grid resistor.

18. The dynamic characteristic of a Class A amplifier is represented satisfactorily within the operating range by a parabola whose vertex is at $i_b = 2$ ma, $e_c = -18$ volts, and passes through $i_b = 10$ ma, $e_c = 0$. Grid bias is -9.

(a) Write the equation of this parabola, using the point Q of zero excitation as the origin of i_p, e_p, coordinates.

(b) An excitation voltage $E_g = 4$ volts (rms) is used. Find the per cent second-harmonic distortion, the steady component of current in the plate circuit, and the rms value of the fundamental-frequency component of plate current.

19. A 2A3 triode is to be used with a 2000-ohm resistance load. Plate battery voltage 360.

(a) What bias voltage will make the quiescent current 62 ma?

(b) Operation as in (a); grid excitation is sinusoidal, at 21.2 volts rms. Find $I_{b\,max}$ and $I_{b\,min}$.

(c) Determine voltage gain, a-c power output, plate dissipation, plate circuit efficiency.

(d) Determine I', I'', I''' (harmonic components).

20. Two tubes, characteristics as in Fig. 9.5, are used in a circuit like Fig. 9.22. $E_{bb} = 400$, $E_{cc} = -95$, $R_L = 400$, $n_2/n_1 = 0.4$; $E_g = 60$ volts rms.

(a) Does this choice of magnitudes result in Class A, B, or C operation?

(b) Draw the equivalent circuit, labeling magnitudes of the circuit elements.

(c) Draw the composite dynamic characteristic, and determine from it the per cent second harmonic distortion, also the per cent third harmonic distortion.

(d) Determine voltage gain, plate circuit efficiency, plate dissipation.

21. Same as Prob. 20, except that $E_{cc} = -40$, $E_g = 10$ (rms).

22. Figure 9.29 illustrates an *amplitude-modulated* a-c voltage. It alternates sinusoidally at a high frequency f_1, the *carrier frequency*, but peak values of the alternation vary as follows:

$$E_{max} = E_a + E_b \cos 2\pi f_2 t$$

Here f_2 is the modulation frequency and is very much less than f_1.

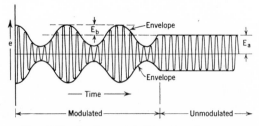

FIG. 9.29   Audio modulation of carrier wave.

(a) Express mathematically the time variation of the instantaneous value of the modulated voltage as illustrated in Fig. 9.29.

(*b*) Expand this trigonometrically into three cosine terms, which will be: (1) a carrier-frequency term in cos $2\pi f_1 t$, (2) a lower sideband term in cos $2\pi(f_1 - f_2)t$, and (3) an upper sideband term in cos $2\pi(f_1 + f_2)t$.

(*c*) A modulated voltage, $E_a = 16$, $E_b = 10$, $f = 1500$, excites a Class B amplifier used as a detector. The circuit is as in Fig. 9.3, the dynamic characteristic being practically a straight line, as in Fig. 9.21. Along this line,

$$e_c = -30 \text{ volts when } i_b = 0$$
$$i_b = 12 \text{ ma when } e_c = 0$$

Grid bias is -30 volts. Write the equation for an oscillographic trace of the plate current, if the oscillograph is only capable of following variations at frequencies less than 5000 cycles per second. (The oscillograph serves as a filter.)

CHAPTER X

AMPLIFIER COUPLING; OSCILLATORS

10.1 Cascading of Amplifiers; Voltage Gain and Decibel Gain. It is frequently necessary to use more than one amplifier, or, according to the more common phraseology, more than one stage of amplification. In multistage amplifiers the output voltage of the first stage is the input voltage (excitation) of the second stage, the output of the second stage the input of the third, and so on. The overall voltage gain of a multistage amplifier is of course the product of the gains of the individual stages.

The term "decibel gain," abbreviated to "db gain," is frequently used.[9K, N] It is a measure of the logarithm of the gain, so that the overall db gain of a multistage amplifier is the sum of the db gains of the individual stages. The definition of the db gain of an amplifier is

$$\text{db gain} = 10 \log_{10} \left(\frac{\text{output watts}}{\text{input watts}} \right) \qquad (10\text{--}1)$$

Decibel gain is thus originally defined as a measure of *power gain* rather than of voltage gain.

This seems a little strange, for one of the useful properties of many amplifiers is that no power is required to vary the grid potential. Thus the power input to the grid is zero; yet according to the definition just stated the db gain of an amplifier measures the ratio of power output to power input.

The explanation of this apparent contradiction is found in early and still current telephone engineering practice. Long-distance telephone circuits employ amplifiers, called "repeaters," located at appropriate distances. Each section of telephone transmission line is connected at its far end to ("terminates in") a resistance. The line current flows through this resistance. The resulting voltage drop across the resistance is the excitation voltage for a repeater. This repeater's load is the next section of transmission line, which terminates in the input resistance of another repeater, whose load is the next section of transmission line, and so on.

This practice has given rise to the telephone engineer's habit of specifying the input and output resistances R_1 and R_2 (the latter heretofore called R_L) for which any given amplifier is suited. The watts input and watts output in (10–1) refer to the power in these resistances, due to a-c input and output voltages E_1 (for E_g) and E_2 (for E_p).

Thus db gain can also be expressed as follows:

$$\text{db gain} = 10 \log_{10} \frac{(E_2{}^2/R_2)}{(E_1{}^2/R_1)} = 20 \log_{10} \frac{E_2}{E_1} \sqrt{\frac{R_1}{R_2}} \qquad (10\text{–}2)$$

If $R_1 = R_2$, as is often true, this simplifies to

$$\text{db (voltage) gain} = 20 \log_{10} \frac{E_2}{E_1} \qquad (10\text{–}3)$$

Only if the input and output resistances are equal does (10–3) give the db gain as defined by (10–1). Equation (10–3) is, however, sometimes used as a definition of the db voltage gain of an amplifier, without regard to the input or output resistances or the power in them.

Note that (10–1) and (10–3) may in general give different results as applied to a given amplifier, each result having a useful meaning if properly interpreted. One is a logarithmic measure of power gain, the other of voltage gain.

10.2 D-C Amplifiers. Each stage of amplification must in general be treated as a distinct unit, with its own real and its own equivalent circuit. However, some provision must always be made for coupling the a-c output voltage of one stage into the grid circuit of the next. It is desirable to do this in a way that permits use of a common d-c source of plate current for all tubes, and of a common source of filament heating current, usually a filament transformer; thus it is desirable to have all cathodes at a common potential.

Figure 10.1 illustrates a multistage amplifier circuit which satisfies these requirements formally. The a-c part of the voltage across each load resistor is also the a-c component of the grid voltage for the succeeding tube. This amplifier contains neither chokes nor condensers; only tubes, batteries, and resistors occur. It is consequently suitable in principle for amplifying d-c and transient, as well as a-c, input voltages. However, this circuit is almost never used for multistage amplification, because of the following practical shortcomings:

(a) Each grid bias voltage is dependent on the steady plate current of the preceding stage, which depends in turn on the preceding grid bias, which depends on the preceding plate current, and so on. Readjustment of bias, plate voltage, or load resistance of any stage necessitates readjustments of grid battery voltages in all succeeding stages.

(*b*) Bias voltages invariably exhibit small-magnitude slow variations, because of various minor effects such as changes in temperatures of batteries, resistors, etc. This "drift" is never more than a very small fraction of the battery voltage, percentagewise, but the "bucking-out" batteries in the grid circuits of Fig. 10.1 have voltages large enough so that a small percentage change may be an important fraction of the small d-c bias voltage required at the grid. Any such small bias drift in an early stage is amplified and appears as a serious shift from the normal bias in later stages.

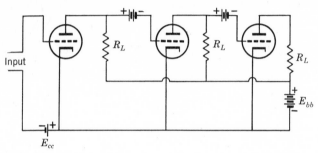

FIG. 10.1 Three-stage amplifier, without condensers or chokes such as are used in the circuits of Figs. 10.3 and 10.4. This circuit is suitable in principle for amplifying d-c, transient, or a-c voltages, but is practically inadequate; see also Fig. 10.2. Cathodes at a common potential, permitting the use of a common filament heater source.

(*c*) The physical bulk of each bias battery introduces a relatively large stray capacitance to "ground," and to bias batteries in other stages. This can provide an unwanted interstage coupling, as between fourth and second, or fifth and third stages, which may produce positive feedback (see Section 10.7) with resulting parasitic oscillations, usually of the "motor-boating" type that periodically damp out, then recur.

(*d*) The bias battery stray capacitance can make the gain fall off rapidly as the frequency rises into the upper audio-frequency range. Thus this circuit may respond inadequately to fast transients.

Figure 10.2 is a diagram of a serviceable type of d-c amplifier, in which the price paid for freedom from the troubles just described is the sacrifice of about half the gain per stage, the use of "regulated power supplies," which hold E_{bb} and E_{cc} constant within very close limits, and the use of high-quality stable precision resistors for R_{g1} and R_{g2}. E_{cc} is of the same order of magnitude as E_{bb}; correct bias is maintained by proper proportioning of R_{g1} and R_{g2}. Note the complete absence of capacitances, or of bulky circuit elements which might introduce stray capacitance; the upper-frequency limit results only from capacitances inherent in the tubes.

The foregoing discussion has illustrated the general nature of the circuit design problem of determining the best way to obtain coupling, yet maintain the proper grid bias at each stage. This problem is universally difficult and expensive with d-c amplifiers but relatively easy with a-c amplifiers. The use of d-c amplifiers should be avoided whenever possible.

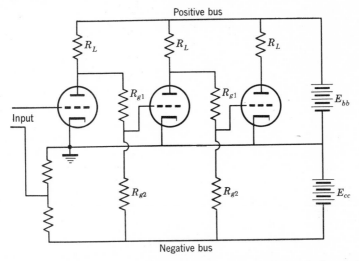

Fig. 10.2 Three-stage d-c amplifier of a useful type, employing both a positive and a negative bus. E_{bb} and E_{cc} are regulated power supplies; E_{cc} is of the same order of magnitude as E_{bb}. Cathodes are at a common potential.

10.3 Transformer and Condenser Coupling. The coupling problem becomes relatively simple with a-c excitation voltages. The output voltage from one stage can then be transmitted to the succeeding grid by means of a condenser or a transformer. Either device provides the necessary d-c insulation, so that "bucking-out" grid batteries are not required. Figure 10.3 illustrates the use of transformers, Fig. 10.4 that of condensers, for coupling between stages. Filament supplies have been omitted from the diagrams. Both arrangements permit the use of common plate, grid, and filament voltage sources.

Load resistors are not needed in the plate circuits of the first two stages in Fig. 10.3 because each transformer has a high a-c primary impedance, which serves the purpose of a load resistance. At normal frequencies these first two stages have the equivalent of infinite a-c load resistances; their load lines are horizontal lines through the operating points.

When coupling is accomplished by means of condensers, as in Fig. 10.4, the resistances marked R_L may in some cases be replaced by chokes. Then the R_G's serve as load resistances. The circuit for each stage is then identical with the parallel-feed amplifier arrangement illustrated in Fig. 9.17.

In an actual multistage amplifier an open circuit exists between grid and filament in each tube. Each amplifier circuit is separated from those adjacent to it by these open circuits. This necessitates completely separate handling of the successive equivalent circuits. The

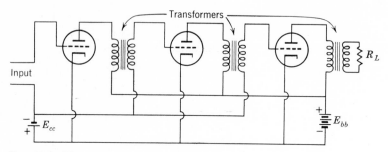

FIG. 10.3   Three-stage amplifier with transformer coupling, suitable for amplifying a-c signals.

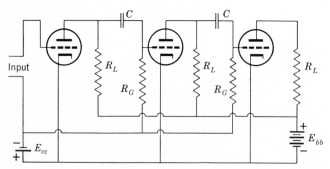

FIG. 10.4   Three-stage amplifier using resistance-condenser coupling (sometimes called RC coupling), suitable for amplifying a-c signals.

gain for each is calculated independently of the others, the total gain being the product of the individual gains. The total phase angle shift is the sum of the individual phase shifts.

At very high frequencies the grid-cathode impedance is not infinite because of interelectrode tube capacitances. Furthermore, the capacitances between the plate and other electrodes in a triode introduce disturbing capacitance coupling between adjacent stages. By the use of pentodes (or screen-grid tetrodes) and of electrostatic shielding between circuits outside the tubes, the a-c electric fields of the various stages can be successfully separated from each other even at high frequencies.

All stages of a multistage amplifier except the final one serve as voltage amplifiers and are therefore designed for substantial voltage gain, as far as choice of load resistance is concerned. The load of the final stage is, however, some useful device, e.g., a speaker for a radio receiver, a relay, an oscillograph element, etc.; the final tube properties are chosen accordingly. The voltage gain of the final stage may be very modest, or even fractional. The type of coupling to the final stage may differ from that to earlier stages, because of the different nature of the tube and its load.

10.4 Resistance-Condenser Coupling. Figures 10.5a and 10.5b are diagrams of the actual and equivalent circuits of a stage of amplification coupled to the grid of the next stage by means of a condenser and resistances. The resistance R_G in the grid circuit of the succeeding stage is large relative to R_L. It is therefore reasonable to assume that at all frequencies the a-c current through R_G and C is negligible relative to that through R_L. Subject to this approximation, the following familiar equation expresses the relation between E_p and E_g for any frequency:

$$\frac{E_p}{E_g} \cong \frac{\mu}{1 + \dfrac{r_p}{R_L}} \tag{10-4}$$

The actual gain E_j/E_g is sharply affected by frequency, because the voltage E_p splits vectorially between the resistance and the condenser in proportion to their impedances. If this is taken into account, the overall gain is, *approximately*, if $R_G \gg R_L$

$$\frac{E_j}{E_g} = \frac{E_j}{E_p}\frac{E_p}{E_g} \cong \frac{\mu}{\left(1 + \dfrac{r_p}{R_L}\right)} \frac{1}{\sqrt{1 + \dfrac{X_C^2}{R_G^2}}} \tag{10-5}$$

Figure 10.5c is the complete vector diagram for the equivalent circuit. An exact expression for gain is obtainable from this vector diagram by a process that closely parallels the derivation of (9-88) for the parallel-feed amplifier. The final result is

$$\frac{E_j}{E_g} = \frac{\mu}{\sqrt{\left(1 + \dfrac{r_p}{R_L} + \dfrac{r_p}{R_G}\right)^2 + \dfrac{X_C^2}{R_G^2}\left(1 + \dfrac{r_p}{R_L}\right)^2}} \tag{10-6}$$

The two terms in the radical are proportional to the components of $-\mu E_g$ that are respectively in phase with and at right angles to E_j.

This permits determination of the cosine of the angle ϕ between E_p and E_g.

It is left as an exercise for the reader to draw the current generator counterparts of Figs. 10.5b and 10.5c and to derive therefrom the current generator counterpart of (10–6), in which g_m appears, but μ does not.

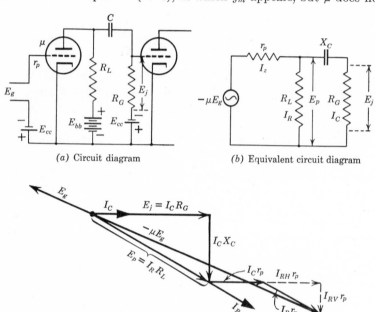

(a) Circuit diagram

(b) Equivalent circuit diagram

(c) Vector diagram for equivalent circuit

FIG. 10.5   Resistance-condenser (RC) coupling.

10.5   Transformer Coupling, Infinite Output Resistance.   Figure 10.6a and the solid lines of Fig. 10.6b illustrate the actual and equivalent circuits of a stage of amplification which is coupled to the grid of the next tube by a transformer of turns ratio $n(= n_2/n_1)$.   The d-c part of the plate current passes through the primary winding of the transformer, which has negligible d-c resistance.   The grid bias voltage for the next stage is applied through the secondary winding.

The secondary of the transformer is open-circuited, so that the primary winding affects the plate circuit behavior exactly as a simple inductance would.   It is therefore represented in the equivalent circuit by the inductance L_P, having reactance X_P ohms. X_P is the "primary reactance," corresponding to the ratio

$$\frac{\text{Primary volts}}{\text{Magnetizing-current amperes}}$$

of an ordinary transformer; X_P must not be confused with the transformer's leakage reactance, which is usually of minor importance in an amplifier.

The statement $E_j = nE_p$ in Fig. 10.6b is an essential part of the equivalent circuit concept. The actual output voltage E_j is taken

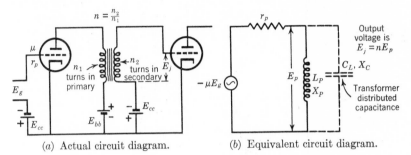

(a) Actual circuit diagram.   (b) Equivalent circuit diagram.

Fig. 10.6 Transformer-coupled amplifier with infinite load impedance. Transformer turns ratio $= n = n_2/n_1$.

from the transformer secondary, which is omitted from the diagram for the sake of simplicity. The gain expression is of course

$$\frac{E_j}{E_g} = \frac{nE_p}{E_g} = \frac{n\mu X_P}{\sqrt{r_p{}^2 + X_P{}^2}} = \frac{n\mu}{\sqrt{1 + \frac{r_p{}^2}{X_P{}^2}}} \qquad (10\text{-}7)$$

If the frequency becomes large enough so that $r_p/X_P \ll 1$, the gain approaches $n\mu$; if the frequency approaches zero, X_P and the gain both vanish.

This equation *apparently* indicates that the gain can be indefinitely magnified by increasing n; this indication is false, for reasons discussed below. It indicates, correctly, that to permit satisfactory operation at low musical frequencies (down toward 20 cycles per second) the primary inductance must be large. Primary inductance is related to the geometry and material of the transformer as indicated by the following equation:

$$L_P = n_1{}^2 \left(\frac{d\Phi}{dn_1 i_b}\right) \qquad (10\text{-}8)$$

Here $d\Phi/dn_1 i_b$ is the slope of the magnetization curve for the iron core of the transformer. The primary inductance can be made large either by making $d\Phi/dn_1 i_b$ large, which requires bulk, weight, and cost in the iron core, or by using a large number of primary turns.

However, the use of many primary turns necessitates the use of a proportionately large number of secondary turns, and with many secondary turns the distributed capacitance of the secondary winding causes loss of amplification at the upper end of the frequency range. This distributed capacitance, which grows rapidly as n_2 increases, is

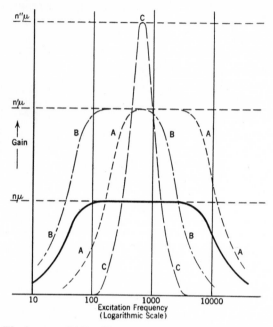

Fig. 10.7 The heavy solid line illustrates the variation of voltage gain with frequency in a transformer-coupled amplifier with infinite load resistance, turns ratio n, no leakage reactance. The effects of changes in turns ratio on frequency response are illustrated as follows, all for the same iron core:

Curve $AAAA$: Turns ratio increased from n to n' by using fewer primary turns; as a result the lower frequency limit is raised.

Curve $BBBB$: Turns ratio increased from n to n' by using more secondary turns; as a result the upper frequency limit is lowered.

Curve CCC: Turns ratio increased by both means; as a result the frequency range is narrowed to a resonant peak at the frequency for which $X_P = X_C$.

represented in the equivalent circuit by a condenser C_L (dotted in Fig. 10.6b) in parallel with L_P. At a sufficiently high frequency this condenser practically short-circuits the transformer secondary, causing the gain to vanish. The gain equation including this capacitance effect is:

$$\frac{E_j}{E_g} = \frac{n\mu}{\sqrt{1 + r_p^2 \left(\frac{1}{X_P} - \frac{1}{X_C}\right)^2}} \tag{10-9}$$

X_L vanishes at low frequencies and X_C at high frequencies, so that the gain vanishes for both high and low frequencies. In the intermediate range, where $r_p/X_P \ll 1$ because L_P is large, and $r_p/X_C \ll 1$ because C is small, the gain approximates $n\mu$. This is illustrated by the solid curve in Fig. 10.7. The intermediate range must include all musical-tone frequencies in an amplifier that is to be used to reproduce music without frequency distortion. With the values of r_p, L_P, and C usually employed, (10–9) does not predict a resonant peak in the gain, despite the appearance of the denominator.

Figure 10.8 illustrates the experimentally measured response to frequency variation in a circuit like that of Fig. 10.6a. Such experimental results agree with the solid-line curve of Fig. 10.7, except for

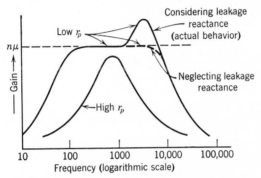

FIG. 10.8 Frequency response of a transformer-coupled amplifier with infinite load resistance, illustrating the effect of leakage reactance.

the sharp rise to a peak just before the high-frequency drop. This peak is due to resonance between the distributed capacitance in the secondary and the leakage reactance of the transformer windings. Leakage reactance has not been indicated in any of the circuit diagrams and has not been taken into account in any of the expressions for gain; thus the simple circuit shown in Fig. 10.6b could never give a gain greater than $n\mu$. The effect of leakage reactance can be accounted for in the equivalent circuit analysis by introducing in Fig. 10.6b a series reactance X_L between r_p and the point where the C_L circuit branches off.

10.6 Transformer Coupling to a Finite Load Resistance. Figures 10.9a and 10.9b illustrate the actual and equivalent circuits if a load resistance is coupled to the plate circuit through a transformer. The load resistance is represented in the equivalent circuit by the magnitude R_L/n^2, rather than by its actual value R_L. (In the equivalent circuit diagram of a transformer all resistances and reactances of the secondary circuit may be treated as though in the primary, provided they are divided by the square of the turns ratio.) The leakage reactances and the resistances of the primary and secondary windings are usually so small, relative appropriately to r_p and R_L/n^2, that their omission introduces no appreciable error. Thus the output voltage $E_j = nE_p$ as before.

Throughout the major part of the normal frequency range of the Fig. 10.9a amplifier the reactances X_P and X_C are both so large relative to R_L/n^2 that they may safely be neglected. The circuit can then

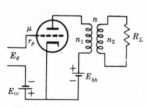

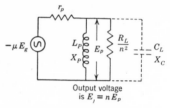

(a) Actual circuit diagram; $n = n_1/n_2$; the output voltage E_j is that across R_L.

(b) Voltage generator equivalent circuit diagram. The dashed portions represent the transformer distributed capacitance.

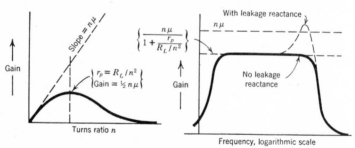

(c) Dependence of gain on turns ratio.

(d) Variation of voltage gain with frequency.

FIG. 10.9   Transformer coupling to a finite load impedance.

be analyzed as though X_P and X_C were removed entirely, corresponding to complete idealization of the transformer. The expression for gain can then be written

$$\frac{E_j}{E_g} = \frac{nE_p}{E_g} = \frac{n\mu}{1 + \dfrac{r_p}{R_L/n^2}} \qquad (10\text{--}10)$$

This shows that, although the transformer magnifies the gain by the factor n, it also shrinks the load by the factor n^2. This latter effect tends to reduce the gain.

If r_p and R_L are both fixed, the gain is roughly proportional to the turns ratio, for moderate values of the turns ratio, whereas for very large turns ratios the gain vanishes, as illustrated in Fig. 10.9c. The solid line represents the gain for various values of n. The dotted line is a tangent to the solid line at the origin; its slope is $n\mu$. The maximum voltage gain occurs at the value of n for which $r_p = R_L/n^2$, that is, at the turns ratio for which the resistances in the equivalent circuit are "matched." The gain at this point is $\frac{1}{2}n\mu$, E_p being just half of $-n\mu E_g$. No advantage is to be gained by using a turns ratio greater than $\sqrt{R_L/r_p}$. If, as sometimes happens, R_L is less than r_p, it may be desirable to use a transformer having more primary than secondary turns, making n fractional.

At low frequencies the effect of X_P, and at high frequencies that of X_C, is important. If, in the equivalent circuit of the parallel-feed amplifier, Fig. 9.17b, the condenser is short-circuited (equivalent to making $X_C = 0$), the circuit of Fig. 10.9b is obtained. It is therefore possible to obtain, for Fig. 10.9, the proper expressions for gain and phase shift in terms of frequency by making $X_C = 0$ in (9–88) and (9–89), and at the same time using R_L/n^2 for R_L, $n\mu$ for μ, and X_P for X_L.

The resulting expressions can be adapted for use at frequencies high enough to involve the distributed capacitance by employing

$$r_p{}^2\left(\frac{1}{X_P} - \frac{1}{X_C}\right)^2 \text{ in place of } \frac{r_p{}^2}{X_P{}^2} \tag{10–11}$$

Figure 10.9d illustrates the general nature of the frequency response so predicted.

10.7 Positive and Negative Feedback; Regeneration. It is possible to couple the output of an amplifier back into the grid circuit, in such a way that the excitation voltage is the input voltage plus or minus some definite fraction of the similarly patterned output. Such an arrangement is said to provide positive feedback (regeneration), or negative feedback.

Negative feedback is employed as a means of reducing harmonic distortion, also as a means of providing impedance transformation, as in a cathode follower circuit, discussed in Section 10.9.

In a stable *regenerative amplifier*, modest positive feedback is employed to provide an increase in the gain. If sufficiently strong positive feedback is employed, an initial voltage impulse anywhere in the circuit tends to be magnified without limit; such behavior is called unstable regenerative action. Most of the electronic circuits used to produce sustained electrical oscillations employ unstable regeneration; see Section 10.10.

The interelectrode capacitances within any vacuum tube provide positive feedback at sufficiently high frequencies. As a result there is a tendency for simple vacuum-tube circuits to exhibit "parasitic oscillations" at frequencies of many megacycles, the tube capacitances providing the feedback.

10.8   Negative Feedback Equations.   There are many ways of providing negative feedback; one of the most common is to use a cathode

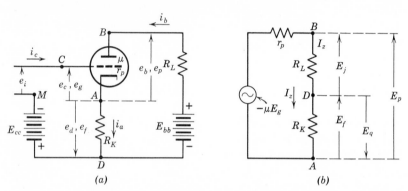

(a)   (b)

FIG. 10.10   A Class A (negative-grid) triode amplifier employing a cathode resistor to give negative feedback. Note that all potentials are measured relative to a zero value at the circuit point A. The sense convention chosen for i_a is such as to agree with the actual direction of flow in R_K.

resistor R_K, as illustrated in Fig. 10.10. In this circuit the input voltage e_i is not applied between cathode and grid, but rather between the new circuit point D and grid, where D is the dividing point between the R_K portion and the R_L portion of the plate circuit loading.

In Fig. 10.10 the grid and plate potentials, e_c and e_b, are still referred to a zero value at the cathode, as is e_d, the (numerically negative) potential of the point D. As to the further symbolism:

e_d, e_f are respectively the total instantaneous value, and the instantaneous value of the varying component, of the voltage across R_K (10–12a)

E_d, E_f are respectively the d-c value, and the rms value of the varying component, of the voltage across R_K (10–12b)

Thus

$$e_d = E_d + e_f \qquad (10\text{--}13)$$

E_g and E_p are, as in circuits previously studied, the rms values of the varying components of the grid-to-cathode and the plate-to-cathode potential differences.

Considering Class A operation, the grid never swings positive; therefore there is no grid current, so that the current i_a in the cathode resistor will be the same as that in the load resistor, that is, $i_a = i_b$; similarly, for the rms a-c values, $I_k = I_p$.

Summation of the voltages from the cathode to the grid around the loop $ADMC$ in the figure gives *

$$e_c = e_d + E_{cc} + e_i \qquad (10\text{--}14)$$

The corresponding relation involving rms a-c voltages is

$$E_g = E_f + E_i \qquad (10\text{--}15)$$

Here E_f is, like E_p, 180° out of phase with E_i, so that, numerically, $E_g < E_i$. Thus the presence of the feedback voltage across the cathode resistor makes the a-c grid excitation voltage E_g be somewhat *less* than the a-c input voltage E_i; thus the feedback is *negative*.

From the equivalent circuit, Fig. 10.10b, $E_f = I_z R_K$, so that the last equation becomes

$$E_g = E_i + I_z R_K \qquad (10\text{--}16)$$

the $I_z R_K$ being subtractive in nature, because of phase relationships. Also from the equivalent circuit

$$I_z(R_L + r_p + R_K) = -\mu E_g \qquad (10\text{--}17)$$

Combination with the preceding equation gives

$$I_z = \frac{-\mu E_i}{R_L + r_p + R_K(1 + \mu)} \qquad (10\text{--}18)$$

Use of $I_z = E_j/R_L$ leads to the gain equation

$$\frac{E_j}{E_i} = \frac{-\mu}{1 + \dfrac{r_p}{R_L} + \dfrac{R_K}{R_L}(1 + \mu)} \qquad (10\text{--}19)$$

Obviously the introduction of R_K has reduced the gain. Note also from (10–18) that the introduction of R_K has reduced I_z; that is, the

---

* If the E_d portion of e_d is the correct bias, there need be no bias voltage source E_{cc}; the circuit is then said to have a "cathode bias."

total plate swing has been lessened, and the harmonic content therefore reduced; see Section 9.20.

To study the effect of the cathode resistor in a pentode having a very large r_p, the current generator concepts are employed. Substitute $\mu = r_p g_m$ in (10–18) and (10–19); then let r_p become infinite, to obtain

$$I_z \cong \frac{-g_m E_i}{1 + g_m R_K} \tag{10–20}$$

$$\frac{E_j}{E_i} \cong \frac{-g_m R_L}{1 + g_m R_K} \quad \begin{bmatrix} \text{for a pentode,} \\ r_p \cong \infty \end{bmatrix} \tag{10–21}$$

10.9 The Cathode Follower Circuit. The cathode resistor of Fig. 10.10a may be used as an output-circuit element, as well as to produce negative feedback. When considering R_K as an output resistor it is convenient, as a mental concept, to transfer the potential reference point to D, rather than A. Thus let

e_q, E_q symbolize the instantaneous value and the rms value respectively of the varying component of the *output* voltage across the cathode resistor (considered as being a positive voltage when the varying component of the potential at A exceeds the varying component of that at D).

From this definition it is evident that

$$E_q \equiv -E_f \qquad e_q \equiv -e_f \tag{10–22}$$

Thus when R_K is thought of as a device used to produce negative feedback, the feedback voltage across it is considered as e_f, polarity e_{AD}, therefore having the same polarity sense convention as e_p; when R_K is thought of as an output resistor, the output voltage across it is considered as e_q, polarity e_{DA}, thus having the same polarity sense convention as e_i.

Thus in Fig. 10.10a *the output voltage e_q is in phase with the input voltage e_i*, both being referred to a basis of potential reference at D, rather than at A. If there exists also an additional output resistor as R_L, it is evident that the two output voltages E_j and $E_q (= -E_f)$ are of opposite polarity, as referred to the circuit point D.

In a *cathode follower* circuit $R_L = 0$, and the only output voltage is E_q across R_K. This output voltage is in phase with and approximately equal to the input voltage; thus the cathode potential faithfully "follows" the input potential as to phase, and approximately as to magnitude. The device is essentially an impedance transformer. The input voltage "looks into" a very high impedance, because the grid draws no

current; therefore the grid voltage will follow faithfully voltage variations of an input source of very high internal impedance; this is necessary in many instrumentation requirements. But the output voltage
E_q is provided by a source (the cathode follower circuit itself) whose
internal impedance is R_K, which may be only a few hundred ohms.
Therefore the output voltage may satisfactorily drive a measuring
device, or a later stage of amplification, whose input impedance is
only a matter of a few thousand ohms.

To obtain the voltage gain equation (the gain is fractional) for a
cathode follower circuit, use

$$I_z = \frac{-E_f}{R_K} = +\frac{E_q}{R_K} \qquad (10\text{--}23)$$

in (10–18); in terms of the current generator concept this gain becomes

$$\frac{E_q}{E_i} = \frac{+1}{1 + \dfrac{1}{g_m}\left(\dfrac{1}{r_p} + \dfrac{1}{R_K}\right)} \qquad [\text{triode}] \qquad (10\text{--}24)$$

In a pentode, $1/r_p$ may be ignorably small relative to $1/R_K$; in that
case, approximately,

$$\frac{E_q}{E_i} = \frac{+1}{1 + \dfrac{1}{g_m R_K}} \qquad \begin{bmatrix}\text{pentode,} \\ r_p \to \infty\end{bmatrix} \qquad (10\text{--}25)$$

Note that the voltage gain of a cathode follower stage is always less
than unity, but usually not much less than unity. For example, g_m
might be 2000 micromhos, and R_K 2500 ohms, making the voltage
gain 0.83.

10.10 Tuned Plate Oscillators. A tuned plate oscillator is one of
many circuit arrangements that can be used to produce sustained
oscillations by regenerative action, that is, by using positive feedback. As illustrated in Fig. 10.11, it is similar to an amplifier in which
the load is a resonant circuit. The load is coupled to the grid circuit by
the mutual inductance M between coils L_P and L_G. Any initial voltage impulse, such as that due to closing a switch that completes the
plate circuit, sets up resonant-frequency electrical oscillations (an a-c
current) in the plate circuit. But for the coupling into the grid circuit,
these oscillations would die out in a few cycles, just as a pendulum
stops swinging unless given cyclic encouragement. As a result of the

coupling into the grid circuit, the grid receives oscillatory excitation of the proper frequency and phase relation to reinforce oscillations already started in the plate circuit, so that they continue indefinitely.

The vector diagram for the equivalent circuit of a tuned plate oscillator is shown in Fig. 10.11c. In preparing this diagram, resonant

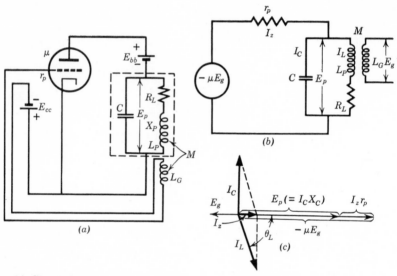

(a) Circuit diagram. The dotted line encloses the "tank circuit." Polarity is correct if L_P and L_G are separated sections of a continuously wound coil.

(b) Equivalent circuit diagram.

$$r_p = \frac{\mu M - L_P}{R_L C}$$

(c) Vector diagram. X_C symbolizes reactance of the condenser C, X_P the reactance of the inductance L_P.

FIG. 10.11 Tuned plate oscillator.

frequency in the "tank circuit" is assumed. Therefore $X_C = X_P$, and $I_C = I_L$. Also, R_L is assumed to be small relative to X_P. From the diagrams:

$$-\mu E_g = I_C X_C + I_L r_p \frac{R_L}{\sqrt{R_L{}^2 + X_P{}^2}} \qquad (10\text{--}26)$$

The excitation voltage can be expressed as

$$E_g = -I_L X_M \qquad (10\text{--}27)$$

where $X_M = 2\pi f M$, the mutual reactance associated with M. The polarity of the coupling must be such as to call for this negative sign.

Use of this equation and of the fact that $R_L \ll X_L$ converts (10–26) into

$$\mu I_L X_M = I_C X_C + I_L \frac{r_p R_L}{X_P} \qquad (10\text{–}28)$$

The currents cancel. It is convenient to interchange X_C and its equal X_P, to give

$$\mu X_M = X_P + \frac{r_p R_L}{X_C} \qquad (10\text{–}29)$$

If the X's are expressed in terms of M, L_P, and C, the $2\pi f$'s cancel, leaving

$$\mu M = L_P + r_p R_L C \qquad (10\text{–}30)$$

The usual form of this is

$$r_p = \frac{\mu M - L_P}{R_L C} \qquad (10\text{–}31)$$

This equation appears at first to indicate that sustained oscillations can result only when the circuit constants are such as to make the right-hand side have a definite value, corresponding to the r_p of the tube used. However, the observed fact is that the circuit oscillates whenever the right-hand side of this equation *exceeds* a definite minimum value.

The reason for this behavior can be clarified by a graphical study of the current-voltage locus for such an oscillating circuit, Fig. 10.12. This locus lies along a straight "load line" because the "tank circuit" of Fig. 10.11 acts like a resistance, in that the total current I_z through it is in phase with and proportional to the voltage E_p. An expression for the apparent shunt resistance R_T of the tank circuit is obtained by observing from the circuit and vector diagrams in Fig. 10.11 that

$$I_z = \frac{E_p}{\sqrt{R_L{}^2 + X_P{}^2}} \frac{R_L}{\sqrt{R_L{}^2 + X_p{}^2}} \cong E_p \frac{R_L}{X_p{}^2} \qquad (10\text{–}32)$$

The ratio of E_p to I_z is R_T, so that

$$R_T \cong \frac{X_P{}^2}{R_L} \qquad (10\text{–}33)$$

The load line in Fig. 10.12 has the slope $-1/R_T$. The tube characteristic curves, so also the locus, level off at a temperature-limited value of current. This upper current limit accounts for the existence of an upper limit to the continued growth of oscillation amplitude.

It is evident that the value of r_p is not the same at all points along the load line. The point Q lies, in Fig. 10.12, at about the height at which the greatest slope of the characteristic curves occurs, so corresponding to the least value of r_p. This establishes the minimum value which the right-hand side of (10–31) can have if oscillations are to persist. At just this least value the oscillations are of very small amplitude. Oscillation over a large voltage range along the load line

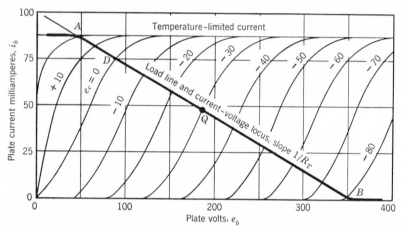

Fig. 10.12 Current-voltage locus for a tuned plate oscillator. The amplitude (voltage swing) will always increase until the appropriately averaged value of r_p is as required by (10–31); see the discussion following (10–33). The increase in r_p is caused by the non-linearity (changing slope) of the characteristic curves. Thus *the amplitude reached is governed by the non-linearities of the characteristics.* This is true of any regenerative electron tube oscillator.

brings the current-voltage locus into regions in which the intersecting plate characteristics have smaller slopes, corresponding to greater local values of r_p than exist near Q. Hence for large-amplitude oscillations the appropriate average value of r_p for a complete cycle of oscillation is much greater than for small-amplitude oscillation. Thus if, in (10–31), M is increased, or R_L or C decreased, making the whole quantity larger, the amplitude of oscillation grows, and with it the average value of r_p. Thus (10–31) remains true even for wide current swings, for an r_p obtained by appropriate averaging.

As long as the current-voltage locus stays within the straight-line range BD, Fig. 10.12, the current I_z and the grid voltage variations are approximately sinusoidal. However, the harmonic components of I_z grow rapidly as operation extends out over the flat horizontal portions to the left of A and right of B, or even into regions to the left of D where the grid voltage wave shape is affected by the flow of grid current. The tank circuit's impedance to these harmonics is very small, but to the fundamental-frequency current very large. Therefore the harmonic components of I_z produce a very small, the fundamental component a very large tank-circuit voltage. For this reason the tank-circuit voltage E_p is very nearly sinusoidal, even at large oscillation amplitudes that make I_z contain pronounced harmonic components. These harmonic components flow through the tank circuit chiefly by way of the condenser.

In oscillators of this and most other types employing regeneration (positive feedback) the grid swings positive during each cycle, so that grid current exists normally during a portion of each cycle. This permits self-biasing, illustrated in Fig. 10.13a. In a self-biased circuit the grid battery is replaced by a small resistance in parallel with a condenser. The voltage drop in the resistance, caused by flow of grid current, provides the grid bias voltage. The condenser is charged during grid-current peaks. By discharging through the resistance during grid-current valleys it maintains the grid bias voltage at a reasonably constant value throughout each cycle.

10.11 Other Regenerative Oscillator Circuits. The essential features of three other types of oscillator circuits that employ positive

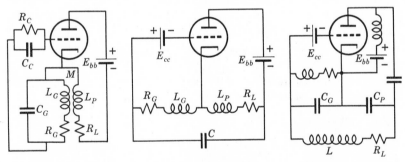

(a) Tuned grid oscillator.   (b) Hartley oscillator.   (c) Colpitt oscillator.

FIG. 10.13 Circuit diagrams for regenerative oscillators. See also Fig. 10.11.
For the tuned grid circuit:

$$r_p = \frac{\mu M L_G - M^2}{R_G L_G C_G}$$

For the Hartley circuit:

$$r_p = \frac{(L_P + M)[\mu(L_G + M) - (L_P + M)]}{C(R_L + R_G)(L_P + L_G + 2M)}$$

feedback are shown in Fig. 10.13. Equations for the tuned grid and Hartley circuits, similar in nature and interpretation to (10–31), appear below the figure.

10.12   Tuned Amplifiers.   In Fig. 10.11a the inductance L_G is connected back into the grid circuit.   If, instead, it is connected in series with the grid of a succeeding stage of amplification, the circuit becomes that of a *tuned amplifier*, which has a large voltage gain for frequencies very close to resonance, but a small voltage gain for all other frequencies.   The equivalent circuit shown in Fig. 10.11b is similarly that of a tuned amplifier as well as of a tuned plate oscillator.   When used as a tuned amplifier the voltage that appears across the secondary terminals of L_G is the excitation voltage of the next stage.

It is left as an exercise for the reader to draw the vector diagram and derive the tuned amplifier gain equation for a general frequency, for which the two reactances are not equal.   A study of a graph of gain vs. the logarithm of the frequency shows that the use of a coil for which $R_L \ll X_P$ favors sharp "tuning."   With such a coil large gain occurs only over a very narrow band of frequencies.

10.13   Dynatron Oscillators.[10a, b]   The screen-grid plate characteristic curve shown in Fig. 6.8 has a negative slope, therefore a negative plate resistance, for a considerable range of plate voltages beyond CC. The volt-ampere curves for electric arcs and glow discharges, also the grid current-grid voltage curves for high-vacuum triodes, exhibit similar negative resistance properties.

Ordinary resistances, which are positive, absorb energy from a-c circuits.   A device for which the a-c resistance is negative can introduce a-c energy into a resonant load circuit like that shown in Fig. 10.14a, the source of energy being the plate battery.   A circuit which employs a negative-resistance volt-ampere curve to produce a-c current is called a "dynatron oscillator."

Dynatron operation can be analyzed by reference to Fig. 10.14b, which shows a negative-resistance portion of a tube characteristic curve.   Note that the present study does not involve a family of tube characteristic curves; operation occurs along one tube characteristic curve only.   The tank circuit in this figure, like the tank circuits in tuned plate oscillators, behaves at resonant frequency like a resistance of $R_T = X_L^2/R_L$ ohms.   During operation as a dynatron oscillator, resonant-frequency current flows through this apparently resistive tank circuit, so that the current-voltage locus must lie along a straight "load line" passing through the operating point and having a slope $-1/R_T$.   The plate voltage at Q is the plate battery voltage, because the resistance R_L is so small that the d-c drop through it is negligible. Three possible load lines, I, II, and III, are illustrated in Fig. 10.14b.

The resonant load circuit requires that the current-voltage locus must lie along one such straight load line.   However, the current-voltage locus must also lie along the tube characteristic curve. Both requirements are simultaneously satisfied when the load line coincides with the tube characteristic, as along a portion of load line II, Fig. 10.14b. For this load line $R_T = r_p$ (evaluated at Q). Oscillation can take place at almost any desired frequency, for there is a wide range of values that L and C can have, yet give to R_T the required magnitude.

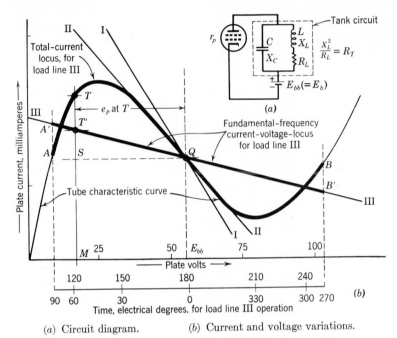

(a) Circuit diagram.   (b) Current and voltage variations.

Fig. 10.14   Dynatron oscillator.

The current in this type of circuit is not *necessarily* oscillating; it might be steady, with voltage and current values as at Q. In order to start oscillation it may be necessary to give the circuit an initial electrical "kick." Making the final connection that completes the plate battery circuit usually accomplishes this purpose, or the condenser may be separately charged, then abruptly connected into the circuit.

Suppose that this latter method is used in a dynatron circuit having resonant-frequency load line II, Fig. 10.14b. The condenser is initially charged to 15 volts or less. Load line II coincides exactly with the tube characteristic curve for about 15 volts each way from Q. As the negative resistance of the tube is exactly equal numerically to the positive apparent resistance of the tank circuit, the net a-c resistance of the oscillating circuit is zero. Oscillations start with an amplitude dependent on the initial charge on the condenser, and continue without change in amplitude. This is analogous to the behavior of a friction-less pendulum, which swings forever with an amplitude dependent on the initial displacement given it. If the condenser is initially charged to 15 volts, the plate voltage will swing to 15 volts above and below Q.

If the tank-circuit constants are such as to produce resonant-fre-quency load line I, the apparent resistance of the tank circuit is greater numerically than the negative plate resistance. Hence the oscillating circuit has a net positive resistance. Behavior is similar to that of a pendulum whose swing involves friction. Oscillations start, but they decay at a rate dependent on the magnitude of the net positive re-sistance.

Suppose that the charged condenser is switched into a circuit having resonant-frequency load line III. Oscillations start as usual with an initial amplitude dependent on the charge on the condenser. However, the amplitude increases at a rate dependent on the net a-c resistance, which is now negative. If the volt-ampere characteristic of the tube were an infinitely long, straight slant line, the oscillation amplitude would increase indefinitely.

Actually the tube characteristic curve cannot continue straight in-definitely; it must eventually bend. The actual current-voltage locus must follow the bends. This at first makes the average plate resistance for the entire cycle have a still greater value than along the straight-line portion, so increasing the rate of growth of amplitude. Soon the swing extends beyond the maximum and minimum points on the curve, so entering regions in which the local contributions to the average plate resistance are positive. Extension of amplitude farther into these regions is accompanied by a change to a progressively less nega-tive plate resistance. Operation stabilizes ultimately at an amplitude for which *the appropriate average* of the plate resistance is $-R_T$.

When dynatron oscillations are of sufficient amplitude to extend into curved parts of the tube characteristic curve, the current in the tube contains harmonics of the fundamental resonant frequency. The im-pedance of the tank circuit is very high to the fundamental frequency, but very low to all its harmonics. Thus, as in a tuned plate oscillator, Section 10.10, the a-c component e_p of plate voltage is almost a pure sine wave, in spite of the presence of pronounced harmonics in the plate current. A time scale, in electrical degrees, for the variation of plate voltage for load line III is shown in the figure.

Two current-voltage loci are needed properly to describe operation in connection with load line III. Current values along one of them,

$A'B'$, follow the fundamental-frequency current variations. The corresponding voltage variation is sinusoidal, for the reasons stated in the previous paragraph, and the tank circuit is resistive. Therefore this locus is a straight line along load line III. The other locus, AB, is a total-current locus and must therefore follow the tube characteristic curve.

The points T and T', describing voltages and currents at about the 57° instant, may be used to contrast these two loci. Here the sinusoidal a-c component e_p of plate voltage has the instantaneous value $\overline{QS}$, as shown in the figure. The total plate current is $\overline{MT}$, the fundamental-frequency component of plate current is $\overline{ST'}$, and the harmonic components total $\overline{TT'}$.

The only important a-c power consumption in such a circuit is that due to the fundamental-frequency current, because the harmonics flow chiefly through the condenser, which has a very small power factor.

PROBLEMS

1. A three-stage d-c amplifier is to employ 6SJ7 pentodes, coupling between stages as in Fig. 10.2. The operating point on the characteristic curves (Fig. 6.15) is to be at $E_c = -2$, $E_b = +160$; $R_L = 20,000$ for all stages. In each grid circuit $R_{g1} = R_{g2} = 1$ megohm. Find the potential at which the positive bus must operate, also the gain per stage, and the total gain, if the negative bus is at -300 volts.

2. (a) Derive equation (10–6), using the Fig. 10.5 vector diagram. (b) Derive an equation for the phase angle between E_j and E_g for this circuit.

3. Circuit as in Fig. 10.5a: $r_p = 12,500$ ohms, $C = 0.0015$ µf, $R_L = 25,000$ ohms, $R_G = 2.5$ megohms. If the rms excitation applied to the first tube is 3 volts, find from (10–6) the excitation voltage of the second tube: (a) at 200 cycles, (b) at 20 cycles; (c) find what per cent of error would result in (a), also in (b), by using (10–5) instead of (10–6).

(d) Find the phase angle between E_j and E_g at 200 cycles and at 20 cycles.

4. Circuit as in Fig. 10.6: $\mu = 8$, $r_p = 5000$, $n_2/n_1 = 3$.

(a) Find what value of L_P will make the voltage gain at 20 cycles be 70.7 per cent of its maximum value, assuming a gain curve of the general type illustrated by the solid line in Fig. 10.7.

(b) What value of transformer distributed capacitance will make the gain at 4500 cycles be 70.7 per cent of its maximum value?

(c) Assume that L_P varies as the square of n_1, and the transformer distributed capacitance as the square of n_2. The turns ratio is increased above the former value of 3 by increasing n_2 in the same ratio that n_1 is decreased. What value of turns ratio, so obtained, will raise the low-frequency 0.707 gain point to 40 cycles?

(d) To what frequency will the high-frequency 0.707 gain point be lowered by this change?

(e) What turns ratio will produce a peaked gain curve (similar to curve CCC, Fig. 10.7) in which the 0.707 points are at 0.8 and 1.25 times the resonant frequency respectively?

5. Add to the circuit of Fig. 10.6b a transformer leakage inductance in series with r_p; then derive, by means of an appropriate vector diagram, an expression for voltage gain of the circuit, including the effects of the distributed capacitance. Show that your equation describes a gain curve similar to the upper solid line in Fig. 10.8 if r_p is small, and similar to the lower solid line if r_p is large.

6. For the amplifier shown in Fig. 10.15 find the generator voltage required to produce 10 watts in the 10-ohm load resistance at a frequency of 200 cycles. The transformer is ideal, that is, it has windings of zero resistance and zero leakage reactance, and the primary and secondary inductive reactances are infinite.

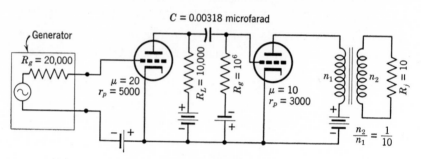

FIG. 10.15   Two-stage amplifier.

7. An R-C coupled amplifier circuit (Fig. 10.5) has the following constants: $R_L = 1000$ ohms, $C = 0.001$ μf, $R_g = 20,000$ ohms, $\mu = 20$, $g_m = 2000$ micromhos. Find the voltage gain at 1000 cycles.

8. A triode with $\mu = 20$ and $r_p = 10,000$ is used as a linear Class A amplifier with R-C coupling; $R_g = 1$ megohm. Find values of R_L and coupling condenser capacitance to make the voltage gain be 15 in the middle frequencies, and to give a low-frequency half-power frequency of 30 cycles.

9. A 2000-ohm resistance load is coupled to a type 2A3 triode by means of an "ideal" output transformer. $E_{bb} = 200$; $E_c = -30$. A small grid-signal voltage, perhaps $E_g = 1$ volt rms, is to be amplified. Find the transformer turns ratio that gives maximum power output.

10. Circuit as in Fig. 10.9a: $n = 3$, $\mu = 8$, $r_p = 10,000$, $R_L = 200,000$. (a) What is the voltage gain of this amplifier for frequencies high enough so that the primary reactance X_P of the transformer can be considered infinite? (b) How large must the primary inductance of the transformer be to make the gain at 50 cycles be 70.7 per cent of its value at 1000 cycles?

11. Circuit as in Fig. 10.9a: $\mu = 8$, $r_p = 10,000$ ohms, $R_L = 1$ megohm. (a) What value of n will give maximum amplification at high frequencies? (b) What two values of n will each give half the maximum possible high-frequency amplification?

12. Circuit as in Fig. 10.10, employing a 2A3 triode in Class A operation. $R_K = 500$, $R_L = 2500$. $I_{b\ max} = 100$ ma, $I_{b\ min} = 80$ ma, $E_b = 400$. (a) By simple numerical additions and subtractions of IR voltage drops, involving also E_b, find the potential of the plate relative to that of the cathode at maximum and minimum plate currents. Locate these points on a set of plate characteristics, and determine the corresponding values of grid potential relative to the cathode. (b) Mark on a circuit diagram the corresponding values of potential relative to

the ground point D, and from them determine E_{cc} and the rms excitation E_i.
(c) Draw on the characteristic set the load line connecting the two extreme points, and by graphical inspection relate its slope to some combination of R_K and R_L. (d) Locate the mid-point on the current-voltage locus, and make a numerical check to see whether or not it corresponds to zero input excitation. (e) From numerical values obtained above, determine the voltage gain; check its value by means of the appropriate equation in Section 10.8.

13. Circuit as in Fig. 10.11, tube characteristics as in Fig. 10.12. Frequency of oscillation is to be 50,000 cycles. Select a set of values of L_P, L_G, C, and R_L that will make r_p be 20 per cent more than the least value possible for a tube having these characteristics; use $X_L = 20R_L$, and let the coefficient of coupling k between L_P and L_G be 0.2. (The coefficient of coupling relates M to L_P and L_G as follows: $M = k\sqrt{L_P L_G}$.)

14. Draw the equivalent circuit and derive the equilibrium equations for r_p for: (a) a tuned grid oscillator, Fig. 10.13a, (b) a Hartley oscillator, Fig. 10.13b.

15. Circuit as in Fig. 10.14a, plate characteristic as in Fig. 6.8, $E_c = -1$. Specify values of E_{bb}, L, C, and R_L that will permit stable 50,000-cycle dynatron oscillations of the type corresponding to load line II, Fig. 10.14b. Make $X_L = 20R_L$.

16. Circuit as in Fig. 10.11, except for use as an amplifier, output voltage being that across the tank circuit, the feedback link omitted.

(a) Derive an expression for tank circuit impedance for the general condition that X_C and X_L are *not* equal.

(b) Using $X_L = 1025$, $X_C = 975$, $R_L = 50$, find the tank circuit impedance.

(c) Using the current generator equivalent circuit, find the voltage gain if $X_C = X_L = 1000$, $R_L = 50$, $g_m = 1500$ micromhos, $r_p = 12,000$.

(d) Find the voltage gain for the (b) condition.

CHAPTER XI

INTRODUCTION TO MICROWAVE ELECTRON TUBE PRINCIPLES

11.1 Electron Tube Behavior at Increasing Frequencies.* As the design frequency of electron tubes has been increased over the years, detrimental effects of interelectrode capacitances, lead-wire inductances, electron transit time (see Sections 2.5 and 2.6), and within-the-tube electromagnetic field propagation effects have had to be dealt with in turn. It has become customary to use the term "ultra-high-frequency," abbreviated uhf, in referring to frequencies, above about 300 megacycles (1-meter wavelength), for which transit time becomes important in space-charge-control tubes of conventional or near-conventional design.

"Microwave" frequencies, within the uhf range, are usually thought of as those permitting use of waveguide techniques, which are convenient above perhaps 2000 megacycles (15-cm wavelength). A waveguide type of transmission line employs a long metal-enclosed region through which electromagnetic waves propagate, there being no electrical insulation associated with the transmission system.

The use of several grids, close spacings to maximize transconductance per unit area, and improved circuit design techniques have served to compensate for interelectrode capacitances, which become important as the frequency rises into the upper audio range, at a few thousand cycles. Lead-wire inductance effects become important at a little below 100 megacycles, and are eliminated by the use of disk seal tubes operating into coaxial-line transmission systems,[11F, I, L, a, b, c, d] in effect making the circuit continuous through the tube envelope; there cease to be lead wires. For use at ultra-high and microwave frequencies, some types of tubes have been built and applied in ways that minimize transit time, by using close spacings or high voltages or both;[11a, b, c, d, F, L] others have employed transit time usefully (klystrons,[11A, F, G, I, L, N, P, R] the dyotron [11e]). Traveling wave amplifiers and magnetrons, useful chiefly at microwave frequencies, employ electron streams that traverse many wavelengths of electromagnetic propagation within the tube at about the phase velocity of the propagation, thus making use

* See textbook references in the bibliography.

of the within-the-tube propagation rather than trying to minimize it. A survey of some of the problems and accomplishments involved in these changes appears in this chapter; more complete treatments appear in *Microwave Electron Tubes*.

Probably the next barrier to be overcome in going to millimeter-wave frequencies well above 30,000 megacycles (1 cm wavelength) will involve the difficulties of producing coherent, noise-free millimeter-wave-length power at a genuinely monochromatic wavelength. It may become necessary to employ incoherent signals, as is done in the optical sciences, and as a corollary to deal with finite bandwidths even for unmodulated waves. The power may have to come from many randomly phased sources, generating intermittently, as with visible light.

Any space-charge-control amplifier tube (triode, tetrode, pentode, etc.) suffers a decline and ultimate vanishing of the useful gain as the frequency increases into a sufficiently high range. For any given tube, disappearance of utility as an oscillator for uhf power generation occurs at a somewhat higher frequency than the cessation of useful amplifier gain. Lighthouse triodes, with cathode-to-grid spacings of the order of 3 mils (about 0.007 mm) will amplify well into the uhf range, but not at microwave frequencies. The Western Electric 416–A triode, cathode-to-grid spacing 0.5 mil (about 0.0012 mm) will amplify at frequencies well into the microwave range.

The next few sections will lay the groundwork for and give explanations of reasons why space-charge-control tubes fail to function at sufficiently high frequencies.

11.2 The Grid Separation Amplifier Circuit.[2b, 11f] In using space-charge-control tubes at ultra-high and microwave frequencies it is usually desirable to employ the grid separation amplifier type of circuit, Fig. 11.1 (sometimes called a "grounded grid" circuit) rather than the familiar cathode separation type of circuit shown in Fig. 9.3a. This is partly because the grid separation circuit is relatively little subject to parasitic oscillations due to interelectrode capacitance feedback, a type of trouble that plagues the other type of circuit unless the grid-plate interelectrode capacitance is extremely small. Also, and equally important, the necessity for disk-seal circuit entrances into the tube makes the grid separation design mechanically simple, in that the grid lies between the cathode and plate electrically as well as structurally. The grid separation circuit has inherently a relatively low input impedance and requires appreciable input power. However, except for internal losses, the uhf input power appears as part of the output power.

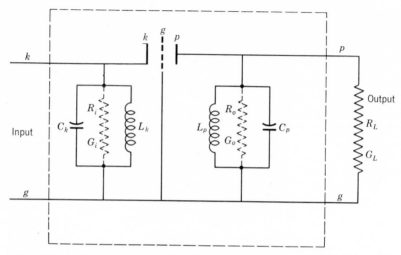

Fɪɢ. 11.1   Grid separation amplifier [11f] commonly used in connection with triode amplifier tubes of the lighthouse and similar types [11a, b] employing disk seals to cathode, grid, and plate.   The input voltage is applied between cathode and grid, and the output appears between grid and plate.   This is basically a low-impedance-input circuit, at any frequency, requiring appreciable input driving power; however, except for internal losses, the input power is transmitted through the tube and is part of the output power.   Only r-f circuit elements are shown in this diagram. R_L is the load; R_i and R_o represent copper loss effects in the resonant circuits.

11.3   Effects of Transit Time on Class C Amplifier Electron Interaction Efficiency.[2b, 11F, L, c, d, h]   It is convenient to discuss the detrimental effects of transit time in space-charge-control tubes in terms of large-signal rather than small-signal operation, because the associated physical events are striking enough to make their nature clearly apparent only when uhf voltages are large.   The same general kinds of effect exist with small-signal excitation.

Figure 11.2 illustrates the plate current and voltage variations typical of reasonably efficient Class C operation at ordinary radio frequencies, the transit angle being ignorably small.   The grid voltage (not shown in the figure) is made to swing positive during a small portion of the cycle, just high enough and long enough to produce the plate current pulse whose "angle of plate current flow" is shown starting a little before moment $ABCD$ and ending just before MN.

Passage of this plate current pulse through a *resonant* load circuit causes the plate voltage variations to be practically sinusoidal, because the resonant circuit has a high impedance to the plate current fundamental-frequency component, and very low impedances to the harmonic components.   At its lowest point the sinusoidal plate voltage wave in

Fig. 11.2 has not quite swung down to zero; thus the "plate swing" is perhaps 85 per cent of the d-c supply voltage E_{bb}.

Every electron that passes from cathode to anode at the moment $ABCD$ receives from the d-c power source E_{BD} electron volts of energy, delivers as plate-dissipation energy E_{BC} electron volts of energy, and

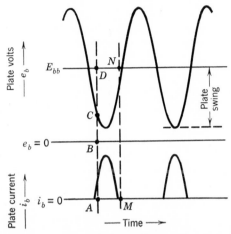

FIG. 11.2   Plate current pulses and plate voltage swing for a Class C amplifier, operating at ordinary r-f frequencies.[2b]   The load is presumed to be a resonant "tank circuit," causing the plate voltage variations to be essentially sinusoidal, even though the plate current passes in pulses.   The "angle of plate current flow" is the duration, in electrical degrees or radians, of the plate current pulse.   The actual flow of plate current is governed chiefly by the grid voltage, not shown in the diagram.   Note that here the phrase "plate swing" signifies only half the total excursion of the plate voltage, a somewhat different meaning from that used in Fig. 9.9.

delivers to the resonant "tank circuit," as a-c power generation, E_{CD} electron volts of energy.   The *electron interaction efficiency* for each such electron is

$$\left.\begin{array}{c}\text{Electron interaction efficiency,}\\\text{for the moment } ABCD\end{array}\right\} = \frac{E_{CD}}{E_{BD}} \qquad (11\text{--}1)$$

The overall electron interaction efficiency (ratio of a-c power generated to d-c power taken from the plate supply) is the weighted average of all such interaction efficiencies.   The relative plate currents at the various instants govern the weighting.   Note that for the moment $ABCD$ the interaction efficiency is reasonably good, being about 70 per cent, whereas the value at moment MN is very poor, perhaps 15 per cent.   This general behavior illustrates an essential principle regarding the generation of a-c electric power by electron interaction with an electric field, as follows:

Whenever an electron moves through an electric field in spite of an opposing force exerted by that field, the electron delivers energy to the circuit of which that field forms a part.

In the present illustration of this principle there exists, in the triode interior, an electric field associated with the r-f circuit system, the field's magnitude being the r-f voltage divided by some interelectrode distance. This r-f field *opposes* the electron's motion, because the r-f potential is more negative at the plate than at the cathode. Thus the electrons in passing to the plate deliver energy to the r-f field, in proportion to its strength. In the low-frequency case, the field does not change during the electron's flight; in the uhf case, the field does change during the flight, but the energy transfer is of the same nature.

Within a triode, the electron is passing through a d-c field that aids its motion at the same time that it passes through the r-f field that opposes its motion. Thus it is at the same time receiving energy from the d-c field and delivering energy to the r-f field. In many uhf devices, for example klystrons and traveling wave amplifiers, the electrons pass through the r-f field subsequent to traversing the d-c field, so that the two energy exchanges occur in sequence.

The following statements as to Class C interaction efficiency in general are reasonably obvious, from a little study of Fig. 11.2: [2b, 9A, C, H, M, 11h]

(a) If the plate swing is inadequate, none of the electrons will experience a high interaction efficiency.

(b) If the angle of plate current flow is very large (as, for example, well in excess of 180°) many of the electrons will experience a very low or even negative interaction efficiency, so that the overall electron interaction efficiency will be poor.

(c) If the plate current pulse were to be shifted substantially away from the minimum point of the plate voltage swing, no electrons would contribute a satisfactory interaction efficiency.

Thus, *at any frequency*, there can be efficient Class C operation only if (a) the plate current swing is reasonably close to 100 per cent (90 per cent is a good value), (b) the angle of plate current flow is small, and (c) the plate current pulse is in phase, or nearly so, with the minimum of the plate voltage swing.

Consider now uhf operation. The electrons now require an appreciable fraction of a cycle to pass through the grid-to-plate region, where the important interaction with the uhf field takes place. Thus an electron might leave the grid location a little before moment *ABCD* and arrive at moment *MN*, in Fig. 11.2. This electron passes about symmetrically relative to the downward swing of the plate voltage; therefore it will have a greater electron interaction efficiency than electrons starting either a little earlier or later. Yet it is obvious that this *one* optimum electron's interaction efficiency will be the average of the efficiencies for all the moments during its flight, and therefore much less than if it had been able to pass in essentially zero time at the lowest point of the plate swing.

This reasoning leads to the following general conclusion:

Good electron interaction efficiency can be obtained only if the grid-to-plate transit angles for most of the electrons are less than perhaps 90°.

This immediately puts an upper limit to the frequency that can be used successfully with any given grid-plate spacing and range of voltages. The voltage enters because it governs the speed of flight across the gap, thereby affecting the transit time.

In evaluating an individual electron's transit time, and in other uhf analytical studies, it is very important to bear in mind that the kinetic energy in electron volts possessed by an electron at any point and moment may in a uhf field be very different indeed from the potential at that point and moment relative to the cathode of origin of the electron. This situation was discussed briefly in item (4) toward the end of Section 2.6. In general the transit velocity is given by the slope of a flight-line diagram, such as Fig. 2.5*a*, and not by employing directly the instantaneous potential at the point and moment in question.

Over all, the above discussion indicates one reason why a given plate current pulse of electrons may give less r-f power output, for given plate swing, when the transit time is long than when it is short. There are other kinds of effects on interaction, of less consequence and more complex in nature, for the most part also tending toward reducing the interaction efficiency.[2b]

11.4 Effects of Transit Time on Input Loading.[2b] The effects of transit time in the input circuit may be studied by the aid of Fig. 2.5*a*. Suppose that the plane $x = s$ represents, not a plate, but the grid plane of a triode, the voltage wave in Fig. 2.5*b* representing the equivalent grid sheet potential. The current pulse that leaves the cathode includes electrons in all flight lines between those starting at 30° and at 150°; only those for flight lines starting prior to 90° pass through the grid plane into the interaction space between grid and plate, where they can be useful. Thus with the current temperature-limited (many Class C devices operate temperature-limited) so that the cathode current density is essentially uniform between 30° and 150°, the plate current pulse will be only half what it would be at low frequencies. Thus it requires a greater "grid drive" to produce any given useful plate current pulse in the uhf range than at ordinary radio frequencies, for the same electrode spacings.

More serious than this is the fact that the electrons that return to the cathode extract power from the input uhf field both going and coming, thus adding to the power drain on the input, in addition to not forming part of the useful current pulse. These electrons strike the cathode with substantial energies, causing cathode back-heating, which may necessitate monitoring the cathode heating power to prevent damage to the cathode from overheating under severe load conditions.

The fraction of the electrons sent back to the cathode is dependent on frequency; this is one reason why input frequency modulation may cause a subsidiary output amplitude modulation.

11.5   Electron Transit Phase Delay.[2b]   It is obvious from Fig. 2.5a, thought of as a cathode-to-grid region, that the useful electrons enter the grid-plate region at a later time, on the average, than the 90° phase position of the maximum point of the grid sheet potential. Thus there is an important *electron transit phase delay* between the upward swing of the equivalent grid sheet potential and the entrance of the driving convection current into the grid-plate interaction space. There will be a still further transit phase delay to the grid-to-plate interaction-space current which drives the load circuit.

These phase delays can be corrected for by circuit adjustments *if they are constant.* However, in general they are not constant. Changes in input signal amplitude cause shifts in phase delay of the plate current pulse, which result in phase modulation of the output incidental to any input amplitude modulation. This can become a very marked effect, because with increasing frequency the first major transit time effect to appear is the electron transit phase delay in the cathode-to-grid region. This comes in at relatively low frequencies because of the low electron velocities in the cathode-to-grid region.

11.6   Cathode Current Density and Anode Dissipation Limitations. For reasons having to do with the 90 per cent plate swing requirement of Fig. 11.2, there is for a given bandwidth of r-f operation an optimum shunt impedance of the output tank-circuit load, for a given d-c voltage.[2b, 11h] Therefore, if the voltage is raised to reduce transit time, thus minimizing the various detrimental transit-time effects, and if the bandwidth is to be maintained, the plate current must also rise in order to maintain the correct shunt impedance. This current increase must be obtained without increasing the input and output capacitances (which involve cathode and anode areas) in order to preserve bandwidth. Therefore (*a*) the output power must increase, (*b*) the cathode current density must increase, and (*c*) the anode power dissipation density must increase. The increases in dissipation and cathode current density can often be provided without great difficulty if the tube is operated at a low duty cycle. Therefore high-voltage, high-power triodes have been used successfully as uhf radar transmitter tubes (below perhaps 1000 megacycles) because this application requires the tubes to carry current only a few microseconds at a time, at a duty factor of the order of $\frac{1}{100}$ to $\frac{1}{1000}$.

Both the anode dissipation and high cathode current density problems become extremely severe for continuous-wave service. Thus uhf tubes are very much easier to build for pulsed than for continuous-wave operation.

11.7 Klystrons (Velocity Modulation Tubes).[11A, F, G, L, N, P, R]   The klystron amplifier, illustrated schematically in Fig. 11.3, employs

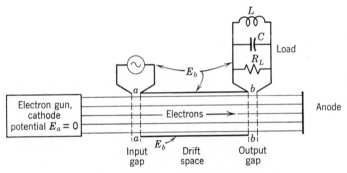

Fig. 11.3 Schematic diagram of a klystron amplifier.

transit time usefully. A beam of electrons, accelerated in an electron gun to kinetic energy E_b electron volts per electron, passes through a very short *input gap*, or "buncher," between two grids, across which a small uhf input voltage is impressed. The electrons then traverse a field-free *drift space* before entering the *output gap* or "catcher." The varying velocities acquired in the input gap cause *bunching* to occur in the drift space; that is, fast electrons catch up with earlier slow ones, causing local concentrations in electron density. Passage of the bunched beam through the output gap causes periodic changes in the charges that are induced on the grids of the gap by the presence of the electrons of the beam. The changing of these induced charges as the bunches go by causes an *induced current* to flow in the resonant output circuits; see the next section for a discussion of induced current. The flow of the induced current through the resonant output circuit, tuned to the input frequency, causes a uhf voltage to appear across the out-

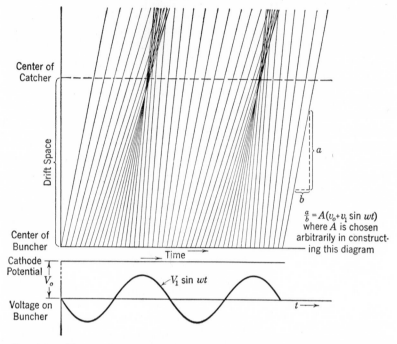

$$\frac{a}{b} = A(v_o + v_1 \sin wt)$$
where A is chosen arbitrarily in constructing this diagram

FIG. 11.4 Electron flight-line (Applegate) diagram for a klystron (reprinted by permission from *Hyper and Ultrahigh Frequency Engineering* by R. I. Sarbacher and W. A. Edson,[11n] published by John Wiley & Sons, 1943). The convergence and crossing of the flight lines indicates the "bunching" of the electrons near the output gap or catcher.

The symbolism is as follows:

V_o = the d-c accelerating voltage of the gun, therefore also the energy in electron volts of the electrons as they enter the input gap, called E_b in this text.

V_1 = the maximum instantaneous value of the uhf voltage across the input gap.

v_0 = the d-c velocity of the electrons within the drift space, this being the electron velocity corresponding to the d-c beam energy V_0 (or E_b).

v_1 = the maximum instantaneous value of the uhf component of the electron velocity in the drift space.

The electron enters the buncher with velocity $v_0 (= \sqrt{2q_e/m_e} \sqrt{V_o})$ and leaves it with velocity $v_o + v_1 \sin \omega t$, as a result of an energy change from V_o to $V_o + V_1 \sin \omega t$. Thus

$$v_o + v_1 \sin \omega t = \sqrt{2q_e/m_e} \sqrt{V_o + V_1 \sin \omega t}$$

$$= v_o \sqrt{1 + (V_1/V_o) \sin \omega t}$$

Because $V_1 \ll V_o$, this becomes

$$v_o + v_1 \sin \omega t \cong v_o + v_o \frac{V_1}{2V_o} \sin \omega t$$

Therefore, in this figure,

$$v_1 = v_o \frac{V_1}{2V_o}$$

put gap, just as the flow of plate current pulses through a triode causes the plate current swing in Fig. 11.2. As in that case, the uhf voltage establishes a uhf field which opposes the movement of the electrons, with a resulting delivery of energy by the electrons to the uhf field; this energy appears as uhf power in the output load resistance R_L. The input and output gaps and the anode may all be at the common d-c potential E_b. The output power is of course obtained at the expense of the kinetic energy of the electrons in the beam, which came originally from the d-c voltage in the gun.

Figure 11.4 is a klystron flight-line (Applegate) diagram, similar in nature to Figs. 2.4 and 2.5a. The electrons leave the input gap with systematically varying velocities, proportional to the slopes of the flight lines. The crossing of the flight lines indicates the overtaking of the slow electrons by the fast ones. Obviously bunches exist where the flight lines are close together. For a detailed analysis of bunch and circuit interactions, see Chapter II in *Microwave Electron Tubes*, and various other books.[11A, F, G, N, P, R]

In order to make such a two-gap klystron become an oscillator, a portion of the output voltage is made to appear across the input gap in proper phase.

In a *reflex klystron* oscillator [11A, F, G, L, N, R] only a single gap is employed, and the *reflector* electrode beyond the gap is held at a d-c potential slightly less than that of the cathode in the gun. Thus the electron's velocities fall to zero and then reverse in direction; the electrons pass back through the gap a second time. With proper transit time between forward and return passages, the single gap acts both as buncher and catcher. By varying the reflector voltage it is possible to achieve modest *voltage tuning*, that is, variation of oscillator frequency in response to this voltage change.

Klystron amplifiers and oscillators have been used extensively in both military and civilian-industry apparatus. Frequencies range from perhaps 1000 megacycles to considerably in excess of 10,000 megacycles. Efficiencies are low, in the range from 5 to an outside figure of perhaps 30 per cent, for power generation devices.

Reflex klystrons are inherently small-signal devices, widely used as local oscillators for radar and radio equipment, at frequencies from perhaps 2000 megacycles to around 60,000 megacycles (5 millimeters wavelength).

11.8   The Induced Current Concept.[11M, g] Figure 11.5a will be used to discuss semiquantitatively the induced current caused by the flow of the bunched beam through the output gap of a klystron. The two sets of grids in the figure bound the output gap; charge q represents a small volume element of electron-borne space charge moving to the right through the gap. Let an imagined potential difference E_h, as due to a battery shown dotted, exist between the two grids, producing an electric field F_h within the gap. The negative volume charge element q will induce positive surface charges on the grid wires. As q moves to the right, the positive induced charges on the right-hand grid will

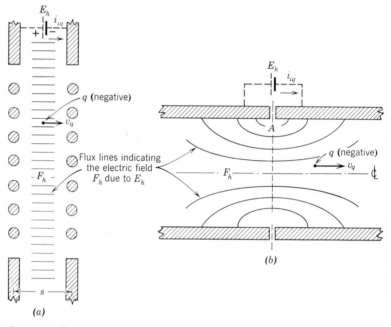

Fig. 11.5 Production of an induced current i_{iq} by the movement at velocity v_q of a volume charge element q.

(a) Normal-flow induced current, such as that caused by passage of electrons through the output gap of a klystron, or between the electrodes of a space-charge-control tube.

(b) Parallel-flow induced current, as within the helix of a traveling wave amplifier, or in the interaction space of a microwave magnetron oscillator.

become stronger, those on the left-hand grid weaker, because of the change in the relative nearness of q to the two grids. The resulting change in surface charge distribution between the two grids requires a flow of *induced current* i_{iq} in the circuit through E_h linking the two grids.

Figure 11.5b illustrates either a pair of metal plates, or, as applied to a traveling wave amplifier study, a longitudinal section of a conducting cylinder, cut transversely at AA, to permit establishing the imagined voltage E_h and resulting field F_h.

According to the fundamental induced current theorem, discussed and demonstrated in Chapter I of *Microwave Electron Tubes*,

$$i_{iq} = \frac{F_h}{E_h} qv_q \cos \theta \qquad (11\text{--}2)$$

where θ is the angle between the directions of F_h and v_q; in Figs. 11.5a and 11.5b, $\theta = 0°$, so that $\cos \theta = 1$.

It is essential to an understanding of the induced current concept to note here that F_h is proportional to E_h, so that the ratio F_h/E_h is not in the least dependent on the *magnitude* of E_h; this ratio depends *only on the geometry of the system*. Thus the magnitude of i_{iq} in (11--2) is not at all dependent on how large or small E_h is. Therefore for convenience E_h may be allowed to approach zero as a limit without changing the meaning of the equation. This implies that the induced current is not changed if E_h is replaced by a short circuit. More generally:

For a given location, velocity, and magnitude of the moving charge, the induced current is in any given geometry the same, regardless of the magnitude or even the existence of an electric field, at the charge location, that is caused by circuit potentials.

An electric field in a klystron gap, or in a traveling wave amplifier or magnetron, may affect the induced current indirectly, by modifying the velocity of charge movement. Such modifications are usually of very little importance in the klystron output gap.

As a first approximation, the grids in a klystron gap may for purposes of analysis be thought of as conducting but completely penetrable flat sheets (the equivalent of imagining the shadow fraction to be zero and the wire-to-wire spacing infinitely small). In that case (11--2) becomes, for the small charge element q,

$$i_{iq} = \frac{qv_q}{s} \qquad (11\text{--}3)$$

where s is the gap spacing.

i_{iq} must, like any electric current, flow in a closed loop. One section of this loop consists of space current within the between-electrode region. Except for the volume actually occupied by q, this space current is displacement current due to changes in the configuration of the field flux joining q to the induced surface charges. This is *not* the field flux shown in Fig. 11.5, in either figure. The induced current as given by (11--2) or (11--3) includes the contributions to space current, due both to the convection current within q and to the displacement current in all of the space, that results directly from the movement of

q. It does not, however, include the displacement current flowing as a result of time variations of electrode potentials; thus *capacitive* current must be separately evaluated. In any calculation involving induced currents:

$$i_{\text{total}} = i_{\text{induced}} + i_{\text{capacitive}} \qquad (11\text{–}4)$$

Study of Fig. 11.5a will show that in the neighborhood of q the space current has a direction perpendicular to the electrode surfaces (the grids being idealized into penetrable equipotentials). In contrast to this, in Fig. 11.5b the space current near q is directed parallel to the electrode surfaces. This explains the appellations normal-flow and parallel-flow for the two figures.

In both figures the conduction-current flow in the metallic circuit occurs entirely on the conductor surfaces, because of the familiar "skin effect" present at high frequencies. In Fig. 11.5b, with E_h replaced by a short circuit, the AA cut disappears completely, so that i_{iq} in (11–2) becomes simply the current due to q that crosses the cut location in the conductor surface. In Fig. 11.5a E_h is replaced, not by a short circuit, but by the resonant load circuit shown in Fig. 11.3 (in reality a resonant cavity), so that i_{iq} becomes the contribution of the q charge element's motion to the load current.

To determine the induced current due to the entire beam, q is first expressed as $\rho\, dV$, where dV is an element of volume, and ρ space charge density. Integration is then carried out over all the volume where space charge is present and for which F_h/E_h has significant values.

11.9 Traveling Wave Devices.[11H, P, j] In the original design of a traveling wave amplifier tube, schematically diagrammed in Fig. 11.6, an electron gun injects an electron beam of energy E_b into the interior of a wire helix. A microwave-frequency uhf signal is applied to this helix at the point of entry of the beam into the helix; a larger signal at this same frequency appears at the output end of the helix.

The uhf current flows spirally around the helix, thus producing in the center an axially directed uhf field that travels longitudinally at a phase velocity slower than that of free-space radio transmission by the pitch factor of the helix. (The pitch factor is the ratio of the length of wire around the helix to the axial length, between any two axial points.) By proper choice of the pitch factor, the traveling wave can be given a phase velocity about the same as the d-c velocity of the electrons in the beam. In a typical device this beam may consist of 1500-volt electrons, corresponding to a pitch factor of about 13. In this case the wavelength of the along-axis uhf wave is about 8 milli-

meters, whereas the useful portion of the helix may be 30 to 50 centimeters long. Thus the interelectrode distance along the beam's travel
is many wavelengths of the useful propagating wave within the
structure.

The interaction between the electrons and the traveling wave, outlined in detail in Chapters VI and VII of *Microwave Electron Tubes*
and in Pierce's book,[11H] is remotely similar to that between the rotor

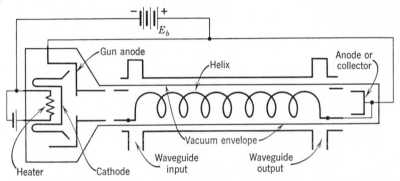

FIG. 11.6   Schematic diagram of a traveling wave amplifier tube using a wire
helix as the uhf circuit element. (Adapted from Fig. 2 in "Travelling-Wave
Tubes," by J. R. Pierce and L. M. Field, *Proc. IRE*, **35**, 108, February, 1947.)

windings and the rotating magnetic field in a polyphase a-c induction
motor or generator. In general, if the electrons are traveling faster
than the uhf field, they can deliver power to the uhf circuit, somewhat
as an induction generator delivers a-c power when the rotor is driven
slightly faster than the "synchronous speed" of the rotating magnetic
field set up by the stator currents. Also, as with the induction ma-
chine, the most effective interaction occurs when there is only a relatively slight difference between the two speeds. If the electrons are
traveling a little more slowly than the uhf field, they will accept power
from it, thus being accelerated, as an induction motor rotor accepts
power when it is running just a little below synchronous speed.

The gross nature of the interaction between the electrons and the
traveling wave may be summarized as follows:

(*a*) The uhf voltage along the helix gives rise to a traveling uhf longitudinal
electric field within the beam.

(*b*) This uhf field causes bunching of the beam; this is *over-run bunching*, totally
different in nature from the drift-space bunching in a klystron (see Chapter VI
in *Microwave Electron Tubes* for a discussion of the different kinds of bunching).

(*c*) The bunched traveling beam gives rise to a longitudinally flowing induced
current in the surface of the helix, somewhat as suggested by Fig. 11.5*b*.

(d) Because of the *characteristic impedance* of the helix, the passage of the induced current results in an addition to the uhf voltage of the traveling wave, which enlarges the original (a) voltage; thus the (a), (b), (c), (d) cycle is again repeated.

The interaction as a whole is a sort of self-reenforcing closed-loop operation. The device may be thought of as an unstable regenerative oscillator, in which the instability appears in the distance rather than in the time dimension. As with any oscillator, nonlinearities of the system set an upper limit to the achievable amplitude. Thus for a given traveling wave device there tends to exist a saturation uhf output power level above which the output cannot rise, regardless of increases in the input.

The decibel power gain is at small power levels proportional to the length, subject, however, to rather severe circuit losses intentionally introduced. This is necessary to prevent reflections back along the tube from the output from causing the device to oscillate rather than amplify. A tube about 30 centimeters long carrying perhaps 10 milliamperes in a 1500-volt beam, in a helix a few millimeters in diameter, might have perhaps 50-db electron interaction power gain. With 30-db intentionally introduced helix loss, this would result in a net small-signal power gain of 20 db. Output powers in the early devices have been modest, from perhaps a few score milliwatts to a very few watts. None of the interaction principles are appreciably sensitive to frequency, for a very wide range of frequencies; thus operation of a given device anywhere in the range from 2000 to 4000 megacycles might easily be obtained.

An *electron wave amplifier* [11i] tube employs two adjacent parallel electron beams having slightly different beam velocities, there being no enclosing helix or other circuit except at the terminations. In an approximate sense, each beam may be thought of as providing the circuit for the other.

11.10   Microwave Magnetrons.[2f, 11C, D, I, L, P, R]   Obviously a traveling wave amplifier can be made re-entrant; that is, it may be looped around so that the output is identified with the input. The device is then an oscillator; it will oscillate at some one specific frequency among those for which the traveling electromagnetic wave experiences an integral number of cycles in traversing the circumference.

A microwave *magnetron oscillator* (see Chapter VIII in *Microwave Electron Tubes*) may be thought of as a *large-signal* re-entrant device of the nature just described. The beam consists of electrons rotating in essentially circular fashion around the axis, somewhat as in Curve 1 of Fig. 2.15, but with an added modest outward radial flow, of magnitude dependent on the uhf power demanded. The counterpart, in the magnetron, of the helix of the traveling wave amplifier may be an array of resonant cavities, as illustrated in Fig. 11.7. The cavities should be thought of as lumped-constant "resonant" circuits, connected to form a sort of lumped-constant re-entrant transmission line.

The magnetron has a great advantage in power conversion efficiency, in comparison with existing klystrons and traveling wave amplifiers.

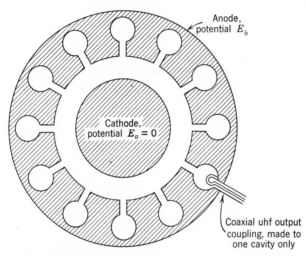

FIG. 11.7 Cathode and anode of cylindrical hole-and-slot multicavity microwave magnetron. Magnetic field parallel to the axis. In operation, there will be a 180° uhf phase difference between adjacent anode segments.

In a magnetron the mechanism of employment of space charge is such that each electron is kept actively circulating and delivering energy to the uhf field until it has given up most of the energy accepted by transfer through the d-c field. Only when an electron has delivered, as uhf energy, nearly all the energy accepted from the d-c field is it permitted to escape to the anode. Thus magnetrons may in some cases operate at as high as 90 to 95 per cent *electron interaction efficiency*. Therefore as uhf power generators they can operate at efficiencies of 50 to 75 per cent, even after accounting for relatively severe uhf copper losses and some cathode back-heating. Magnetron oscillators are used both as continuous-power and pulsed-power generators, at frequencies from 300 megacycles to well above 10,000 megacycles. Power levels range from perhaps ½ watt to many kilowatts as continuous-wave generators, and up to more than a megawatt peak power as pulsed generators. Magnetron oscillators can also be built to operate at low audio and power frequencies; below the uhf range they are built as "split-anode" devices operating on a negative-resistance principle.

Figure 11.8 presents a somewhat idealized set of d-c volt-ampere characteristic curves for a microwave magnetron oscillator. They

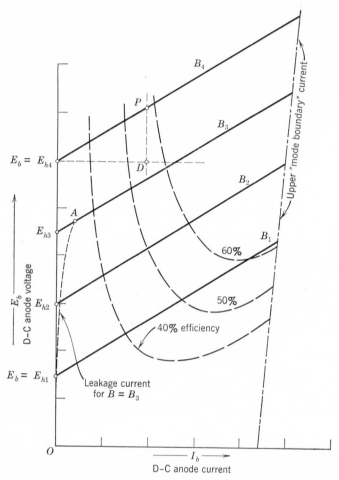

FIG. 11.8 Idealized d-c operating characteristics of a magnetron. Solid lines are d-c volt-ampere curves for values B_1, B_2, B_3, etc., of magnetic flux density. E_{h1}, E_{h2}, etc., are corresponding threshold voltages. Dashed lines are illustrative constant-efficiency contours.

might, for example, apply to a 50-watt magnetron for operation at 3000 megacycles, the voltages then ranging up to 1200 volts or so, and the currents up to 100 milliamperes, for a magnetic field strength of 2000 gausses.

With any given axial magnetic field (for example B_3) existing in the magnetron interaction space, little or no current flows as the plate voltage is first increased upward from zero; this is consistent with the concept of "magnetic cut-off" discussed in connection with Fig. 2.14. In an ideally perfect magnetron oscillator, no current at all would flow before E_b reaches the threshold voltage E_{h3}. At the threshold voltage E_{h3} that corresponds to the design frequency of the resonators and to the magnetic flux density B_3, d-c current begins to flow, and the magnetron begins to oscillate, generating microwave power at its resonant frequency. Note that the threshold voltage is much below the normal d-c magnetic cut-off voltage; thus the operation as an oscillator permits electrons to reach the anode that could not do so if there were no uhf field present in the interaction space. Further increase of anode voltage E_b above E_{h3} leads to a roughly linear increase of I_b with E_b. The *modulation impedance* of the device is the slope of the d-c characteristic curve, as between E_{h4} and point P along the volt-ampere curve that applies for the magnetic field strength B_4. In general the volt-ampere curves do not extend indefinitely to higher values; beyond some reasonably definite "mode boundary" value of I_b the magnetron cannot be operated, at least as a power generator at the desired frequency; it may or may not operate at some other, undesired, frequency.

As illustrated, there exists a different threshold voltage and associated volt-ampere curve for each value of magnetic flux density, the threshold voltage being a linear but not a proportional function of the magnetic flux density, according to the following "Hartree" equation:

$$\frac{E_h}{E_0} = 2\frac{B}{B_0} - 1 \qquad (11\text{-}5)$$

In this expression, B is the existing magnetic flux density, E_0 is the kinetic energy that an electron has when circulating in synchronism with the uhf electromagnetic field at anode radius, and B_0 is related to E_0 just as B is related to E_b in (2–92). That is, B_0 is the magnetic flux density that would cause magnetic cut-off to occur at $E_b = E_0$ for the existing geometry. In useful devices values of the ratio B/B_0 are likely to be between 2 and 5.

In an actual operating magnetron a small *leakage current* will flow to the anode at voltages below the threshold, the magnetron not then being in an oscillating condition. Thus the actual curve between the origin and the more or less straight-line oscillating volt-ampere curve is not quite vertical, being shaped more as indicated by the line OA in Fig. 11.8, for the B_3 condition.

CHAPTER XII

RANDOM VELOCITIES OF GAS PARTICLES *

12.1 The Maxwellian Energy Distribution Function. The more general form of the Fermi distribution function (8–19) is [7A, B, 8A, B, D, G, H]

$$\left.\begin{array}{c}\text{Fractional occupancy of} \\ \text{the shell at energy } E\end{array}\right\} = \frac{1}{1 + B \exp (E/E_T)} \qquad (12\text{–}1)$$

where the symbolism is as in Chapter VIII, and, in addition,

> B is a constant (that is, a quantity not dependent on E) whose value is determined by the requirement that the integral of dN_s [particles per shell, (8–20a)] over all values of energy shall equal N, the total particle density per unit volume. In general, B depends on the density and mass of the particles, and on the temperature.

In order to permit comment on the nature of the integration to determine B, the integral can be expressed as follows, using as the integrand a modified form of (8–20a):

$$N = \left[\frac{2\pi G(2mq_e)^{3/2}}{h^3} \right] \int_{E=0}^{E=\infty} \left(\frac{1}{1 + B \exp (E/E_T)} \right) \sqrt{E}\, dE \qquad (12\text{–}2)$$

> where G is a "weighting" quantity, being 2 for the electrons in a metal, because of their spin, and 1 for gas particles.
>
> m is the mass of a particle, m_e for the electrons in a metal, m_g for gas particles.

The integral in this equation is a function of B and of E_T; the expression as a whole is an equation for the determination of B.

For an electron gas in a metal, the quantity in brackets is very small (because $m = m_e$), and N is very large (because metals are dense); therefore the integral must be a very large quantity. In order for the integral to be large, B must be extremely small, because, with E_T at its room-temperature value of about 0.04, exp E/E_T becomes rapidly large for increasing E_T. Integration using formula E, Table IX, will show that (12–2) is satisfied when the (8–19) form of the Fermi distri-

---

* General bibliography references are 12A, B, C, D, 1I, J, K, 7A, B, 8B, G, H.

bution function is used, with N very large and m very small. In this operation $B = \exp(-E_F/E_T)$.

For ordinary gases $m = m_g$, which is greater than m_e by about 10^5; also, N for such a gas is less than N in a metal by at least 10^4; thus for an ordinary gas the integral in (12-2) must be less by a factor of the order of 10^{11} than it is for the electron gas in a metal. This requires that B in the Fermi distribution function shall be very large indeed; in that case the 1 in the denominator becomes unimportant for practically all values of E, so that *for an ordinary gas* the Fermi distribution function becomes:

$$\left.\begin{array}{l}\text{Fractional occupancy of the}\\ \text{shell at energy } E, \text{ for a}\\ \text{Maxwellian distribution}\end{array}\right\} = \frac{1}{B}\exp\frac{-E}{E_T} \qquad (12\text{-}3)$$

With the 1 in the denominator of (12-2) dropped, integration is straightforward; use $E/E_T = r^2$, and employ Table IX. The result is the Maxwell-Boltzmann distribution:

$$\frac{dN_c}{dE} = \frac{2N}{\sqrt{\pi}}\sqrt{\frac{E}{E_T{}^3}}\exp\frac{-E}{E_T} \qquad (12\text{-}4)$$

Here dN_c has been used with the same meaning as dN_s, to agree with later symbolism in this chapter. This form is radically different from (8-20a) in that it does not involve the Fermi-level energy E_F in any way, whereas it does involve N as a directly proportional factor.

Note relative to the electrons-in-the-metal distribution (8-20a) that, for electron energies large enough so that $(E - E_F)/E_T \gg 1$, the distribution is of the (12-4) form, because the term containing B in the denominator of the Fermi function is large enough to mask the 1 term. Thus, in the "tail of the distribution curve," the energy distribution function for the electrons is of the same nature as the Maxwellian energy distribution (12-4). This is why thermionically emitted electrons have on emergence a Maxwellian distribution; they are all electrons from the tail of the (8-20a) distribution curve.

12.2 Mechanistic Derivation of the Maxwellian Distribution Function.[12A, D] It is desirable to present a derivation of the Maxwellian distribution function on the basis of ordinary particle mechanics. To do so it is necessary to introduce the concept of velocity space, illustrated by Fig. 12.1.

Just as many velocity points exist in the three-dimensional velocity space as there are gas particles in unit volume of real space, each velocity point being placed in accordance with the proper u, v, w components of the total velocity, which is symbolized as c. Thus u, v, w are respectively the instantaneous velocities of a particle in the x, y, z directions. It is convenient to introduce a symbol η (eta) to describe the concentration of points in velocity space. Just as N stands for the

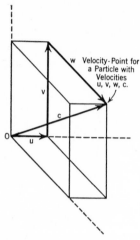

number of particles per unit volume anywhere in real space, so η stands for the number of particles per cubic meter per second at any location in velocity space. There are N points altogether in the velocity space.

dN_c will now be defined as the number of particles per cubic meter having velocities between c and $c + dc$, regardless of the direction of motion. It is, therefore, the number of points within a *spherical shell of velocity space* of radius c, thickness dc. The quantity dN_u is similarly defined as the number of points within a plane "slice," perpendicular to the u axis, located u from the origin and with thickness du.

Fig. 12.1   Coordinate system for velocity points.

No one direction of motion can have preference over any other, if the gas as a whole is stationary; therefore the number of particles in any spherical shell must be equally distributed throughout it. Hence η can be expressed by dividing dN_c by $4\pi c^2 \, dc$, the volume of the shell; thus

$$\eta = \frac{dN_c}{4\pi c^2 \, dc} \tag{12-5}$$

Now consider a slice of thickness du at u. Divide the slice into small rings about the axis, each of radius s and extent ds, where $s^2 = v^2 + w^2$ (s is obviously perpendicular to u). All points of each ring are at a common distance $c = \sqrt{u^2 + s^2}$ from the origin; therefore η is uniform within each ring, and the number of points in each is $2\pi\eta s \, ds \, du$. Integration over all rings gives the number of points in the slice. Thus

$$dN_u = \int_{s=0}^{s=\infty} 2\pi\eta s \, ds \, du \tag{12-6}$$

The objective of this section's analysis is the determination of the dependence of η on the energy E. This involves attention to the interchange of energy and momentum at collisions between the particles, in an equilibrium state. For convenience in studying collision rates, imagine the velocity space to be divided into identical rectangular cells, having edge dimensions du, dv, dw. Each cell is large enough to contain the velocity points for a very great number of particles, yet small enough so that its edge dimensions are very small relative to the average particle velocity.

The rate of collisions between particles in the ith cell and those in the jth cell, where i and j are indices identifying any two randomly chosen cells, is proportional to the product of the number of velocity points in the two cells. Thus, mathematically:

$$G_{ij} = g_{ij}n_i n_j \, \Delta t \qquad (12\text{–}7)$$

where G_{ij} is the number of collisions of particles initially in cell i with particles initially in cell j, within the time interval Δt.

n_i, n_j are respectively the numbers of particles in cells i and j.

g_{ij} is a proportionality factor depending on the size and shape of the particles.

To illustrate this, suppose that

$$n_i = 3, \text{ consisting of particles } A, B, C \qquad (12\text{–}8a)$$

$$n_j = 2, \text{ consisting of particles } D, E \qquad (12\text{–}8b)$$

Then suppose that there occur per second 50 of each of the following kinds of collisions:

	BA	CA	DA	EA	
AB		CB	DB	EB	
AC	BC		DC	EC	(12–9)
AD	BD	CD		ED	
AE	BE	CE	DE		

This is a square array with the items AA, BB, etc., left out, as a particle cannot very well collide with itself. There are

$$(5 \times 5) - 5 = 20 \text{ kinds of collisions} \qquad (12\text{–}10a)$$

therefore

$$20 \times 50 = 1000 \text{ collisions per second of all kinds} \qquad (12\text{–}10b)$$

The G_{ij} collisions are underlined in the array; there are 6 kinds of them, so that there are

$$6 \times 50 = 300 \text{ collisions of } i \text{ with } j \text{ particles} \qquad (12\text{–}11)$$

In this case (12–7) takes the form

$$300 = 50 \times 3 \times 2 \qquad [\Delta t \text{ being 1 second}] \qquad (12\text{–}12)$$

Thus the factor g_{ij} is in this case 50.

Of the $g_{ij}n_in_j\,\Delta t$ collisions, a certain number will result in the particles involved appearing in particular randomly chosen cells k, l. Of
course the sum of the energies and the sums of the momenta for the
i, j cells must be the same as the corresponding sums for the k, l cells,
in order to satisfy the laws of conservation of energy and momentum. Call the number of collisions that result in change to k, l cells
$g_{ij}{}^{kl}n_in_j\,\Delta t$. Thus

$$G_{ij}{}^{kl} = g_{ij}{}^{kl}n_in_j\,\Delta t \qquad (12\text{--}13)$$

where $G_{ij}{}^{kl}$ stands for the number of collisions between i, j particles
that result in change to the k, l cells.

$g_{ij}{}^{kl}$ is a factor dependent on particle size and shape, very much
less than g_{ij} (in the ratio of the chance of an i with j collision resulting in change into the *particular* cells k, l).

There is a converse relation

$$G_{kl}{}^{ij} = g_{kl}{}^{ij}n_kn_l\,\Delta t \qquad (12\text{--}14)$$

describing change into i, j cells as a result of the occurrence of collisions of particles in k cells with particles in l cells.

There are two basic principles, regarding this collision mechanism,
that lead directly to the Maxwell-Boltzmann distribution relations:

(a) A sufficient condition for an equilibrium state to exist is that the
rate at which changes occur from the i, j cells into the k, l cells equals
the inverse rate, that is

$$G_{ij}{}^{kl} = G_{kl}{}^{ij} \qquad [\text{equilibrium condition}] \qquad (12\text{--}15)$$

(b) It is reasonable to accept the principle of *detail balancing*, sometimes also called the principle of *microscopic reversibility*,[12D, a] applying
to the size and shape coefficients, stated as

$$g_{kl}{}^{ij} = g_{ij}{}^{kl} \qquad [\text{detail balancing}] \qquad (12\text{--}16)$$

A simple mental concept of detail balancing is stated below Fig.
12.2, which portrays a collision between two spherical particles following
the paths PP' and QQ' respectively, coming in from P and Q.

Comparison of (12–13) and (12–14) in the light of the (12–15) and
(12–16) statements shows that

$$n_in_j = n_kn_l \qquad (12\text{--}17)$$

This may be written

$$\ln n_i + \ln n_j = \ln n_k + \ln n_l \qquad (12\text{--}18)$$

Furthermore, the conservation of energy requires that

$$E_i + E_j = E_k + E_l \tag{12-19}$$

where

E_i, E_j, E_k, E_l are the respective kinetic energies (in electron volts) associated with the i, j, k, l cells.

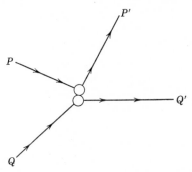

FIG. 12.2 Colliding spherical gas particles. Equation (12–16) states the detail balancing hypothesis, which is that:
The probability of departure with directions and speeds as at P', Q', *if* approach occurs with the P, Q directions and speeds, is the same as:
The probability of *departure* with the P, Q directions and speeds, if *approach* were to occur with directions and speeds as at P', Q'.
The randomness as to departure conditions, for given approach velocities, exists because of the various possible orientations of the axis through particle centers at collision.

The presumption that some sort of equilibrium-state energy distribution exists implies that

$$n \text{ is some function of } E; \text{ thus } E = E(n) \tag{12-20}$$

where n, E apply to any and all cells, including the i, j, k, l cells. Study of the algebra involved will show that, with i and j chosen completely arbitrarily, the only form that the function $E(n)$ can have, to satisfy both (12–18) and (12–19), is

$$\ln n = bE + a \tag{12-21}$$

where b and a are as yet completely arbitrary constants. To demonstrate that this form is adequate, multiply (12–19) by b, and add a twice to each side; the resulting form is

$$bE_i + a + bE_j + a = bE_k + a + bE_l + a \tag{12-22}$$

This is obviously in complete agreement both with (12–18) and (12–21).

If one were to try a different function, for example

$$\ln n = bE^2 + a \qquad (12\text{–}23)$$

(12–18) would not be satisfied.

Equation (12–21) can also be written

$$n = (\exp a)(\exp bE) \qquad (12\text{–}24)$$

or, more usefully,

$$n = A \exp bE \qquad (12\text{–}25)$$

where A and b are two constants to be evaluated (in the next section) on the basis of the following two conditions:

(a) The total number of points in the velocity space is equal to N (the concentration of particles per unit volume of metric space).

(b) The kinetic energy, integrated over all the particles, is the product of the total number of particles by their average energy.

b is of necessity negative; if it were positive the number of particles per shell would become rapidly greater for more remote points in velocity space, leading to an infinite total number of particles.

With b negative, (12–25) is seen to have the same general form and meaning as (12–3) and is the simplest form of expression of the Maxwellian distribution function.

12.3   Forms of the Maxwellian Distribution Equations.[12A, B, C, D]   In this section the conditions (a) and (b) stated following (12–25) will be employed to establish the significance of the constants A and b.

It is evident that $1/b$ has the dimensions of energy per particle (in electron volts) and is negative. It will be recalled that in electric circuit studies involving the discharge of a condenser C through a resistance R the transient voltage decay equation is, in volts e,

$$e = E_0 \exp\left(\frac{-t}{RC}\right) \qquad (12\text{–}26)$$

and that the quantity RC is called the *time constant* of the circuit. Similarly in the present case it is convenient to define an *energy constant* of the distribution thus:

$$-\frac{1}{b} = \left\{ \begin{array}{l} \text{In electron volts, the energy per particle} \\ \quad \text{that is ``characteristic'' of a particular} \\ \quad \text{Maxwellian energy distribution} \end{array} \right. \qquad (12\text{–}27)$$

Symbolize this characteristic energy per particle as E_T; thus E_T is *defined*, for present purposes, as

$$E_T = -\frac{1}{b} \qquad (12\text{–}28)$$

It will turn out that in a Maxwellian distribution the *average* energy per particle is proportional to E_T, and that this average energy is measured by something that is called "temperature," so that it is convenient to call E_T the "voltage equivalent of temperature." However, the primary reason why *this particular* definition of E_T is used is that it makes the exponent in (12–25) have the simplest possible form.

A derivation based on quantum mechanics, and remotely similar to the one just given, leads to the more general Fermi distribution function (12–1).[7A, 8B, E, G, H] In that derivation the first-appearing form of the function is

$$\text{Fractional occupancy of} \atop \text{the shell at energy } E \Big\} = \frac{1}{1 + B \exp bE} \qquad (12\text{–}29)$$

The quantity E_T is, as in (12–28), defined so as to make the exponent as simple as possible. In both cases the quantity T called temperature, involved in the general branch of science called thermodynamics, is related to E_T as follows, as first stated in (7–3a).

$$kT = q_e E_T \qquad (12\text{–}30)$$

It is also convenient to define a characteristic velocity; thus let

ζ (zeta) symbolize the velocity per particle that corresponds to the energy per particle characteristic of the temperature T.

Mathematically, this requires that

$$\tfrac{1}{2}m\zeta^2 = kT = q_e E_T \qquad \begin{bmatrix} \text{this is the energy per} \\ \text{particle characteristic} \\ \text{of the temperature } T \end{bmatrix} \qquad (12\text{–}31)$$

The phrase "energy per particle characteristic of the temperature T" used here, and implied in (12–27), means merely that, if this particular value of energy per particle is used in the equations, the mathematical forms will have the maximum simplicity. It *does not* imply that E_T is the average energy, or the most probable energy, or that it has any other similarly unique physical significance, although it may and does become these for certain special cases. The *particular* definitions (12–31) involving E_T, kT, and ζ are employed because they make the exponents simple.

In (12–25) A is a constant independent of E; the size of cell du, dv, dw used in the preceding sections is also a constant independent of E. Therefore it is acceptable to introduce a new constant D, also independent of E, defined by

$$A = D \, du \, dv \, dw \qquad (12\text{–}32)$$

Thus (12–25) now becomes

$$n = \left(\exp \frac{-E}{E_T}\right) D \, du \, dv \, dw \tag{12-33}$$

It is evident from the definition of η, early in Section 12.2, and from the definition of the n's following (12–7), that

$$n = \eta \, du \, dv \, dw \tag{12-34}$$

Comparison of the last two equations shows that

$$\eta = D \exp \frac{-E}{E_T} \tag{12-35}$$

Recall now the relation between total velocity c and total energy E, for any point in velocity space:

$$\tfrac{1}{2}mc^2 = q_e E \tag{12-36}$$

Use in the preceding equation of this and (12–31) leads to

$$\eta = D \exp \frac{-c^2}{\varsigma^2} \tag{12-37}$$

Equation (12–5) can now be employed as follows:

$$N = \int_{c=0}^{c=\infty} dN_c = \int_{c=0}^{c=\infty} 4\pi c^2 \eta \, dc \tag{12-38}$$

Introduction of the preceding equation leads to

$$N = 4\pi D \int_{c=0}^{c=\infty} c^2 \exp \frac{-c^2}{\varsigma^2} \, dc \tag{12-39}$$

In these equations, N = particles per unit volume of metric space, also total particles in velocity space. Equation (12–39) can also be written

$$N = 2\pi^{3/2}\varsigma^3 D \frac{2}{\sqrt{\pi}} \int_{c=0}^{c=\infty} \frac{c^2}{\varsigma^2} \exp \frac{-c^2}{\varsigma^2} \, d\,\frac{c}{\varsigma} \tag{12-40}$$

Integration by means of Table IX gives

$$N = \pi^{3/2}\varsigma^3 D \tag{12-41a}$$

from which

$$D = \frac{N}{\pi^{3/2}\varsigma^3} \tag{12-41b}$$

Therefore, from (12–37),

$$\eta = \frac{N}{\pi^{3/2} \zeta^3} \exp \frac{-c^2}{\zeta^2} \qquad (12\text{–}42)$$

This permits (12–5) to take the very useful form stating the number dN_c of particles in the hollow spherical velocity-space shell at radius c:

$$dN_c = \frac{4N}{\sqrt{\pi}} \frac{c^2}{\zeta^2} \exp \frac{-c^2}{\zeta^2} \, d\frac{c}{\zeta} \qquad (12\text{–}43)$$

This is the same as (12–4), but expressed for velocities rather than energies.

This completes the employment of condition (a), stated below (12–25), to eliminate A in favor of N.

The employment of condition (b) can be introduced as follows:

$$N\bar{E}_c q_e = \int_{c=0}^{c=\infty} \tfrac{1}{2} mc^2 \, dN_c = \int_{c=0}^{c=\infty} \tfrac{1}{2} mc^2 \cdot 4\pi c^2 \eta \, dc \qquad (12\text{–}44$$

where $\bar{E}_c$ is the average total kinetic energy per particle, in electron volts. Both sides of this expression state the total kinetic energy, in joules, for $\bar{E}_c q_e$ is the average energy in joules.

Introduction here of (12–42) for η, and rearrangement, gives

$$N\bar{E}_c q_e = Nm\zeta^2 \frac{2}{\sqrt{\pi}} \int_{c=0}^{c=\infty} \frac{c^4}{\zeta^4} \exp \frac{-c^2}{\zeta^2} \frac{dc}{\zeta} \qquad (12\text{–}45a)$$

Integration by means of Table IX gives

$$N\bar{E}_c q_e = N(\tfrac{3}{4} m\zeta^2) \qquad (12\text{–}45b)$$

Both sides still state total energy per cubic meter, in joules. Of course the N's cancel; it is convenient to use the (12–31) statement of the characteristic energy to convert this to

$$\bar{E}_c q_e = \tfrac{3}{2}(\tfrac{1}{2} m\zeta^2) = \tfrac{3}{2} kT = \tfrac{3}{2} E_T q_e \qquad (12\text{–}46)$$

Thus condition (b) following (12–25) has been employed to relate the arbitrary constant $-b = 1/E_T$ to the average energy $\bar{E}$, in the forms

Average energy per parti-
cle, Maxwellian distri-
bution
$$\left. \begin{array}{l} \\ \\ \\ \end{array} \right\} \quad \begin{array}{l} = \bar{E}_c = \tfrac{3}{2} E_T \quad \text{[electron volts]} \quad (12\text{–}47a) \\[2mm] = \tfrac{3}{2} kT \quad \text{[joules]} \quad\quad\quad (12\text{–}47b) \end{array}$$

It is convenient at this point to complete the determination of dN_u, introduced by (12–6). In carrying out the integration, note that, in velocity space,

$$c^2 = u^2 + s^2$$

and also that therefore

$$\exp \frac{-c^2}{\zeta^2} = \exp \frac{-u^2}{\zeta^2} \exp \frac{-s^2}{\zeta^2} \tag{12–48}$$

The integral (12–6) then takes the form

$$dN_u = \frac{N}{\sqrt{\pi}} \exp \frac{-u^2}{\zeta^2} d\left(\frac{u}{\zeta}\right) \int_{(s/\zeta)=0}^{(s/\zeta)=\infty} 2\frac{s}{\zeta} \exp \frac{-s^2}{\zeta^2} d\left(\frac{s}{\zeta}\right) \tag{12–49}$$

Integration by means of Table IX gives the very useful form for the number of particles dN_u in the velocity-space "slice" at velocity u:

$$dN_u = \frac{N}{\sqrt{\pi}} \exp \frac{-u^2}{\zeta^2} d\left(\frac{u}{\zeta}\right) \tag{12–50}$$

Graphical illustrations of this relation and of (12–43), the corresponding total-velocity distribution relation, appear in a later section.

12.4 Terminology for Distribution Relations. This section presents grouped statements of the meanings of various old and new symbols used in the presentation of detail facts regarding particle velocity distributions.

Group I. Temperature (see Section 7.3).

kT, $E_T q_e$, $\frac{1}{2}m\zeta^2$, are all equal to one another; each describes in a particular way the kinetic energy, in joules per particle, that is "characteristic" of the temperature T for any gas.

k = Boltzmann's gas constant, 1.380×10^{-23} joule per particle per degree Kelvin.

q_e = the electronic charge, 1.602×10^{-19} coulomb per electron.

m = the mass per gas particle. For gas molecules, m can be determined by multiplying the electronic mass, m_e, by the *mass ratio*.

m_e = the mass of an electron, 9.11×10^{-31} kilogram.

m/m_e = the *mass ratio;* numerically, $m/m_e = 1822 \times$ molecular weight of gas particle. $\tag{12–51}$

T = temperature of the gas in degrees Kelvin.

E_T = the voltage equivalent of the temperature T; see (12–31);

$$T = 11{,}610 E_T \tag{12–52}$$

ζ = the velocity corresponding to the characteristic temperature energy; for purposes of calculation, using (2–5),

$$\zeta = \frac{5.93 \times 10^5 \sqrt{E_T}}{\sqrt{m/m_e}} \qquad (12\text{--}53)$$

also, from the equality between kT, $\frac{1}{2}m\zeta^2$, and $E_T q_e$:

$$\zeta = \sqrt{\frac{2kT}{m}} = \sqrt{\frac{2q_e E_T}{m}} \qquad (12\text{--}54)$$

Group II.   Individual Velocities and Energies.

u, v, w are respectively x-, y-, and z-directed velocities of a particle. c is the total velocity of a particle regardless of its direction, that is,

$$c^2 = u^2 + v^2 + w^2 \qquad (12\text{--}55)$$

s is the resultant of v and w, that is,

$$s^2 = v^2 + w^2 \qquad (12\text{--}56)$$

E_u, E_v, E_w, E_c, are respectively the energies, in electron volts, associated with the u, v, w, and c velocities. A typical relation is

$$u = \frac{5.93 \times 10^5 \sqrt{E_u}}{\sqrt{m/m_e}} = \sqrt{\frac{2q_e E_u}{m}} \qquad (12\text{--}57)$$

du, dc, dE_u, dE_c, etc., are small increments of the corresponding velocities and energies. See under dc in Group IV for a comment on their magnitudes.

$R^2 = c^2/\zeta^2 = E_c/E_T$; R is the ratio of an individual particle's total velocity to the characteristic velocity ζ.   (12–58)

$r^2 = u^2/\zeta^2 = E_u/E_T$; r is the ratio of a particular particle's x-directed velocity to the characteristic velocity.   (12–59)

Group III.   Average and Root-Mean-Square Velocities and Energies.

$\bar{c}$, $\bar{R}$ are average values of c, R.

$\bar{u}$, $\bar{r}$ are the averages *of the positive values only* of u, r; overall averages are zero.

$\bar{\bar{c}}$, $\bar{\bar{u}}$, $\bar{\bar{R}}$, $\bar{\bar{r}}$ are rms values of c, u, R, r.

$\bar{\bar{c}}^2$, $\bar{\bar{u}}^2$, $\bar{\bar{R}}^2$, $\bar{\bar{r}}^2$ are, therefore, the *averages of the squares* of c, u, R, r.

$\bar{E}_c$, $\bar{E}_u$ are average total and average x-directed kinetic energies, in electron volts.

Since R^2, c^2, and E_c are, from their definitions in Group II, directly proportional to one another, their averages, $\overline{\overline{R}}^2$, $\overline{c}^2$, and $\overline{E}_c$ are also proportional, and by the same proportionality factors. $\overline{r}^2$, $\overline{u}^2$, and $\overline{E}_u$ are similarly proportional. Therefore

$$\overline{\overline{R}}^2 = \frac{\overline{\overline{c}}^2}{\alpha^2} = \frac{\overline{E}_c}{E_T} \tag{12-60}$$

$$\overline{r}^2 = \frac{\overline{\overline{u}}^2}{\alpha^2} = \frac{\overline{E}_u}{E_T} \tag{12-61}$$

Group IV.   Concentrations of Particles.

N = concentration, that is, total number of particles per cubic meter.

N_c = the number of particles per cubic meter with total velocities greater * than a value c.

$p_c = N_c/N$ = (a) the fraction, of the total number of particles, that have at any given moment total velocities greater than c; also (b) the *probability* that any particle has a velocity greater than c.

dN_c = the number per cubic meter with total velocities between * c and $c + dc$, where

dc = an increment of c small relative to the range of velocities considered, yet large enough so that dN_c is a very large number.   The other incremental quantities listed in Group II are similarly proportioned.

$dp_c = dN_c/N$ = (a) the small *fraction* of the total number of particles that have velocities between * c and $c + dc$; also, (b) the *probability* that any particle's total velocity is between * c and $c + dc$.

N_u = the number per cubic meter with x-directed velocities greater * than a value u.

$p_u = N_u/N$ = (a) the fraction, of the total number of particles, that have at any given moment x-directed velocities greater than u; also (b) the *probability* that any particle has an x-directed velocity greater than u.

dN_u = the number per cubic meter with x-directed velocities between * u and $u + du$; as with dc, the increment du must be small, yet dN_u must be a large number.

$dp_u = dN_u/N$ = (a) a small *fraction;* also (b) a *probability*, both as for dp_c except that x-directed instead of total velocities are involved.*

* See comments as to sign, associated with (12–67) through (12–71).

12.5 Maxwellian Distribution Curves and Averages for Total Velocities.[12A, B, D]

The ordinary gas distribution has been presented, earlier in this chapter, in the *velocity distribution* form of (12–43):

$$dN_c = \frac{4N}{\sqrt{\pi}} \frac{c^2}{\zeta^2} \exp \frac{-c^2}{\zeta^2} d\frac{c}{\zeta} \qquad (12\text{–}62)$$

and in the *energy distribution* form (12–4), which can be stated

$$dN_c = \frac{2N}{\sqrt{\pi}} \sqrt{\frac{E_c}{E_T}} \exp \frac{-E_c}{E_T} d\frac{E_c}{E_T} \qquad (12\text{–}63)$$

These equations state the same set of facts in two different ways.

The velocity distribution form is more conveniently expressed in terms of the probability, or fraction p_c, defined in Group IV of the preceding section as $p_c = N_c/N$, and in terms of the dimensionless ratio $R = c/\zeta$, defined in Group II; thus (12–62) becomes

$$\frac{dN_c}{dR} = \frac{4N}{\sqrt{\pi}} R^2 \exp(-R^2) \qquad (12\text{–}64)$$

also written

$$\frac{dp_c}{dR} = \frac{4}{\sqrt{\pi}} R^2 \exp(-R^2) \qquad (12\text{–}65)$$

These equations were originally derived by Maxwell and by Boltzmann. Hence they are said to describe the Maxwellian or Maxwell-Boltzmann velocity distribution. They are charted graphically in Fig. 12.3 for the following form of (12–62):

$$\frac{dp_c}{dc} = \frac{4}{\sqrt{\pi}\zeta} \frac{c^2}{\zeta^2} \exp \frac{-c^2}{\zeta^2} \qquad (12\text{–}66)$$

The three curves in Fig. 12.3a are of a type sometimes called *integrated distribution curves*. They describe, in a manner convenient for quantitative use, the Maxwellian distribution of total velocities in an ordinary gas for three different temperatures, low, intermediate, and high.

Ordinates in Fig. 12.3a describe the fraction, p_c, of the total number of particles, whose total velocity exceeds a value c measured along the horizontal axis. It will be seen that, for all three temperatures, about 57 per cent of the particles have velocities greater than the characteristic velocity ζ for that temperature. The meanings of the differential quantities dc and dp_c are indicated near the upper end of the intermediate-temperature curve.

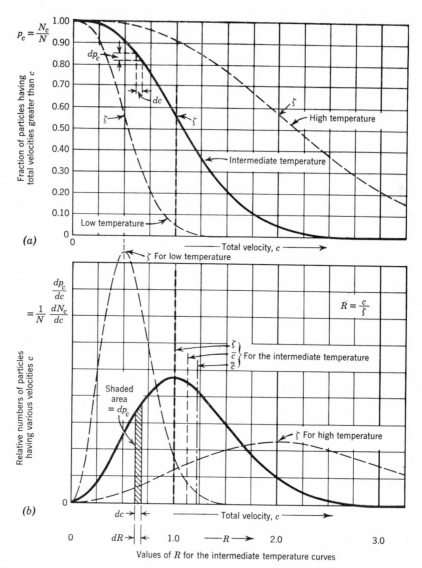

FIG. 12.3   Maxwellian total velocity distributions.

(a) Integrated distributions, total Maxwellian velocities, equation (12–67).
(b) Distributions of total Maxwellian velocities, equation (12–66).

The scale of values of R applies *only* to the solid-line curves, in (a) and (b).

Figure 12.3b contains three *distribution curves* [12A, B, C] that correspond to the *integrated distribution curves* of Fig. 12.3a. The area, from some velocity $c = c$ out to $c = \infty$, under one of the curves in the lower figure, is just the ordinate of the corresponding curve in the upper figure, hence the word "integrated" in the name for the upper curves. The *area* under an *increment, dc,* of a distribution curve is just dp_c, as it describes the increment of height in the corresponding integrated distribution curve. The total area under each of the lower curves must be just 1.00, as that is the maximum height of each upper curve. It follows that the ordinates of the lower ones are the slopes of the corresponding upper ones, except for a difference in sign.

There is an incongruity as to algebraic sign in this graphical presentation, in that the slopes of the integrated distribution curves in Fig. 12.3a are negative, whereas the derivatives are represented in Fig. 12.3b as being positive. There is a little problem in interpretation of symbols that causes this, as follows:

As originally stated, the physical concept associated with dN_c indicates that it is the number of particles (per unit volume) whose total velocities are greater than c and less than $c + dc$. As so introduced, dN_c is obviously a numerically positive quantity, for one does not talk of there being a negative number of particles in a certain region. Careful mathematical interpretation would imply the definition of a quantity $N_{\text{below } c}$, where

$N_{\text{below } c}$ = The number of particles whose total velocities are less than c (12–67)

Then obviously $N_{\text{below } c}$ increases as c increases, thus

$$\frac{dN_{\text{below } c}}{dR} \quad \left[\begin{array}{l}\text{is numerically positive; this is the physical} \\ \text{meaning of (12–64).}\end{array}\right] \quad (12\text{–}68)$$

On the other hand, N_c, as defined in Group IV of the preceding section, is the number of particles per unit volume whose velocities exceed a value c, that is, more completely,

$$N_c \equiv N_{\text{above } c} = \text{The number of particles whose total velocities}$$
$$\text{are greater than } c \qquad (12\text{–}69)$$

Then obviously $N_{\text{above } c}$ *decreases* as c increases; that is,

$$\frac{dN_{\text{above } c}}{dR} \quad \left[\begin{array}{l}\text{is numerically negative; thus the slopes of the} \\ \text{integrated distribution curves in Fig. 12.3}a\text{ are} \\ \text{negative.}\end{array}\right] \quad (12\text{–}70)$$

Thus from a mathematically careful standpoint:

The integrated distribution curves of Fig. 12.3a are plotted in terms of
$N_{\text{above } c}$; whereas (12–71)
The distribution curves of Fig. 12.3b are plotted in terms of $dN_{\text{below } c}/dc$.

On balance, it has seemed less confusing, in the mathematical treatments that follow, to treat dN_c, and similarly dN_u, as absolute-value quantities, thus ignoring altogether this question of sign, rather than to adopt the mathematically careful procedure of using one symbol for $dN_{\text{above } c}$ and another symbol for $dN_{\text{below } c}$. Similarly dp_c and dp_u are treated as absolute-value quantities.

Distribution curves are not as satisfactory as integrated distribution curves for direct quantitative work. They are, however, graphically suggestive of the values of average and rms velocities, and of the corresponding Group III ratios; it is the distribution-curve equation that is used in determining various averages mathematically.

The rms velocity ratio $\overline{\overline{R}}$ is the radius of gyration, referred to the zero-velocity axis, of the geometric figure described by the distribution curve. The steps in its determination are as follows:

(*a*) The incremental area dp_c under the distribution curve at any increment dR is expressed from (12–65).

(*b*) This incremental area is multiplied by the second power of R, because the "second moment," or moment of inertia, of the figure is used in obtaining the radius of gyration.

(*c*) All such products are summed by integrating from $R = 0$ to $R = \infty$.

(*d*) The result of the integration is divided by the area under the curve (in this case 1.00) thus giving $\overline{\overline{R}}^2$, where $\overline{\overline{R}}$ can be variously described as the rms value of R, the radius of gyration of the figure, and—because of the fact that the area is 1.00—the second moment of the figure.

The mathematical statement of these operations is:

$$\overline{\overline{R}}^2 = \frac{\displaystyle\int_{R=0}^{R=\infty} R^2 \frac{4}{\sqrt{\pi}} R^2 \exp(-R^2)\, dR}{1.00} = \frac{4}{\sqrt{\pi}} \frac{3}{8} \sqrt{\pi} = \frac{3}{2} \qquad (12\text{–}72)$$

See Table IX for this integral.

Thus for the total-velocity Maxwellian distribution

$$\overline{\overline{R}}^2 = \frac{3}{2} \qquad \overline{\overline{c}}^2 = \frac{3\varsigma^2}{2} \qquad (12\text{–}73a)$$

Use of this in (12–58) leads to

$$\overline{E}_c = \tfrac{3}{2} E_T \qquad (12\text{–}73b)$$

This is in agreement with (12–47) and confirms the statements made in Section 7.3. Another form of this average energy relation is

$$\overline{\overline{c}} = \sqrt{\tfrac{3}{2}}\,\varsigma = 1.224\varsigma \qquad (12\text{–}73c)$$

The *average* values $\bar{c}$ and $\overline{R}$ are found similarly; in the operation corresponding to (*b*) above, the incremental area is multiplied by the first instead of the second power of R, for $\overline{R}$ is the distance to the center of gravity of the distribution-curve figure. The results are

$$\overline{R} = \frac{2}{\sqrt{\pi}} \qquad (12\text{--}74a)$$

$$\bar{c} = \frac{2\zeta}{\sqrt{\pi}} = 1.128\zeta \qquad (12\text{--}74b)$$

The occurrence of the crests of the distribution curves of Fig. 12.3b at points for which $c = \zeta$ illustrates why the characteristic velocity ζ is sometimes called the *most probable velocity*. These curves are higher at the points where $c = \zeta$ than elsewhere; therefore more particles must have velocities near to ζ than similarly near to any other velocity.

12.6   Equations for Total-Velocity Maxwellian Integrated Distribution Curves. The equation for the integrated distribution curves of Fig. 12.3a is obtained by integration of (12–65), indicated as follows:

$$p_c = \frac{N_c}{N} = \frac{4}{\sqrt{\pi}} \int_{R=R}^{R=\infty} R^2 \exp\left(-R^2\right) dR \qquad (12\text{--}75)$$

From Table IX, integration gives

$$p_c = \frac{N_c}{N} = \frac{2}{\sqrt{\pi}} R \exp\left(-R^2\right) + (1 - \operatorname{erf} R) \qquad (12\text{--}76)$$

The *error function*, also called the *probability integral*, used here, is defined as

$$\operatorname{erf} R = \frac{2}{\sqrt{\pi}} \int_{R=0}^{R=R} \exp\left(-R^2\right) dR \qquad (12\text{--}77)$$

Tables of values of erf R, corresponding to upper limits between 0 and 3.0, will be found in Pierce's Tables of Integrals.[1U] Erf R rapidly approaches unity as R rises above 1.5, so that for large values of R the first term alone of (12–76) gives a good approximation to p_c; see also (12–79).

The following *asymptotic series* gives values for erf R that are satisfactory, for most purposes, when R is greater than about 2.0:

$$\operatorname{erf} R = 1 - \frac{\exp\left(-R^2\right)}{R\sqrt{\pi}} \left[1 - \frac{1}{2R^2} + \frac{1\cdot 3}{(2R^2)^2} - \frac{1\cdot 3\cdot 5}{(2R^2)^3} + \cdots \right] \qquad (12\text{--}78)$$

As usual with series of this type, the successive terms first decrease, then increase. Since the error in a numerical value for such a series is not greater than the last term used, maximum accuracy is obtained by stopping with the smallest term, though often sufficient accuracy results from the use of only a very few terms. This is particularly true in the asymptotic series expression that results from combining (12–76) and (12–78), which is

$$p_c = \frac{N_c}{N} = \frac{\exp{(-R^2)}}{R\sqrt{\pi}} \left[2R^2 + 1 - \frac{1}{2R^2} + \frac{1 \cdot 3}{(2R^2)^2} - \frac{1 \cdot 3 \cdot 5}{(2R^2)^3} + \cdots \right]$$

(12–79)

12.7   Curves and Equations for x-Directed Maxwellian Velocity Distributions. Figures 12.4a and 12.4b are respectively integrated distribution curves and distribution curves for x-directed components of Maxwellian velocities. The unit of measure along the horizontal scale is r, the ratio of a particular x-directed velocity to the characteristic velocity. Because of this choice of scale units, both curves can serve for any temperature for which the distribution is Maxwellian. Of course y-directed and z-directed velocity distributions are identical with those for x-directed velocities.

From (12–50), the equation for the distribution curve, Fig. 12.4b, is
12A, B, C

$$\frac{dp_u}{dr} = \frac{1}{\sqrt{\pi}} \exp{(-r^2)} \qquad \text{or} \qquad \frac{dN_u}{dr} = \frac{N}{\sqrt{\pi}} \exp{(-r^2)} \quad (12\text{–}80)$$

The equation for the integrated distribution curve, Fig. 12.4a, is

$$p_u = \frac{N_u}{N} = \frac{1}{\sqrt{\pi}} \int_{r=r}^{r=\infty} \exp{(-r^2)}\, dr = \frac{1}{2}(1 - \operatorname{erf} r) \quad (12\text{–}81)$$

If the asymptotic series for erf r is used, p_u becomes

$$p_u = \frac{\exp{(-r^2)}}{2r\sqrt{\pi}} \left[1 - \frac{1}{2r^2} + \frac{1 \cdot 3}{(2r^2)^2} - \frac{1 \cdot 3 \cdot 5}{(2r^2)^3} + \cdots \right] \quad (12\text{–}82)$$

The distribution curve in Fig. 12.4b is symmetrical about zero, because as many particles must be moving east as are moving west, if the gas as a whole is to remain stationary. Hence the true average x-directed velocity is zero, just as the true cyclic average value of a sine-wave alternating current is zero. Yet just as the average value of a *half-wave* of alternating current is of interest, so here the average velocity among the half of the particles with positive velocities is of interest and is described by $\bar{u}$. Hence $\bar{r}$ is the distance from the zero axis to the center of gravity *of one "wing"* of Fig. 12.4b. $\bar{\bar{r}}$ is the radius of gyration of either or both wings.

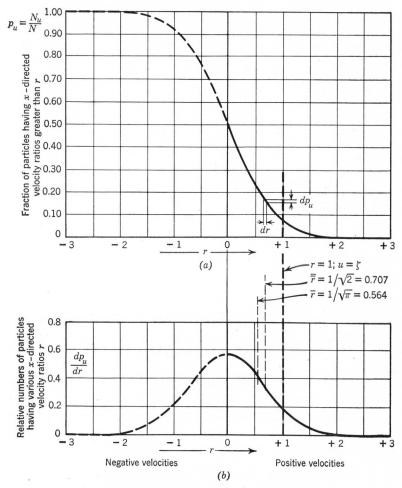

Fig. 12.4   Maxwellian x-directed velocity distribution.

(a) Integrated distribution curve, equation (12–81).
(b) Distribution curve, equation (12–80).

Integrations similar to that in (12–72), applied, however, as to $\bar{r}$, to only one wing, lead to the following results:

$$\bar{r} = \frac{1}{\sqrt{\pi}} \qquad \text{so that} \qquad \bar{u} = \frac{\zeta}{\sqrt{\pi}} = 0.564\zeta \qquad (12\text{–}83)$$

$$\bar{\bar{r}} = \frac{1}{\sqrt{2}} \qquad \text{so that} \qquad \bar{\bar{u}} = \frac{\zeta}{\sqrt{2}} = 0.707\zeta \qquad (12\text{–}84)$$

These can be used to relate energies, as follows:

$$\bar{\bar{r}}^2 = \frac{\bar{\bar{u}}^2}{\bar{\zeta}^2} = \frac{\bar{E}_u}{E_T} = \frac{1}{2} \tag{12-85}$$

On comparing (12–73a) and (12–85), it appears that the average x-directed energy is, in agreement with what is called the *principle of equipartition of energy* (equipartition among the degrees of freedom), one-third of the average total translational energy, that is,

$$\bar{E}_u = \tfrac{1}{2}E_T \quad \text{and} \quad \bar{E}_u = \tfrac{1}{3}\bar{E}_c \tag{12-86}$$

12.8   Rate at Which Gas Particles Arrive at a Boundary Wall.[12A, B, C]

The derivation of equations for thermionic emission, and various gaseous conduction problems, require a knowledge of how many gas particles or electrons hit per second per unit area of an enclosing boundary wall because of their random motions; also of the number that so hit with x-directed energies exceeding any given value.

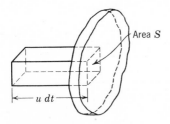

Area S

u dt

FIG. 12.5   Rate of arrival at a wall of particles with velocity u.

Figure 12.5 illustrates a portion of an enclosing wall. It is desired to determine how many particles strike per unit area of this wall in a short time interval, dt. The figure shows imaginary boundaries of a boxlike region adjacent to the wall, the two ends each having area S. The length perpendicular to the wall is u dt, where u is any particular x-directed velocity. Any particle *within this region* that has a velocity between u and u + du at the beginning of the interval dt will of course arrive at the wall by or before the end of the interval. The y- and z-directed velocities are of no consequence, for during dt as many particles of any selected x-directed velocity will enter from one side of the boxlike region as leave from the opposite side.

Thus the number of particles with velocities between u and u + du that during dt strike the area S on the wall is just the number that were in the boxlike region at the beginning of dt. This number is the volume uS dt of the region multiplied by dN_u, the number of such particles per unit volume. Mathematically:

$$\left. \begin{array}{l} \text{Number of particles with veloci-} \\ \text{ties between } u \text{ and } u + du \text{ that} \\ \text{strike the area } S \text{ in } dt \text{ seconds} \end{array} \right\} = uS\,dt \cdot dN_u \tag{12-87}$$

Division by $S\,dt$ gives the number of particles of the selected velocity that arrive per unit area per second, symbolized by dL_u:

$$dL_u = u\,dN_u \quad \begin{bmatrix} \text{particles arriving per unit area per} \\ \text{second with velocities between } u \\ \text{and } u + du \end{bmatrix} \quad (12\text{--}88)$$

Then L, the number of particles of all velocities that arrive per unit area per second, is obtained as

$$L = \int_{u=0}^{u=\infty} u\,dN_u \qquad (12\text{--}89)$$

To express L for a Maxwellian distribution, employ (12–80) for dN_u, and express u as $r\zeta$, giving

$$L = \zeta \int_{r=0}^{r=\infty} r\,dN_u = \frac{N\zeta}{\sqrt{\pi}} \int_0^\infty r \exp(-r^2)\,dr \qquad (12\text{--}90)$$

On integration this becomes

$$L = \frac{N\zeta}{2\sqrt{\pi}} \quad \begin{bmatrix} \text{Maxwellian particles arriving} \\ \text{per second per unit area of} \\ \text{bounding surface} \end{bmatrix} \qquad (12\text{--}91)$$

L_u, the number of particles arriving per unit area per second with x-directed velocities exceeding some definite value u, is obtained as follows:

$$L_u = \int_{u=u}^{u=\infty} u\,dN_u \qquad (12\text{--}92)$$

Thus a lower limit $r = r$ is used in employing (12–90) to evaluate L_u; this gives

$$L_u = \frac{N\zeta}{2\sqrt{\pi}} \exp \frac{-u^2}{\zeta^2} \qquad (12\text{--}93)$$

The *integrated velocity distribution* among arriving particles is, by definition

$$\frac{L_u}{L} = \frac{\text{Rate of arrival of particles with } x\text{-directed velocities greater than } u}{\text{Rate of arrival of particles with all velocities}} \qquad (12\text{--}94)$$

From (12–93) and (12–91) this is

$$\frac{L_u}{L} = \exp \frac{-u^2}{\zeta^2} \qquad (12\text{--}95a)$$

that is,

$$\frac{L_u}{L} = \exp(-r^2) \qquad (12\text{--}95b)$$

The corresponding velocity distribution equation is

$$\frac{d(L_u/L)}{dr} = 2r \exp\left(-r^2\right) \tag{12–96}$$

12.9 Distribution of Initial Velocities at a Boundary Wall and among Thermionic Electrons.[7B, a, 15a, b] Figure 12.6 is a graph of the velocity distributions described by (12–95) and (12–96), being the velocity distributions, on arrival, of Maxwellian gas particles striking an enclosing wall.

Analytical theory based on (8–20a), as applied to (12–90) and the concept of thermionic emission outlined in Section 8.6, leads to Dushman's equation (7–2), and also to the prediction that electrons emitted from a thermionic surface possess *on emergence* a Maxwellian distribution of velocities corresponding to cathode temperature, although they do not have such a distribution in the interior.   Therefore Fig. 12.6 and equations (12–95) and (12–96), expressed for cathode temperature, describe the initial-velocity distributions *among electrons emerging from a thermionically emitting surface.* This has been confirmed by experiment.

As applied to Fig. 8.10, initial velocity signifies an escaping electron's velocity where the zero level of potential energy is reached or crossed, whether the potential-energy line is that corresponding to space-charge-limited (upper line) or temperature-limited (lower line) conditions. However, (12–95) and (12–96) express the velocity distribution among thermionic electrons for all surfaces, therefore for all work functions. Thus the addition of an increment of work function does not alter the velocity distribution.   Similarly, the appearance of the potential-energy crest due to space charge, Fig. 8.10, does not alter the velocity distribution among the escaping electrons, because it appears to them just the same as an increment of work function.   Thus (12–95) and (12–96) express the velocity distribution among the electrons escaping past the crest of Fig. 8.10 (the dip of curve 4 in Fig. 8.9), as well as among the electrons emitted from a temperature-limited surface.

Thus, in Fig. 8.10, the electrons that reach or pass the zero level on the way out have the (12–95) and (12–96) distribution.   Only the high-energy electrons of this group reach the potential-energy crest; however, on the way to the crest they lose just enough energy to make the distribution among them the same as exists among the larger number that just reach the zero level.   See Section 12.14 for a rigorous proof of this concept.

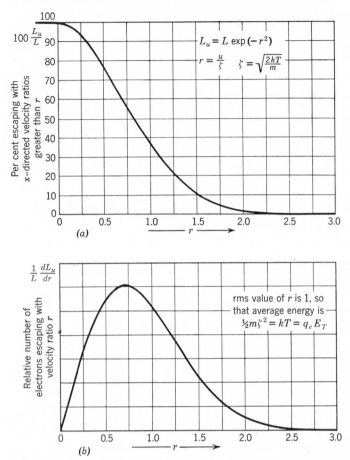

FIG. 12.6 Time-exposure-over-a-surface velocity distribution of thermionically emitted electrons, also of Maxwellian gas particles striking a boundary.
(a) The integrated distribution curve, from (12–95).
(b) The distribution curve, from (12–96).

The distribution illustrated by Fig. 12.6 has the following interesting properties, determined by the method of (12–72):

Average x-directed velocity: $\dfrac{\sqrt{\pi}\,\zeta}{2} = 0.887\zeta$ \hfill (12–97a)

Root-mean-square x-directed velocity: ζ \hfill (12–97b)

Average energy due to x-directed motion: E_T \hfill (12–97c)

Most probable (crest, Fig. 12.6b), x-directed velocity: $\dfrac{\zeta}{\sqrt{2}}$ \hfill (12–97d)

The velocity distribution curves and equations presented prior to Fig. 12.6 have one characteristic in common: they describe in one way or another the range of individual velocities or energies as measured by a "snapshot observation throughout a volume." For example, Figs. 12.3 and 12.4 specify percentages among particles that are observed to be present

(a) within a given volume
(b) at a given instant.

In sharp contrast to this, the curves in Fig. 12.6 describe a distribution as recorded by a "time-exposure observation over a surface." That is, Fig. 12.6a specifies percentages among all the particles that are observed to reach or pass through

(a) a given area
(b) during any given time interval, say 1 second.

With this contrast in mind, the differences between Figs. 12.4 and 12.6 may be itemized as follows:

(a) A particle cannot arrive at a surface while going away from it; therefore only positive velocities appear in Fig. 12.6. In contrast with this, the curve in Fig. 12.4b is symmetrical about zero velocity, because a snapshot throughout a volume must record as many easterly as westerly motions.

(b) A particle cannot reach or cross any surface while standing still; therefore the curve in Fig. 12.6b has zero ordinate at zero velocity. Comparison shows that in Fig. 12.4 the maximum ordinate occurs at zero velocity; that is, a snapshot throughout a volume discovers more particles near to zero velocity than similarly near to any other x-directed velocity.

(c) During an appreciable time interval an individual particle may shuttle back and forth in an enclosure many times, hitting the surfaces on each round trip. Rapidly moving particles make more round trips per second, so hit more times per second, than slowly moving ones. For that reason the average x-directed energy of the particles on arrival at a surface is greater than the average observed throughout a volume; it is just twice as great, in a Maxwellian distribution.

12.10 Average Energies of Arriving Maxwellian Particles and of Escaping Electrons. The Ideal Gas Law.[12A, B, C] Only x-directed movement brings particles to a y, z surface, so that there is no tendency for particles with large sideways velocities to hit more often than those with small sideways velocities. Time-exposure observations over a y, z surface must, therefore, record just the y- and z-directed velocity distributions that result from snapshot observations throughout a volume, Fig. 12.4. Only the x-directed distribution is recorded differently by the two methods of observation.

From the preceding section, the average energy of x-directed motion of Maxwellian particles on arrival at a surface is E_T. From (12–86), the average snapshot-throughout-a-volume energy of y- and z-directed motion among such particles is $\frac{1}{2}E_T$ for each of the other two directions. Therefore the average total energy of Maxwellian particles on arrival at a surface is $E_T + \frac{1}{2}E_T + \frac{1}{2}E_T = 2E_T$, as stated in Section 7.3.

The distribution of velocities among electrons thermionically emitted being Maxwellian, and corresponding to cathode temperature, the average outwardly directed energy among such electrons must be E_T, and the average total energy $E_T + \frac{1}{2}E_T + \frac{1}{2}E_T = 2E_T$, where E_T is the voltage equivalent of cathode temperature.

Each gas particle on arriving at a boundary wall possesses a momentum mu normal to the wall; it rebounds elastically from the wall, with resulting change of momentum $2mu$. The number of such boundings per unit area is as given by (12–91), and the average value of u involved is given by (12–97a) as $\sqrt{\pi}\,\zeta/2$. Therefore the total rate of change of momentum per unit area, or *pressure*, is

$$\text{Pressure, newtons per square meter} = \frac{N\zeta}{2\sqrt{\pi}} \times 2m\frac{\sqrt{\pi}\,\zeta}{2}$$

$$= N \cdot \frac{1}{2}m\zeta^2 = NkT \quad (12\text{–}98)$$

Thus the Maxwellian velocity distribution is in agreement with the familiar ideal gas law.

12.11   Shot Effect and Thermal Noise Voltages within Conductors; Noise Level.[12E, b]   The term "noise level" referred originally to the intensity of miscellaneous noises that speech or music must rise above in order to be clearly audible. In a busy street, the noise level has to do with the amount and kind of traffic passing; in a telephone receiver or radio speaker, it depends on small current variations which result from various properties of the transmission system. The word "noise" suggests variations within the frequency range audible to human ears, but the phrase "noise level" describes the intensity of miscellaneous troublesome variations of currents, voltages, or radiations, at all frequencies.

Various sources of noise are present in any circuit containing a vacuum-tube amplifier, no matter how much care is taken in the circuit assembly, because they result from the electrons' random motions. The two important causes of such noise are the raindrop patter of electrons on the plate, called "shot effect" from the similarity to a shower of small shot,[12E, b] and the random motions of the electrons within conductors, usually referred to by the phrase *thermal agitation*.[12E] The origins of noise and noise problems are discussed in Chapter VI of *Fundamentals of Physical Electronics.*

Shot noise is less in a space-charge-limited device than in a comparable temperature-limited device, by a factor of perhaps 10 or 20, because the random variations in thermionic current density cause compensating variations in the magnitude of the negative potential dip just outside the cathode, the noise-produced changes in plate current then being much reduced.[12b]

An important property of shot noise and thermal noise is that the mean square noise current $\overline{i_n^2}$ or voltage $\overline{e_n^2}$ is proportional to the band width Δf of the frequency spectrum passed by the amplifier involved. Mathematically:

$$\text{Shot noise current:} \quad \overline{i_n^2} = 2I_b q_e \, \Delta f \qquad (12\text{–}99a)$$

where I_b is the d-c plate current, q_e the electronic charge; and

$$\text{Thermal noise voltage:} \quad \overline{e_n^2} = 4RkT \, \Delta f \qquad (12\text{–}99b)$$

where R is the resistance of the conductor involved, T is its temperature, and k is Boltzmann's gas constant.

The ultimate limit to attainable sensitivity in any radio or telephone receiver, or any sensitive measuring instrument, is the ratio of the signal strength to the noise level, that is, the signal to noise ratio.

12.12   Random Current Density in an Ion or Electron Gas.[15A, a, b] There is a marked similarity between the mechanism of electric conduction in a metal and that in the *plasma*, or conducting region, in a gas-discharge device, for in both the current is carried primarily by the "drift" of an electron gas; see Section 15.6.

In both metals and plasmas the space charge that might be expected to result from the presence of the electrons is neutralized by an equal concentration of positive ions. The ions are atoms that have each contributed an electron to the make-up of the electron gas. One important contrast between metallic and gaseous conduction is that, in a metal, the positive ions are fixed in position, whereas in a plasma they are free to move. Because of their large mass, they move so slowly that the ion drift motion makes a negligible contribution to the current flow. Their laterally outward diffusion *owing partly to random motions* is important, however, because it ultimately removes them from the plasma. Continuous energy input is necessary to replace them.

This explains in a general way the interest in what is called the *random ion current density* in a plasma. Section 12.8 deals with the rate of arrival of particles at a small area on a boundary wall; that analysis applies equally well to a small imaginary area located anywhere within the body of the gas. Equation (12–91) therefore describes the rate at which particles pass per unit area through from one side to the other of any such internal area. If the particles are ions, they carry a current, called the random ion current, through the chosen area. The random ion current in one direction across any internal area is the same as that in the reverse direction, so that the concept of random ion current flow does not imply a net transfer of charge from one part of the gas to another.

The magnitude of the random ion current density in a plasma is obtained by multiplying (12–91) by the electronic charge; thus

$$J_{ri} = \frac{N_i q_e \zeta_i}{2\sqrt{\pi}} \qquad (12\text{–}100a)$$

Here J_{ri} = random positive ion current density.

$\quad N_i$ = positive ion concentration.

$\quad \zeta_i$ = the velocity characteristic of the temperature of the ionic gas; see (12–31) and (12–53).

The similar expression for random electron current density J_{re}, the i subscripts being changed to e throughout, with obvious significance, is

$$J_{re} = \frac{N_e q_e \zeta_e}{2\sqrt{\pi}} \qquad (12\text{–}100b)$$

Even though $N_e = N_i$ in a plasma, J_{re} is hundreds of times larger than J_{ri}, primarily because the random currents are proportional to the ζ's, which vary inversely as the square roots of the masses, and ions have very much larger masses than electrons. In addition, experiments show that the electron temperature is often many times that of the ions.

12.13   Sheath Penetration by Electrons in a Conducting Gas.[15A, a, b] For reasons to be discussed in Section 16.7 a "potential barrier" often exists between the main body of a conducting gas and a boundary wall. This barrier obstructs the flow of electrons to the wall. The term barrier is used to remind the reader of the work-function barrier that similarly obstructs the escape of electrons from a metal. The barrier now under discussion is simply a drop in potential that occurs within a thin region, often called a "sheath," adjacent to the wall; see

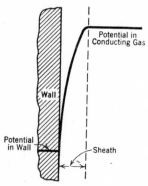

FIG. 12.7 Sheath adjacent to the boundary wall of a conducting gas.

Fig. 12.7. The potential drop through the sheath is intimately associated, by way of Poisson's law, with the positive space charge that exists within it because of the absence of electrons.

A few high-random-energy electrons penetrate through the sheath from plasma to wall in spite of the barrier it presents, in much the way that a few electrons escape from a hot metal in spite of the work-function barrier. The expression for the electron current density that passes through the sheath in spite of the obstruction offered is obtained from (12–93) by multiplying by q_e and using $u = u_s$, where it is the electrons for which $u \geq u_s$ that will penetrate. This gives

$$J_{es} = \frac{N_e q_e \zeta_e}{2\sqrt{\pi}} \exp \frac{-u_s^2}{\zeta_e^2} \qquad (12\text{–}101)$$

also expressible as

$$J_{es} = \frac{N_e q_e \zeta_e}{2\sqrt{\pi}} \exp \frac{-E_s}{E_{Te}} \qquad (12\text{–}102)$$

and from (12–100b) as

$$J_{es} = J_{re} \exp \frac{-E_s}{E_{Te}} \qquad (12\text{–}103)$$

The symbolism here is the same as in (12–100b), with the following additions:

J_{es} = current density due to passage of electrons through the sheath.

E_s = potential difference that the electrons must overcome in penetrating the sheath.

E_{Te} = voltage equivalent of electron temperature.

u_s = x-directed velocity necessary for penetration.

It will be shown in the next section that the "time-exposure-over-a-surface" velocity distribution among originally Maxwellian electrons that succeed in penetrating a sheath is also Maxwellian, and at the same temperature. Consequently the penetrating electrons reach the wall with average energies $\frac{1}{2}E_{Te} + \frac{1}{2}E_{Te} + E_{Te} = 2E_{Te}$.

12.14   Penetrating Electrons Possess a Maxwellian Distribution.
It is desirable to demonstrate that the velocity distribution and the
temperature are the same at impact with the wall as among the larger
number of electrons that enter the sheath, for the Fig. 12.7 situation
represented by (12–103).   Let u', r', E_u' symbolize the values *on
arrival at the wall* of the x-directed (toward-the-wall) velocities, velocity
ratios, and kinetic energies of electrons whose x-directed velocities,
velocity ratios, and kinetic energies were u, r, E_u on entering the
sheath from the plasma at the outer face of the sheath.   Then

$$u'^2 = u^2 - u_s{}^2; \text{ also } r'^2 = r^2 - r_s{}^2 \qquad (12\text{–}104)$$

because the conservation of energy requires that

$$E_u' = E_u - E_s \qquad (12\text{–}105)$$

and squares of velocities vary in proportion to energies.   Also, let

L_u' symbolize the rate of arrival at the wall of electrons having
x-directed velocities exceeding u'.

L' symbolize the rate of arrival of electrons of all velocities at
the wall.

L_u symbolize the rate of arrival *at the sheath edge*, from the plasma,
of electrons having x-directed velocities exceeding u.

L symbolize the total rate of arrival of electrons from the plasma,
at sheath edge.

The integrated time-exposure-over-a-surface velocity distribution
among all the electrons arriving from the gas at the sheath edge is, as
in (12–94),

$$\frac{L_u}{L} = \frac{\displaystyle\int_u^\infty u \, dN_u}{\displaystyle\int_0^\infty u \, dN_u} \qquad (12\text{–}106)$$

L_u and L are expressed here as in (12–92) and (12–89).   If the arriving
electrons possess a Maxwellian distribution, dN_u is expressible from
(12–80), giving

$$\frac{L_u}{L} = \frac{\zeta_e \displaystyle\int_r^\infty r \exp\left(-r^2\right) dr}{\zeta_e \displaystyle\int_0^\infty r \exp\left(-r^2\right) dr} = \exp\left(-r^2\right) \qquad (12\text{–}107)$$

where u has been replaced by $r\zeta_e$.   This equation is identical with
(12–95b).

The integrated time-exposure-over-a-surface distribution *at plasma-sheath edge,* among electrons destined to penetrate the sheath, is obtained by using L' rather than L in the denominator of (12–107), that is,

$$\frac{L_u}{L'} = \frac{\int_u^\infty u \, dN_u}{\int_{u_s}^\infty u \, dN_u} \qquad (12\text{–}108)$$

Note that u_s rather than zero is used as the lower limit of the denominator integral, because it is the electrons for which $u > u_s$ that penetrate the sheath, thus comprising the L' flow. As before, use $u = r\zeta_e$ and the Maxwellian form (12–80) for dN_u; (12–108) then becomes

$$\frac{L_u}{L'} = \frac{\zeta_e \int_r^\infty r \exp\left(-r^2\right) dr}{\zeta_e \int_{r_s}^\infty r \exp\left(-r^2\right) dr} = \exp\left(-r^2 + r_s{}^2\right) \qquad (12\text{–}109)$$

Obviously $L_u = L_u'$, because u and u' are the velocities, at outer sheath face and at wall, of identical particles. Replacing L_u by L_u' in (12–109) and employing (12–104) gives

$$\frac{L_u'}{L'} = \exp\left(-r'^2\right) \qquad (12\text{–}110)$$

This is identical in form with (12–107). Thus it has been shown that the electrons arriving at the wall have the same velocity distribution as exists among the larger number that enter the sheath, and are therefore at the same temperature.

This argument demonstrates the statement made in Section 12.9, relative to Fig. 8.10 or curve 4 of Fig. 8.9, that the electrons passing the negative dip (potential-energy crest) outside a thermionic cathode do so with the same Maxwellian distribution that they possess on reaching the zero level at the cathode surface.

12.15   Richardson's $T^{\frac{1}{2}}$ Equation for Thermionic Emission.[7B, C] Early attempts were made to explain thermionic emission from metals by assuming an internal electron gas possessing a Maxwellian velocity distribution. Such treatment leads quite obviously to an expression for thermionic current density J_{th} identical in form with (12–102). Work function E_W is used in place of E_s, and the distinction between net and gross work function disappears; the E_T corresponding to the temperature of the emitter is used in place of E_{T_e}. As ζ is proportional to the square root of the temperature, the following general form appears, introduced by Richardson and at one time widely used:

$$J_{th} = aT^{\frac{1}{2}} \exp \frac{-E_W}{E_T} \qquad (12\text{-}111)$$

Here a and E_W are empirically determined. See the discussion following (7–9) for the reasons for preferring the (7–2) form containing T^2.

12.16 Equilibrium between Different Potentials in an Enclosure; the Boltzmann Relation. Figure 12.8 represents an enclosure containing an electron gas, its space charge being everywhere just neutralized by relatively stationary positive ions. The dotted vertical lines in the middle indicate that the enclosure is screened into two compartments differing in potential by E_s volts, as suggested by the potential lines at the bottom of the figure. Electrons pass freely through the screens. The potential within each compartment is uniform. Situations similar to this occur in some gaseous-conducting devices.

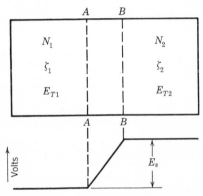

Fig. 12.8 Equilibrium between electron gases at different potentials.

Random electron velocities must in general result in a flow of electrons both ways through the boundary zone, though the flow from left to right is affected by the potential difference between the compartments. Since any electron as it leaves or enters a compartment has some kinetic energy of motion, the electron flow results in a two-way energy transfer. The rates of flow of particles, also the rates of transfer of energy, are equal in the two directions when the following equilibrium conditions exist:

(a) $E_{T1} = E_{T2}$ (that is, the electron temperatures are equal) (12–112)

(b) $$\frac{N_1}{N_2} = \exp \frac{-E_s}{E_T} \qquad (12\text{-}113)$$

where N_1 and N_2 are the respective electron concentrations.

This illustrates the "Boltzmann relation," which in general specifies just such an exponential relation, involving the temperature, for the *equilibrium* distribution of particles among various available energy states, which may be of a great variety of types.

Equation (12–80) can be used to illustrate the application of the Boltzmann relation to the distribution of x-directed gas particle energies. Consider two increments of x-directed velocities with equal dr's, but widely differing x-directed energies E_u' and E_u'', as follows:

$$dN', dr \quad \text{at} \quad r' = \sqrt{\frac{E_u'}{E_T}} \qquad (12\text{--}114)$$

$$dN'', dr \quad \text{at} \quad r'' = \sqrt{\frac{E_u''}{E_T}} \qquad (12\text{--}115)$$

Divide the (12–80) form using the first set by that containing the second; the result is

$$\frac{dN'}{dN''} = \exp\left(-\frac{E' - E''}{E_T}\right) = \exp\frac{-\Delta E}{E_T} \qquad (12\text{--}116)$$

which is identical in nature with (12–113).

No general demonstration of the Boltzmann equilibrium relation will be given here, but the derivation of (12–113) will be presented.* Assume that equilibrium of electron flow and of energy transfer exists between the two compartments of Fig. 12.8. Equality of the electron temperatures in the two regions has not yet been demonstrated, so distinct symbols E_{T1} and E_{T2}, ζ_1 and ζ_2, will be used for the characteristic electron temperature energies and velocities. The current due to electron flow across screen AA from left to right is the random current density for the compartment 1. That in the reverse, barrier-penetrating direction, is given by an expression like (12–103), using the concentrations and temperatures for compartment 2. The requirement that these two flow rates be equal is stated as:

$$\frac{N_1\zeta_1}{2\sqrt{\pi}} = \frac{N_2\zeta_2}{2\sqrt{\pi}} \exp\frac{-E_s}{E_{T2}} \qquad (12\text{--}117)$$

Electrons passing from left to right through screen AA have time-exposure-over-a-surface total average energies $2E_{T1}$; those passing

---

* The derivation given here parallels one given by Loeb (12B–109) relative to the mechanism of evaporation and condensation at a liquid surface.

through it in the reverse direction have similar total average energies $2E_{T2}$. (It was demonstrated in Section 12.14 that the velocity distribution and therefore the average energy, among particles that penetrate to AA, are the same as among the larger number that arrive at BB.) Hence the equality of energy transfer is expressed by multiplying the rate of electron movement each way by the average energy carried, as follows:

$$\frac{N_1 \zeta_1}{2\sqrt{\pi}} 2E_{T1} = \frac{N_2 \zeta_2}{2\sqrt{\pi}} 2E_{T2} \exp \frac{-E_s}{E_{T2}} \qquad (12\text{--}118)$$

Comparison with (12–117) shows that

$$E_{T1} = E_{T2} \qquad (12\text{--}119)$$

That is, in the equilibrium condition the temperatures must be equal. On using this fact in (12–117) the ζ's cancel, leaving just (12–113).

Suppose that N_1 and N_2 differ by only a small amount dN, and that E_s becomes a differential increment dE. Equation (12–113) can then be written

$$\frac{N + dN}{N} = \frac{\exp[-(E + dE)/E_T]}{\exp[-E/E_T]} = \exp \frac{-dE}{E_T} \qquad (12\text{--}120)$$

As dE/E_T is very small, a series expansion of the exponential reduces this to

$$1 + \frac{dN}{N} = 1 - \frac{dE}{E_T} \qquad (12\text{--}121)$$

or

$$\frac{dN}{N} = -\frac{dE}{E_T} \qquad (12\text{--}122)$$

which is the differential form of the Boltzmann relation.

PROBLEMS

1. The electron gas of a certain gas discharge has a temperature of 15,000° K and a Maxwellian velocity distribution.

(a) What is the voltage equivalent of this temperature?

(b) How large a fraction of the total number of electrons have total velocities exceeding 6×10^6 meters per sec?

(c) How large a fraction have x-directed velocities exceeding 6×10^6 meters per sec?

(d) What kinetic energy, in electron volts, corresponds to this velocity?

2. (a) What percentage of the particles in a Maxwellian distribution have total velocities greater than the average total velocity?

(b) What percentage have energies greater than the average total energy?

(c) What percentage have positive x-directed velocities greater than the average positive x-directed velocity?

(d) What percentage have energies due to positive x-directed motion that are greater than the average x-directed energy?

3. What percentage of the particles in a Maxwellian distribution have total velocities greater than 10 times the characteristic velocity? What percentage have total energies greater than 10 times the characteristic energy?

4. Derive an expression for the number of Maxwellian gas particles whose velocities in all directions *perpendicular to some definite axis* have values between s and $s + ds$ (see Section 12.2).

5. What is the most probable total energy, in terms of E_T, in a Maxwellian distribution? The most probable x-directed energy?

6. Suppose that the distribution of velocities v among falling raindrops is expressible mathematically as follows:

$$dN_v = \frac{N}{b\sqrt{\pi}} \exp\left[-\frac{(v-a)^2}{b^2}\right] dv$$

N is the number of raindrops per cubic foot, a is a characteristic velocity in feet per second, and b is a velocity roughly descriptive of the deviation of individual velocities from the characteristic velocity.

(a) Plot the corresponding distribution curve of dN_v/dv against v, letting $b = a/10$. Locate points $v = a - b$, $v = a$, $v = a + b$.

(b) Write the equation for and plot the corresponding integrated distribution curve.

(c) Derive mathematical expressions for the average, most probable, and rms velocities, in terms of a and b.

In carrying out (b) and (c) it is not unreasonable to make the approximation that the integral from $v = 0$ to $v = v$ is the same as the integral from $v = -\infty$ to $v = v$. Strictly speaking, this is absurd, as it implies the inclusion of negatively falling raindrops. However, with $b = a/10$ the error introduced is very small, and the forms become much simpler mathematically as well as easier to understand.

7. The supposed raindrop velocity distribution of the preceding problem describes a "snapshot throughout-a-volume" distribution. Using that distribution:

(a) Derive an expression for the number of raindrops striking 1 sq ft of ground per second.

(b) Derive expressions for the time-exposure-over-a-surface velocity distribution and the integrated velocity distribution among the raindrops as they strike the ground.

(c) Determine the average velocity among the arriving drops.

(d) Determine the average energy among the arriving drops, each of mass m (in pound units).

(e) How large a fraction of the drops strike the ground with velocities greater than $a + b$? With velocities less than $a - b$?

The simplifying approximation suggested in the previous problem is also applicable here.

8. In an electron gas having 10^{18} electrons per cubic meter at 20,000° K:

(a) How many electrons having x-directed energies exceeding 10 volts will strike the enclosing boundary per square meter per second?

(b) What will be the average x-directed energy of these electrons?

(c) What will be their average total energy?

(d) Answer (b) and (c) for the same group of electrons *after they have passed through a 10-volt barrier encountered at the surface,* and compare the results with the same quantities as determined for *all* the electrons striking the wall and not encountering a barrier.

9. Suppose that there exists a velocity distribution, among a set of particles, which has the following general law:

$$\frac{dN_c}{dR} = NKR^3 \exp\left(-R^2\right)$$

Here dN_c is the number of particles, out of a total of N per unit volume, whose velocities lie between c and $c + dc$; also $R = c/\zeta$, where ζ is some characteristic velocity, and K is a constant, to be chosen to satisfy the requirement that the integrated distribution curve accounts for 100 per cent of the particles between velocities of zero and infinity.

Find the *average* value of the velocity, and determine K.

10. For the electron gas in a metal, having the zero-temperature Fermi distribution (Chapter VIII):

(a) Find the average total and the average x-directed kinetic energy, as percentages of the Fermi-level energy.

(b) Find the average total and the average x-directed velocity, as percentages of the velocity corresponding to the Fermi-level energy.

CHAPTER XIII

IONIZATION AND EXCITATION OF ATOMS *

13.1 The Function of Positive Ions in Gaseous-Conducting Devices. The electron tubes so far studied in this text contain only negatively charged current-carrying particles, that is, electrons. In contrast to this, gas-filled electron tubes, mercury-arc rectifiers, gas and vapor light sources, electric arcs, glow discharges, sparks, etc., contain charged particles of both signs, for the most part in approximately equal concentrations. Yet in them, as in high-vacuum electronic devices, the important current flow is that due to electron movement. The positively charged particles present are positive ions. Their mass per particle is so much greater than that of the electrons that they move relatively very slowly; in mercury vapor the velocity ratio is about 1 to 605. Hence the rate of charge transfer due to positive ion motion is an insignificant part of the total current.

Yet in spite of the fact that positive ions carry so little current, their presence makes the current-voltage relation altogether different from what it is without them. When they are not present, as in high-vacuum electronic devices, the current density due to electron movement is limited by space charge. When they are present, and equal in concentration to the electrons, there is no space charge, and the electron current density may reach tremendously large values even though the potential gradient is small.

Interest in regard to the ions in gaseous electrical discharges centers around the manner and rate of their appearance and disappearance. It is important to know where they come from and where they go, and at what energy cost. If they are present, electron space charge is neutralized and large currents can flow in response to a small potential difference; if they are absent, current flow can take place only under the influence of a high potential, no matter how freely electrons may be supplied.

In an ionized gas, and in a metallic conductor, current flow consists of an electron "wind" passing through a region populated by positively

---

* See bibliography references 13A, B. The suggestions and criticisms made by Dr. S. A. Goudsmit relative to Chapter XIII were very helpful to the author. Additional reference books are 1I, J, K, 13C, D, E.

charged particles which are relatively stationary. The positively charged particles of a metal are the atoms of its structure; they may be called positively charged because each has contributed its outer electron to the electron wind that blows through the lattice-work of atoms. The heat motions of these atoms are vibratory in nature, so that each one retains its average position relative to its neighbors. In an ionized gas the positively charged particles are gas ions whose random heat motions carry them throughout the body of gas; however, relative to the electron wind that constitutes the current, they are practically at rest.

13.2   Energy Required for Ionization; Energy-Level Diagrams. The arrangement of electrons around atomic nuclei was discussed in Section 8.1. A positive ion is an atom or molecule from which an outer electron has been removed. Just as an electron can be removed from a metallic surface only by the introduction of energy (heat energy in thermionic emission), so an electron can be removed from a particle of gas or vapor only by the contribution of energy. The least amount of energy necessary to remove a single electron from a metal surface is definite and measurable; it is called the work function and is usually a matter of a few electron volts. The least energy that can remove an electron from a gas particle is similarly definite and measurable in electron volts. It is called the *ionizing potential* and is between 5 and 25 volts for most gas and vapor atoms.

Energy-level diagrams similar in principle to those employed in work-function representation are useful in the study of ionization and kindred processes in gases. Figure 13.1 compares the energy-level diagram for an atom of sodium vapor with a metal-conductor type of diagram. To emphasize the similarity, the work function of the metal on this diagram has been indicated as being the same as the ionizing potential of sodium. Below the line that is described as the "normal level" there are, in both diagrams, "occupied" or "filled" levels, representing the energy states of the electrons present in the metal or in the atom. The metal has a very large, but finite, number of filled levels, there being one for each free electron in the metal. In a sodium-vapor atom there are altogether eleven filled levels, corresponding to the eleven electrons that form the "atmosphere" around the atomic nucleus. These eleven occur in groups as indicated; first two close together, then eight, then one alone.

The quantitative parallelism between Figs. 13.1a and 13.1b is limited to the spacing between the normal and zero levels, for the bottom metal level is likely to be between 2 and 20 volts below the one here called normal, as compared with a matter of thousands of volts for the sodium-vapor atom.

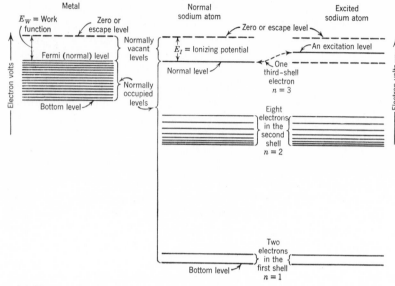

(a) Energy levels for the free electrons in a metal, as in Fig. 8.2.

(b) Energy levels for the 11 electrons of a sodium atom's "electron atmosphere" in the *normal state* of the atom.

(c) Similar to (b), in an *excited state* of the atom.

Fig. 13.1 Comparison between an energy-level diagram for a metal and an energy-level diagram showing the normally occupied levels in a sodium atom.

13.3 Excited States of Atoms. Figures 13.1a and 13.1b represent minimum-energy conditions: in the metal, that of absolute zero temperature; in the atom, the "normal state." This means the condition in which most atoms are found in gases at ordinary room temperatures. If an atom or a piece of metal initially in the minimum-energy or normal state receives energy from an outside agent, one or more of the electrons must rise out of a level that is normally filled into one or more of those ordinarily vacant. The normally vacant levels lie above the normal level in both metal and atom. In the metal the rising electrons ordinarily come from the normal level or those just below it. In a gas atom just the normal-level electron is elevated into one of the higher normally empty positions.

When this has happened an atom is said to be *excited*, or in an *excited state*, or to have an electron in an *excitation level*.[1J] Figure 13.1c is an energy-level diagram for an excited atom. An electron ordinarily occupies an excitation level for only a very brief period of time, of the order of a hundredth of a microsecond (10^{-8} second). As it drops to a lower excitation level or to the normal level, energy is released. This energy usually appears as radiation. The amount of energy released in the return to the normal state is exactly the amount originally required to cause elevation to the excited state, and is measured by the spacing between the levels on the diagram.

If an atom receives energy in excess of that needed to lift an electron to the zero level, the electron escapes from the atom altogether, so converting the atom to an ion.

13.4 Transitions between Levels. In electrical discharges atoms are continually being raised from the normal into excited states by collisions with other particles. This activity is the result, directly or indirectly, of the acceleration of charged particles by the electric field between the electrodes. As the affected atoms return to the normal state, they radiate energy electromagnetically, sometimes in the form of visible light. This gives rise to the luminosity of arcs, sparks, and glow discharges.

An *ionizing collision* is one in which the outer electron of an atom is lifted past the ionization level and escapes. Enough ionizing collisions must occur in an electrical discharge to maintain the necessary ion concentration in spite of the gradual lateral movement of ions out of the path of the discharge. *Exciting collisions* lift electrons into excitation levels. Exciting collisions occur very much more frequently than do ionizing collisions.

The vertical spacing between any two levels is proportional (*a*) to the amount of energy that must be imparted to an atom by a collision in order to produce a shift from the lower to the upper of the pair, and, therefore, from (13–6), (*b*) to the *reciprocal of the wavelength*, that is, to the *number of waves per centimeter*, of the electromagnetic radiation emitted during the downward shift. Thus the particular kinds of radiation sent out by a conducting gas are determined by the spacings between the various excitation levels.

The excitation levels lie above the normal level and below the ionization level. Hence the portions of energy-level diagrams that lie between these two extremes are especially interesting and useful. In fact, the phrase energy-level diagram usually refers to this portion alone, illustrated for sodium in Fig. 13.2*b*, and for neon and mercury in later figures. The proper placement of the excitation levels for the various elements is determined by analysis of spectral photographs that record, experimentally, the wavelengths of the spectral lines.

The usual cycle of energy changes from normal state to excited state, then back to normal state again, consists of abrupt elevation of an electron to some excitation level, followed by a cascading back to the

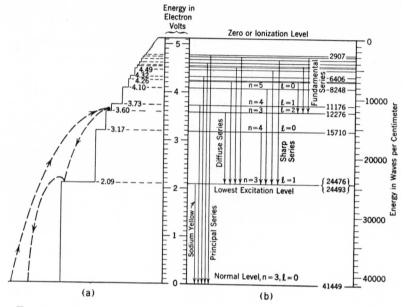

Fig. 13.2   Energy levels and transitions for a sodium atom.   (See Table XI.)

normal level by a series of long or short downward *transitions* between levels. The following typical cycle for a sodium atom is illustrated in Fig. 13.2*a*.

(1) A fast-moving electron strikes a sodium atom and causes a shift from the normal level to one that is 3.60 volts above normal. The attacking electron goes on its way with kinetic energy reduced by the amount given to the atom.

(2) The atom remains in this excited 3.60-volt state for an uncertain but extremely short period of time, of the order of 10^{-8} second.

(3) A transition (abrupt shift downward) occurs, terminating at the 2.09-volt level. Simultaneously a light impulse is radiated whose energy is correspondingly $3.60 - 2.09 = 1.51$ electron volts, at a definite wavelength.

(4) Hesitation again occurs for perhaps a hundredth of a microsecond; then

(5) Another transition carries the atom to the normal state. At the same time a 2.09-volt light impulse is released. This impulse has the yellow color that is used as a chemical test for the presence of sodium. In fact, each transition corresponds to some one definite line in the spectrum of sodium.

Figure 13.2*a* illustrates the cycle just described as the trajectory of a ball that has been thrown up a flight of stairs, only to bounce down again. The particular height to which it rises depends on the energy initially received.

Often the return to the normal state from a particular excited state may take place in any of a variety of ways. A single transition directly to the normal state may occur, or the return to normal may take place in two, three, or several transitions.

The probability of a transition from the 3.60-volt level in sodium to either the 3.17-volt level or the normal level is practically zero. Such transitions are never observed experimentally; they are called *forbidden* transitions. Those that do occur are called *permitted* transitions. On energy-level diagrams vertical lines are drawn connecting levels between which transitions are permitted; this has been done in Fig. 13.2b.

The spectrum of a sodium-vapor light source contains a spectral line corresponding to each one of the vertical lines in Fig. 13.2b, for, each time a permitted transition occurs, light of its characteristic wavelength is emitted. Some of the permitted transitions are more likely to occur than others and so occur more often. This is a partial explanation of the differences in the intensities of the various colors of light produced by a given source.

13.5   Electron-Volt Measure of the Color of Light. The proportionality between the energy released in a transition and the number of waves per centimeter of the resulting radiation arises out of the fact that light emission invariably occurs in impulses of definite energy content, variously called *photons, light quanta,* and *light particles.*

The energy of a photon is proportional to the light frequency, according to the equation

$$W_{ph} = hf \qquad \text{[joule units]} \qquad (13\text{--}1)$$

Here W_{ph} is the photon's energy in joule units, f the radiation's frequency in cycles per second, and h a universal (Planck's) constant, of value 6.624×10^{-34} joule-second, as introduced in Section 8.7.

If the photon energy is expressed in electron volts E_{ph},

$$W_{ph} = E_{ph}q_e = hf \qquad (13\text{--}2)$$

This rearranges into

$$E_{ph} = \frac{h}{q_e}f = 4.13 \times 10^{-15}f \qquad \begin{bmatrix} \text{energy per photon,} \\ \text{in electron volts} \end{bmatrix} \qquad (13\text{--}3)$$

In all free-space electromagnetic radiations, whether radio waves, heat, light, X rays or cosmic rays, wavelength λ times frequency must give the velocity of light c, that is

$$\lambda f = c \qquad (13\text{--}4)$$

If λ is wavelength in centimeters, and f is cycles per second, c must of course be 3×10^{10} centimeters per second. If λ is in meters, c is 3×10^{8} meters per second.

Combination of (13–3) and (13–4) gives

$$E_{ph}" = \frac{hc}{q_e}\frac{1}{\lambda} \tag{13–5}$$

Energy-level information is usually expressed in values of $1/\lambda$, stated as *waves per centimeter*. Numerically,

$$E_{ph} = 12400 \times 10^{-8}\frac{1}{\lambda_{cm}} \quad \begin{bmatrix} \text{energy per photon,} \\ \text{in electron volts} \end{bmatrix} \tag{13–6}$$

The wavelength of visible or near-visible radiations is often measured in *angstrom units*, which are units of length each 10^{-8} centimeter long.

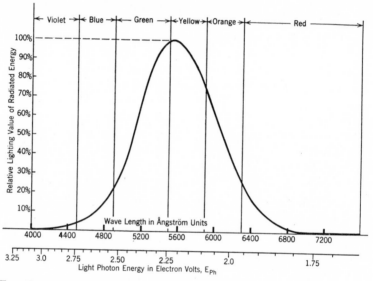

Fig. 13.3 Relative sensitivity of the human eye to light of various colors. (Reproduced from *Lighting Data*, Bulletin LD-114 D of the General Electric Company.)

Equation (13–6) can be written as follows in terms of $\lambda_{\text{Å}}$, wavelength in angstrom units:

$$E_{ph} = 12400\frac{1}{\lambda_{\text{Å}}} \tag{13–7}$$

Light wavelengths are also measured in *microns*. A micron is 10^{-6} meter, 10^{-4} centimeter, 10^4 angstrom units. Thus

$$E_{ph} = 1.240\frac{1}{\lambda_{\text{microns}}} \tag{13–8}$$

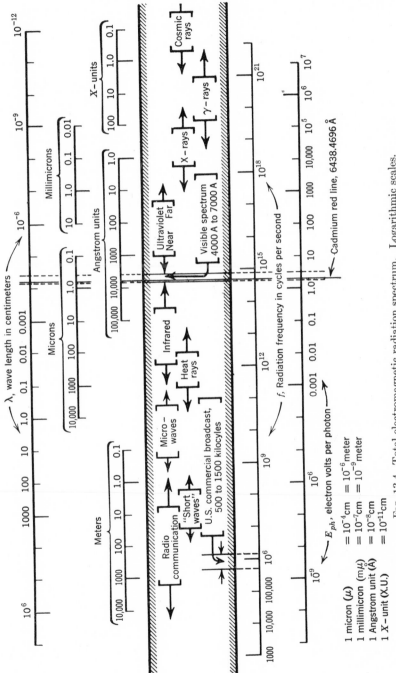

FIG. 13.4   Total electromagnetic radiation spectrum.   Logarithmic scales.

Equations (13-6) and (13-7) are easy to bear in mind and serve two useful purposes:

(a) Equation (13-6) shows that $1/\lambda_{cm}$, the number of waves per centimeter, is a directly proportional measure of the energy per photon; and

(b) Equation (13-7) permits description of the color of light in electron volts, as it relates E_{ph} directly to $\lambda_{\text{Å}}$, the most common wavelength measure in referring to colors.

Figure 13.3 is a graphical representation of the sensitivity of the human eye to light of various colors. Figure 13.4 gives the approximate wavelength and electron-volt limits for the various kinds of electromagnetic radiations that human experience encompasses.

13.6 Scales on Energy-Level Diagrams. The left-margin scale on Fig. 13.2b is divided in electron volts and has its zero at the normal level; this is the most satisfactory scale to use when considering rates and probabilities of excitation and ionization. The right-margin scale is divided in waves per centimeter, also called wave numbers. Its zero is at the zero level. It is used in calculating wavelengths corresponding to the various transitions, and in analyses leading to the placement of levels.

The wave-number difference between the 2.09-volt level and the normal level is $41449 - 24476 = 16973$. This describes sodium's characteristic yellow light in waves per centimeter. Its reciprocal, 5890×10^{-8} centimeter, or 5890 angstrom units, is the corresponding wavelength. The same result can be arrived at by using the voltage scale. The energy difference between these two levels is 2.09 electron volts, which when used in (13-7) gives 5890 angstrom units for $\lambda_{\text{Å}}$. The placement of the zero at the top of one scale and at the bottom of the other is done as a matter of convenience in the particular services for which each scale is used.

13.7 Resonance Radiation; Photoelectric Ionization. The light-producing transitions from high to low levels are reversible, within certain limitations. In particular, an atom may be excited by the absorption of a photon, *provided the energy of each photon is the same or very nearly the same as the energy difference of the transition*. This gives rise to *resonance radiation*.

Imagine that light from a monochromatic (single-wavelength) light source falls on a glass tube containing sodium vapor. If the color (wavelength) of the monochromatic light is varied in the direction of increasing energy, from infrared on up, there is at first no effect on the sodium vapor. The light passes through it with only slight diffusion.

However, when the light source begins sending out 2.09-volt photons, the entire sodium-vapor chamber becomes itself a light source *of the same color*, sending radiations in all directions. Various atoms are being raised to the 2.09-volt excited states by the incoming light; on their return to normal states 2.09-volt radiation occurs. This resonance radiation originates in the sodium-vapor tube, but the energy for it comes from the monochromatic light source.

If the monochromatic light source begins sending out light carrying more than 2.09 electron volts per photon, resonance radiation stops, and the sodium-vapor tube becomes dark again. The reason for this is that the probability of absorption of a photon is very small unless the photon's energy is just the amount required to raise the atom to an excited state. In contrast to this, excitation by impact may result from collisions with particles having a considerable range of energies above the required value. The difference arises from the fact that a photon must give up all or none of its energy; a moving particle may give up any fraction of its energy.

If the incoming photon's energy is sufficient, ionization may occur; the resulting ions are said to be produced by photoelectric action. The analogy with the energy-level diagram of a solid piece of metal (Fig. 13.1) can now be reversed. *Photoelectric emission* from a metal results when incoming photons have sufficient energy to raise internal electrons from the uppermost filled ("normal") level to the zero or escape level; see the next chapter.

13.8   Atomic Number; Isotopes. Each atom of an element normally consists of (*a*) a positively charged central nucleus which contains almost all of the atomic mass, and (*b*) a surrounding atmosphere of electrons whose arrangement accounts for most of the element's chemical and physical properties.

The atomic number Z is the number of electrons in the atmosphere of an atom when the atom as a whole is electrically neutral; it is therefore also a measure of the positive charge on the nucleus. The mass of an atomic nucleus is almost all due to the protons and neutrons it contains, which have each the same mass as a hydrogen nucleus. Neutrons are electrically neutral, but each proton has a positive charge numerically equal to the charge on an electron.[13C]

Atoms having the same atomic number but different atomic weights are called *isotopes;* [1J, 13C] see Table II. For example, the nucleus of one kind of neon has a mass about 20 times, of the other kind 22 times, that of a hydrogen nucleus. Yet both are neon, for the atomic number is 10 for both kinds. As neon occurs in nature, the two are always mixed in such proportions as to give an average atomic weight of 20.2.

The atomic number of mercury is 80; its average atomic weight, 200.61, is the composite result of a mixture of seven isotopes, of atomic weights 202, 200, 199, 198, 201, 196, in that order of prominence. Sodium's atomic number is 11; there is only one kind of sodium, of atomic weight 23. Deuterium, or "heavy hydrogen" is an isotope of hydrogen.

13.9 Energy Levels As Related to Electron Motions. An atom of sodium vapor that is struck by a fast-moving electron may have the outermost one of the eleven electrons in its atmosphere driven away by the impact. This will happen only if the kinetic energy of the on-coming electron is at least 5.12 volts, and the geometry of the collision favorable. If the resulting sodium *ion* is again hit by a high-speed electron, it may lose its tenth electron, now the outermost one. The energy required for this operation is 47 volts. With sufficiently elaborate equipment it is possible to rob atoms of two, three, four, or even more electrons. If all the electrons are removed, the atom is said to be *stripped*.

An atom from which one or more electrons have been removed of course exerts an attraction on any lone electron that may enter its field. The motion of a roving electron during approach toward an atomic nucleus that has been stripped of its electronic atmosphere is remotely similar to that of a comet approaching the sun. The electron, like the comet, loses potential energy and gains kinetic energy as it comes near to the heavier body. In both cases mutual attraction draws the smaller body inward, while centrifugal force tends to drive it farther out.

A comet approaching from the remote heavens possesses at every point in its path enough kinetic energy to carry it back to infinite space again. It will begin orbital motion around the sun only if, while in the sun's gravitational field, it loses by collision, friction, or otherwise, an appreciable portion of the kinetic energy that would normally carry it away again. An electron *invariably* loses energy while approaching a stripped atomic nucleus, for any electrical particle that undergoes acceleration radiates energy electromagnetically. Hence any electron that approaches at all closely is presumably captured and pursues a path that carries it repeatedly around the nucleus.

Because the electron is continually losing kinetic energy by radiation, its velocity and centrifugal force should become continually less, permitting the radius of its path to become smaller and smaller. According to this reasoning the path should be a flat spiral centering at the nucleus. But motion in any path that repeatedly encircles the nucleus is essentially periodic, and therefore subject to the quantum limitation that requires the action per cycle to be an integral multiple of h; see

Section 8.7. This requirement, combined with that of centrifugal balance, restricts the possible radii to certain discrete values, and compels successive abrupt reductions in radius of path rather than a gradual decrease.

Each possible radius corresponds to a particular level on an energy-level diagram. In pursuing the orbital path corresponding to a given level the electron radiates no electromagnetic energy. A transition between levels corresponds to an abrupt shift to a smaller orbit, along with a sudden release of a single impulse of radiant energy. Thus the impulse-like nature of light and the intermittent nature of the movement toward the nucleus are mutually interdependent, both being quantitatively related to the action unit h.

13.10 Energies of the Levels; One Electron in a Nuclear Field.
The necessity for balance between centrifugal force and inverse-square-law attraction of the stripped nucleus requires, for a circular path, that [1J]

$$\frac{m_e v^2}{r} = \frac{Z q_e \cdot q_e}{4 \pi \epsilon_0 r^2} \qquad (13\text{--}9)$$

where Z = nuclear atomic number.
q_e = electronic charge.
m_e = electronic mass.
v = linear velocity in the path.
r = radius of the path.

The limitation of cyclic action to h-units (see Section 8.7) requires that

$$\int_{s=0}^{s=2\pi r} m_e v \, ds = 2\pi r m v = nh \qquad (13\text{--}10)$$

Here ds is incremental distance around the circumference, and n is any whole number. Equations (13–9) and (13–10) permit the elimination of v and subsequent determination of the radius of the orbit for any particular value of n.

The energies rather than the radii are of interest, however. Potential energy W_p of the electron's position is its charge $(-q_e)$, multiplied by the potential, $Z q_e / 4 \pi \epsilon_0 r$; that is,

$$W_p = -\frac{Z q_e^2}{4 \pi \epsilon_0 r} \qquad \text{[joule units]} \qquad (13\text{--}11)$$

This assumes that the potential energy is zero at an infinite radius, decreasing to negative values as the radius becomes finite; the zero of potential energy, like that of electric potential in a circuit, may always be selected arbitrarily. Kinetic energy W_k is of course $\frac{1}{2}mv^2$. It may be expressed by canceling an r in (13–9) and dividing by 2. This leads to the expression

$$W_k = + \frac{Zq_e^2}{8\pi\epsilon_0 r} \tag{13–12}$$

The net energy W is the algebraic sum of the two kinds:

$$W = W_p + W_k \tag{13–13}$$

$$= -\frac{Zq_e^2}{4\pi\epsilon_0 r} + \frac{Zq_e^2}{8\pi\epsilon_0 r} \tag{13–14}$$

that is,

$$W = -\frac{Zq_e^2}{8\pi\epsilon_0 r} \tag{13–15}$$

An expression for W which does not involve either the radius or velocity is obtained by multiplying (13–9) and (13–15), then substituting into the result a value for v^2r^2 obtained from (13–10). These operations give

$$W = \frac{Z^2 q_e^4 m_e}{8\epsilon_0^2 h^2} \frac{1}{n^2} \tag{13–16}$$

All the factors except n and Z that appear here are fundamental physical constants, and n is any whole number. Bear in mind that the energy calculated by using (13–15) or (13–16) *is the energy necessary to remove the electron to infinity.*

The atomic number of hydrogen is 1. Therefore if $Z = 1$ in (13–16), and n is given values from unity up, the energies for the various levels in a hydrogen atom's energy-level diagram should and do result. Similarly, if $Z = 2$, those for once-ionized helium's diagram result, and, if $Z = 3$, those applicable to twice-ionized lithium, and so on.

It has just been explained how and why each level of a single-electron energy-level diagram corresponds to a particular value of n, called the quantum number for that level. The greatest value n can have is infinity. This corresponds to the ionization level, for which the energy is zero. The least value n can have is 1. The atomic number for hydrogen is also 1; the use of $n = 1$ and $Z = 1$ in (13–16) gives an energy in joule units that corresponds to 13.53 electron volts. This is the energy of the normal level. Since that for the ionization level is zero, the energy difference between these two extreme levels is that of the lower one. Therefore the ionizing potential of atomic hydrogen should be and is 13.53 volts.

13.11   Limitations of the Orbital Physical Picture. The locations of the energy levels for the various elements have been rather well explained by extensions and modifications of this theory of electron motions.   The physical picture of planetary pellet-like electrons surrounding a nucleus that grows out of such treatment is called the "Bohr atom model." [1J]

Some of the modifications employed are very striking.   Elliptical orbits must be used; each electron is assumed to spin on its own axis, like the earth; also, the relativity change in mass of an electron, as its velocity varies around an elliptical orbit, is taken into account.   Finally there is necessary a wave-mechanical denaturing of the electrons themselves, by which each one partakes of some of the aspects of a cloud-like wave train encircling the nucleus.

Throughout all these changes in the physical picture the essential features of the mathematical expressions remain the same.   Although the simple picture of planetary pellet-like electrons is inaccurate in detail, it leads to useful approximations to the major aspects of atomic behavior.

13.12   Three-Dimensional Quantization. The circular motion assumed in the derivation of (13–16) is a very specialized kind of orbital motion, in that the *angular* position only of the electron varies.   In a sense circular motion is one-dimensional, for it is completely described by variations in a single (angular) coordinate.

Since space is three-dimensional, an electron's velocity may have three mutually perpendicular components.   Each component of motion is periodic, so that an electron may have three different quantum numbers.

A similar situation was encountered in Section 8.7, where particles were thought of as being contained within a cubical box.   The restraining walls of a box are plane surfaces; similarly, the barriers that prevent the escape of electrons from metals or metallic crystals are the work functions of plane surfaces.   This suggested quantization in rectangular coordinates.   The total quantum number n was expressed as

$$n = \sqrt{n_u{}^2 + n_v{}^2 + n_w{}^2} \qquad (13\text{--}17)$$

because the total kinetic energy was found to be proportional to $n_u{}^2 + n_v{}^2 + n_w{}^2$.   These three contributing n's, n_u, n_v, and n_w, are the quantum numbers that correspond to the velocity components in the x, y, and z directions respectively.

The force that acts on the electrons near a nucleus is centrally directed.   This makes suitable a quantization in spherical or "polar"

402   IONIZATION AND EXCITATION OF ATOMS

coordinates,[13B-22] Fig. 1.13, rather than in rectangular coordinates. The three polar quantum numbers are n_r, n_θ, and n_ϕ, corresponding to variations in r, θ, and ϕ. In this polar system, r is the radius from an origin at the nucleus, θ is the angle between the radius and the polar axis, and ϕ is a measure of revolution around the polar axis.

The total quantum number is given by

$$n = n_r + n_\theta + n_\phi \tag{13-18}$$

This definition is used because mathematical analysis shows that for periodic motion in the force field of a central nucleus the kinetic energy is inversely proportional to $(n_r + n_\theta + n_\phi)^2$.

The change from the relation $n = \sqrt{n_u^2 + n_v^2 + n_w^2}$ used in Chapter VIII to $n = n_r + n_\phi + n_\theta$ used here is necessary only because the electric forces on the electrons around an atomic nucleus are centrally directed and so induce motions of polar rather than rectangular nature. *In both situations n is chosen so that the energy is dependent on n^2.*

The use of polar coordinates requires the selection of some given direction in space as that of the polar axis. In atomic study the direction chosen is that of whatever magnetic field exists. The field may be small, perhaps weaker than the earth's magnetic field. Yet in general there is at all points in space some magnetic field, so also some one direction that has unique magnetic significance.

13.13   The Exclusion Principle; Grouping of the Levels. A sodium nucleus that has captured just one electron must be expected to gather in ten more eventually, because eleven are required to neutralize the nuclear charge. As in the case of gas particles in a box, only one electron can have the motions that correspond to a given combination of quantum numbers [13B-144] (see Section 8.8). The final state of each one of the eleven must therefore be different from the states of all the others. There are correspondingly eleven separate, occupied energy levels in the normal state of a sodium atom.

The various orbits in which these eleven electrons travel are in general elliptical. The major axis of each orbital path depends on the total quantum number. The various ellipses have varying degrees of flatness and lie in different planes; that is, they have different *eccentricities* and *orientations*.

The most important differences between them have to do with the lengths of the major axes and the eccentricities. These differences can be illustrated by a two-dimensional study, because each ellipse is two-dimensional in nature, the third dimension entering only in relation to the orientation. For this purpose let $n_\theta = 0$, only n_r and n_ϕ having values. Mathematical analysis shows that the resulting quantized motion is truly elliptical, with the nucleus at one focus of the ellipse. The length of the major axis is found to be directly proportional to n^2, and the energy inversely proportional to n^2. For given length of major axis, the minor axis is proportional to n_ϕ. When $n_\phi = n$, the major and minor axes are equal, so that the motion is circular. These relations are illustrated in Fig. 13.5.[1J]

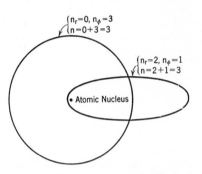

It has just been pointed out that the energy of an electron depends on the total quantum number; of course a given total quantum number can result from a variety of combinations of the component quantum numbers. Therefore more than one electron can have the same energy. For example, an elliptical orbit for which $n_r = 2$, $n_\phi = 1$, calls for the same energy as the elliptical one for which $n_r = 1$, $n_\phi = 2$, and the circular one for which $n_r = 0$, $n_\phi = 3$.

FIG. 13.5 Circular and elliptical orbits having the same total quantum number and therefore the same energy. The major axis of the ellipse is the same as the diameter of the circle. The minor axis of the ellipse is proportional to n_ϕ.

This explains why the energy levels occur in groups, as illustrated in Fig. 13.1b. The total quantum number is the same for all the levels in a group, and the energies are approximately the same within low-lying groups. The small differences in energy between the levels within a group result from minor differences in the energy contributions from the different components of motion.

13.14 Shells. The different quantum-number groups of electrons are often spoken of as *shells*. The reason for this is that the various groups are located at progressively greater distances from the nucleus. Equation (13–15) indicates that the mean orbital radius should vary approximately inversely as the energy, therefore directly as n^2. The proportionality between the length of the major axis and n^2 bears this out.

For reasons detailed in the next section, a shell whose total quantum number is n contains $2n^2$ possible energy states, or energy levels. This is illustrated in Fig. 13.1. Sodium has two electrons in the first, closest-in shell with lowest-lying levels, eight electrons in the second, and one lone one as a start in the third.

The path of the lone third-shell electron is a very flat, elongated ellipse. As illustrated in Fig. 13.5, such a path brings the electron traveling along it much closer to the nucleus than does a circular path. This outer electron's orbit is at one end *well inside the second shell of electrons*. It is said to pursue a *penetrating* orbit.

The ten electrons of the first two shells serve, for regions beyond them, as an effective screen of $\frac{10}{11}$ of the nuclear charge. Therefore for the portion of this elongated path that is *outside* the second shell, the eleventh electron lies in a central force field due to a charge of $+q_e$. For the portion of the path *inside* the second shell it lies in a much stronger field. The average effect of the nucleus on this penetrating electron is therefore greater than it would be on a nonpenetrating one.

Thus the *effective nuclear charge* is greater for a penetrating than for a nonpenetrating orbit. In (13–16), Z stands for the nuclear charge. Evidently a penetrating electron must have, according to this equation, a greater negative energy, and so occupy a lower level, than a nonpenetrating one having the same total quantum number.

For example, if sodium's outermost electron normally pursued a nonpenetrating path, it should be possible to calculate the ionizing potential of sodium by using $n = 3$ and $Z = 1$ in (13–16). Such treatment predicts an ionizing potential of only 1.51 volts. The actual ionizing potential is obtainable from this equation by using $n = 3$, $Z = 1.84$. This indicates that for the actual penetrating orbit pursued in the normal state of the atom the effective nuclear charge is 1.84.

One of sodium's excitation levels has an energy of 1.51 electron volts (measured from the ionization level). This level presumably corresponds to a nonpenetrating orbit for which $n = 3$.

13.15   Magnetic Quantization: $2n^2$. This question naturally arises: Why can the nth shell contain $2n^2$ electrons, but no more?

The periodic motions of an electron in the central force field around an atomic nucleus are a composite of:

(a) Variations in r, that is, in closeness to and remoteness from the origin at the nucleus; the corresponding quantum number is n_r.

(b) Continuous rotation about the polar axis, that is, a continuous increase in ϕ. The corresponding quantum number is n_ϕ. Since the electron carries an electric charge, this continuous rotational motion constitutes an electric current and produces a magnetic field. The rotation may be either clockwise or counterclockwise, so that the magnetic field may have either of two opposite polarities. Some magnetic field exists at all points in space, and the direction of the polar axis is that of the magnetic field. The magnetic energy due to the combination of the external field with that produced by the electron is different for the two directions of electron motion. For this reason there can be *two* energy states for each numerical value of n_ϕ, except when $n_\phi = 0$. Each state can be occupied by an electron.

Because n_ϕ is magnetic in nature, it is often called m_l. The significance of the subscript l will appear later.

(c) Oscillations of the polar angle θ, which must always take place between 0 and π (radians). Since θ does not increase continuously, there are not two oppositely directed kinds of θ motion with differing energies. The quantum number is n_θ.

The mathematical statements of these quantizations are as follows:

$$n_r h = \oint m_e v_r \, dr \qquad (13\text{--}19a)$$

$$n_\phi h = \oint m_e r^2 \sin^2 \theta \, \frac{d\phi}{dt} \, d\phi \qquad (13\text{--}19b)$$

$$n_\theta h = \oint m_e r^2 \, \frac{d\theta}{dt} \, d\theta \qquad (13\text{--}19c)$$

The results of spectrographic study indicate that each electron spins on its own axis, as does the earth. Such spinning of electric charge produces a magnetic field. The rate of spin, as measured by action in h-units, is always the same, but the magnetic field may be oriented either with or against the polar-axis field. The spin quantum number m_s is always $\frac{1}{2}$, so that the change from one orientation to the opposite is accompanied by a shift of a single h-unit. For any given array of the quantum numbers n_r, n_ϕ, and n_θ there are two half-quantum spin states, one for each spin orientation. That is, m_s may be either $\frac{1}{2}$ clockwise, or $\frac{1}{2}$ counterclockwise.

Table X lists the various combinations of n_r, n_ϕ, and n_θ that are possible for each of several total quantum numbers.[13B-145] It also indicates how the $2n^2$ levels in a shell differ from one another. The symbol l is used for the quantity $m_l + n_\theta$ (identical with $n_\phi + n_\theta$). Thus m_l can never be greater than l, and it is equal to l when $n_\theta = 0$. This usage is a helpful simplification in dealing with circular or elliptical orbits which are two-dimensional.

It has been found that actual atomic behavior, as recorded by spectral lines, is best approximated by using, in numerical formulas, values that are slightly greater than the integral values 0, 1, 2, 3, etc., in place of l. For some purposes $l + \frac{1}{2}$ works best; for others $\sqrt{l(l+1)}$. However, these best approximations never require the use of numerical values greater than n. If the numerical value to be used in place of l is slightly greater than l, but does not exceed n, it is apparent that l does not exceed $n - 1$.

The restriction, in Table X, of values of l to not more than $n - 1$

is in accord with the situation outlined in the previous paragraph, as well as in accord with known placement of electrons in shells. The usage outlined in the previous paragraph also makes the use of the value 0 for l, apparently requiring the electron to collide with the nucleus, not wholly unreasonable, because the numerical value used is not quite zero.

Within each shell, the energy states available to the electrons are classified into subgroups, according to the values of l. Letters are ordinarily used to describe the l's according to the following code:

$$\text{Letter symbol:} \quad s \quad p \quad d \quad f \quad g \quad h \quad i$$
$$\text{Value of } l: \qquad 0 \quad 1 \quad 2 \quad 3 \quad 4 \quad 5 \quad 6$$

$$(13\text{--}20)$$

By reference to Table X it will be seen that, in any shell, a completed s subgroup contains 2 electrons, a completed p subgroup 6 electrons, a completed d subgroup 10 electrons, and so on.

In general, an atom whose outermost aspect is a completed subgroup is relatively stable chemically. Thus the stability of atoms for which the static models have cubical outer aspects (see Fig. 8.1) is due to the fact that just enough electrons are present to fill the p subgroup.

There are no elements whose outer aspects are completed third shells. Thus argon has 8 electrons in the third shell (see Table II), but the next element, potassium, places its additional electron in the fourth shell. The reason for this "jump" is explained in the following paragraph.

The first fourth-shell electron pursues a penetrating orbit, for its angular momentum is small ($l = 0$) while its radial motion is large ($n_r = 4$). On the other hand, the last 10 third-shell electrons have more nearly circular, nonpenetrating orbits ($l = 2$, $n_r = 1$). It was pointed out in Section 13.14 that electrons in penetrating orbits are exposed to relatively large effective nuclear charges, and have relatively large (negative) energy values. The effective nuclear charge of the first fourth-shell orbit is enough larger than that of the last subgroup of third-shell orbits to more than compensate for the increase in total quantum number from 3 to 4, in the establishment of energy values. Therefore the energy level for the first fourth-shell energy state lies below that for the last 10 third-shell states and so is occupied before the last 10 third-shell levels.

If the spectrum of sodium is analyzed with reference to Table X, it appears that the normal level of sodium's energy-level diagram is one for which $n = 3$, $n_r = 3$, $l = 0$. The usual sodium spectrum corresponds to an energy-level diagram having four levels for which $n = 3$. Their l-values are 2, 1 (a pair), and 0, as marked in Fig. 13.2b.

According to Table X there should be six levels having $n = 3, l = 1$. Yet only two appear in the diagram. Actually all of the six states of motion can exist, but their energies all have either the 24476 or the 24493 value, so that they are shown as a pair. If a strong magnetic field is applied to a discharge while the spectral lines are being observed, the differences in magnetic energies of the clockwise and counterclockwise rotations become more pronounced, and each member of the pair splits up into three distinguishable levels. This spectral change is called the "Zeeman effect." [13B-69] Many other levels are similarly affected. A somewhat similar behavior in the presence of a strong electric field is called the "Stark effect." [13B-78]

13.16 Action and Angular Momentum. One of the concepts that is very useful in the analysis of electronic motions is that of *total angular momentum*, symbol J. The only angular momentum possessed by sodium's eleventh electron in the normal state is that due to electron spin, for $l = 0$. In the $n = 3, l = 1$ state it has angular momentum due both to *rotation* and *spin*. The total angular momentum J is the vector sum of these. Vectorial summation of angular momenta is accomplished by the use of vectors pointed along the axis of the rotation, in the direction of a right-handed screw's advance. If the motions of more than one electron are effective in causing the differences between the levels, *the total angular momentum is the vector sum of the momenta for all the active electrons.*

The actual vector summation is, in atomic analysis, always made in terms of quantum units. This is possible because action and angular momentum have the same dimensional formula, and are subject to corresponding action limitations. To illustrate this the action integral for circular motion, which is

$$\int_{s=0}^{s=2\pi r} m_e v \, ds = 2\pi r m_e v = nh \qquad (13\text{--}21)$$

may be rewritten in polar terminology, in the form

$$\int_{\phi=0}^{\phi=2\pi} I\omega \, d\phi = 2\pi I\omega = n_\phi h \qquad (13\text{--}22)$$

Here I, ω, ϕ signify moment of inertia, angular velocity, and rotational angle. Equation (13–22) can be rewritten as an equation for the angular momentum $I\omega$, as follows:

$$I\omega = \frac{n_\phi h}{2\pi} \qquad (13\text{--}23)$$

This shows that the action limitation in general requires angular momentum to be an integral multiple of $h/2\pi$.

With this relationship in mind, it is intelligible to say that the total angular momentum of sodium's normal level ($n = 3$, $l = 0$) is half of an h-unit, or $\frac{1}{2}(h/2\pi)$, for the only angular motion is that due to spin. On the other hand, the total angular momentum corresponding to the $n = 3$, $l = 1$ level is, in $h/2\pi$ units, either

$$J = 1 + \tfrac{1}{2} = 1\tfrac{1}{2}$$

or

$$J = 1 - \tfrac{1}{2} = \tfrac{1}{2}$$

(13–24)

These two forms correspond to the two opposite possibilities in the angular combination of these motions. The term values of these two levels are respectively 24492.83 and 24475.65 waves per centimeter. For $n = 3$, $l = 2$ there are again two possibilities, $J = 2 + \frac{1}{2} = 2\frac{1}{2}$ and $J = 2 - \frac{1}{2} = 1\frac{1}{2}$. The energy values for these two levels are normally indistinguishable experimentally.

Sodium is said to have a one-electron spectrum, in that the energy changes all result from variations in the motion of one electron outside a stable $2 + 8$ group. In contrast, mercury is said to have a two-electron spectrum, involving two electrons outside a stable $2 + 8 + 18 + 32 + 18$ array; see Table II.

13.17   Identification of Levels. The levels of an atom's energy-level diagram are identified quantitatively by their *term values*, in waves per centimeter, and qualitatively by a symbolic notation. The notation in this text is that used by Bacher and Goudsmit.[13A] The information conveyed by the notation includes: (*a*) descriptions of the *electron configurations*, that is, statements of the values of n and l for the various electrons, (*b*) indications as to the various ways in which angular momenta of individual electrons combine to give different values of total angular momenta, and so different energy values, (*c*) numerical values of total angular momentum J, and (*d*) information indicating between what levels transitions may occur.

13.18   Energy Levels for the Arc Spectrum of Sodium. Table XI lists the term values and symbolic notations for the excited states of a sodium atom, sometimes described as the energy states of the NaI spectrum. They are also referred to as the energy states of the *arc spectrum* of sodium, because transitions between them produce the light radiated by a sodium vapor arc. The arc spectrum of sodium is said to be a one-electron spectrum, because the differences between the energies of the levels are due entirely to changes in the angular momenta and radial movements of one lone third-shell electron outside a stable 2 + 8 array.

If this outer electron is entirely removed, further contributions of energy operate on one of the eight second-shell electrons. The resulting energy states are those of the NaII spectrum, also called the *spark spectrum* of sodium, because much of the light radiated by an electric spark in sodium vapor is due to transitions between the NaII energy states. The spark spectrum of sodium is similar to the arc spectrum of neon (NeI), for both are produced by 2 + 8 electron arrays. The ionization level of the NaI spectrum is the normal level of the NaII spectrum.

Table XI has four columns, with entries describing, for each level, the *term value*, the *configuration*, the *symbol*, and the *J-value*, with meanings as follows:

13.19 Term Values. The numbers in the term value column measure, in waves per centimeter, the distances of the levels below the ionization or zero level. The *reciprocal* of the difference between two term values gives the wavelength, in centimeters, of the radiation corresponding to a transition between those levels.

13.20 Configuration. The *numerals* in the configuration description give values for the total quantum numbers n for the various electrons. The *letters* describe the angular quantum numbers $l(= m_l + n_\theta)$, according to the following code:

$$\text{Letter symbol:} \quad s \quad p \quad d \quad f \quad g \quad h \quad i$$
$$\text{Value of } l: \quad 0 \quad 1 \quad 2 \quad 3 \quad 4 \quad 5 \quad 6 \tag{13-25}$$

The exponents to the l-value letters indicate the number of electrons having the specified values of n and l. For example, the description of sodium's normal, unexcited configuration can be explained as follows:

The whole: $1s^2\ 2s^2\ 2p^6\ 3s$
Its parts: $1s^2$: two electrons for which $n = 1, l = 0$
(these constitute the first shell)
$2s^2$: two for which $n = 2, l = 0$
(these begin the second shell)
$2p^6$: six for which $n = 2, l = 1$
(these complete the second shell)
$3s$: one for which $n = 3, l = 0$
(this one is alone in the third shell)

The configurations for the various levels in any one spectrum are ordinarily alike except for the last few electrons. It is usually necessary to give the descriptions only for those that change. For example, in sodium's arc spectrum only the eleventh electron changes its n and l values, so that it is sufficient to abbreviate to $3s$ the description of the configuration of the normal level, and to $3p$ that for the 24493 and 24476 levels. The yellow light characteristic of sodium is due to transitions from the $3p$ to the $3s$ configuration.

13.21   Symbols. Within a given configuration, the various electron angular momenta may combine vectorially in a number of different ways to give a variety of energies, and so various levels. To each of these there corresponds a symbol, found in the symbol column. In text references the values of J are usually appended as a subscript to the symbols, but they appear in a separate column in the table. Thus the complete symbol for sodium's $3s$ level is $^2S_{\frac{1}{2}}$; those for the two $3p$ levels are $^2P_{\frac{1}{2}}{}^\circ$ and $^2P_{1\frac{1}{2}}{}^\circ$.

The levels of any spectrum can be segregated into an *odd* group and an *even* group, the *odd* terms being identified by the superscript $^\circ$. Thus the $^2S_{\frac{1}{2}}$ level is an even one, the $^2P_{\frac{1}{2}}{}^\circ$ and $^2P_{1\frac{1}{2}}{}^\circ$ levels odd ones. Transitions must in general take place from odd levels to even levels, or vice versa.

The upper prefix ^{2} to the symbols for the sodium terms indicate that they belong to sets of terms which for the most part are made up of close pairs, called doublets. One-electron spectra contain doublets, two-electron spectra singlets *and* triplets. The expected "multiplicities" increase systematically with the number of electrons involved.

The complete qualitative description of a level or term includes a statement of its configuration followed by the symbol for the individual level. Sodium's normal state is a $1s^2\, 2s^2\, 2p^6\, 3s\ ^2S_{\frac{1}{2}}$ level; the description may be abbreviated to $3s\ ^2S_{\frac{1}{2}}$.

13.22   The Meanings of Symbols. The tendency of individual momenta of an outer group of one, two, three, or more electrons to combine according to a certain definite system forms the basis for the choice of symbols. When the system is followed exactly the atom is said to exhibit complete "Russell-Saunders coupling." Complicated spectra follow this system only approximately or not at all. In neon's arc and sodium's spark spectra (NeI and NaII) the deviations from Russell-Saunders coupling are so great that the usual symbolism cannot be used. An arbitrary identification of terms in order of energy values is adopted for these spectra.

The ideal Russell-Saunders combination pattern is as follows:

(1) The individual l-values add *vectorially* in as many different ways as will give integral results. The resultant, called L, may be 0, 1, 2, 3, 4, etc., in units $h/2\pi$. L is correspondingly described by the capital letters S, P, D, F, G, etc. This is

suggestive of the l-value symbolism. Small letters code the values of angular momenta for individual electrons; capital letters similarly code the vectorial summation of the l-values for an electron group. The individual values and their vector summation must be integral multiples of $h/2\pi$ units.

(2) The individual spin values add vectorially in as many different ways as give (a) integral values if there is an even number of spin values, (b) half-integral values if there is an odd number of spin values. The resultant is the total spin vector, sometimes called S. Care must be taken not to confuse this S with the description of L when of value zero.

(3) The vectors L and S combine *vectorially* to give J-values. They combine in as many ways as will result in: integral values if the spin vector is a whole number, half-integral values if the spin vector is a half number.

13.23   Symbols for Sodium. Suppose that this combination pattern is applied to sodium's two $3p$ levels, 24493 and 24476. Sodium has a one-electron spectrum, so that just one l-value, that of the eleventh electron, contributes to L. Therefore when the value of l is $p(=1)$, that of L is $P(=1)$. The spin of only the eleventh electron contributes to S; the value of S is therefore $\frac{1}{2}$. J may then be either:

$$J = 1 \oplus \tfrac{1}{2} = \tfrac{1}{2};$$

$L = 1$

$\longrightarrow$

$\longrightarrow\!\!\leftarrow\!\!-$

$J = \tfrac{1}{2}\ S = \tfrac{1}{2}$

$${}^{2}P_{\frac{1}{2}}{}^{\circ}\quad 24493 \quad (13\text{--}27a)$$

or

$$J = 1 \oplus \tfrac{1}{2} = 1\tfrac{1}{2};$$

$L = 1 \quad S = \tfrac{1}{2}$

$\longrightarrow\!\!\longrightarrow$

$\longrightarrow$

$J = 1\tfrac{1}{2}$

$${}^{2}P_{1\frac{1}{2}}{}^{\circ}\quad 24476 \quad (13\text{--}27b)$$

These two terms constitute a *doublet*. The levels of one-electron spectra generally occur in pairs (doublets), one for each manner of addition of the spin vector. Sometimes the separation between the levels of a pair is so small as to escape observation.

The symbol for sodium's normal level is ${}^{2}S_{\frac{1}{2}}$. This suggests that it should be one of a pair of doublets and indicates that its J is $\frac{1}{2}$. As for all one-electron levels, the value of L is the same as that of l; here it is $S(=0)$. The value of J is as usual $L + S$, which, however, gives in this case *only one* half-integral result, that is,

$$J = 0 \oplus \tfrac{1}{2} = \tfrac{1}{2} \qquad\qquad {}^{2}S_{\frac{1}{2}}\ 41{,}449.0 \qquad (13\text{--}28)$$

$\frac{1}{2}$ can add vectorially to 1 to give two half-integral results, but $\frac{1}{2}$ added vectorially to zero gives only $\frac{1}{2}$. One member of the expected doublet does not exist. Yet the symbol is given the doublet marking because its spin vector is such as to lead normally to doublet expectation; it belongs to a doublet system and is so marked. All the levels of sodium's arc spectrum belong to doublet systems.

13.24   J-Values. For convenience, and because of their importance, values of total angular momentum of the active electron or electrons are entered in separate columns in Tables XI, XII, XIII, and XIV, rather than being appended as subscripts to the energy-level symbols. The significance of these J-values is briefly discussed in Section 13.16, and their utility in the next section.

13.25.   Selection Principles. Some transitions between levels are *permitted*, others *forbidden*. Spectral theory explains why this is true, but the explanation is too intricate to present here. The *selection rules* are in general as follows: [13A-16]

(1) Transitions occur only from odd to even or even to odd levels. For even levels, the arithmetical sum of all the l-values is even; for odd levels, it is odd.

(2) In any permitted transition J changes by $+1$, 0, or -1, except that transitions requiring changes from $J = 0$ to $J = 0$ are forbidden.

(3) In any permitted transition the l-value for the shifting electron changes by either $+1$ or -1.

(4) The n-value can change by any amount.

(5) Transitions requiring shifts in the values of n or l for more than one electron are very infrequent and in most cases forbidden.

Additional selection rules still further contrast permitted and forbidden transitions. Some, like the fifth rule above, are only approximate and serve chiefly to differentiate between expected intensities of the corresponding spectral lines.

13.26   Series of Levels in Sodium. The transitions marked on Fig. 13.2b have been arranged so as to group together those that correspond to various important *spectral series*. The transitions that give rise to a series of spectral lines terminate at a common level. They originate at members of a *series of levels* which have successively different values of n, but identical values of l and of J, and therefore identical symbols.

The names given to the NaI series of spectral lines are partly descriptive, partly misleading. The "principal series" contains the most pronounced lines, the first one of them being the yellow light characteristic of sodium. The names "diffuse" and "sharp" indicate the character of the spectral lines of the respective series. The transitions of the "diffuse series" originate at levels that are very close doublets (12276, $^2D_{1\frac{1}{2}}$, $^2D_{\frac{1}{2}}$, for example). The transitions of the "sharp series" originate at levels that are not doublets, even though they bear doublet symbols (8248, $^2S_{1\frac{1}{2}}$, for example), for reasons explained in the discussion following (13–28). There is nothing especially fundamental about the series so named.

13.27. Mercury. Table XII contains the various descriptive names, numbers, and symbols, and Fig. 13.6 the energy-level diagram, for the arc spectrum of mercury. This is a two-electron spectrum, for

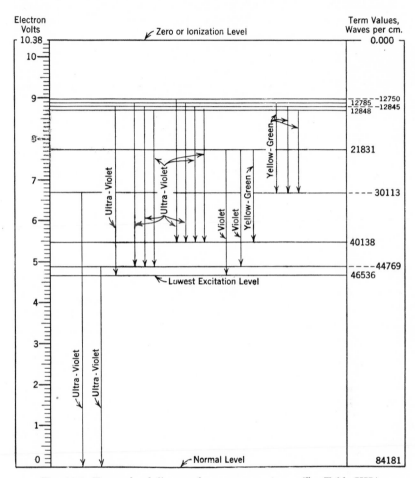

FIG. 13.6 Energy-level diagram for a mercury atom. (See Table XII.)

there are two active ($6s^2$) electrons outside a stable $2 + 8 + 18 + 32 + 18$ array.

The occurrence of singlets and triplets, typical of two-electron spectra, is well illustrated by the four $6s6p$ levels. The two active electrons have the l-values $s(= 0)$ and $p(= 1)$. Since 1 and 0 can add vectorially to give only a single positive result, $L = 1(= P)$. The total spin vector S may be either $\frac{1}{2} \oplus \frac{1}{2} = 1$ or $\frac{1}{2} \oplus \frac{1}{2} = 0$. Vector addition of the value 1 for S to the value 1 for L gives three possible values for J, corresponding to the following triplets:

$$J = 1 \oplus 1 = 0;$$

$^3P_0{}^\circ$ 46536   (13–29a)

$$J = 1 \oplus 1 = 1;$$

$^3P_1{}^\circ$ 44769   (13–29b)

$$J = 1 \oplus 1 = 2;$$

$^3P_2{}^\circ$ 40138   (13–29c)

If the value 0 for S is used, there can be just one J-value, corresponding to the following *singlet:*

$$J = 1 \oplus 0 = 1; \qquad J = L = 1 \qquad ^1P_1{}^\circ \quad 30113 \quad (13\text{–}30)$$

Sometimes a "triplet" level occurs alone. For example, the $6s7s$ configuration has for L the value zero, and has only two terms, one for each value of S, as follows:

$$J = 0 \oplus 0 = 0 \qquad {}^1S_0 \qquad \text{singlet system}$$
$$J = 0 \oplus 1 = 1 \qquad {}^3S_1 \qquad \text{triplet system} \qquad (13\text{–}31)$$

This latter term is symbolized as a triplet because unit spin vector can ordinarily add to the L-vector in three different ways. Thus in mercury most of the other levels for which the spin-vector is 1 occur in three's. This one occurs alone because zero added to unity can give only one vectorial result, by contrast with three vectorial integral results when added to any integral value of L other than zero.

13.28   Mercury Metastable States.   The levels 46536 $6s6p$ $^3P_0{}^\circ$ and 40138 $6s6p$ $^3P_2{}^\circ$ are of particular interest because no transitions can take place downward from them. Neither of these permits a shift to the normal level, for in one J would have to change from 0 to 0, which is forbidden, in the other from 2 to 0, likewise ruled out. There cannot be a shift from the $6s6p$ $^3P_2{}^\circ$ level to either of the two lower $6s6p$ levels (46536 and 44769) because there would be no change in l in such transitions.

Therefore a mercury atom that through accident of collision, or by transitions from higher levels, reaches either the 46536 or the 40138 state remains there until impact with another particle occurs. There can be no escape from these levels to the normal level by the release of radiant energy. Since the likely duration of these states is many thousands of times that of any of the other levels, they are called *metastable states*.[13B-44]

Atoms in metastable states have important effects in electric arcs and glow discharges. For example, mercury may be ionized in two steps, the first step creating a metastable state, the next causing a further shift up to the ionized level. An atom so ionized has received its 10.38 electron volts of energy in two successive steps, neither step requiring more than 6 volts.

An atom in a metastable state possesses energy that can be released by contact. For example, if a metastable atom whose energy is 4.65 volts comes into contact with a metal surface that has a 3-volt work function, there is a substantial likelihood that an electron will leave the surface. The electron may in fact be ejected with a kinetic energy equal to $4.65 - 3.0 = 1.65$ electron volts. The mercury atom returns to its normal state simultaneously with the electron ejection. Similarly a 5.43-volt metastable atom can ionize a sodium atom by accidental contact, for sodium's ionizing potential is only 5.12 volts. If two 5.43-volt metastable atoms collide, one may be ionized while the other returns to the normal state.

13.29 Negative Term Values. Most of mercury's energy levels represent situations in which only one electron has been shifted from the normal 6s condition. However, two $6p^2$ levels have been observed, although they occur only infrequently. It takes *more* energy, by about one electron volt, to produce either of these $6p^2$ levels than to produce ionization. They therefore lie above the zero level and are said to have *negative* term values, -7860 and -9798.

13.30 Light from Mercury Vapor and from Sodium Vapor; Fluorescence. As indicated in Fig. 13.6, the arc spectrum of mercury includes both violet and yellow-green transitions. The violet ones occur much oftener than the yellow-green ones. The violet light produced by a mercury-vapor arc is therefore usually so intense as to mask the yellow-green light, in spite of the latter's much greater relative lighting value per unit of energy (see Fig. 13.3). By using an enclosing tube made of amber glass that restricts the emergence of violet light but not of yellow-green light, a mercury discharge may be made to give green illumination.

The ultraviolet radiations from a mercury arc are effectively stopped by the walls of the enclosing tube, if the tube is made of glass. Quartz is transparent to ultraviolet radiation. It is the near ultraviolet radiation from a mercury arc that has therapeutic value, so that mercury-arc tubes employed for medical purposes are made of quartz. The 1850 angstrom radiation from mercury arcs is rather strong, and harmful physiologically. For this reason quartz mercury-vapor lamps should be used only as directed by a competent physician.

The transitions in the mercury spectrum that produce visible light originate rather high up in the mercury energy-level diagram, Fig. 13.6. For example, that from 21831 to 44769 (violet, 4360 Å, 2.85 volts) can occur only after at least a 7.74-volt excitation. Suppose that an atom in a mercury arc receives by electron impact 7.74 electron volts of energy, lifting it into the 21831 energy state. It may subsequently radiate visibly 2.85 electron volts of this during transition to the 44769 energy state. The energy remaining, 4.89 electron volts, is then radiated in the ultraviolet (2530 Å), giving "light" which is not useful from the standpoint of illumination. It may be said that the *luminous efficiency* of this cycle of operations from normal state to normal state again is $2.85/7.74 = 0.367$, or 36.7 per cent.

Mercury's metastable states add to the overall efficiency of a mercury arc as an illuminant, because many light-producing cycles may begin and end at metastable states. For example, suppose that a 3.07-volt electron impact lifts an atom from hesitation in the 46536 metastable state to the 21831 condition. The atom may then immediately return to the 46536 state for further hesitation, then repeat the experience. Each such cycle produces 3.07-volt (violet) light, and has 100 per cent luminous efficiency. Of course there is no assurance that the descent from the 21831 level will take place along the transition leading back to the level from which the cycle started. If the descent happens to follow the transition leading to the 44769 energy state, further nonluminous descent to the normal state immediately occurs. There can be no appreciable hesitation in the 44769 state, so that there is no chance for electron impact while there.

The more opportunities there are for high-efficiency luminous cycles in a discharge, the greater overall efficiency is possible. For this reason sodium vapor gives excellent efficiency as an illuminant.[15H,I,r] The light-producing cycle consisting of electrical elevation from sodium's normal level to the 24493 level or its twin, with immediate return, is 100 per cent efficient and terminates at the normal state. Thus sodium operates very efficiently to and from its normal state, but the most efficient processes in mercury (also in neon) require sufficient energy input to the discharge to favor high concentrations of metastable particles. Some practical difficulties have had to be overcome in using sodium-vapor light sources, because rather high operating temperatures are necessary to vaporize sodium and keep it vaporized. The yellow light from sodium does not provide pleasing general illumination, but it has been found occasionally useful for street lighting.

Very successful techniques have been developed for converting the line-spectrum type of light from mercury and other gases, used in gas discharges, into white light suitable for general illumination, by inter-action of the line-spectrum light with layers of fluorescent *phosphors* coated on discharge-tube walls. In this way common store and home fluorescent lights are made to produce essentially white light.[3K, L, 15H, I, J, r]

In conversion of light by fluorescence, individual photons are ab-sorbed by molecules of the phosphor (Section 3.5), and part of the energy so received is immediately reradiated. There is always some energy loss in the conversion, so that the energy per photon of the re-radiated light is less than that of the incident light. This explains why it is possible to scatter sodium yellow light into the orange and red parts of the visible spectrum, but not into the blue and green parts. Ultraviolet radiation from mercury can be converted into visible light by fluorescence, but infrared radiation cannot.

13.31 Neon. Table XIII contains the term values, and Fig. 13.7 an energy-level diagram, for the arc spectrum of neon.[13A-312] In order to avoid confusion, only the transitions that produce visible light are shown, except that two ultraviolet transitions terminating at the normal level are included. The features of special interest are as follows:

(*a*) There is so little adherence to Russell-Saunders coupling that the levels within each configuration are numbered consecutively, in-stead of being given coded letter symbols.

(*b*) Not more than one electron at a time ever moves out into the third shell, so that the $2p^5$ group is a part of all the configurations. The electron array $1s^2\,2s^2\,2p^5$, sometimes called the ion on which the levels are built, itself has a variety of energy states *similar to those in a one-electron spectrum*. This behavior illustrates the general principle that a subgroup lacking just one electron of completion behaves in general like a single electron. The angular momenta (magnetic quan-tum numbers m_l, Table X) of the electrons within any completed sub-group combine to give zero total angular momentum. The omission of the final electron from the group, therefore, leaves the resultant of the m_l's at just the value which that one would produce if it were alone in its subgroup. The energy levels of the $2p^5$ group in neon may thus be

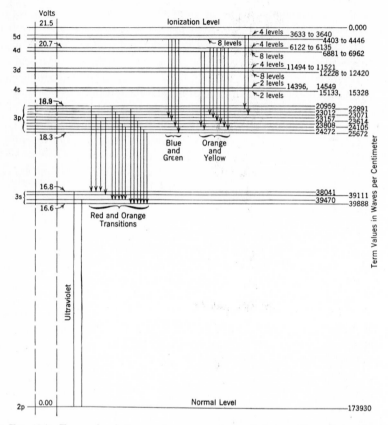

FIG. 13.7   Energy-level diagram for a neon atom.   Only transitions giving rise to visible light are shown, except for two terminating at the normal level.   Not to scale.   (See Table XIII.)

said to be those due to the ghost of the missing electron.   Such a one-electron set of levels consists of doublets (see Section 13.23); the important doublet of the $2p^5$ neon ion consists of the following:

$$1s^2 \quad 2s^2 \quad 2p^5 \; (^2P_{1\frac{1}{2}})$$
$$1s^2 \quad 2s^2 \quad 2p^5 \, (^2P_{\frac{1}{2}})$$

(13–32)

Thus in the 25671.65 $2p^5$ $(^2P_{1\frac{1}{2}})$ $3p$ 1_1 energy state of neon there is a $3p$ electron outside of a $^2P_{1\frac{1}{2}}$ ion, while in the 23157.34 $2p^5$ $(^2P_{\frac{1}{2}})$ $3p$ 7_1 state there is a $3p$ electron outside a $^2P_{\frac{1}{2}}$ ion.

(c) There is an older notation for the neon spectrum; the older notation is included in Table XIII because many references to the neon spectrum will be found in which the older notation is used.

(*d*) The transitions between the $3p$ and the $3s$ levels produce most of the red light that is characteristic of neon.

(*e*) There are the following two important metastable states:

$$39887.61 \quad 2p^5 \, (^2P_{1\frac{1}{2}}) \, 3s \, 1_2{}^\circ$$
$$39110.81 \quad 2p^5 \, (^2P_{\frac{1}{2}}) \, 3s \, 3_0{}^\circ \tag{13--33}$$

A shift to the normal level from the first of these would require J to change by 2, hence is forbidden. For the second, $J = 0$, as for the normal level, and transition between two $J = 0$ levels is forbidden. Therefore transitions cannot occur from either of these levels to the normal. Many of the red transitions terminate on one or another of these two metastable states.

(*f*) The lowest excited state (39887.61, metastable) is 16.6 volts above the normal. Most of the levels from which visible light originates are a few volts higher than this. It is apparent that individual luminous cycles from normal state to normal state are very inefficient. As in mercury, cycles beginning and ending at the metastable states are efficient light producers.

(*g*) Metastable neon atoms have such high energy content that they are able to ionize, by contact, atoms of many other gases which can be mixed with neon in a discharge tube. Examples of such gases are mercury, sodium, and argon.

(*h*) In a mixture that includes neon and some gas having low exciting and ionizing potentials, a low voltage gradient may introduce only enough electronic energy to excite and ionize the gas of lower ionizing energy. In that case the neon takes no part in the electrical discharge. At high voltage gradients in the same mixture the neon may become active. Luminous tubes that for the most part are blue, but have constricted portions that are red, make use of this behavior. The current must be the same at all points along the tube. Therefore the current density, and along with it the voltage gradient, must be greater in the constricted than in the other portions. This increased gradient results in excitation and ionization of neon, with resulting production of red color in the constricted parts.

13.32 Copper. The arc spectrum of copper is of interest partly because copper arcs occur frequently in engineering work, and partly because copper's quartet terms illustrate more complicated vector combinations of angular momenta than occur in either sodium or mercury. Table XIV contains some of the more important term values for CuI.

In the normal state of copper there is a lone fourth-shell electron outside a completed third shell; that is, there is a $2 + 8 + 18 + 1$

electron array. A one-electron spectrum might be expected. Actually the arc spectrum of copper results from two rather distinct sets of energy states. One set is built on a $3d^{10}$ ion, corresponding to the one-electron expectation. Examples of this are $3d^{10}\ 4s\ ^2S_{\frac{1}{2}}$ at 62308.00 (the normal level); $3d^{10}\ 4p\ ^2P_{\frac{1}{2}}{}^{\circ}$ and $^2P_{1\frac{1}{2}}{}^{\circ}$ at 31772.698 and 31524.314; $3d^{10}\ 5s\ ^2S_{\frac{1}{2}}$ at 19170.791.

The other set results from the activities of a $2 + 8 + 17 + 2$ array. It therefore consists of levels built on a $3d^9\ 4s$ ion. This set of levels produces what is essentially a three-electron spectrum, the three active electrons being the two in the fourth shell and the ghost of the one missing from the third-shell d group; see item (b), in the preceding section.

The terms built on the $3d^9\ 4s$ base provide an interesting illustration of the Russell-Saunders vector combination pattern for various angular momenta.[13B-108] For example, there are many energy states having the configuration $3d^9\ 4s\ 4p$. The three electrons that are active in this configuration have l-values of $d(= 2)$, $s(= 0)$, and $p(= 1)$. The vector sum can be

$$L = 2 \oplus 0 \oplus 1 = 1 \qquad\qquad (13\text{–}34a)$$

or

$$L = 2 \oplus 0 \oplus 1 = 2 \qquad\qquad (13\text{–}34b)$$

or

$$L = 2 \oplus 0 \oplus 1 = 3 \qquad\qquad (13\text{–}34c)$$

The spin vector S is the half-integral vector sum of the three individual spin values and has values as follows:

(a) If the first two of the three spin values add up to 1, S may be either $\frac{1}{2}$ or $1\frac{1}{2}$, thus

$$S = (\tfrac{1}{2} \oplus \tfrac{1}{2}) \oplus \tfrac{1}{2} = 1 \oplus \tfrac{1}{2} = \tfrac{1}{2} \quad \text{or} \quad 1\tfrac{1}{2} \qquad (13\text{–}35a)$$

(b) If the first two of the three add up to 0, S is $\frac{1}{2}$, thus:

$$S = (\tfrac{1}{2} \oplus \tfrac{1}{2}) \oplus \tfrac{1}{2} = 0 \oplus \tfrac{1}{2} = \tfrac{1}{2} \qquad (13\text{–}35b)$$

This shows that S may have the value $\frac{1}{2}$ in either of two different ways; the two different ways give rise to different term values.

The L and S vectors add in all possible ways, vectorially, subject to the limitation that the resultant J must be a half-number, since the spin vectors are both half-numbers. The various combinations are as follows:

When $L = 1$ and $S = \frac{1}{2}$:   (13–36a)

$$J = 1 \oplus \tfrac{1}{2} = 1\tfrac{1}{2}$$
or $$J = 1 \oplus \tfrac{1}{2} = \tfrac{1}{2}$$

Four $^2P°$ doublet terms:
if $S = 1 \oplus \frac{1}{2}$, at   if $S = 0 \oplus \frac{1}{2}$, at
16428.659   5964.26
16487.0   3943.27

When $L = 1$ and $S = 1\frac{1}{2}$:   (13–36b)

$$J = 1 \oplus 1\tfrac{1}{2} = 2\tfrac{1}{2}$$
or $$J = 1 \oplus 1\tfrac{1}{2} = 1\tfrac{1}{2}$$
or $$J = 1 \oplus 1\tfrac{1}{2} = \tfrac{1}{2}$$

Three $^4P°$ quartet terms:
23289.348
22194.01
21364.27

When $L = 2$ and $S = \frac{1}{2}$:   (13–36c)

$$J = 2 \oplus \tfrac{1}{2} = 2\tfrac{1}{2}$$
or $$J = 2 \oplus \tfrac{1}{2} = 1\tfrac{1}{2}$$

Four $^2D°$ doublet terms:
if $S = 1 \oplus \frac{1}{2}$, at   if $S = 0 \oplus \frac{1}{2}$, at
16135.158   5656.52
15709.66   3617.14

When $L = 2$ and $S = 1\frac{1}{2}$:   (13–36d)

$$J = 2 \oplus 1\tfrac{1}{2} = 3\tfrac{1}{2}$$
or $$J = 2 \oplus 1\tfrac{1}{2} = 2\tfrac{1}{2}$$
or $$J = 2 \oplus 1\tfrac{1}{2} = 1\tfrac{1}{2}$$
or $$J = 2 \oplus 1\tfrac{1}{2} = \tfrac{1}{2}$$

Four $^4D°$ quartet terms:
18794.05
17901.732
17763.847
17392.39

and so on. There are altogether, according to this combination system, the following terms for the $3d^9\,4s\,4p$ configuration:

Two pairs of P doublet terms:	16487 16429	and	5964 3943
Two pairs of D doublet terms:	16135 15710		5656 3617
Two pairs of F doublet terms:	18582 17345		6278 4189

(13–37)

Three P quartet terms: 23289, 22194, 21364.

Four D quartet terms: 18794, 17901, 17764, 17392.

Four F quartet terms: 21398, 21155, 20745, 20005.

The ionizing potential of copper, 7.68 volts, corresponds to the highest level of the *one-electron* set of levels. The zero level is therefore 7.68 volts above the normal level. However, it requires more than 7.68 electron volts to excite a copper atom to many of the levels in the three-electron set, so that many of copper's term values are negative. None of the negative ones are listed in Table XIV. If a copper atom receives between 7.68 and about 9 electron volts of energy, it may be ionized, or it may be lifted to one of the negative levels without ionization.

PROBLEMS

1. The term values for three of the energy levels for an argon atom are: 23009; 33968 (a metastable level); 127104 (the normal level).

(*a*) Calculate the ionizing potential of argon. (*b*) What is the wavelength, in angstrom units, of radiation resulting from a transition from the 23009 level to the 33968 level? In what part of the spectrum does this lie? (*c*) How much energy, in electron volts, may a metastable argon atom in the 33968 level release at a collision?

2. Suppose the important "term values" in the energy-level diagram for an atom are: 115240 (normal state), 42080 (lowest excited state), 39875, 39100, 31250, 20040, 12330, 0 (ionized state).

(*a*) Find the ionizing potential and the lowest excitation potential.

(*b*) Find the wavelength in angstrom units of the light produced by a transition from the 12330 level to the 31250 level.

(*c*) An atom of this substance experiences a transition of the (*b*) type, as the aftermath of being hit by an electron. What is the least energy that the hitting electron must possess to have this effect?

(*d*) If the hitting electron actually possessed an energy of 37 electron volts before the collision, what was its velocity after the collision? (Assume that the atom neither gains nor loses kinetic energy of motion as a whole during the collision.)

(*e*) In a plasma in a gas made up of atoms of this substance the electron temperature is 14,800° K (see Chapter XV). The electrons collide with atoms. Assume that the ratio of the number of collisions involving an electron whose energy is E or more electron volts to the total number of collisions is the factor $\exp(-E/E_{Te})$. If there are 10^{12} collisions per microsecond involving electrons with ionizing energy, how many will there be involving electrons able to produce excitation of some sort?

3. Suppose that an atom of neon in the higher of neon's two metastable states collides with a normal-state atom of argon, and that as a result of the collision the neon atom returns to the normal state and the argon atom is ionized. If the surplus energy all appears as kinetic energy of the electron ejected from the argon atom, what is its velocity?

4. An electron whose kinetic energy is 25 electron volts strikes and ionizes a normal-state mercury atom. If the velocity of the atom is not changed by the collision, with what velocity will the electron proceed after the collision?

5. In a region containing a mixture of neon and mercury, a neon ion collides with a mercury atom, with the result that the mercury atom is ionized, and the neon atom returns to the normal state. How much kinetic energy is released?

6. The wavelength of the characteristic red line used as a chemical test for the presence of cadmium is 6438 Å. If a particular source emits this red light to the extent of 6×10^{-8} watt, how many photons are radiated per microsecond?

7. A mercury atom in the lower metastable state strikes a surface whose work function is 2.0 volts, and as a result an electron is ejected from the surface. If after striking the surface the mercury atom has a kinetic energy of one electron volt, find (a) the maximum velocity that the ejected electron can have, and (b) the velocity of the mercury atom after striking the surface.

8. A metastable mercury atom, energy 4.65 electron volts, strikes a diatomic molecule. As a result the molecule is dissociated into two atoms, the mercury atom returns to the normal state, and the three resultant particles depart from the encounter with a total energy, divided unequally among them, of 3 electron volts. What is the energy of dissociation of the diatomic molecule?

9. Referring to Fig. 13.6, consider an atom in the 12848 energy state. This atom can, according to the figure, spontaneously shift out of that state in any one of at least three different ways. Describe its subsequent history for each of the three ways, with particular attention to the end condition.

10. What must be the temperature of sodium vapor to just permit a collision between a stationary atom, and one having 15 times the average energy, to result in the production of yellow light caused by transitions from the lowest excited state to the normal state? How large a percentage of the atoms have 15 times the average energy?

11. Calculate from theoretical considerations, of the Section 13.10 type, the energy in electron volts required to remove the second of helium's electrons, also that required to remove the third of lithium's electrons.

12. What is the "effective nuclear charge" for the orbit pursued by the outermost electron, in a sodium atom in the lowest excited state? In a sodium atom in the 8248 state?

13. Determine theoretically the least excitation potential of a hydrogen atom, employing the fact that the ionizing potential is 13.53 volts.

14. Refer to Fig. 13.7. An electron with kinetic energy of 6 electron volts strikes a neon atom in the metastable 39888 level. As a result the neon atom is lifted to the 6122 level (it is *not* ionized), and cascades back to the normal state in three transitions, hesitating at 23071 and 39470. (a) With what velocity does the electron continue on after the collision? (The atom's velocity is unchanged.) (b) What are the wavelengths and "colors" of the three photons emitted? (c) What is the efficiency of conversion of energy into visible light for this event, *relative to the maximum possible efficiency obtainable* if all light affected the eye as strongly as 5600 angstrom light does? (Thus your answer takes into account a physiological factor.)

15. Refer to the energy-level diagram for mercury, Fig. 13.6, in connection with a mercury-vapor fluorescent light. An electron possessing 7.3 electron volts of kinetic energy strikes a normal-state mercury atom and causes the atom to be excited into the 44769 state. A photon is radiated as a result of the transition from 44769 to the normal state. This photon strikes the fluorescent "phosphor" on the interior wall of the tube, causing emission (from a phosphor atom) of a photon of wavelength 4800 Å, the energy not required for this purpose appearing as heat in the phosphor.

(a) What is the ratio of *useful* light energy produced to original energy of the electron? (b) If 6×10^{18} such occurrences take place per second, how many watts of heat power do they cause to appear in the phosphor? (c) If the light from the phosphor had been 5400 Å, would the light appear to the eye more or less brilliant? (d) At 5400 Å would the answer to (a) be greater or less than at 4800 Å?

16. (a) What are the wavelengths of the radiations produced by the two mercury transitions (Fig. 13.6) that terminate at the normal level? (b) State the wavelength of a prominent violet line in the arc spectrum of mercury. (c) Explain by reference to Table XII how the selection rules indicate that the (b) transition is a permitted one. (d) How much energy must be given to a mercury atom in the normal state to put it into condition to radiate this kind of light?

17. (a) Using color boundaries as in Fig. 13.3, and neon term values as stated in Table XIII and Fig. 13.7, select a pair of neon levels between which a transition producing red light is permitted, the lower level of the pair being metastable. Identify the selected levels by stating their term values. (b) State the wavelength of the transition between the selected levels. (c) How much energy must be given to a neon atom in the normal state to put it into condition to make this transition?

18. The term values of the important energy levels for copper are given in Table XIV.

(a) Draw to scale an energy-level diagram for copper (use single lines to represent groups of close levels). Label clearly the zero level, the normal level, and the level that corresponds to the lowest excited state. Show permitted transitions in the usual way; in order to determine which transitions are permitted, use the selection rules stated in Section 13.25. (b) Is the lowest excited state metastable? (c) Select a pair of levels between which a green light transition is permitted. State the wavelength of the selected transition.

CHAPTER XIV

PHOTOSENSITIVE DEVICES

14.1 Photoelectric Emission. As stated in Section 13.5, radiant energy is transferred to electrons or atoms in discrete energy units of magnitude hf joules, where f is the radiation's frequency in cycles per second, and h the ultimate unit of action. The light-quantum (photon) energy in electron volts, symbol E_{ph}, is defined by the relation

$$E_{ph}q_e = hf \qquad (14\text{--}1)$$

Here q_e is, as usual, the electronic charge. If radiation of E_{ph} electron volts per photon strikes a surface whose work function E_W is less than E_{ph}, some of the electrons within the metal will be ejected out of it. Each one that emerges does so because it acquires from a photon the kinetic energy necessary to carry it past the work-function barrier at the surface (Fig. 8.2). This behavior is called photoelectric emission of electrons. In photoelectric devices the electrons are emitted into regions that are either entirely free from gas (vacuum phototubes) or contain an inert gas at a low pressure (gas phototubes).

14.2 Summary of Photoelectric Emission Phenomena. * The following important generalizations can be made regarding the photoelectric emission of electrons from metal surfaces:

(a) Emission cannot occur unless

$$E_{ph} \geqq E_W \qquad (14\text{--}2)$$

This limitation exists because each electron's ejection results from the action of a single photon; there is no cumulative effect. The reasonableness of (14–2) is apparent from Fig. 8.2. The highest-energy (Fermi-level) electrons lack E_W electron volts of having enough kinetic energy to escape beyond the metal boundary. As an individual electron can receive only E_{ph} electron volts of energy from the entering light, it is evident that no electron can be ejected by light for which $E_{ph} < E_W$. Equation (14–2) expresses this limitation, which gives rise to the concepts "threshold frequency" and "threshold wavelength" for

---

* See bibliography references 1J, K, 14D, E, F, G, H, a, b, c.

a surface. These quantities are the values of frequency and wavelength that correspond to the condition $E_{ph} = E_W$. Thus

At the threshold frequency: $\qquad hf = E_W q_e \qquad (14\text{–}3)$

Emission occurs only for values of E_{ph} and of frequency at or above the threshold, therefore only for wavelengths at or below threshold values. As E_{ph} is between 1.75 and 3.0 volts for visible light (see Fig. 13.3), a photoelectric surface must have a work function within or below this range to be sensitive to visible light.

(b) When the energy per photon of the incident light is somewhat greater than the work function, i.e., greater than the threshold value,

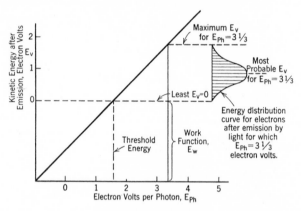

Fig. 14.1 Kinetic energies of photoelectrically emitted electrons.

electrons can escape at a substantial rate. A very few of the electrons within the metal (1) possess the Fermi-level energy before accepting the photon's energy, (2) are close to the boundary and so lose no energy by internal encounters prior to emergence, and (3) after accepting the photon's energy have a direction of motion perpendicular to the boundary. For these few electrons the kinetic energy E_v after escape is just $E_{ph} - E_W$. This is the maximum energy of emergence. Most of the escaping electrons have less than this energy, for they (1) have initially less than Fermi-level kinetic energy, (2) lose energy due to internal encounters, and (3) approach the surface from the interior at some angle less than 90°. In general, then,[14a, b, c]

$$E_v \leqq E_{ph} - E_W \qquad (14\text{–}4)$$

Figure 14.1 illustrates this relation. Another form of it is

$$\tfrac{1}{2} m_e v^2 \leqq hf - E_W q_e \qquad (14\text{–}5)$$

(c) The energy distribution (not velocity distribution) of the emitted electrons is approximately symmetrical about the median between zero and the maximum possible value, as indicated at the upper right of Fig. 14.1.

(d) The intensity of the incoming light (watts per unit area) has no effect whatever on the maximum electron energy after escape, or on the energy distribution among the escaping electrons; these quantities are controlled entirely by the light frequency, as described under (b) and (c).

(e) The number of electrons ejected per second is directly proportional to the intensity of the incident light, provided the wavelength, angle of incidence, and polarization of the light remain unchanged.

(f) The response or sensitivity of a photoelectric tube as a whole, or of unit area of a sensitive surface, may be expressed variously by stating:

(1) The *quantum yield*, also called the *quantum efficiency*, as a fraction, or a percentage. When expressed in per cent, it is the number of electrons emitted per hundred incident photons. The quantum efficiency is usually not more than a few per cent.

(2) The *photoelectric yield*, in amperes per watt of light energy input; this is the same as coulombs emitted per watt-second of light energy. Photoelectric yield and quantum yield are related as follows:

$$\text{Amperes per watt} = \frac{\text{Quantum yield}}{E_{ph}} \qquad (14\text{--}6)$$

(3) The amperes (or microamperes) per lumen; the basis of reference is the visual response to the light rather than its intensity in watts per square meter.[14A]

(g) The magnitude of the response to light, whatever the manner of its description, is extremely sensitive to details of surface preparation. Composite surfaces consisting of a few successive thin layers, sometimes monomolecular, of selected substances, can be made to have very high photoelectric sensitivities.

(h) As the light frequency rises above the threshold value, the sensitivity at first increases rather rapidly. This is due to the following obvious facts: as E_{ph} increases, (1) electrons initially below the Fermi level can be emitted, thus increasing the population available; (2) electrons initially in the Fermi level can lose energy internally after accepting a photon, yet be able to emerge; and (3) electrons with the maximum internal energy $E_{ph} + E_W$ can arrive at the boundary a little slantwise, yet be able to escape; compare with the (a) comments. In general, for a clean metal surface, the increase in sensitivity is believed to continue indefinitely, but at a decreasing rate, as suggested by the dotted curve in Fig. 14.2. However, in corresponding curves for specially prepared phototube surfaces, pronounced humps appear just above the threshold, as in the solid-line curve of Fig. 14.2.

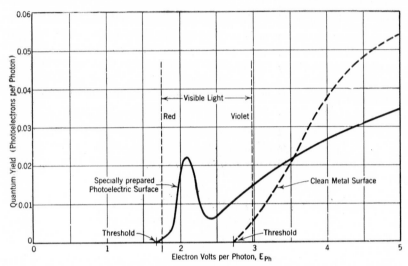

Fig. 14.2 Illustrative color-sensitivity curves for photoelectric surfaces. The crest just above threshold energy in the solid-line curve illustrates the "selective photoelectric effect." Note that the light-filtering effect of the glass envelope may cause the quantum yield for a phototube as a whole to decline at high photon energies, although the yield from the surface itself continues to increase, as shown here.

(i) If there is any time lag between initial light incidence and electron ejection, it is less than 10^{-8} second.

(j) Light can cause the transfer of electrons from one material directly into another against a retarding potential-energy barrier, such as the contact difference of potential between metals. Light affects the various "rectifier" photocells in this way.

(k) In a semiconductor (Section 8.12) light photons may increase the conductivity by giving energy to electrons in filled levels or in donor impurity levels, thereby lifting these electrons either into running levels or into acceptor impurity levels, thus producing mobile electrons and mobile holes.

(l) Photoelectric emission is not materially changed by variations in temperature, unless such variations are so extreme as to modify the structure of the emitting surface. The minor effects that pronounced temperature changes do have are quantitatively in accord with the properties of the electron gas within a metal, which acquires an energy distribution as indicated by Fig. 8.4b as the temperature increases.

14.3   Geometric and Physical Optics.[14A, B, C]   The underlying principles of photoelectric behavior as just outlined are simple to state and use, and the circuits immediately associated with photosensitive devices are for the most part equally simple. However, most engineering applications of photosensitive devices require very careful attention to *optical* problems. In the field of such engineering applications there have been more outstanding successes, and more failures, as a result of thorough analysis, or otherwise, of the optical problems, than because of matters relating to the electrical components or circuits.

It is therefore very strongly urged that anyone engaging in the study or engineering use of photosensitive devices acquire a good working mastery of the principles of *geometric optics* [14B] and at least a familiarity with the concepts of *physical optics*.[14B, C]   Geometric optics deals with optical focusing systems, employing mirrors, lenses, prisms, etc.; physical optics deals more with the properties of components of such systems and includes attention to refraction, polarization, diffraction and diffraction gratings, the origin of rainbows, and, in general, matters closely related to the wave nature of light.

14.4   Color Sensitivity; Selective Photoelectric Emission.[14D, E, F, a, b, c, d, e]   The dotted curve in Fig. 14.2 is typical of quantum yield curves for clean metal surfaces. For specially treated surfaces employed in commercial phototubes, the solid-line curve is fairly typical, in that it rises to and falls sharply away from a maximum at a photon energy between 25 and 75 per cent above the threshold.[14D, E]   Surfaces exhibiting one or more of these maxima are said to have a "selective photoelectric effect."

Color sensitivity or quantum yield curves for complete phototubes may be very different from those for the photoelectric surfaces within the tubes, because the glass walls are more transparent to some wavelengths than to others. Glass is opaque to ultraviolet light, so that the color sensitivity curves of glass envelope tubes decline as E_{ph} rises above the visible range, instead of rising more or less continually as do the curves for the surfaces themselves.

Many different, rather complex manufacturing formulas are used for preparing special surfaces for commercial phototubes, for example, the cesium layer on a mixed cesium oxide and silver oxide surface.[14e]

The location of the threshold and the location and prominence of the crest, or crests, are extremely sensitive to the details of surface preparation. It is almost impossible to keep manufacturing processes sufficiently uniform to meet anything approaching close tolerances as to reproducibility of characteristics from tube to tube. The locations and prominence of the crests are considerably affected by changes in light polarization, if the light strikes the surface at an angle that is less than 90°.

Theoretical developments based on the energy distribution of Fig. 8.4b, obeying the Fermi distribution equation (8–20a), have led to very satisfactory explanations of the shapes of clean-metal quantum yield curves just above their threshold, even in regard to the rather minor effects of temperature changes.[14d] However, no very convincing or complete theoretical explanations have yet been advanced for the shapes of the various experimentally obtained quantum yield curves for ·composite surfaces; see Chapter IV in *Fundamentals of Physical Electronics* for comments.

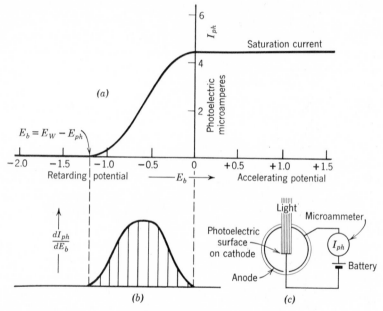

(a) Directly observed integrated distribution curve. Light is of constant intensity, energy per photon E_{ph} electron volts.

(b) Distribution curve.

(c) Phototube and circuit.

FIG. 14.3 Energy distribution among photoelectrons, central cathode vacuum phototube. Potentials *electrostatically* measured.

14.5 Volt-Ampere Response of a Vacuum Phototube in Which the Electron Receiver Surrounds the Emitter.[14D, E, F] Figure 14.3c illustrates a geometrical arrangement in which nearly all emitted electrons *must* travel toward the opposite electrode, regardless of the directions of their initial velocities, because the electron-receiving anode quite

completely surrounds the electron-emitting cathode. Such a device is called a *central cathode* phototube.

Figure 14.3a illustrates the kind of volt-ampere curve to be expected (for monochromatic light) with this geometry when the interelectrode region is completely evacuated, as in a vacuum phototube. Note that potentials are *electrostatically* measured. (As explained later in Section 14.7, contact differences of potential must be taken into account in preparing a curve like that in Fig. 14.3a from experimental data.) Note that, if there is zero potential difference between the electrodes, all emitted electrons reach the receiving surface; hence no increase in current results from making the receiving surface positive. A tube of this type is said to "saturate" at zero voltage. The current indicated for negative voltages flows because of the initial electron energies.

14.6 Energies of Photoelectrically Emitted Electrons. The electrons ejected from a surface photoelectrically all acquire E_{ph} electron volts of energy from the incoming light. However, they start from various energy levels, lose various amounts of energy on the way out, and approach the surface internally at a variety of angles. Therefore the energies of the escaping electrons are distributed between zero and the maximum $E_{ph} - E_W$ as illustrated at the upper right of Fig. 14.1.[1J, 14D, E, F, a, b, c] The negative portion of the Fig. 14.3a volt-ampere curve is an integrated distribution curve for the photoelectron energies, and Fig. 14.3b is the corresponding distribution curve.[14a] If the receiving electrode is negative by more than $E_{ph} - E_W$ volts, no electrons can reach it. The fastest electrons barely reach it if the potential difference is just $E_{ph} - E_W$. At each potential between this negative extreme and zero, the observed current measures the number of electrons whose initial energies exceed the energy described by that potential, thus providing the integrated distribution curve information.

Available evidence indicates that the directions of the initial velocities are symmetrically distributed about a normal to the surface, regardless of the angle of incidence of the light, or of its polarization.[14D, b] If the incident light is polarized and makes an angle less than 90° with the surface, there will be a component of the light wave's electric vector perpendicular to the surface. It appears that the presence of this component favors a relative increase of the initial velocity component normal to the surface. See also Chapter IV in *Fundamentals of Physical Electronics*.

14.7 Effects of Contact Difference of Potential in a Phototube.[14a] Contact difference of potential between electrode materials (Sections 8.24 and 8.25) must be taken into account in interpreting measurements of small potential differences between phototube electrodes, if such measurements are made by ordinary electromagnetic (D'Arsonval) meters. The order of magnitude of contact differences of potential is the same as that of the energies of the emitted photoelectrons; the field produced by it is just as real as that due to a battery, but meters depending on current flow do not register its effects. The potential scale in Fig. 14.3a corresponds to electrostatic potential measurements, which do register the effects of contact difference of potential.

Suppose that in the Fig. 14.3c circuit the work functions of the emitting and receiving surfaces are 1.8 and 4.0 volts respectively. The anode's receiving surface is then 4.0 − 1.8 = 2.2 volts below the emitter's potential when the battery voltage is zero. If violet (3.0-volt) light strikes the emitting surface, the fastest ejected electrons have 3.0 − 1.8 = 1.2 electron volts of kinetic energy. This is not enough to carry them to the opposite electrode against the 2.2-volt field established by the contact difference of potential, so that the current is zero when the battery voltage is zero. Current will then first appear when an increasing battery potential reaches 1.0 volt. An electrostatic voltmeter across the tube then registers a negative 1.2-volt potential (2.2 − 1.0 = 1.2) which the fastest ejected electrons can just overcome. Saturation occurs when the battery potential is 2.2 volts, just enough to compensate for the 2.2-volt contact difference of potential between cathode and anode. Thus under these illustrative conditions cut-off and saturation occur at electrostatically measured potential differences of −1.2 and 0.0 volts respectively, as illustrated in Fig. 14.3a.

14.8 Volt-Ampere Response of a Vacuum-Type Phototube in Which the Emitter Surrounds the Receiver.[14D, E, F] Phototubes are usually built with a small electron-receiving electrode located at a little distance from a large-area cathode, which may in an extreme case nearly surround the anode, as in Fig. 14.4b. This *central anode* arrangement permits the effective use of a large photoelectrically active surface.

In a central anode vacuum-type tube, saturation occurs as before, but at a much higher voltage, as illustrated in Fig. 14.4a. At zero potential difference (electrostatically measured) only a very few electrons reach the receiver. Although at this potential condition many electrons are emitted and there is no energy barrier to obstruct their approach to the central receiver, very few happen to be aimed directly at the receiver. Most of them strike and re-enter the emitter. With sufficiently sensitive meters it is possible to measure currents down to a cut-off at $E_W - E_{ph}$ volts, as with a central cathode tube.

When the anode is made positive, in a central anode tube, there is a definite field drawing electrons toward the center. If this field is strong enough, all electrons reach the anode, producing saturation. At voltages above the zero-field value but below saturation many electrons are deflected toward the central anode but acquire sufficient kinetic energy to carry them orbitally around it and into the emitter again.

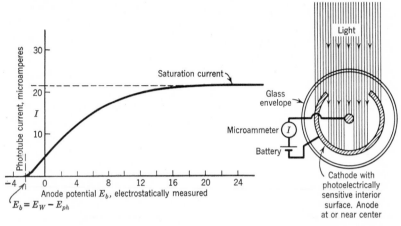

(a) Volt-ampere curve at constant light intensity, energy per photon E_{ph} electron volts.

(b) Phototube and circuit.

Fig. 14.4   Central anode vacuum-type phototube with cylindrical cathode.

14.9 Photomultiplier Tubes.[14f]   A photomultiplier tube employs photoelectric emission, secondary emission, and rather complex electron ballistics to provide extreme sensitivity to very small changes in light intensity.   As illustrated in Fig. 14.5, such a device contains a photoelectric cathode, several *dynodes* (secondary emitting anodes; see Section 6.7), and an anode.   The first dynode might be at 75 volts, the second at 150 volts, etc., relative to the cathode, in a high-vacuum envelope.   The signal input illuminates the photoelectric cathode; the photoelectrons strike the first dynode, producing substantial secondary emission therefrom.   The second dynode is placed so as to cause a gradient *at the first dynode* accelerating the secondary electrons *toward the second dynode*.   This process is repeated for perhaps ten dynodes. At each dynode the secondary emission ratio might be perhaps 2 to 3.[6d] Suppose that the secondary emission ratio is 3, for each of ten dynodes. Then any change in initial photoelectric current is amplified by a factor $3^{10} = 520{,}000$; this order of magnitude of amplification can be attained in commercial photomultipliers.

The secondary emission ratio of the dynodes will not in general be precisely constant,[6d, e, 14f] either from tube to tube or from time to

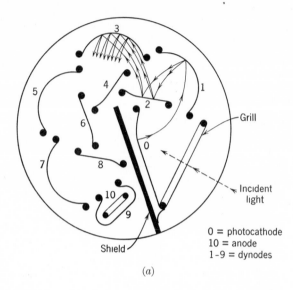

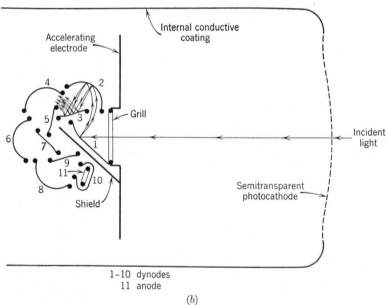

FIG. 14.5 Illustrative schematic arrangements of electrodes in photomultiplier tubes. (Reproduced by permission of the Radio Corporation of America.) (a) The 931-A tube. (b) The 5819 tube employing a large-area semitransparent photocathode.

time in a given tube. When a photomultiplier tube is cut into a circuit after being idle for several hours, the amplification may decline substantially, at first rapidly, then more slowly. Minutes may be required to reach stability under given conditions of voltage and average illumination. Yet this does not imply a large change in the secondary emission ratio, for if in a 10-dynode tube the secondary emission ratio declines by 10 per cent, the amplification will decline to $(0.9)^{10} = \frac{1}{3}$ of its former value. Thus extremely close tolerances must be held on the secondary emission ratio to maintain even modest reproducibility and stability in use.

The electron ballistics of photomultiplier design represent very interesting illustrations of step-by-step trajectory determinations, described relative to Figs. 2.7 and 2.8.

14.10 Use of Gas To Amplify Photoelectric Currents.[14E, F]   The electron emission from photoelectric surfaces is small, being measured in microamperes even in phototubes exposing considerable sensitive area to light. By introducing an inert gas at a low pressure the photoelectric current may be amplified without seriously modifying the response to light. At the same time the volt-ampere characteristic is changed in a way beneficial for circuit use. The gas must be inert (chemically inactive) to avoid deleterious chemical effects on the photoelectric surface. It must also not be readily absorbed by the metallic parts of the tube. Argon, neon, and helium have been used.

The amplification is a result of the production of ions at a rate proportional to the photoelectric emission current. The amount of gas amplification (rarely more than ten to one) is dependent on the gas pressure in the tube, the requirements for excitation and ionization of the gas, the applied potential, and the interelectrode geometry.

Figure 14.6a represents a phototube in which the cathode and the anode are parallel planes. The light ejects electrons from the cathode photoelectrically to the extent of J_{ph} amperes per unit area. J_{ph} is proportional to the light intensity, dependent on the wavelength of the incoming light, and entirely independent of the anode potential. For simplicity of analysis, end effects will be neglected.

The type of volt-ampere curve to be expected with this geometry is illustrated in Fig. 14.6b. Whether the tube is evacuated or gas-filled, the current reaches the value I_{ph}, corresponding to current density J_{ph}, at about zero volts, as in Fig. 14.3. All emitted electrons then reach the anode. If there is no gas in the tube, the current remains constant at this value for all positive anode voltages.

If inert gas is present at a pressure of a few millimeters of mercury, the volt-ampere curve is the same as without gas until the anode voltage rises above the ionizing potential of the gas. The increase in current above I_{ph} after the ionizing potential is passed is due to an ion-and-electron current in the gas that is proportional to I_{ph}. Because the additional current is proportional to the photoelectric emission current, ordinates of the volt-ampere curve increase in proportion to any increase in light intensity. This proportionality exists only as long as the illumination is not excessive.

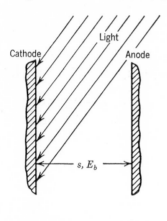

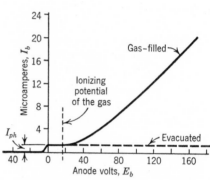

(a) Geometrical arrangement.

(b) Volt-ampere curves, monochromatic light of constant intensity.

FIG. 14.6 Effect of inert gas in a phototube with parallel plane electrodes.

Thus the gas amplifies the photoelectric current, the amplification ratio being I_b/I_{ph}. The amplification increases with rising anode voltage, as indicated by the solid volt-ampere curve in Fig. 14.6b.

14.11 Mechanism of Gas Amplification; Elastic and Inelastic Collisions. [1J, K, 12C, 15A, B, C, D, E, F, G, a] If in Fig. 14.6a the anode-to-cathode voltage is E_b and the anode distance is s, the electric field F in the intermediate region is

$$F = -\frac{E_b}{s} \qquad \text{[volts per meter]} \qquad (14\text{--}7)$$

An electron photoelectrically ejected from the cathode is accelerated by this field. Acceleration continues unchecked until collision with a gas particle takes place. Many collisions occur before the anode is reached.

A collision may be *elastic*, like that between billiard balls; then the total kinetic energy and the x, y, z momentum components are differently divided between the particles after collision but have the same combined value as before. Or a collision may be *inelastic;* then it results in excitation or ionization of the atom, with consequent absorption of energy, so that the total kinetic energy and combined momentum components are not conserved.

Suppose that the gas is argon, ionizing potential 15.7 volts, lowest excitation potential 11.5 volts, atomic weight 39.9, mass ratio m_g/m_e = 1822 × 39.9 = 72,800. Photoelectric devices ordinarily operate at room temperature, that is, in the neighborhood of 300° K. This is low enough so that for most purposes the thermal motions of the gas atoms may be neglected.

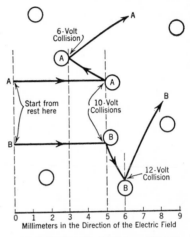

Consider a collision between one of the argon atoms and an electron that has acquired 10 electron volts of energy from the field. Because this is not enough energy either to excite or ionize the argon atom, the collision must be an *elastic one.* Then, although the electron may rebound with greatly changed *direction* of motion, it loses very little energy. As Loeb points out, the result is like that of throwing a tennis ball at a boat; not very much energy is imparted to the boat, because its mass is so large relative to that of the ball; see Chapter VII in *Fundamentals of Physical Electronics.*

FIG. 14.7   Typical electron trajectories *AAAA* and *BBBB.* The circles represent gas particles.

Because an electron on the average transfers only a very small fraction of its energy to an atom during an elastic collision, a 10-volt electron is still a 10-volt electron after making an elastic collision. As long as the collisions are elastic, and the kinetic energy given to the atoms is negligible, *an electron's energy change depends only on its progress in the direction of the field.*

Suppose, for example, that the anode potential and spacing are 100 volts and 5 centimeters respectively, making the potential gradient 2 volts per millimeter, as in Fig. 14.7. If, as in trajectory *AAAA* in that figure, the encounter just after a 10-volt collision happens to be on the rebound, 2 millimeters behind the 10-volt collision, the electron strikes with only 6 volts of energy and must make another elastic collision. The *BBBB* trajectory illustrates a rebound that advances the electron in the direction of the field. The electron enters the second *BBBB* collision with 12 volts of energy, for it has advanced 1 millimeter in the direction of the field since the first collision.

This second *BBBB* collision may or may not be an elastic one. The electron enters it with enough energy to cause excitation, for the least excitation energy of argon is 11.5 electron volts. If excitation does occur, the electron emerges from the collision with only 0.5 volt of energy and begins a new sequence of elastic collisions, during which it again builds up to excitation or higher energy.

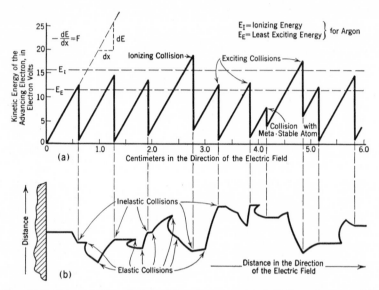

FIG. 14.8 Advance of an electron driven by an electric field through argon at low pressure. (*a*) Energy variations. (*b*) Path of the electron's motion.

But excitation may not occur at the second *BBBB* collision. When the electron's energy exceeds the excitation energy, there is a definite *probability of excitation;* perhaps between 3 and 30 per cent of the 12-volt collisions result in excitation. If excitation does not occur, the collision is an elastic one; the electron travels on, still with its 12 volts of energy. It advances, acquiring more energy, until an inelastic collision does occur.

If the first inelastic collision occurs after the electron's energy has exceeded the ionizing potential, there is a definite probability, but not a certainty, that ionization will occur; see Chapter VII in *Fundamentals of Physical Electronics.*

Thus, as an electron travels toward the anode, its energy builds up, drops off, builds up, drops off, in the manner illustrated by Fig. 14.8*a*.

Each slant line represents the building-up process and may include many free paths, as shown in Fig. 14.8b. The inelastic collisions result in vertical drops in the energy line; the elastic collisions have no effect on the shape of this line, for they do not affect the electron's energy. Ordinarily the peaks in the sawtooth line must lie above the dotted excitation-energy line at 11.5 volts. Very rarely a peak like that at about 4.2 centimeters may occur, as a result of a collision with a metastable atom which can accept less than 11.5 electron volts of energy. Ionization is represented on the sawtooth diagram by a vertical drop of 15.6 volts.

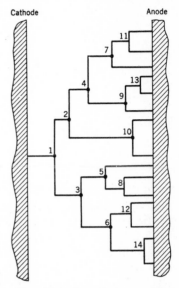

Amplification of the initial photoelectric current results from the fact that each ionizing collision results in the production of a new electron as well as an ion. The new electron pursues its own journey to the anode, exciting and ionizing atoms as it goes. Each electron so produced makes more electrons. The more electrons there are, the faster the electron stream grows. Figure 14.9 illustrates how the ionizing collisions make each original photoelectron become the parent of an extensive genealogical tree. In that figure, 14 ionizing collisions are represented, so that 15 electrons enter the

FIG. 14.9 One electron emitted from the cathode; 14 ionizing collisions; 15 electrons enter the anode.

anode as a result of one's leaving the cathode. If this represented the average behavior in a particular device, the actual tube current would be 15 times the photoelectric emission current.

The large mass and size of the ions produced by electron impact make their drift toward the cathode occur slowly, even when accelerated through substantial fields. Experiments have shown that ions are very unlikely to make either exciting or ionizing collisions with atoms or molecules.

14.12 Dependence of Amplification on Electrode Spacing and on Ionization Rate; "Townsend" Current.[14g, 15A, B, C, D, E, F, G] The amplification obtained by the use of gas in a phototube depends chiefly on: (a) the spacing between the electrodes, and (b) a coefficient symbolized as α ("Townsend's alpha") which stands for *the number of ionizing collisions per unit distance of an electron's advance.* Each such collision produces a new electron. α depends on the gas concentration, on the exciting and ionizing potentials and probabilities for the gas used, and on the ratio of field strength to gas concentration.

Suppose that L electrons per unit area per second cross a plane distant x from the cathode of Fig. 14.6a, moving toward the anode. In going a differential distance dx, each one of them produces $\alpha\,dx$ ions, and the same number of electrons. This results in a change dL in the electron flow, thus

$$dL = L\alpha\,dx \qquad (14\text{--}8a)$$

In terms of the electron current density J_e, obtained by multiplying L by the electronic charge, this is

$$dJ_e = J_e\alpha\,dx \qquad (14\text{--}8b)$$

Integration between $x = 0$ and $x = s$ gives J_e at the anode, which is of course the plate current J_b; thus

$$J_b = J_{ph}\exp\,\alpha s \qquad (14\text{--}9)$$

where J_{ph} is the current density at $x = 0$, photoelectric in origin. This expresses the proportionality of the tube current to the photoelectric emission current. Because the proportionality factor is an exponential function of αs, the amplification increases rapidly with increase in the spacing, and with any growth in α, for example as a result of an increase in the voltage between the electrodes.

The current represented by the J_b flow of electrons to the anode (with also of course a corresponding flow of ions to the cathode) is an example of a kind of current called "Townsend current," characterized by the fact that a reasonably adequate analysis can be made by studying the behavior of *individual* current-carrying particles. In Townsend current flow generally the initiating electrons may be introduced by radiation that is not at all in the visible spectrum (see Fig. 13.4), or by impact of particles of radioactive origin (beta rays, alpha rays, neutrons). Also, the initiating electrons may appear anywhere in the space between cathode and anode; they do not necessarily start from the cathode in the more *general* Townsend current problem. See also Section 15.1.

14.13   Dependence of Townsend's α on Gas Concentration and on Field Strength.[14g, 15A, B, C, D, E, F, G]   There is implicit in Fig. 14.7 the concept of *electron mean free path*, that is, the average distance traveled by an electron between successive collisions with gas particles. Note that the length of an individual free path is measured *along the path* and not along a straight line from one collision to the next. In the analysis of mean free paths in Sections 15.11 and 15.12, it is shown that the following relation provides a reasonably satisfactory approximation to the mean free path of an electron:

$$l_n = \frac{1}{\pi b^2 N_g} \qquad (14\text{--}10)$$

Here N_g = the gas-particle density (particles per unit volume).

     b = the radius of the gas particle, assumed to be spherical in shape.

     l_n = a somewhat formalized value of the electron mean free path; see (15–19).

This is a reasonable enough relationship, indicating as it does that the electron mean free path varies inversely as the concentration of gas particles, and inversely as the cross-sectional area of the gas particle. At any given gas temperature, as for example 273° K, the mean free path varies inversely as the gas pressure. See values of l_{no}, Table XV, for approximate magnitudes at a pressure of 1 millimeter of mercury.

Townsend's α depends on pressure and on electric field strength by way of the mean free path, in a manner that will be brought out by a comparison of Figs. 14.10a, 14.10b, and 14.10c. All three diagrams are similar in nature to Fig. 14.8a.

Note the use of an abscissa scale measuring distance in the direction of the electric field in l-units. The length of an l-unit may be identified, as to concept, with the value of l_n as given in (14–10). In advancing a distance of one l-unit in the direction of the field, an electron may make very many collisions, because of violent sideways motions that may cause it to travel many l-units of total distance during each single l-unit of forward motion.

The top one of the three sawtooth diagrams, Fig. 14.10a, represents a typical electron's energy variation along the anode-to-cathode journey when the gas concentration is so low that there are very few collisions. The electron mean free path is very long. The collisions that do occur involve considerable energy; however, experiments have shown that the mean free paths of high-velocity electrons are relatively long and that only a moderate fraction [15q] of the collisions with energies well above ionizing energy result in ionization. Thus because collisions of all kinds occur infrequently, and only part of those that do occur are ionizing collisions, very few new electrons are produced by electron impact when the gas pressure is low. Most electrons, like the one whose uneventful journey is diagrammed in Fig. 14.10a, pass directly to the anode without experiencing either exciting or ionizing collisions. α is very small and the phototube current is very little, if any, greater than the photoelectric emission current. There is little or no gas amplification.

In Fig. 14.10b (note the change in the vertical scale) the behavior is indicated for a very great gas concentration. There are many colli-

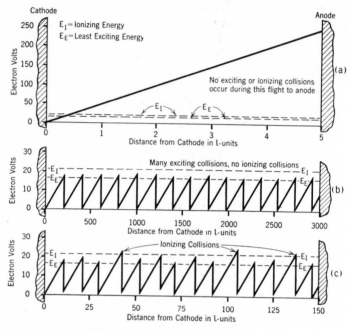

(a) Low gas concentration.
(b) High gas concentration.
(c) Intermediate gas concentration.

FIG. 14.10 Dependence of ion production on gas concentration at constant field strength. An l-unit of distance is a formalized value of electron mean free path; see (14–10). l_n in the text symbolizes the length of an l-unit.

sions per millimeter of path, so many, in fact, that long before an electron acquires ionizing energy it experiences an exciting collision that drops its energy back nearly to zero. Again ionization is very unlikely, α is very small, and there is little or no gas amplification.

Figure 14.10c illustrates the behavior for an intermediate gas concentration. There are not so many collisions per volt along the rising front of a sawtooth as in Fig. 14.10b, because the gas particles are farther apart. After the E_E level is passed, along any one rising front, there is an appreciable probability of any collision's being inelastic and so terminating the sawtooth. However, there are not nearly so many opportunities for such termination, per volt of rise, as in Fig. 14.10b, so that occasional sawteeth in Fig. 14.10c do rise above the ionization level E_I. Some of the collisions that terminate these tall sawteeth result in ionization of gas particles and consequent introduction of new electrons. α has an appreciable value, and there may be considerable gas amplification. At ordinary room temperatures and modest electric fields, this situation exists when the gas pressure is a few millimeters of mercury.

14.14 Similitude Relations Involving α.[14g, 15A, B, C, D, E, F, G] In Chapter VIII of *Fundamentals of Physical Electronics*, and in various other reference texts, it is shown that

$$\frac{\alpha}{F} = f_1(Fl_n) \qquad (14\text{--}11)$$

where F is the electric field strength, and $f_1(Fl_n)$ is an empirically determinable function of Fl_n, in that in $f_1(Fl_n)$ the quantities F and l_n occur only as the product Fl_n. Note here that

$$Fl_n = \begin{pmatrix} \text{volts} \\ \text{per} \\ \text{meter} \end{pmatrix} \times \begin{pmatrix} \text{meters} \\ \text{per} \\ l\text{-unit} \end{pmatrix} = \begin{pmatrix} \text{volts} \\ \text{per} \\ l\text{-unit} \end{pmatrix} = \begin{pmatrix} \text{slope of a} \\ \text{sawtooth,} \\ \text{in Fig. 14.10} \end{pmatrix} \qquad (14\text{--}12)$$

Thus, according to (14–11), the quantity α/F depends on field strength and on mean free path by way of their product Fl_n. This dependence can equally well be stated as

$$\frac{\alpha}{F} = f_2\left(\frac{1}{Fl_n}\right) \qquad (14\text{--}13)$$

Graphically, $f_1(Fl_n)$ and $f_2(1/Fl_n)$ have, point for point, identical ordinates, plotted, however, with respect to reciprocally related abscissas.

Multiply (14–11) through by l_n; rearrangement then gives

$$\alpha l_n = Fl_n f_1(Fl_n) = f_3(Fl_n) \qquad (14\text{--}14)$$

where $f_3(Fl_n)$ has an obvious meaning.

Equation (14–10) indicates an inversely proportional relation between the formalized mean free path l_n and gas concentration N_g,

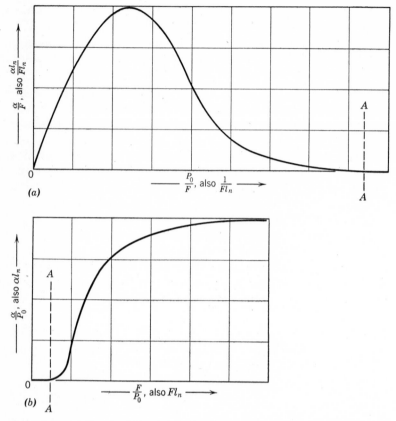

Fig. 14.11 (a) Graph of the similitude relation $\alpha/F = \phi(P_0/F)$, where α is the number of new electrons produced by ionizing collisions per unit distance of an electron's advance. $\alpha/F = 0$ for values of P_0/F greater than at AA. (b) Graph of the similitude relation $\alpha/P_0 = \psi(F/P_0)$. Note that $\alpha/P_0 = 0$ for values of F/P_0 less than at AA.

which is proportional to the gas pressure. Therefore (14–13) and (14–14) can be restated respectively as

$$\frac{\alpha}{F} = \phi\left(\frac{P_0}{F}\right) \tag{14–15}$$

$$\frac{\alpha}{P_0} = \psi\left(\frac{F}{P_0}\right) \tag{14–16}$$

where P_0 is the pressure, in millimeters of mercury, corresponding to the gas concentration N_g at a temperature of $273°$ K.

$\phi\left(\dfrac{P_0}{F}\right)$, $\psi\left(\dfrac{F}{P_0}\right)$ are, as suggested by the equation forms, empirically determined functions of the respective arguments.

Under standard atmospheric conditions, temperature $273°$ K, pressure 760 millimeters of mercury, there are 2.687×10^{25} particles per cubic meter (the Loschmidt number) for any gas. Therefore the pressure P_0, at this temperature, corresponding to a concentration N_g particles per cubic meter, is given by

$$P_0 = \frac{760 N_g}{2.687 \times 10^{25}} = 2.83 \times 10^{-23} N_g \qquad (14\text{--}17)$$

P_0 is in millimeters of mercury; N_g in particles per cubic meter.

Either (14–15) or (14–16) will permit the determination of α for any combination of electric field strength and gas concentration, within the range of P_0/F for which empirical evaluations of the functions ϕ, ψ have been made, for any particular gas. They may appropriately be called "similitude" relations for α, because of the concept, inherent in their origin, that the formalized mean free path is treated as the unit of distance governing the behavior. See Section 16.2 for another illustration of similitude.

Figures 14.11a and 14.11b illustrate the general shapes taken by the (14–15) and (14–16) functions. On both figures variables αl_n, $F l_n$ are also indicated. The rise of α/F in Fig. 14.11a to a maximum at an intermediate value of P_0/F is consistent with the comparison of Figs. 14.10a, 14.10b, and 14.10c, made in the previous section.

14.15   Gas Amplification Limited by Space Charge.[14F–VII, 14E–III]   In a phototube employing gas amplification many more electrons arrive per second at the anode than are photoelectrically emitted from the cathode. However, the current entering at one terminal must be the same as the current leaving at the other. Therefore as many electrons must leave the cathode per second, in one way or another, as enter the anode.

Each collision that produces a new electron also produces a new ion. The electric field causes the ions to drift to the cathode. On arrival at the cathode each ion steals an electron from the cathode surface and becomes a neutral gas particle again; this is the mechanism by which the additional electrons leave the cathode.

In a planar device, as illustrated in Fig. 14.12, the current near the anode is obviously all electron-borne, but that near the cathode chiefly ion-borne, if the gas amplification is substantial. The ions move very slowly, the electrons rapidly, because of the large mass ratio (see Sections 15.13 through 15.15); therefore, from the equation of flow, $J = \rho v$, there will be very little space charge near the anode, but substantial positive space charge near the cathode. This leads to potential distributions as indicated in Fig. 14.12. The gentle gradient evident in the central and near-anode regions may reduce α there, making the amplification less for intense than for moderate illumination.

In a typical commercial phototube, having a large-surface-area cathode and a rodlike, small-surface-area anode, the geometry causes

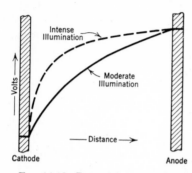

the current density to be low where the gradient, and therefore also the velocity, is low, and to be high where the velocity is high. The geometry thus largely compensates for the space-charge effect.

When the phototube current is large because of intense illumination, there may occur abrupt initiation of a glow discharge, the mechanism being as described in Sections 17.2, 17.6, and 17.7. Such a glow discharge is self-sustaining, and its current is in no way dependent on the illumination of the tube.

FIG. 14.12 Potential distribution in a planar gas-filled phototube, showing the effect of positive space charge when illumination becomes intense.

Passage of glow discharge current for more than a brief moment will destroy the sensitivity of the tube.

14.16 Volt-Ampere Properties of Gas-Filled Phototubes; Simple Phototube Circuits.[14E, F, G, H, 18D, E, F, G]   Figure 14.13a illustrates volt-ampere characteristics for a gas-filled phototube. A destructive glow discharge is initiated if operation is carried across the dotted curve *ABC*. The widening of the dotted line *AB* to a dotted region *BC* indicates that above *B* the transition from the ordinary light-controlled phototube current to a self-sustaining glow discharge takes place gradually rather than abruptly.

In a simple d-c phototube circuit, Fig. 14.13b, the effect of changes in light intensity is predictable by means of a load line, as in amplifier circuit analysis; see Figs. 9.4 and 9.5. Such a load line appears in Fig. 14.13a, corresponding to the circuit of Fig. 14.13b. The equation of the load line is

$$e_b = E_{bb} - i_b R_L \qquad (14\text{--}18)$$

where E_{bb} is the d-c source voltage, R_L the load resistance, and e_b and i_b plate voltage and plate current. The load line is the locus of i_b, e_b

values as the light varies. If the light were to vary periodically between 0.2 and 0.4 lumen, i_b would vary between the intersections of the load line with the 0.2- and 0.4-lumen curves. This is between about 5 and 7.5 microamperes; the plate swing would be between about 58 and 40 volts.

Because of the approximate proportionality between i_b and e_b for constant illumination, as indicated by Fig. 14.13, a gas-filled phototube acts much like a resistance of magnitude inversely proportional

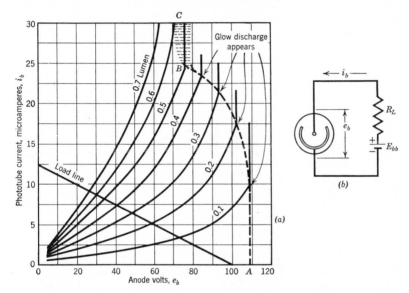

FIG. 14.13 (a) Volt-ampere characteristic curves for a gas phototube, intensity of illumination being the parameter; also, a load line corresponding to the simple d-c circuit shown in (b).

to light intensity. It is of course also a rectifier, permitting current flow only in one direction.

An a-c component of current can exist in a phototube circuit either because there is in the circuit an a-c voltage source, or because the light intensity varies periodically.

Suppose that steady light, of such intensity as to produce the solid volt-ampere line in Fig. 14.14a, strikes the tube in the circuit of Fig. 14.14b. E_i represents an a-c voltage introduced by a transformer. The magnitude of the a-c voltage E_j that appears across R_L can be predicted by means of the equivalent circuit in Fig. 14.14c. r_p should be defined, as in amplifying tubes, as $\partial e_b/\partial i_b$; it is approximately an inverse function of the light intensity.

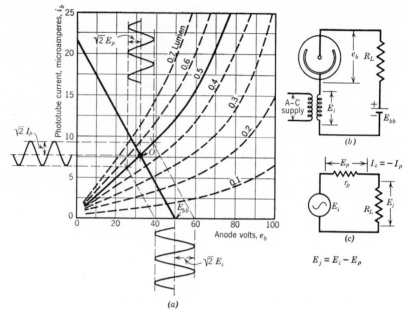

(a) Tube characteristics and load line.

(b) Actual circuit.

(c) Equivalent a-c circuit. $r_p = \dfrac{\partial e_b}{\partial i_b}$

FIG. 14.14   Gas-filled phototube in a circuit containing an a-c as well as a d-c voltage.

A method of representing the effects of periodic variations in light intensity, with fixed plate battery voltage, is illustrated in Fig. 14.15.

14.17   Semiconductor Photocells and Metal Plate Rectifiers.[8C, I, J, 14D, E, F, G, H, h, i, j]   In the photoelectric tubes so far described in this text, the power associated with current flow in the external circuit is provided by the d-c voltage source, the magnitude of the current being controlled by the light. In a semiconductor photocell, illustrated in Fig. 14.16a, the incoming light is the energy source. There is no auxiliary battery. The light penetrates through a thin metal film to the boundary between film and semiconductor (see Section 8.12). Both cuprous oxide (CuO_2) and selenium serve satisfactorily as the semiconducting material.

---

* For material covering fundamental principles of semiconductors as used in these devices, see bibliographical references 8A, D, E, F, G, I, J.

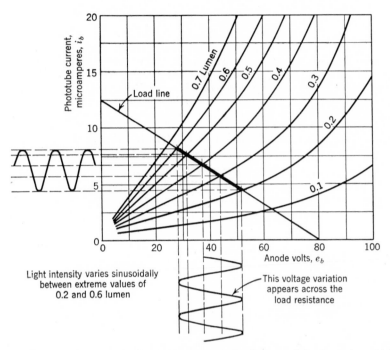

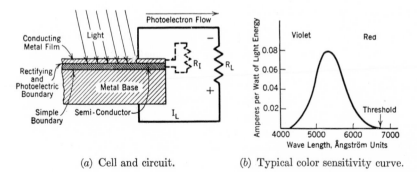

FIG. 14.15 Variations in phototube current and voltage resulting from sinusoidal variations in light intensity. The heavy portion of the load line is the current-voltage locus.

(a) Cell and circuit.   (b) Typical color sensitivity curve.

FIG. 14.16 Semiconductor rectifier-type photocell.

Either of two kinds of boundaries may exist between a metal and a semiconductor (or within a semiconductor), as follows:

(a) A *rectifying and photoelectric boundary* [14h] may be formed by sputtering (see Section 16.3) a thin film of metal over the surface of the semiconductor. Or, an extremely thin layer of cuprous oxide may be formed over copper by heating the copper in air at 1050° C, then annealing at 600° C. Other methods are used with selenium. An *n-p* or *p-n* junction *within* germanium (p. 234) is such a boundary.

(b) A *simple boundary* is formed by pressing the metal onto the semiconductor. A simple boundary has neither rectifying nor photoelectric properties.

A semiconductor "sandwich" as illustrated in Fig. 14.16a has one each of the two kinds of boundaries. Such a device serves as a rectifier when used with an a-c power source and load; semiconductor photocells are therefore sometimes called rectifier-type photocells. The electrons in such a rectifier flow reasonably freely from copper to oxide, but the resistance to flow from oxide to copper is very high. One sandwich rectifies satisfactorily with an a-c source of a few volts. Stacks of sandwiches serve well as rectifiers for a-c potentials of several hundred volts; this is the nature of *metal plate* rectifier units.

When used as a photocell, the penetration of light to the rectifying and photoelectric boundary causes electrons to be "lifted" by the photon energy across this boundary in the high-resistance direction, that is, from semiconductor to conducting film. They then return to the oxide either through the external circuit, or through the internal resistance R_I.

A semiconductor rectifier-type photocell is essentially a current rather than a voltage generator; it is able to drive its current against load potentials of a very few volts. At a given light intensity and wavelength, electrons constituting some definite current are transferred photoelectrically from semiconductor to metal. A satisfactory equivalent circuit is shown in Fig. 14.17a. R_I is the internal shunt resistance opposing passage of the photoelectrons back through the rectifying and photoelectric boundary; R_L is the load resistance. When R_L is a current meter of very low resistance, the cell is short-circuited. Practically all the photoelectrons then pass through the meter, and but very little return current flows internally. The current through the short-circuiting meter is then directly proportional to the light intensity, as indicated by the straight line through the origin in Fig. 14.17b. C represents the internal capacitance of the cell.

When R_L is large, nearly all the photoelectrons return internally, through R_I. The measured external voltage is then the potential drop through the internal parallel path. This internal drop depends on the internal current and might therefore be expected to be proportional to light intensity. However, the rise in terminal voltage results in a decrease in R_I, so that the open-circuit voltage is only approximately proportional to light intensity, as indicated by the curved line in Fig. 14.17b.

R_I varies inversely with cell area, so that it is undesirable to have more cell area than is exposed to light, if the return current is to be kept to a small fraction of the generated current.

The photoelectric yield and quantum yield of rectifier photocells are much greater than those for the photoelectrically emitting surfaces

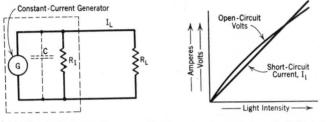

(a) Equivalent circuit.   (b) Response to variations in light intensity.

Fig. 14.17 Semiconductor rectifier-type photocell properties.

used in vacuum and gas-filled phototubes. The overall sensitivity, in current units per lumen, of a rectifier-type photocell is likely to be a little better than that for a gas-filled phototube.

Rectifier-type photocells are advantageously simple and economical. However, it is not feasible with such cells, as it is with photoelectric emission cells, to make the currents in relatively high-voltage circuits directly dependent on illumination. Rectifier photocells usually cannot be used to excite the grid circuits of vacuum-tube amplifiers, whereas emission phototubes are well adapted to such use.

14.18 Photoconducting Cells.[*][8I, J, i, 14D, E, F, i, j] In the photosensitive devices so far discussed light produces a transfer of electrons across some kind of potential barrier, thereby causing or modifying electron flow in an external circuit.

In a photoconducting cell, illumination causes a decrease of the electrical resistance of a semiconductor. Germanium, selenium, alloys of selenium and tellurium, and a thallous oxysulphide (in the "thalofide" cell), lead sulphide, and lead selenide are semiconductors whose resistance is decreased by illumination, and have therefore been used in photoconducting cells.[8I, 14i, j] Details of behavior are in accordance

* See footnote on p. 448.

with the semiconductor energy levels discussed in Section 8.12. Photoconductive cells are very useful in the infrared portion of the spectrum (see Fig. 13.4).

A photoconducting cell is designed to require the current from an external circuit to flow along a very thin layer of the light-sensitive semiconducting material. If a thick layer were used, the portion receiving light would constitute but a small part of the total resistance, because of the relatively shallow penetration of light.

When light strikes a selenium cell, the resistance changes very rapidly at first, later slowly but for a long time. The amount of the change is relatively greater at low than at high temperatures, because the resistance of selenium decreases more rapidly with rise in temperature than with increase in illumination.

Experiments indicate that there are two distinct kinds of current flow in semiconductors whose resistance changes with illumination [8I, J, i, 14i, j] Thus a distinction is made between "primary" current and "secondary" current. The primary current is directly proportional to the light intensity and appears as soon as light strikes the cell. The secondary current is not always directly proportional to light intensity, and minutes may be required for it to reach final value after a change in light intensity.

14.19   Time Lag in Photosensitive Devices. [8I, J, 14D, E, F, G, h, i, j, k]   There is no measurable time lag between the application of a light beam and the emission of photoelectrons from the cathode of a phototube. Therefore vacuum phototubes respond faithfully to variations of light intensity at frequencies of many megacycles. Interelectrode capacitance may affect appreciably the *circuit* response at very high frequencies. [14k]

Gas phototubes exhibit significant time lags. [14k] The establishment of the equilibrium current for any given illumination requires the accumulation of a positive space charge near the cathode; see Section 14.15. This accumulation takes appreciable time because of the relatively slow drift motion of the positive ions. Because of the time lag, the current in a gas-filled phototube circuit does not follow light variations faithfully at radio frequencies. The response is usually satisfactory at frequencies within the audio-frequency range (up to ten or fifteen thousand cycles per second).

In semiconductor rectifier-type photocells there is no time lag between application of light and the photoelectric transfer of electrons from semiconductor to conductor. However, the geometry of such a cell makes its capacitance relatively large; thus for high-frequency illumination the equivalent circuit must include a condenser, shown dotted in Fig. 14.17a. At sufficiently high frequencies this condenser constitutes an internal short circuit.

Photoconducting cells may exhibit pronounced time lags, if "secondary" current is prominent, because of the delay in the establishment of the final value of secondary current.[8I, J, 14D, E, F, i, j]

PROBLEMS

1. A certain photoelectric surface has a work function of 2.5 volts. Will it emit photoelectrons when exposed (a) to red light? (b) to violet light? (c) What color of light has the threshold wavelength for this surface? (d) The exposure is to ultraviolet light, wavelength 1850 Å. What is the energy, in electron volts, of the fastest emitted photoelectrons?

2. The characteristic curves of Fig. 14.13 were taken from published data on an early gas phototube. Assume (incorrectly) that in this tube the anode and cathode are parallel planes 0.4 cm apart.

(a) From the curve for 0.1 lumen, using a point at 80 volts, 3.8 μa, and assuming that i_{xh} for 0.1 lumen is 0.2 μa, determine Townsend's α for the 80-volt condition.

(b) What should be the corresponding (planar-geometry) values, at 80 volts, of i_{ph} and i_b for 0.4-lumen illumination?

(c) What should be the effect, on the ratio of i_b at 0.4 lumen to that at 0.1 lumen, of the use of cylindrical geometry, as suggested by Fig. 14.13b?

3. If, in Fig. 14.6, $s = 5$ cm, what is Townsend's α, when E_b is (a) 60 volts, (b) 160 volts? (c) The gas pressure is originally 2 mm of mercury. What new value of pressure will make α at 160 volts the same as it was formerly at 60 volts?

4. Two gases have the same ionizing potential, the same probability of ionization, and the same atomic radius, but the least excitation potential is much less for one than for the other. At moderate gas concentrations, which gas will have the larger value of α? Which will serve most effectively for gas amplification?

5. (a) In Fig. 14.13, if $E_{bb} = 100$, what is the smallest R_L that can be used without initiating a glow discharge at very intense illumination?

(b) With this load resistance, what is i_b at 0.1 lumen illumination? at 0.7 lumen?

6. In Fig. 14.14b, let $E_{bb} = 100$, $R_L = 5,000,000$, $E_i = 10$. Find E_p and I_p when illumination is (a) 0.1 lumen, (b) 0.7 lumen. (c) For which illumination are the harmonics in I_p most pronounced?

7. Conditions as in Prob. 5, except that there is an inductive reactance $X_L = 2,500,000$ ohms in series with the 5,000,000-ohm R_L. Illumination 0.7 lumen. Assume $I_p = 5$ μa and is sinusoidal. Determine the instantaneous values of the excitation voltage e_i when the instantaneous value i_p of the a-c component of plate current is (a) at its greatest positive value, (b) at its greatest negative value, (c) zero but increasing, (d) zero but decreasing.

8. Conditions as in Fig. 14.15, sinusoidally varying illumination. Plot a curve of i_b vertically, illumination horizontally. Your curve is qualitatively similar to the dynamic characteristic of a triode. By a method similar to that outlined in Section 9.20, determine the per cent second-harmonic distortion in I_p and E_p.

CHAPTER XV

CURRENT FLOW IN GASES *

15.1 Distinction among Electric Arcs, Glow Discharges, and Townsend Currents;[15A, C, D, c] **Spark Discharges.** On the basis of volt-ampere characteristics (see Fig. 15.1) and external appearances it is convenient to distinguish between three very different kinds of steady-flow gaseous conduction of electric current. In order of increasing current magnitude, these are Townsend currents,[15D, E, F] glow discharges, and electric arcs.

Townsend currents are typically measured in microamperes or fractions of microamperes. They may begin to be measurable at around 25 to 50 applied volts and in general increase more rapidly than in proportion to the voltage. The upper limit of voltage for Townsend currents is determined by the appearance of a glow discharge, or an electric arc, or a transient arc called a spark; such a change may occur at perhaps 75 to many thousands of volts, depending on electrode spacing, gas pressure, and the gas employed. Glow-discharge currents are usually measurable in tens or hundreds of milliamperes, at voltages of perhaps 75 to 1000; observations on glow discharges are ordinarily made at gas pressures ranging from a few hundredths of a millimeter to a few millimeters of mercury. The upper limit to glow-discharge current is established by an abrupt transition to an arc. Electric-arc currents range from a few hundred milliamperes to hundreds of thousands of amperes, at relatively low voltages (usually less than 100 volts overall, except for very long arcs). Electric arcs are obtainable at any gas pressure from perhaps a few tenths of thousandths of a millimeter of mercury up to indefinitely many times atmospheric pressure. There is no upper limit to the current an electric arc may carry, except the survival of the environment; large-current arcs are very destructive.

Problems involved in the initiation of arcs and glow discharges are discussed in Chapter XVII, also in Chapter IX of *Fundamentals of Physical Electronics*. Townsend-current flow is an essential element in the mechanisms of starting electric arcs and glow discharges.

---

* See especially the bibliography references 15A, B, C, D, G, *a*, *c*, *f*, *g*, *i*, *k*, *m*, *n*, 16*f*.

Gas amplification in a phototube, discussed in Sections 14.10 through 14.15, represents the behavior of a particular variety of Townsend current. That analysis illustrates a distinguishing characteristic of Townsend currents: a reasonably adequate treatment of their behavior can be built up from a study of the orderly behavior of *individual charge-carrying particles.*

Much more evident in engineering experience are the larger currents carried by *group movements of particles,* of such complexity that analysis must deal with behavior of the groups rather than of individual particles; this is the nature of current flow in glow discharges, electric arcs, and electric sparks. These statistically studied discharges are characterized by the "plasma" type of conduction,[15A, B, C, D, G, f, g, i, n, 16f] mentioned briefly in Sections 12.12 and 12.13, and dealt with in the present and following chapters, and also in Chapters X and XI of *Fundamentals of Physical Electronics.*

Probably the most familiar form of electric arc is that drawn between two separating contacts, as between the blade and jaw of a knife switch. Such an arc consists chiefly of a well-defined and extremely hot core, of small diameter, surrounded by a flame. The core terminates at extremely hot, well-localized, small electrode areas called the *cathode spot* and the *anode spot.*

Arcs in gases at low pressure do not usually have well-localized, extremely hot anode spots, nor well-defined arc cores, but many of them do have small, well-localized, very hot cathode spots. The cathode "hot spots" of mercury-pool-type mercury-vapor rectifiers dodge about erratically on the mercury surface. Many commercially used mercury-vapor rectifying tubes have electrically heated oxide-coated cathodes that release electrons thermionically; arcs in such devices do not have cathode spots.

A typical light pattern for a glow discharge is shown in Fig. 16.1b. The most familiar form of glow discharge is that in colored commercial display lights. The most striking form is the laboratory display which exhibits *striations,* that is, alternate bright and dark regions, in the positive column.

The mechanism by which electrons are relased from the cathode of a glow discharge demands an overall discharge potential of at least 75 volts, more often several hundred volts, whereas electric arcs can be maintained by much smaller voltages. Current densities in glow-discharge cathode spots are small fractions of a per cent of those in the very much smaller and hotter arc cathode spots. A glow discharge cannot exist adjacent to a thermionically emitting cathode; rather, an arc will be formed.

Spark discharges should be thought of as high-energy-density, transient forms of electric arcs. The spectrum from a spark differs from that from an arc because of the greater energy density.

15.2   Definite Values of Arc Current, Not of Arc Voltage, Required by Circuits.   An arc in a knife switch is in reality part of the switch, for the circuit is not open until the arc breaks. The electric arcs in circuit breakers and in gas-filled electronic rectifying devices are parts of switching mechanisms. A six-phase power rectifier is essentially a high-speed switching device that performs the same functions as the rotating commutator of a d-c generator.

Now it is typical of any switch, and of any arc used as a switch, that the current is either zero, or has a magnitude determined almost entirely by the external circuit. The voltage across a current-carrying switch or arc switch is then just the small value necessary to compel passage of the required current. Thus external circuit conditions impose a definite arc current, not a definite arc potential, in an arc used as a switch.

A d-c electric welding arc is not used as a switch, yet it is the welding current, not the voltage, that is selected by the operator to suit the work he is doing. Power supply equipment for electric-arc welding is built to maintain the current constant at some selected value, the arc voltage varying according to changes in arc length. Electric arcs formerly used for street lighting operated at substantial currents and moderate voltages and hence were always used in series rather than in parallel. Power was supplied to them by current generators rather than by voltage generators. Thus the circuits used for arc welding and for street lighting arcs impose definite arc currents, not definite arc potentials. The same is true in most other industrial applications of electric arcs.

In view of these facts, it is desirable to approach most problems of arc behavior by assuming current magnitudes dependent on circuit conditions external to the arcs, and working toward evaluation of the voltages required to maintain the arcs.

15.3   Electrical Discharge Volt-Ampere Characteristics.   Figure 15.1 illustrates in a rather general way the types of volt-ampere relationships to be expected for the three different kinds of current flow that can take place between metallic electrodes (the cathode not being a thermionic emitter). The choice of coordinates—voltage horizontal, current vertical—is in agreement with the accepted method of presenting plate characteristic curves of vacuum tubes, as in Fig. 9.5b. Usual engineering practice has been to present arc-discharge characteristics the other way, with the current coordinate horizontal, as in

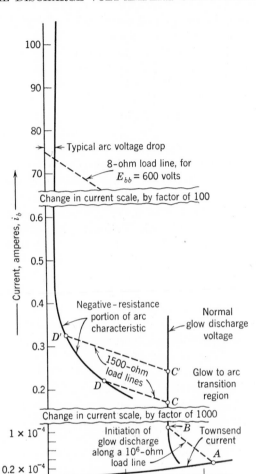

FIG. 15.1 Illustrative volt-ampere relationship for gaseous conduction between metallic electrodes (cathode not a thermionic emitter). This complete pattern of behavior, from very small currents through moderately large currents, is usually thought of in terms of engineering devices or laboratory apparatus employing gases or vapors (e.g., mercury vapor) at low pressures, from perhaps 0.01 to 10 millimeters of mercury. However, all aspects of the curve can be observed at atmospheric pressure; one manner of occurrence of a glow discharge at atmospheric pressure is as a transient phase in the reignition of a moderate-current power-frequency a-c arc, during the process of cyclic current reversal; see Section 17.14. If the cathode is a thermionic emitter, the glow discharge portion of the curve will be absent, and an arc can exist at very small currents.

Fig. 17.3. For the purpose of coordination with circuit studies that may employ either high-vacuum or gas tubes (rectifier circuits, in particular), it is desirable to achieve familiarity with gas-discharge characteristics in the coordinates used in Fig. 15.1. The accident of historical precedent should not be given over-riding importance, as compared with convenience-in-use concepts.

In the coordinate system of Fig. 15.1, the load line concept can be immediately transferred from Fig. 9.5b to the gas-discharge representation. For example, imagine that Townsend currents are being measured by the use of an apparatus employing a 1,000,000-ohm load resistor in series with a variable-voltage power supply and the gas-discharge device. At some point such as A along the Townsend-current curve the voltage is high enough so that a glow discharge will be initiated, following principles described in Section 17.2. The abrupt shift to the glow-discharge characteristic must take place between two points that are both on the load line for the circuit at the moment of change. Thus the glow-discharge current and voltage will be as at point B after the change, if the breakdown to the glow is initiated when the voltage across the device reaches the value at A.

If a 10,000-ohm load resistor were to be used, the current would jump abruptly by about 7000 microamperes, rather than by 70 microamperes. This very large abrupt current change might cause serious over-current damage to the instrument being used to measure the Townsend current; this is an important problem in experimentally studying gas-discharge characteristics. Partly because of this it has been customary in such experimentation to employ relatively high d-c power supply voltages, and correspondingly high series resistances.

It is usually possible to determine by experiment a reasonably definite and repeatable value of "breakdown voltage," as at A in Fig. 15.1, at which a glow discharge or arc is initiated. Note particularly that:

(a) The breakdown voltage, as at A, is dependent on electrode spacing and gas concentration according to *Paschen's law*, Section 17.8; this law states in principle that the breakdown voltage is a fairly complicated function of the length of the gap between electrodes, *as measured in mean-free-path units* (l-units, as used in Fig. 14.10). For most engineering devices (but there are very important exceptions) this makes the breakdown voltage increase about in proportion to electrode spacing and to gas pressure. Thus the point A could be moved outward indefinitely along the Townsend-current line; however, breakdown *cannot* in general occur at potentials *below* the glow-discharge voltage, no matter how close together the electrodes may be.

(b) The glow-discharge voltage is, under the usual conditions described as a "normal glow discharge," dependent primarily on the gas employed and the material used for the cathode; see Section 16.1. Thus the potential after breakdown, as at B, Fig. 15.1, is roughly independent either of electrode spacing or gas concentration, over very wide ranges of both quantities.

It is reasonably evident that, if the breakdown voltage were very large (for the electrode material and gas supposedly employed in producing the Fig. 15.1 curves) and the load resistance sufficiently small, the load line would not intersect the glow-discharge portion of the volt-ampere characteristic at all. In that case breakdown occurs directly to the electric-arc condition, there being no intermediate glow-discharge state.

In accordance with (a) above, some engineering devices may have breakdown potentials only moderately higher than the glow-discharge voltage, whereas others employing the same gas and electrode materials may have breakdown potentials of thousands of volts, many times the glow-discharge voltage. In the latter case, when breakdown does occur, it will be to an arc rather than to a glow discharge.

The elapsed time after applying a voltage at or a little above the breakdown value at A, Fig. 15.1, and before the abrupt change from A to B takes place, may vary considerably from test to test, for voltages a very little above the breakdown potential. However, a fairly definite average time to breakdown is usually determinable. This average time to breakdown for small over-voltages is measurable in microseconds or fractions of microseconds at atmospheric pressure, in milliseconds at pressures of a few millimeters of mercury, and perhaps in seconds at still lower pressures. In all cases, however, there is a reasonably definite minimum potential below which breakdown will not occur, no matter how long a time may have elapsed subsequent to the application of the voltage.

The transition from glow to arc, as along the 1500-ohm load line CD, or along $C'D'$, displays a less regular behavior than the initial breakdown to the glow. When the current is a little below the value as at C, Fig. 15.1, the glow-discharge current might flow for many minutes, perhaps even an hour or so, without showing any signs of instability, then abruptly and without warning shift to D. The probability of such an abrupt transition's occurring within any given small interval of time is greater for a larger current, as at C', than for a smaller current as at C. Presumably there is for any given physical arrangement a definite minimum current below which the transition to arc cannot take place.

The time lag to voltage breakdown follows the general type of probability analysis [17d] given in Section 18.18 for the firing time of an ignitron type of mercury-pool rectifier tube.[18b] Probably that analysis can be extended, in principle, to include the glow-to-arc transition, the independent variable being current rather than voltage, the average time again being very short at atmospheric pressure, and longer for lower pressures.

In Fig. 15.1 the 8-ohm 600-volt load line shown terminating at 75 amperes is illustrative of the application of the diagram to a mercury-pool-type 60-cycle power rectifier. The voltage terminus of the load line varies cyclically in magnitude. For this 8-ohm load line, at the moment illustrated, the a-c supply voltage is 600, and the tube drop about 15 volts; thus the momentary conversion efficiency, from a-c power to d-c power, is $585/600 = 97.5$ per cent.

The electric-arc portion of the Fig. 15.1 volt-ampere curve is shown as having a negative-resistance section, ending in a minimum value of arc voltage, or "arc drop"; then the curve exhibits a very gradual rise of arc voltage with increasing current. For very large power rectifiers the arc drop may be only 15 to 20 volts at currents of many thousand of amperes.

The glow-discharge curve may also show a decline to a minimum, with subsequent very gradual rise; the glow-discharge voltage can, however, in a properly designed tube, be sufficiently constant over a wide range of current values to serve as a voltage-regulating device, as in the VR-75, VR-105, and VR-150 commercial tubes.

If the cathode is a thermionic emitter, the glow-discharge phase of the characteristic is completely absent, and the very-small-current portion is subject to a rather different interpretation than that applied to the Townsend-current portion of the Fig. 15.1 curve. There will still be a distinct and rather marked increase in arc drop for very small currents, although the equivalent of the breakdown potential will in general be a very small fraction of its value for an unheated metallic electrode.

Electric arcs operating along the negative-resistance portion of the arc characteristic have been used as the active elements in negative-resistance oscillators.

Further comments relative to arc characteristic curves appear in Sections 17.11, 17.12, and 17.13.

15.4 Plasmas and Plasma Boundaries.[15A, B, C, D, G] Electric arcs ordinarily carry large currents at low voltages, glow discharges small currents at relatively high voltages. However, there is much greater similarity between electric arcs and glow discharges than is usually realized; their contrast in appearance and in electrical characteristics are so prominent as to mask the essential similarities in their internal makeup. The contrasts between them are incidental to the existence of different mechanisms of electron release from the cathode. Both can exist at either high or low gas pressures, and both assume definite normal cross sections unless restricted to smaller ones by physical boundaries.

A discharge of either type consists essentially of:

(a) A main current-carrying region, named by Langmuir the *plasma*.[15n, 16f] A plasma is similar to the interior of a metal conductor in that it contains electrons and positive ions in equal concentrations, hence no space charge, and a considerable drift current of electrons can be driven through it by a moderate potential gradient.

(b) A set of plasma boundary regions, analyzed in Chapter XVI, which have properties very different from those of the plasma. For example, space charge is a prominent feature of the boundary regions.

The plasma of an electrical discharge usually has a different potential from the regions outside it. Figures 15.2a, 15.2b, and 15.2c illustrate typical longitudinal and transverse potential variations for electric arcs. Transverse variations are shown both for an atmospheric-pressure arc in open air, and for an arc at a low pressure, perhaps 1 millimeter of mercury or less, in a metallic vacuum enclosure. The curves and bends in the potential lines in these figures indicate the existence of considerable amounts of space charge in the boundary regions. There is usually a slight radial gradient in a plasma, as shown in both transverse diagrams.

Plasma boundary regions may be classified as:

(a) The *cathode fall space*, containing the *cathode fall of potential*, located between plasma and cathode. Arcs and glow discharges differ primarily as to conditions in this one boundary region, through which the main electron stream enters from the cathode. The cathode fall of potential of a glow discharge is often a matter of hundreds of volts, whereas the cathode fall of potential of an arc is of the order of magnitude of the ionizing potential of the active gas, so always less than 25 volts; see the next section for the use of this as a criterion for distinguishing an arc from a glow discharge. The cathode fall of potential may be less than the ionizing potential, but it does not exceed the ionizing potential, in an arc. The various problems regarding the initiation of an arc or glow, that is, arc-over, sparking, arc reignition, and electrical breakdown generally, have to do with the setting up of the cathode fall space mechanism for electron release from the cathode surface.

(b) The *anode fall space*, containing the *anode fall of potential*, between anode and plasma. The main electron stream leaves through this boundary region.

(c) All other boundary regions, whether between plasma and free space, or between plasma and material surfaces. In this book these regions will sometimes be called "inactive boundary regions," more often by the widely used name "sheaths." [15h, n, 16f, 18m] The current through the inactive boundary regions is either zero or small and is incidental to the main current. The sheath around the grid of a grid-controlled gas rectifier (thyratron) is an example of an inactive boundary region through which there is some current flow.

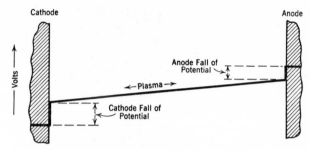

(*a*) Longitudinal potential distribution in an arc.

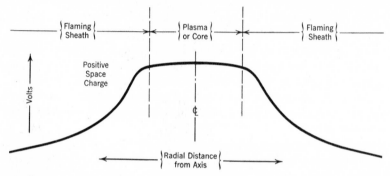

(*b*) Detail of transverse potential variation for an open-air arc, core diameter perhaps a very few millimeters; see Section 16.12.

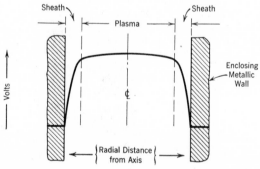

(*c*) Detail of transverse potential variation for a low-pressure arc in a metallic enclosure, plasma diameter perhaps a very few centimeters.

FIG. 15.2   Potential variations in and around an electric arc. Note that within the plasma there is little or no space charge, because ions and electrons are present in about equal concentrations. The sheaths contain substantial space charge.

15.5   Criterion for Distinction between an Arc and a Glow Discharge.   A criterion, proposed by Compton [15c] and quite universally accepted, for unambiguously distinguishing between an electric arc and a glow discharge may be expressed as follows:

An electric arc is a current-carrying gas discharge in which the cathode fall of potential is of the order of magnitude of the ionizing potential of the gas or vapor involved in the conduction.

This criterion is unmistakable and convenient, because experimentally observed discharges have cathode fall potentials that are either (a) at or below ionizing potentials, or (b) higher than the 70 volts and up typical of low-current, cold-cathode discharges. Cathode fall potentials in the in-between range are in general not observed.

15.6   Properties of a Plasma.*   A plasma contains gas particles, electrons, and positive ions, the latter two kinds of particles in essentially equal concentrations. The ion-electron concentration is rarely more than a very few per cent, more often a small fraction of a per cent, of the gas-particle concentration. A drift current of electrons, driven by the relatively gentle longitudinal electric field, accounts for the observed current flow. The longitudinal ion drift current is negligibly small because the ions are too heavy to move rapidly; the radial ion drift current is important, as it represents the principal cause of loss of ions from the plasma.

The radial ion motion takes place because of

(a) The existence of a pronounced concentration gradient of ions, the ion and electron density generally decreasing from the center outward, resulting in an ion diffusion current,

(b) The existence of a very gentle radial electric gradient, as suggested in Figs. 15.2b and 15.2c.

These two types of flow are intimately connected; see the *ambipolar diffusion* analysis [15A,G,n] and related studies in Chapter X in *Fundamentals of Physical Electronics.*

The longitudinal electric gradient accelerates the electrons, giving them kinetic energy, which appears first as energy associated with movement in the direction of the field. This originally directed kinetic energy is immediately scattered into random directions and magnitudes, giving the electrons a high average random energy, that is, a high temperature.

If the gas pressure is low, the electron temperature becomes much higher than that of the gas, or of the ions, often exceeding $15,000°$ K [15k, l, m, n, r, 16e, f] The simultaneous existence of different temperatures in the

* In the bibliography, see 15A, B, C, D, G, e through s, y, 16f.

same region is easily explainable by means of heat transfer concepts. It is a familiar fact that a heated substance has a higher temperature than an adjacent unheated substance, even though the two are in intimate contact. Heat energy flows from the heated to the unheated substance at a rate dependent on the temperature difference and the intimacy of contact. In a plasma the electrons are heated by the receipt and subsequent scattering of energy from the electric field; the ions and gas particles are not so heated. The ions also are accelerated by the field, but power input is the product of force by drift velocity, and the ion drift velocity is very small, so that direct input of energy from field to ions occurs at a very modest rate.

Because the electrons are heated as a result of exposure to the field, while the gas particles are not, the electrons must be hotter than the gas particles. At low pressures, heat transfer from the electrons to the gas particles occurs very slowly, because at elastic collisions the light electrons rebound from the much heavier ions with very little transfer of energy per collision, and there are relatively few collisions. Therefore at low pressures there can and does exist a large temperature difference between electrons and gas particles. Much of the energy given up by the electrons is transferred by means of exciting and ionizing collisions, which extract kinetic energy from (i.e., cool) the electrons but do not heat the gas particles.

At pressures up toward atmospheric there are enormously many collisions, so that the heat transfer occurs rapidly in spite of the very small energy exchange per collision. Therefore there can be only a very small temperature difference between the electrons and the gas particles; near to and above atmospheric pressure there is essentially thermal equilibrium as between electrons, gas particles, and ions.

The electron temperature must always be high enough so that a few electrons have energies sufficient to cause ionization at collisions with gas particles. This is necessary because the slow radial drift motions of the ions cause them all eventually to reach and pass through the lateral plasma boundaries; this loss of ions must be made up by the production of fresh ions within the plasma.

Loss of ions by recombination of electrons and ions to form neutral particles is negligible *in plasmas*, for reasons discussed in the next section. Recombination occurs freely beyond plasma boundaries.

15.7 Recombination Occurs in Boundary Regions, Not in Plasmas. Practically no recombination of electrons and ions to form neutral particles occurs in plasmas.[15A, B, C, D, G, a, m, n, u] Analyses of the mechanisms of recombination have indicated that the probability of attachment of two approaching charged particles is very small if the relative velocity of approach is high. Also, *large* attachment energy favors the existence of a *small* probability of attachment.[15a, u]

The average velocity is high among plasma electrons, because of their small mass and high temperature. Therefore there are in a plasma only very few low-velocity electrons, yet only low-velocity ones are at all likely to recombine. Furthermore, the energy of attachment (that is, the ionizing potential) for direct electron-ion joining is relatively large. Thus the rate of direct electron-ion recombination in a plasma is negligible. The rate of a two-stage recombination process, involving negative ion formation by electron attachment to a gas particle, followed by mutual neutralization at collision between this negative ion and a positive ion, is also negligible, largely because plasma conditions are not favorable to the survival of the negative ion between the two events. The energy of electron attachment in the negative ion is so little that it is easily dislodged, either by even very-low-energy collisions, or by low-energy photons (heat radiation).

However, in the relatively low-energy-density and relatively cool fringe or "flaming sheath" around an unrestricted plasma, for example an open-air arc, recombination occurs rapidly; see Section 16.12.

In either high-pressure or low-pressure plasmas the presence of any material surface in the path of ion and electron lateral motion precipitates recombination on the surface. Electrons enter or attach themselves to the surface, and ions steal them from it by contact. Thus material-surface plasma boundaries are "ion sinks." This ion-removing property of material surfaces explains the effectiveness of many design features used in a-c circuit breaker construction. It is important to make the ion concentration in circuit-breaker arcs fall off as nearly as possible in proportion to the cyclic decrease in arc current, in order to discourage arc reignition after the cyclic current zero; see Section 17.14. Removal of ions, called deionization, is favored by a large exposure of the plasma to surfaces. Forcing the arc to play in narrow slots increases the plasma surface exposure, and the introduction of oil spray exposes the plasma to oil drop surfaces. Individual oil drops do not last long, for the energy released at their surfaces by recombination heats them rapidly to vaporization.[17l]

Whatever the details of the situation, ions and electrons within a plasma rarely recombine, whereas those that adventure outside a plasma recombine very quickly.

15.8 Scattering of Electron Energies. Experiments have shown that at pressures so low that the electron mean free path [equation (15–21)] is several centimeters, plasma electrons do in fact have essentially Maxwellian velocity distributions. Collisions of electrons with gas particles are, in such plasmas, so infrequent as to invalidate any attempt to account for the randomizing of electron energies by a collision mechanism. There are not enough collisions to do the job.[15n, y]

The originally directed energies of such low-pressure plasma electrons can acquire the observed Maxwellian random energies only as a result of an exchange of energy between electrons. Those that acquire energy become the high-velocity members of a Maxwellian distribution; those that lose it, the low-velocity members. The question arises: What mechanisms are possible for this electron-to-electron interaction, if collisions with gas particles are ruled out?

Wherever electrons and ions are present in unequal densities, space charge exists, and the potential gradient is modified as required by Poisson's equation. This is a form of gross-aspect or *macroscopic* interaction, introducing an effect on a large group of particles in one region as the result of the existence of another remotely located group. Such gross-aspect interaction does not produce scattering of electron energies.

Superposed on this macroscopic interaction will be a similar *microscopic* effect closely related to plasma oscillations (Section 15.17). There always exist, in any gas, small random local and time-varying deviations in particle concentration, above and below a mean. The less the particle density, the larger the percentage deviation from the mean, within any given small volume. Such rapidly changing deviations in electron density within a plasma give rise, by way of Poisson's equation, to similar time-varying deviations of potential about a mean. Thus presumably the line representing the actual potential distribution between a cathode and an anode through a plasma must have pronounced, small-scale, irregular, unstable variations above and below the smooth line (Fig. 15.2a) that represents the average condition; similar local transverse potential variations are to be expected. Thus the plasma may be likened to a stretched tarpaulin flapping in a strong wind. The fluttering-potential hills and valleys can make major contributions toward randomizing the electron energies.

Interaction on a still finer ultramicroscopic scale may exist. Neutral gas particles may be thought of, electrically, as dipoles, quadripoles, etc. At distances greater than the collision radius, such particles exhibit electric field forces varying inversely as the third or higher powers of the distance, as contrasted with the inverse square dependence of the coulomb field of an electron or a positive ion. Therefore the coulomb fields of electrons or ions may be able to produce direct effects on other individual charged particles at distances many times those for which their interactions with neutral gas particles can occur. Statistical analysis shows that such direct interactions between electrons tends toward randomization of their energies. Any such effect increases greatly as the electron density goes up, because it involves, inversely, the square of the mean distance between adjacent electrons.

At high gas pressures, as in open-air arcs, the electron mean free path is short enough so that collisions between electrons and gas particles can account for the conversion of electron energies from directed to random form. Studies by Suits and others [15f, g] show that in atmospheric-pressure arcs there exists essentially thermal equilibrium among gas particles, ions, electrons, and even the excited states of gas particles. This implies that the densities of gas particles in various excited states should obey the Boltzmann relation (see Section 12.16). For an excited state, the exponent in the Boltzmann relation is E_e/E_T, where E_e is the excitation energy.

In view of the experimental evidence for energy scattering, and related considerations just discussed, electrons in both low-pressure and high-pressure plasmas will be considered to possess Maxwellian velocity distributions.

15.9 Plasma Cross Section; Equilibrium and a Least-Energy Requirement.[15A, C, G, f, k, n, y] The plasmas of atmospheric-pressure arcs and glow discharges, also of low-pressure ones in chambers large enough to permit unlimited expansion, are observed to have more or less definite cross sections. The cross-sectional area of a plasma grows as the current increases, the current density changing but little. The restriction to a definite cross section can be explained reasonably well on the basis of equilibrium conditions and a least-energy requirement.[15n, y] The magnetic "pinch effect" force, that acts radially inward on any current carrier, may be partly responsible for the restriction of plasmas to limited cross sections.

A plasma must satisfy two equilibrium requirements, as follows: (a) the rate of ion production within the plasma volume must equal the rate of ion loss laterally through the boundary; and (b) the rate of energy input (current times voltage) must equal the rate of energy loss through the boundary surfaces. This energy loss includes that due to radiation, heat conduction, and the removal of energy of ionization in the escaping ions.

As indicated earlier, arc circuits demand definite arc *currents* and provide whatever arc voltages the specified currents require. At any given gas concentration the two equilibrium requirements just stated can be satisfied, for any given arc current, by a plasma of almost any cross section.

However, if the cross section were to be very large, there would be a high rate of energy loss because of the large exposed boundary surface, and a considerable gradient would be required to introduce the energy necessary to maintain equilibrium. A very small cross section would also result in high total energy loss, because the plasma temperatures and charged-particle concentrations would be so great as to make the energy loss *per unit boundary area* excessive. At some intermediate cross section the product of exposed boundary area by the energy loss per unit area has a minimum value; an arc of this cross section requires the least energy for its maintenance and is the one automatically assumed by the arc.

Because energy and ions pass out through the boundary surfaces, but are produced within the plasma volume, the least-energy *shape* of plasma cross section is that having a minimum ratio of surface to volume, which is a circle. If physical boundaries restrict the plasma to a smaller cross section than that naturally assumed, or to a noncircular section, the gradient and overall voltage become greater than without the restriction; this is significant in the design of circuit breakers for electric power systems.

The cross section of a high-pressure arc is much smaller than for a low-pressure one, because the mean free path is the yardstick by which a discharge lays out its own pattern. If the yardstick is small, as at high pressure, the diameter will be small. This is an illustration of "similitude"; see Section 16.2.[15f, n, y, 17l]

15.10 Criterion by Which the Value of the Plasma Longitudinal Gradient Is Established. In the light of the concept that a gas-discharge circuit imposes a certain current, and provides whatever voltage the discharge then demands, the discussions of the last several sections may be summarized into the following statement of the criterion by which the longitudinal gradient is determined:

The potential gradient along the plasma must be large enough to cause the rate of power introduction into the plasma electron stream to be great enough, to make the electron temperature become high enough, to cause ionizing collisions to occur with sufficient frequency to provide replacements for the ions lost at the lateral boundaries.

The rate of ion loss at the lateral boundaries is discussed briefly in the next chapter.[15f, k, n, y]

15.11 Distributions of Free Paths of Particles.* The velocities of drift of electrons and ions in response to electric fields, and the rates of production of ions by collisions of electrons with gas particles, depend on the individual "free paths," these being the distances traveled by particles between collisions. The free path length is measured along

* In the bibliography, see 12A, B, C, D, 15A, B, C, D, G, a, v.

the path traveled. The term *mean free path*, symbolized l, of course signifies the average free path.

It has been pointed out earlier that the electron mean free path (or sometimes the ion mean free path) is a sort of yardstick by which a gas discharge lays out its own pattern, or by which electrode spacings and sizes should be measured in studying the dependence of properties of the discharge on environmental geometries.

Figure 15.4 illustrates the distribution of free paths relative to the mean. Approximate mathematical expressions for the free path distribution and for the mean free path are derived in the following paragraphs. The method involves probabilities or "chances" and can be illustrated by the following example. Suppose that it is required to estimate the chance that a football player will gain between fifteen and sixteen yards on a play. In order to make this gain he must first succeed in advancing fifteen yards, then he must be stopped within the next one yard. Two distinct chances are involved: first, that of advancing any amount greater than fifteen yards; second, that of being stopped within one yard.

Suppose that, in the game in question, it is reasonable to expect him to gain fifteen yards or more in 5 per cent of the plays; that is, the probability of his advancing fifteen or more yards is 0.05. Suppose also that he has a 20 per cent chance of being downed in any one yard that he reaches; that is, the probability of his being stopped in any one yard is 0.20. The probability of going more than fifteen yards, then being stopped within the sixteenth yard, is the first probability multiplied by the second, that is

$$0.05 \times 0.2 = 0.01 \qquad (15\text{--}1)$$

This set of events should therefore be expected to occur in about one per cent of the plays. The chance of his going *more* than sixteen yards is that of going more than fifteen, minus that of stopping within the sixteenth yard, or $0.05 - 0.01 = 0.04$.

Now to return to the gas particles: let the solid-line, crosshatched circle at A, Fig. 15.3, represent a gas particle at a moment when it has already advanced distance x from the point of the last collision, and the dotted-line crosshatched circle at B the same particle after it has gone distance dx farther. The increment dx corresponds to the one yard between fifteen and sixteen in the football example. Presume that all gas particles are spheres of radius b. If the *center* of any other approaches closer than $2b$ to the center of the one illustrated, collision takes place. Spheres of radius $2b$ are drawn at both positions in the figure to indicate the limit of approach of other noncolliding particles.

Let P_x symbolize the probability that a gas particle will go a distance greater than x without collision; that is, it is the ordinate of the inte-

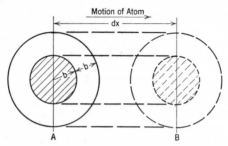

FIG. 15.3   Increment dx of an atom's free path. Volume swept out in distance dx by imaginary sphere of radius $2b$ is $\pi(2b)^2\,dx$. Chance of collision therein is $N\pi(2b)^2\,dx$.

grated distribution curve, Fig. 15.4a. When the football player's x was fifteen yards, his P_x was 5 per cent.

Let $p\,dx$ symbolize the probability of a collision's terminating the free path within the distance dx; thus $p\,dx$ corresponds to the football player's 20 per cent chance of stopping in any one yard.

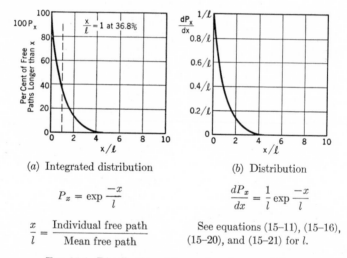

(a) Integrated distribution

$$P_x = \exp\frac{-x}{l}$$

$$\frac{x}{l} = \frac{\text{Individual free path}}{\text{Mean free path}}$$

(b) Distribution

$$\frac{dP_x}{dx} = \frac{1}{l}\exp\frac{-x}{l}$$

See equations (15–11), (15–16), (15–20), and (15–21) for l.

FIG. 15.4   Distribution of free paths of gas particles.

The *change* dP_x in P_x while dx is being traversed is of course the probability of reaching and passing x without collision, but of experiencing a collision before $x + dx$ is reached. Therefore dP_x is the product of (a) the probability of advancing a distance greater than x, by (b) that of stopping within dx. This product is negative, because P_x decreases as x increases. Mathematically,

$$dP_x = -P_x \cdot p\, dx \qquad (15\text{-}2)$$

This can be written

$$\frac{dP_x}{P_x} = -p\, dx \qquad (15\text{-}3)$$

and integrated into

$$\ln P_x = -px + K \qquad (15\text{-}4)$$

or

$$P_x = \exp(-px + K) \qquad (15\text{-}5)$$

The probability of a free path's terminating at a distance greater than zero is 100 per cent, so that $P_x = 1$ when $x = 0$. Hence the integration constant K vanishes, giving

$$P_x = \exp(-px) \qquad (15\text{-}6)$$

The quantity p is determinable in the gas particle case from the fact that $p\, dx$ must be the probability of collision with another gas particle within the distance dx. While going from A to B, Fig. 15.3, the sphere of radius $2b$ sweeps out a volume $\pi(2b)^2\, dx$. The chance of collision meanwhile is that of finding the center of another particle within this volume, which is the volume itself multiplied by the concentration N_g of particles. Therefore, for spherical gas particles,

$$p\, dx = N_g \cdot \pi(2b)^2\, dx \qquad (15\text{-}7)$$

so that

$$p = 4\pi N_g b^2 \qquad (15\text{-}8)$$

This derivation for p has assumed all particles but the one illustrated in Fig. 15.3 to be stationary. Actually, they have Maxwellian velocities, which make some particles initially in the volume $4\pi b^2\, dx$ move out in time to escape being hit, and make others move in from the outside in time to be hit. Analysis shows the chance of moving in to be greater than that of moving out, so the actual probability of collision within dx is greater than that given by (15-8), by the factor $\sqrt{2}$.[12A, B, D, 15B, a, q, w] With this relative-velocity correction

$$p = 4\sqrt{2}\,\pi N_g b^2 \qquad (15\text{-}9)$$

Use of this in (15-6) gives

$$P_x = \exp(-4\sqrt{2}\,\pi N_g b^2 x) \qquad (15\text{-}10)$$

Let a distance l_g be defined as

$$l_g = \frac{1}{4\sqrt{2}\,\pi N_g b^2} \quad \left[\begin{array}{l}\text{called } \textit{Maxwell's mean free path,} \\ \text{for a spherical gas particle mov-} \\ \text{ing among others like itself}\end{array}\right] \quad (15\text{--}11)$$

Equation (15–10) can then be written

$$P_x = \exp\frac{-x}{l_g} \qquad (15\text{--}12)$$

This is the equation for the integrated distribution curve of Fig. 15.4a. Its negative derivative is the equation for the free-path distribution curve, Fig. 15.4b, that is,

$$\frac{dP_x}{dx} = -\frac{1}{l_g}\exp\frac{-x}{l_g} \qquad (15\text{--}13)$$

For this particular distribution the two curves have identical shapes.

The average free path is obtained by averaging the distribution equation, (15–13), in the usual way, as described in Section 12.5; the result is l_g, which justifies calling l_g the mean free path, as in (15–11).

15.12   Approximate Magnitudes of Mean Free Paths.*   Gas particles are far from being perfectly elastic spheres, as was assumed in the derivation based on Fig. 15.3. Therefore the meaning to be attached to the "radius" b is rather uncertain, and different experimental values for b result from different methods of measurement of the mean free path. Table XV presents useful approximate information as to values of b for various gases. It also gives *millimeter* values of a sort of standard-of-comparison mean free path symbolized as l_{go}, and defined in *meter* units by applying (15–11) to a particular standard pressure and temperature, thus

$$l_{go} = \frac{1}{4\sqrt{2}\,\pi N_q b^2} = \frac{1.592 \times 10^{-24}}{b^2} \quad \left[\begin{array}{l}\text{Maxwell's mean free path, in} \\ \text{meter units, at } 273^\circ \text{ K and} \\ \text{a pressure of 1 millimeter} \\ \text{of mercury, for gas particles} \\ \text{moving among themselves}\end{array}\right]$$

$$(15\text{--}14)$$

Here N_q is the number of gas particles per cubic meter of any gas at 273° K and a pressure of 1 millimeter of mercury. Use of the Losch-

---

* In the bibliography, see 12A, B, C; 15A, B, C, D, G, a, q, v, w.

midt number, Table I, shows that

$$N_q = \frac{2.687 \times 10^{25}}{760} = 3.536 \times 10^{22} \qquad \begin{bmatrix} \text{gas particles per cubic meter,} \\ \text{for any gas, at a pressure} \\ \text{of 1 millimeter of mercury,} \\ \text{temperature 273° K} \end{bmatrix}$$

$$(15\text{--}15a)$$

The ideal gas law may be expressed as follows in terms of units presently useful, first for any pressure and temperature condition, then for a standard condition useful in vacuum practice:

$$P_g = 1.036 \times 10^{-25} N_g T_g \qquad \begin{bmatrix} \text{at any pressure and temper-} \\ \text{ature} \end{bmatrix} \qquad (15\text{--}15b)$$

$$1 = 1.036 \times 10^{-25} N_q \times 273° \qquad \begin{bmatrix} \text{at a pressure of 1} \\ \text{millimeter of mer-} \\ \text{cury, temperature} \\ \text{273° K, therefore} \\ \text{concentration } N_q \text{ as} \\ \text{in (15--15a)} \end{bmatrix} \qquad (15\text{--}15c)$$

Here P_g = gas pressure in millimeters of mercury.

T_g = gas temperature in degrees Kelvin.

N_g = gas concentration at temperature T_g, pressure P_g.

The proportionality factor 1.036×10^{-25} has been determined by employing in this last equation the value of N_q from (15–15a).

From (15–11), if b is considered to have the same value for all pressures and temperatures (this is true in relation to pressures, but only a rather poor first approximation in relation to temperatures; see Cobine [15A]) l_g will vary inversely as the gas concentration, that is

$$\frac{l_g}{l_{go}} = \frac{N_q}{N_g} \qquad (15\text{--}16a)$$

Here N_q/N_g can be expressed by dividing (15–15c) by (15–15b), leading then to the useful form

$$l_g = l_{go} \frac{1}{P_g} \frac{T_g}{273} \qquad (15\text{--}16b)$$

Actually, b decreases appreciably with increasing temperature, because a high energy of mutual approach permits particles to come closer together before significant deflection than in case of a low energy of approach.

The mean free paths of positive ions, even when moving among gas particles of their own kind, are affected by various complicating factors discussed in Chapter VII in *Fundamentals of Physical Electronics.* The most obvious effect differentiating the mean free path of an ion from that of a gas particle is the fact that the ion may be driven by an electric field and therefore may have a much higher total velocity than the gas particles among which it moves. Kinetic theory analysis shows that for perfectly elastic spherical particles this difference in velocity can be accounted for by expressing the ion mean free path as follows:

$$l_i \cong \frac{1}{4\pi N_g b^2 \sqrt{1 + (\overline{c_g^2}/\overline{c_i^2})}} \qquad (15\text{--}17)$$

where $\overline{c_i^2}$, $\overline{c_g^2}$ are the mean square velocities of the ions and gas particles respectively.

l_i is the mean free path of an ion among gas particles of its own kind, for example, a mercury ion in mercury vapor.

It is evident from (15–17) that:

(a) If the ions and gas particles have the same mean square velocity, the radical in the denominator becomes $\sqrt{2}$, so that the equation for l_i then becomes the same as that for l_g in (15–11).

(b) If the ions have a much higher mean square velocity than the gas particles, the radical in the denominator becomes unity.

Therefore, to a first approximation,

$$l_i \cong l_g \qquad \left[\begin{array}{l}\text{if the ion temperature is the same as the gas} \\ \text{temperature}\end{array}\right] \qquad (15\text{--}18a)$$

$$l_i \cong \sqrt{2}\, l_g \qquad \left[\begin{array}{l}\text{if the ion temperature is very much} \\ \text{greater than the gas temperature}\end{array}\right] \qquad (15\text{--}18b)$$

The important conclusion to be drawn here is that marked differences in mean square velocities that may exist between gas particles and ions will have only modestly important effects on ion mean free path estimates. This is true because the factor of uncertainty in experimental knowledge of the value of either l_i or l_g is likely to be substantially greater than the $\sqrt{2}$ factor differentiating (15–18a) from (15–18b).

For mercury ions in mercury vapor, $l_{go} = 0.024$ millimeter is frequently employed. This value was used by Compton and Van Voorhis [15q] in 1925, and checks back (by way of an early book by Dushman [2E]) to viscosity measurements. German workers tend to use

$l_{go} = 0.0165$ millimeter, as given in the table on page 39, Vol. I, of Engel and Steenbeck.[15G]   See Table XV for l_{go} values for other gases.

The mean free path of an air molecule at atmospheric pressure and room temperature is about 10^{-5} cm.

A formal expression for the mean free path of an *electron* is obtainable by recognizing that the space occupied by an electron is negligible relative to that of a gas particle, so that the crosshatched circles in Fig. 15.3 shrink to points representing the electron. b is still the gas-particle radius.   As collision occurs if an electron approaches within a distance b of the center of a gas particle, the sphere that describes the limit of approach without collisions has a radius b rather than $2b$.   The volume swept out during the electron's advance from A to B, Fig. 15.3, becomes $\pi b^2 \, dx$.   Because of the large mass ratio, the electron is moving so rapidly that the gas particles may be considered at rest; therefore the $\sqrt{2}$ relative-velocity factor is not used. $\pi b^2 \, dx$ is related as before to the mean free path, so that:

$$\left.\begin{array}{l}\text{The mean free path of an electron moving} \\ \text{among solid-elastic-sphere gas particles}\end{array}\right\} = l_n = \frac{1}{\pi N_g b^2} \quad (15\text{--}19)$$

Note that, with b considered constant, l_n becomes an inversely proportional measure of gas concentration; l_n is frequently used in just this way.

Table XV presents values for a sort of standard-of-comparison electron mean free path l_{no}, defined as

$$l_{no} = \frac{1}{\pi N_q b^2} = 4\sqrt{2}\, l_{go}$$

$$= \frac{4\sqrt{2} \times 1.592 \times 10^{-24}}{b^2}$$

$$\left[\begin{array}{l}\text{standard-of-comparison mean free} \\ \text{path for an electron moving among} \\ \text{solid-elastic-sphere gas particles,} \\ \text{temperature of the gas } 273° \text{ K,} \\ \text{pressure 1 millimeter of mercury}\end{array}\right]$$

$$(15\text{--}20a)$$

The counterpart of (15–16b) is

$$l_n = l_{no} \frac{1}{P_g} \frac{T_g}{273} \quad \left[\begin{array}{l}T_g \text{ in degrees Kelvin} \\ P_g \text{ in millimeters of mercury}\end{array}\right] \quad (15\text{--}20b)$$

The variation with temperature as well as with pressure is satisfactorily expressed by this relation.   The velocities of the electrons are enormously greater than those of the gas particles, for any gas temperature. Therefore changes of gas temperature have no particular effect on l_n, except as indicated by (15–20).

Actually, the last two equations lead to a rather arbitrarily established approximation to the electron mean free path. Note that they are based ultimately on nonelectrical measurements that permit determination of gas-particle free paths, then modified to give electron mean free paths by use of the theoretically determined factor $4\sqrt{2}$. Direct electrical measurements have shown that the *probability of collision* [comparable with p in (15–9), not very well named] of an electron with a gas particle is strongly dependent on the energy of the attacking electron (the Ramsauer effect) because of the complex detail structure of the outer aspect of any atom or molecule. Reasonably good agreement has been attained between the quantum-mechanical theories of this dependence and experimental determinations.

Thus

$$\frac{1}{p_{eo}} = l_{eo} = l_{eo}(E) \tag{15–21a}$$

symbolizes the fact that the mean free path of an electron having energy E electron volts is a function of E, this function being different for each gas. Here l_{eo} is the *Ramsauer* mean free path, and p_{eo} the "probability of collision" at 273° K and 1 millimeter of mercury pressure. Obviously, as in (15–20b)

$$l_e = l_{eo} \frac{1}{P_g} \frac{T_g}{273} \tag{15–21b}$$

where l_e is the energy-dependent Ramsauer mean free path at temperature T_g and pressure P_g.

Table XVI is a chart containing the essential information relative to the dependence of l_{eo} on E for a number of gases, in terms of its reciprocal p_{eo}.

In engineering devices employing gaseous conduction the electron energies are always distributed according to some more or less well-determined energy distribution, as for example the Maxwellian distribution corresponding to a particular electron temperature. The actual mean free path is therefore $\overline{l_e}$, which is l_e averaged with proper weighting for the energies; similarly for standard conditions there is an averaged l_{eo}. The values l_n and l_{no} as in (15–20) are employed because there is no satisfactory knowledge, either from theory or experiment, as to the properly weighted and averaged values $\overline{l_{eo}}$; see the handling of a similar problem by Kenty, Easley, and Barnes.[15j]

15.13 Electron Mobility Relations.* In any plasma practically all the current flow between anode and cathode is accounted for by the longitudinal *drift motion of the electrons* that takes place as a result of

* In bibliography, see 12B, C, 15A, B, C, D, G, K, *a, j, m, n, p, s, u, w, x.*

the gentle longitudinal electric gradient that sustains the discharge. The electron drift current density J_e is related as follows to the electron concentration N_e, the electron drift velocity v_e, and the electronic charge q_e:

$$J_e = N_e q_e v_e \tag{15–22}$$

Electron *mobility* g_e is defined in terms of v_e and field strength F by the relation

$$v_e = g_e F \quad \text{[this defines the electron mobility } g_e] \tag{15–23}$$

Mobility is expressed in meters per second per volt per meter. Similar equations relating to ion motions are obtained by using subscripts i instead of e.

During each free path the forward component of motion of an ion or electron, of mass m, is increased by means of an acceleration $q_e F/m$ caused by the electric field of strength F. Each free path terminates in a collision. Most of the collisions are elastic, not inelastic (see Section 14.11), although the few inelastic collisions have important effects.

Consider an elastic collision between a moving electron and a stationary gas particle. If the electron strikes squarely head-on, the forward component of the electron's velocity will be just reversed, as is that of a tennis ball which makes a direct hit on a post and bounces directly backward. If the electron makes only a grazing collision, its forward velocity component is unchanged, as when a tennis ball barely grazes the side of a post. In the course of many collisions, these two extreme kinds occur with equal frequency, so that the average persistence of forward motion as between them is zero. Any particular angle of partially reversing bounce can be similarly paired with the same angle of forward glancing bounce to give an average of zero forward persistence. Thus on the average the forward energy acquired by the electron between collisions is immediately converted into randomly directed energy, *providing the particle hit remains stationary.* In collisions between electrons and gas particles, the gas particles hit do for all practical purposes remain stationary, because of the large mass ratio.

Thus there is, *on the average,* no persistence of forward motion into subsequent free paths, in the case of collisions between electrons and gas particles.

For this reason a fairly good approximation to the average drift velocity v_e of an electron is the average of the forward velocities that would be acquired during individual free paths if there were zero forward motion at the beginning of *each* free path. The average velocity during any uniform acceleration a enduring for time t after a start from rest is $\frac{1}{2}at$. Therefore if t represents the time between collisions, and if the forward velocity is zero at the beginning of *each* free path,

$$v_e = \frac{1}{2}\frac{q_eF}{m_e}t \tag{15–24}$$

The average time between collisions is $l_e/\overline{c_e}$, the mean free path l_e divided by the average velocity. (A car going 60 miles an hour passes a town every quarter of an hour if the towns are 15 miles apart; $^{15}\!/_{60} = \frac{1}{4}$.) $\overline{c_e}$ is the average electron total velocity regardless of direction. The use of $l_e/\overline{c_e}$ for t gives

$$v_e = \frac{1}{2}\frac{q_eF}{m_e}\frac{l_e}{\overline{c_e}} \tag{15–25a}$$

The derivation just given has assumed all free paths to be equally long. A derivation that is similar to the above but takes into account the free path distribution of Fig. 15.4 leads to

$$v_e = \frac{q_eFl_e}{m_e\overline{c_e}} \tag{15–25b}$$

$\overline{c_e}$ will be evaluated differently for different situations. In a plasma the electron random velocities greatly exceed the drift velocities, so that (12–74b) may be used for $\overline{c_e}$. Equation (15–25b) ignores the actual velocities with which free paths begin.

Expressions that take these into account have been derived for v_e and g_e, employing the assumption that the random velocities are Maxwellian and that the gas particles are solid elastic spheres, with results as follows: [12B, 15A, B, C, D, G, a, w]

Due to Langevin: [15w, B]

$$v_e = \frac{3}{4}\frac{q_eFl_e}{m_e\overline{c_e}} = 0.75\frac{q_eFl_e}{m_e\overline{c_e}} \tag{15–26a}$$

$$g_e = \frac{3}{4}\frac{q_el_e}{m_e\overline{c_e}} = 0.75\frac{q_el_e}{m_e\overline{c_e}} \tag{15–26b}$$

Due to Compton,[12B, C, 15a, w] according to a derivation appearing in Chapter X of *Fundamentals of Physical Electronics*,

$$v_e = \frac{8}{3\pi}\frac{q_eFl_e}{m_e\overline{c_e}} = 0.85\frac{q_eFl_e}{m_e\overline{c_e}} \tag{15–27a}$$

$$g_e = \frac{8}{3\pi}\frac{q_el_e}{m_e\overline{c_e}} = 0.85\frac{q_el_e}{m_e\overline{c_e}} \tag{15–27b}$$

$\overline{c_e}$ may depend on the electric field strength F, so that these equations for v_e do not necessarily imply a linear dependence of v_e on F. Thus g_e may itself be a function of field strength.

Uncertainties as to values to be used for l_e and $\overline{c_e}$ are likely to be considerably greater than the numerical differences between (15–25a), (15–25b), (15–26a), and (15–27a), so that the selection between them is more or less arbitrary. In specific problems involving numerical values the usual important need is to establish the order of magnitude of v_e or g_e; uncertainty by a factor of 2 or 3 is in many cases not disturbing. The important conclusion to be drawn from a comparison of these four equations for v_e is that *they resemble one another so closely.* Many authors quite properly use (15–25b) because of its simplicity of form and the ease of statement of its origin; in this text the Compton forms (15–27) will be used.

A convenient manner of employment of the drift velocity equations will be outlined using (15–27a). It is presumed that T_e and E_{Te}, the electron temperature and its voltage equivalent, are known as a result of probe measurements, as outlined in Section 16.11. For l_e there can be used the value of l_n obtained from (15–20a), (15–20b), and Table XV; this is only a rough approximation, because of the variation of l_e with electron energy,[15v] as mentioned briefly at the end of Section 15.12; see Table XVI. It does, however, have the correct order of magnitude, which is the primary need. It is presumed that the longitudinal electric field strength F is known, as, for example, by probe measurements of plasma potential at various points; see Fig. 16.3a and Section 16.11. From (12–74b) and (12–54),

$$\overline{c_e} = \frac{2\zeta_e}{\sqrt{\pi}} = \frac{2}{\sqrt{\pi}} \sqrt{\frac{2q_e}{m_e}} \sqrt{E_{Te}} \qquad (15\text{--}28)$$

Introduction of this into (15–27a) and use of l_n for l_e leads to

$$v_e = \frac{2}{3\sqrt{\pi}} \sqrt{\frac{2q_e}{m_e}} \frac{Fl_n}{\sqrt{E_{Te}}} \qquad (15\text{--}29a)$$

also expressible as

$$v_e = 5.93 \times 10^5 \frac{2}{3\sqrt{\pi}} \frac{Fl_n}{\sqrt{E_{Te}}} = 5.93 \times 10^5 \times 0.376 \frac{Fl_n}{\sqrt{E_{Te}}} \qquad (15\text{--}29b)$$

from which v_e can be evaluated.

To obtain the ratio v_e/ζ_e of drift to characteristic random velocity, divide (15–29a) by (12–54) and simplify; the result is

$$\frac{v_e}{\zeta_e} = \frac{2}{3\sqrt{\pi}}\frac{Fl_n}{E_{Te}} = 0.376\,\frac{Fl_n}{E_{Te}} \qquad (15\text{–}29c)$$

In a typical low-pressure plasma, F might be 0.1 volt per centimeter, and l_n about 1 centimeter; E_{Te} might be 2 volts, making $Fl_n/E_{Te} = \frac{1}{20}$. This illustrates the fact that in all cases it will be found that $v_e \ll \zeta_e$; the plasma electron drift velocity will always be very small relative to the random electron velocities.

Non-plasma electrons, as in Townsend currents, Fig. 15.1, must be studied by an analysis based on the sawtooth type of diagram, Fig. 14.10; see Chapter VIII in *Fundamentals of Physical Electronics*.

It is important always to bear in mind that *all equations for electron and ion drift velocity give only rough approximations to the true values*.

15.14   Ion Mobility Relations.[12B, 15B, G, a, k, m, n, o, p, s, w]   The equation

$$v_i = g_iF \qquad \text{[this defines the ion mobility } g_i] \qquad (15\text{–}30)$$

is the counterpart of (15–23), in that it relates ion drift velocity v_i to ion mobility g_i. The chain of logic leading to the electron drift velocity and mobility equations can be applied to positive ion drift velocities and mobilities. However, the following significant differences appear:

(a) *Weak-Field vs. Strong-Field Conditions.* A major distinction must be made between weak-electric-field conditions, for which the ion and gas-particle mean energies (described in terms of ion and gas temperatures) are about the same, and strong-electric-field conditions, for which the ion temperature greatly exceeds the gas temperature. In the weak-field cases the total velocities for the ions and gas particles are about the same, whereas in the strong-field cases the total velocities for the ions greatly exceed those for the gas particles. The weak-field *ion* drift velocity equations differ somewhat in form from the strong-field equations. Electron drift velocity equations do not exhibit this difference, because the electron velocities enormously exceed the gas-particle velocities, regardless of equality or inequality of electron and gas particle temperatures.

(b) *Mean Free Path Dependence on Random Velocities.* The ion mean free path should be expressed in the (15–17) form which accounts for the fact that the total velocities of the ions and gas particles may either be about the same or markedly different for the contrasting weak- and strong-field circumstances. It is frequently convenient, in dealing with ions moving among gas particles of their own kind (for example, mercury ions in mercury vapor) to use in (15–17) the relation

$$\frac{\overline{c_g^2}}{\overline{c_i^2}} = \frac{T_g}{T_i} = \frac{E_{Tg}}{E_{Ti}} \qquad \begin{bmatrix} \text{for ions among gas par-} \\ \text{ticles of their own kind,} \\ \text{so that } m_g = m_i \end{bmatrix} \qquad (15\text{–}31)$$

Here T_i, E_{Ti}, T_g, and E_{Tg} describe respectively the ion and gas temperatures and voltage equivalents of temperature, measuring the respective random energies.

(c) *Persistence of Forward Motion.* If a positive ion, having been accelerated by the electric field, makes a direct hit on a gas particle of equal mass, the gas particle will just come to rest; the forward persistence is zero. If it makes a grazing collision, the forward persistence is 100 per cent. The average condition lies between these extremes, obviously a substantial percentage, as compared with zero average persistence for electrons; see the discussion preceding (15–24). Forward persistence obviously tends to increase the mobility.

These (a), (b), and (c) considerations can be illustrated by extreme cases. For the weak electric field, from (a), $T_i = T_g$, so, from (15–31), $\overline{c_i^2} = \overline{c_g^2}$; thus (15–17) reduces to (15–19), therefore, approximately

$$l_i \cong l_g \qquad [\text{in a weak electric field, for which } Fl_g \ll E_{Tg}] \qquad (15\text{–}32)$$

This is subject to pronounced modifications owing to induced dipole moments in the gas particles,[15B] as discussed in Chapter VII of *Fundamentals of Physical Electronics*, but is adequate for a study of concepts. As the field increases from weak to strong values, the ratio $\overline{c_g^2}/\overline{c_i^2} = E_{Tg}/E_{Ti}$ in (15–17) approaches zero, because the ion temperature becomes much greater than the gas temperature. Therefore the radical in (15–17) approaches unity, so that, to a first approximation

$$l_i \cong \frac{1}{4\pi N_g b^2} = \sqrt{2}\, l_g \qquad \begin{bmatrix} \text{in a strong electric field,} \\ \text{for which } Fl_g \gg E_{Tg} \end{bmatrix} \qquad (15\text{–}33)$$

It will be seen, from the elementary form (15–25b), that in so far as the mean free path is concerned, the growth of the field strength from weak to strong values should tend to increase the ion mobility. In contrast with this mean free path effect, which involves $\overline{c_i}$ only indirectly, there is a direct effect caused by the appearance of $\overline{c_i}$ in the denominator of the elementary form (15–25b). This direct effect tends to make the ion mobility decrease as $\overline{c_i}$ rises with a growing Fl_g.

A Compton derivation [15a, w] [see also (15–27)] treats these two conflicting tendencies in combination; the net result, in form applicable either to weak or strong electric fields, is

$$v_i = \frac{8}{3\pi} \frac{q_e}{m_g} \frac{F}{4\pi N_g b^2} \frac{1}{c_i} \sqrt{1 + \frac{\overline{c_g}^2}{\overline{c_i}^2}} \qquad (15\text{–}34)$$

The use of (15–11), also of (15–31), permits this to be expressed as

$$v_i = \frac{8\sqrt{2}}{3\pi} \frac{q_e}{m_g} \frac{Fl_g}{\overline{c_i}} \sqrt{1 + \frac{E_{Tg}}{E_{Ti}}} \qquad (15\text{–}35a)$$

$$g_i = \frac{8\sqrt{2}}{3\pi} \frac{q_e}{m_g} \frac{l_g}{\overline{c_i}} \sqrt{1 + \frac{E_{Tg}}{E_{Ti}}} \qquad (15\text{–}35b)$$

These are in form convenient for comparison with equations (15–27) for electrons.

The extreme values the radical can take are: unity, when $E_{Ti} = E_{Tg}$ (weak field), and $\sqrt{2}$, when $E_{Ti} \gg E_{Tg}$ (strong field). Thus the extreme change in the appearance of these equations between the weak-field and the strong-field cases is by the factor $\sqrt{2}$. This is relatively insignificant, for uncertainties in experimentally available magnitudes for l_g represent a greater factor than this.

Note particularly the following weak-field form, for which the radical has the $\sqrt{2}$ value:

$$v_i = \frac{16}{3\pi} \frac{q_e}{m_g} \frac{Fl_g}{\overline{c_i}} \qquad \begin{bmatrix} \text{weak electric fields,} \\ \text{for which } Fl_g \ll E_{Tg}, \\ \text{so that } E_{Ti} = E_{Tg} \end{bmatrix} \qquad (15\text{–}36a)$$

This is also expressible as

$$v_i = 0.85 \frac{2q_e}{m_g} \frac{Fl_g}{\overline{c_i}} \qquad \begin{bmatrix} \text{if } Fl_g \ll E_{Tg}, \\ E_{Ti} = E_{Tg} \end{bmatrix} \qquad (15\text{–}36b)$$

There is an obvious need here to be able to find E_{Tg}. The gas within a laboratory discharge tube or an industrial gas tube must exceed the temperature of the enclosing vacuum envelope sufficiently to transfer to the envelope the heat generated in the gas by the discharge. Kenty, Easley, and Barnes [15j] made gas temperature determinations in a mercury-argon discharge of the fluorescent lamp type, at argon pres-

sures between 1 and 5 millimeters of mercury. They found temperature rises of the gas above the glass envelope to lie between 10° and
60° C, at wall temperatures ranging from 230° to 350° K.

The temperature rise above the walls was found to be approximately
proportional to the gas pressure, which suggests that in most industrial
gas tubes the gas temperature is approximately that of the walls, because most such tubes operate at pressures much lower than used in
these experiments. However, their envelope temperatures range to
considerably higher values than 350° K. Because in the drift velocity
equations E_{Tg} ordinarily occurs to the $\frac{1}{2}$ power, no great precision in
the knowledge of its value is usually needed.

15.15 Approximate Magnitudes of Ion Drift Velocities. Determination of the ranges of Fl_g over which weak-gradient and strong-
gradient behaviors apply is important in any quantitative problem.
This implies determination of the ion temperature in the "terminal-
energy" condition usually achieved, in which the rate of gain of energy
by an ion from the field equals the rate of loss to gas particles at elastic
collisions.[15A, B, G, a, w, x] (The ions do not make appreciable exciting or
ionizing collisions with gas particles, at ion energies achieved in either
strong-gradient or weak-gradient conditions.) The terminal energy
problem is analyzed in some detail in Chapter VIII of *Fundamentals
of Physical Electronics*. The results will be summarized here.

At very weak fields, the terminal-energy ion temperature is the same
as the gas temperature. Above a not sharply defined range of Fl_g
values, the ion temperature becomes approximately proportional to
Fl_g, making $\overline{c_i}$ in (15–36) proportional to $\sqrt{Fl_g}$, so that for these higher
field strengths:

$$v_i \text{ varies as } \sqrt{Fl_g}, \text{ not as } Fl_g \qquad (15\text{–}37)$$

Before stating quantitatively the weak-field and strong-field ranges,
(15–36a) will be rearranged to express v_i in terms of E_{Ti}, the procedure
being the same as in similarly converting v_e to the (15–29a) form. The
result is

$$v_i = \frac{2}{3} \sqrt{\frac{2}{\pi}} \sqrt{\frac{2q_e}{m_g}} \frac{Fl_g}{\sqrt{E_{Ti}}} \sqrt{1 + \frac{E_{Tg}}{E_{Ti}}} \qquad (15\text{–}38a)$$

which can also be expressed

$$v_i = \frac{5.93 \times 10^5}{\sqrt{m_g/m_e}} \times 0.53 \frac{Fl_g}{\sqrt{E_{Ti}}} \sqrt{1 + \frac{E_{Tg}}{E_{Ti}}} \qquad (15\text{–}38b)$$

Also, the ratio of drift velocity to the random velocity ζ_i characteristic of the ion temperature can be set up in a manner analogous to (15–29c); the form is

$$\frac{v_i}{\zeta_i} = \frac{2}{3}\sqrt{\frac{2}{\pi}\frac{Fl_g}{E_{Ti}}}\sqrt{1 + \frac{E_{Tg}}{E_{Ti}}} \qquad (15\text{–}39a)$$

that is,

$$\frac{v_i}{\zeta_i} = 0.53\,\frac{Fl_g}{E_{Ti}}\sqrt{1 + \frac{E_{Tg}}{E_{Ti}}} \qquad (15\text{–}39b)$$

The terminal-energy analysis shows that strong-gradient, weak-gradient, and intermediate-gradient conditions may be distinguished on the basis of the magnitude of the ratio Fl_g/E_{Tg}, as follows:

Case I.   Strong Electric Gradients.

$$\text{When } \frac{Fl_g}{E_{Tg}} \geqq \text{ about 6, then } E_{Ti} \cong 0.8\,Fl_g \qquad (15\text{–}40)$$

(The original numerical form is $E_{Ti} = \sqrt{2/3}\,Fl_g$.)   Use of this converts (15–38a) into

$$v_i \cong \sqrt{\frac{4}{3\pi}}\sqrt{\frac{2}{3}}\sqrt{\frac{2q_e}{m_g}}\sqrt{Fl_g} \qquad \text{[strong gradients]} \quad (15\text{–}41a)$$

becoming numerically

$$v_i \cong \frac{5.93 \times 10^5}{\sqrt{m_g/m_e}} \times 0.59\sqrt{Fl_g} \qquad \text{[strong gradients]} \quad (15\text{–}41b)$$

Also, (15–39) becomes

$$\frac{v_i}{\zeta_i} \cong \sqrt{\frac{4}{3\pi}} = 0.65 \qquad \text{[strong gradients]} \qquad (15\text{–}42)$$

Note that, in this strong-gradient case, the ion drift velocity is only a little less than the random velocity characteristic of the temperature.

The strong-gradient point of view can be pushed to a still further extreme, for which no collisions occur because l_i has become large relative to the length of path of ion motion being considered.   This is the situation within the sheath adjacent to a metallic plasma boundary, or adjacent to a grid or probe, as suggested by the sharp potential drop through a very thin sheath in Fig. 15.2c; see Section 16.7.   In this case the velocity in the direction of the field is obtained from the energy equation (5–2), with m_g used for m_e; this concept replaces that of a mobility-governed drift velocity.   The random ion velocities are now merely those inherited from the ion temperature at the start of the free fall and are superposed on the free-fall velocity; of course the free-fall velocity rapidly becomes so large as to mask the random velocities.

Case II. Weak Electric Gradients.

$$\text{When } \frac{Fl_g}{E_{Tg}} \gtrless \text{ about } \frac{1}{2}, \text{ then } E_{Ti} \cong E_{Tg} \qquad (15\text{–}43)$$

This converts (15–38a) into

$$v_i \cong \frac{4}{3\sqrt{\pi}} \sqrt{\frac{2q_e}{m_g}} \frac{Fl_g}{\sqrt{E_{Tg}}} \qquad \text{[weak gradients]} \qquad (15\text{–}44a)$$

becoming numerically

$$v_i \cong \frac{5.93 \times 10^5}{\sqrt{m_g/m_e}} \times 0.75 \frac{Fl_g}{\sqrt{E_{Tg}}} \qquad \text{[weak gradients]} \qquad (15\text{–}44b)$$

Also, (15–39) becomes

$$\frac{v_i}{\varsigma_i} = \frac{4}{3\sqrt{\pi}} \frac{Fl_g}{E_{Tg}} = 0.75 \frac{Fl_g}{E_{Tg}} \qquad \text{[weak gradients]} \qquad (15\text{–}45a)$$

As here $(Fl_g/E_{Tg}) \gtrless \frac{1}{2}$, one may restate this as

$$\frac{v_i}{\varsigma_i} \gtrless \begin{Bmatrix} \text{about } \frac{1}{3}, \text{ and decreasing to} \\ \text{lower values as } Fl_g \text{ declines} \end{Bmatrix} \qquad (15\text{–}45b)$$

Thus over the entire weak-gradient range the drift velocities are modest fractions of the random velocities, becoming very small fractions as Fl_g/E_{Tg} declines.

Case III. Intermediate Gradients.

$$\text{When } \frac{1}{2} < \frac{Fl_g}{E_{Tg}} < 6, \text{ then } E_{Tg} < E_{Ti} < 0.8Fl_g \qquad (15\text{–}46)$$

Here E_{Ti}/E_{Tg} is given by the following approximate dimensionless-ratio equation for the ion temperature under terminal-energy conditions:

$$\frac{E_{Ti}}{E_{Tg}} = \frac{1}{2} + \frac{1}{2} \sqrt{1 + \frac{8}{3} \left(\frac{Fl_g}{E_{Tg}}\right)^2} \qquad (15\text{–}47)$$

This reduces to the Case I and Case II values at the extremes. With E_{Ti}/E_{Tg} known, values of v_i and v_i/ς_i are obtained from (15–38) and (15–39).

For all cases, strong, weak, and intermediate gradients, the above relations can be very useful first approximations. They are only approximate, primarily because of the uncertainties surrounding the relationship between l_i and l_g, and the values of l_g itself, also because of the not altogether valid assumption, employed in certain steps of the terminal-energy analysis, that the random velocities are Maxwellian and are large relative to the drift velocities.

The ratio Fl_g/E_{Tg} takes on values from perhaps 10^{-8} to 10^{+6} in engineering apparatus of various kinds; in most cases the ratio lies outside the (15–46) range and so can be treated by either the Case I or the Case II relations. Thus in the majority of cases, either (a) the ion temperature is determined entirely by the electric gradient, being unaffected by the gas temperature, or (b) the ion temperature is the same as the gas temperature. However, a number of plasma problems of engineering interest do involve values of Fl_g/E_{Tg} which lie within the Case III range.

15.16 Ratio of Drift Current Density to Random Current Density. It is frequently desirable to know the ratio of the drift current density $N_e v_e q_e$, or $N_i v_i q_e$, to the corresponding random current density, as given by (12–100). Thus, in general,

$$\frac{\text{Drift current density}}{\text{Random current density}} = \frac{Nvq_e}{(N\zeta q_e/2\sqrt{\pi})} = 2\sqrt{\pi}\,\frac{v}{\zeta} \quad (15\text{--}48)$$

Application of appropriate forms for v/ζ will show that:

For strong gradient (Case I) ions, not in general being plasma ions, from (15–42) and (15–48):

$$\frac{\text{Drift current density}}{\text{Random current density}} \cong \frac{4}{\sqrt{3}} \cong 2.3 \quad (15\text{--}49)$$

Thus in strong-gradient situations the ion drift current density is materially greater than the random ion current density, by a factor that is about the same for all large gradients. The precise numerical value 2.3 is not dependable, but the concept is correct.

For weak gradient (Case II) ions, including many but not all plasma conditions, from (15–45a) and (15–48):

$$\frac{\text{Drift current density}}{\text{Random current density}} = \frac{8}{3}\frac{Fl_g}{E_{Tg}} = 2.67\,\frac{Fl_g}{E_{Tg}} \quad (15\text{--}50a)$$

For plasma electrons, from (15–29c) and (15–48)

$$\frac{\text{Drift current density}}{\text{Random current density}} = \frac{4}{3}\frac{Fl_n}{E_{Te}} = 1.33\,\frac{Fl_n}{E_{Te}} \quad (15\text{--}50b)$$

A comparison of the last two equations is significant, for in any plasma F is of course the same for the two equations. As indicated below (15–29c), it is reasonable to expect that Fl_n/E_{Te} will be perhaps $\frac{1}{20}$ or less. Plasma ion conditions range somewhat both ways from the boundary between weak and intermediate gradients; therefore from (15–43) it is reasonable to expect that for plasma ions Fl_g/E_{Tg} will be within a factor of perhaps 2 or 3 one way or the other of $\frac{1}{2}$.

Therefore from (15–50a) and (15–50b) it may be expected that, as to orders of magnitude:

For plasma conditions:

$$\frac{\left[\begin{array}{c}\text{Electron drift}\\\text{current density}\end{array}\right]}{\left[\begin{array}{c}\text{Electron random}\\\text{current density}\end{array}\right]} = \left[\begin{array}{l}\text{A very markedly small}\\\text{fraction, usually of the}\\\text{order of }\frac{1}{20}\text{ or less, for}\\\text{any plasma}\end{array}\right] \quad (15\text{--}51a)$$

$$\frac{\left[\begin{array}{c}\text{Ion drift}\\\text{current density}\end{array}\right]}{\left[\begin{array}{c}\text{Ion random}\\\text{current density}\end{array}\right]} = \left[\begin{array}{l}\text{Ranging modestly both}\\\text{ways from 1, probably}\\\text{being below 1 in more}\\\text{cases than above 1}\end{array}\right] \quad (15\text{--}51b)$$

15.17 Plasma Electron and Ion Characteristic Frequencies.[15A, G, a, y] In Chapter X of *Fundamentals of Physical Electronics* equations are derived for the plasma electron characteristic frequency, at which sustained internal plasma oscillations occur, and at which interchanges of energy with microwave-frequency radiations are possible. These resonances involve the propagation of what may be called space-charge waves.

The plasma electron characteristic frequency f_e is

$$f_e = \frac{q_e}{2\pi}\sqrt{\frac{N_e}{\epsilon_0 m_e}} = 9.05\sqrt{N_e} \quad (15\text{--}52)$$

where N_e is of course expressed in electrons *per cubic meter*. As an illustration, when there are on the average 10^{12} electrons per cubic *centimeter* (a possible value for a mercury-vapor plasma), N_e in (15–52) is 10^{18}, making $f_e = 9050$ megacycles. This illustrates the fact that typical plasma electron characteristic frequencies lie within the range of well-established microwave-frequency measurement techniques; measurements of f_e are sometimes employed for the determination of plasma electron density. Equation (15–52) is identical with the equation for the "critical frequency" for an electron density N_e in the ionosphere; radio waves of lower frequency than this (a few mega-cycles) are totally reflected back to the earth's surface from the iono-sphere.

The plasma ion characteristic frequency, of more complex de-pendence, is given by [15A, a]

$$f_i^2 = \cfrac{1}{\cfrac{4\pi^2 \epsilon_0 m_g}{N_i q_e^2} + \cfrac{m_g \lambda^2}{k T_e}} \tag{15-53}$$

Here λ is the wavelength of the propagation taking place within the plasma; the denominator term involving λ corresponds to a sort of electroacoustical propagation in which the *electron* temperature is in-volved. Whenever the electroacoustical propagation is significantly involved, λ is related to the dimensions of the enclosure.

Obviously when λ is small, the frequency expression has a form resembling (15–52). When λ is large, the electroacoustical propagation predominates, with a propagation velocity characteristic of the *electron* temperature, even though it is the *ion* mass that is involved.

PROBLEMS

1. As explained in Section 15.8, local random variations in charged-particle concentrations may result in local random variations in plasma potential. Suppose that at a certain moment a local region has the one-dimensional sinusoidal potential variation of Fig. 15.5. The uniform positive ion concentration is 10^{12} per cu cm;

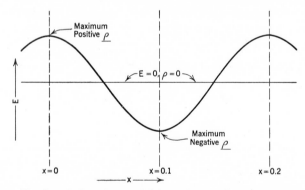

Fig. 15.5   Local variation of potential in a plasma; distances in centimeters.

at the potential crests the electron concentration is 0.1 per cent greater than this, at the valleys 0.1 per cent less. Find the potential difference between crest and valley.

2. (a) In Fig. 14.10b, determine the slope of the rising front of each sawtooth, in electron volts per *l*-unit; see (14–12).

(b) Calculate the average velocity of electron drift taking place in Fig. 14.10b, assuming that all sawteeth terminate at the excitation energy and begin again at zero energy.

3. Experiments show that an electron's mean free path in a certain gas varies with the electron's total velocity c as follows, at $40°$ C and a gas pressure of 10 mm of mercury: $l_c = (4 \times 10^{-10})c$. (This is similar to the Table XVI information.)

(a) Write the corresponding equation for $273°$ K and 1 mm of mercury gas pressure.

(b) At $40°$ C, 10 mm pressure, how many collisions per second will be made, in this gas, by an electron whose velocity has a constant value c, its mean free path being l_c?

(c) Use the above relation between l_c and c in setting up an integral from which the number of collisions per electron per second can be determined, the electrons having a Maxwellian velocity distribution. Remember that the Maxwellian expression for dN_c/N stands for the *fractional time per second during which an electron's velocity lies between c and $c + dc$*, as well as for the fractional number of electrons having this velocity at any one instant. Do not carry out the integration; merely set up the integral.

4. A certain plasma in mercury vapor has the following attributes: $N_e = N_i = 10^{11}$ electrons, also ions, per cu cm; $N_g = 10^{14}$ mercury atoms per cu cm; $T_g = 400°$ K.

(a) Find the value F_1 of electric gradient such that when $F \geqq F_1$ the ion drift velocity varies about as $\sqrt{F}$; state ion temperature and ion drift velocity for $F = F_1$.

(b) Find the value F_2 of gradient such that when $F \gtreqless F_2$ the ion drift velocity varies about as F. State ion temperature and ion drift velocity for $F = F_2$.

(c) State electron drift velocity as a function of F, if the electron temperature is $23,200°$ K.

5. In a certain plasma, in order to produce ions rapidly enough to make up for loss by diffusion through the boundaries, the electron temperature must be $16,000°$ K. Gas-particle radius is 2×10^{-8} cm; the atomic weight of the gas is 40; there are 3×10^{14} atoms per cu cm. The ion temperature is $8000°$ K, the gas temperature $400°$ K. Determine: (a) the gas pressure, (b) ion and electron mean free paths, (c) ion and electron mobilities.

CHAPTER XVI

PLASMA BOUNDARY REGIONS

16.1   The Cathode Spot and Cathode Fall Space of a Glow Discharge. Plasma boundary regions were classified in Section 15.4. The active boundary regions of a glow discharge will be discussed in connection with Fig. 16.1, which illustrates a typical glow-discharge potential variation and light pattern.

The cathode fall space, which emits little or no light, extends outward some distance from the cathode spot area. The termination of the cathode fall space on the side toward the plasma is marked by the edge of the negative glow. Beyond the negative glow there can usually be observed a less brilliant region called the Faraday dark space, which merges into the luminous positive column or plasma. The cathode spot is sometimes covered by a luminous layer aptly described as the "velvety glow."

The velvety glow, cathode fall space, negative glow, and Faraday dark space are all parts of the plasma boundary region through which the electron stream enters from the cathode. The properties of these bright and dark regions are described in various books and technical papers.[15A, C, D, E, G, 16a]

In either a glow discharge or an arc the between-cathode-and-plasma boundary region accommodates the mechanism for causing emergence from the cathode of enough electrons to carry the current demanded by the circuit. A glow-discharge cathode is bombarded by positive ions accelerated by passage through the cathode fall of potential. Each of these on striking the cathode removes from it the electron required for recombination to form a neutral gas particle. The part of the current so accounted for is called the *positive ion current* at the cathode.[16b]

The ion bombardment of the cathode causes ejection from it of additional electrons,[16a, b] besides those required for recombination, in much the way primary electrons produce secondary electrons at the dynodes of photomultiplier tubes. Also, there is photoelectric emission from the cathode due to high-energy photons resulting from exciting collisions of electrons with gas particles in the negative glow and plasma.[15B] The flow toward the plasma of electrons released by positive ion bombardment *and* by photoelectric action constitutes the *electron current* at the cathode.   The total current through the cathode fall space is the sum of the electron and positive ion currents.

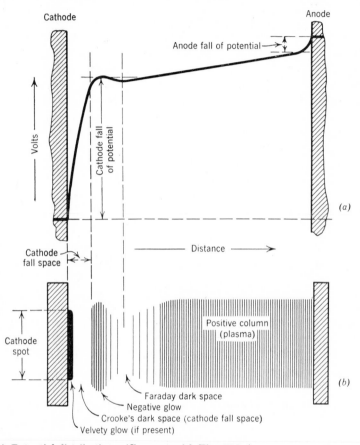

(*a*) Potential distribution.   (Compare with Fig. 15.2*a*.)

(*b*) Illustrative light pattern.   Positive column, negative glow, and velvety glow are often brightly but differently colored.

FIG. 16.1   Glow discharge properties.

The thickness of the cathode fall space (distance it extends outward from the cathode) is, as to order of magnitude, an electron mean free path.   Thus the edge of the negative glow roughly marks the termination, with resultant excitation and ionization, of the first free flight of the electrons released from the cathode.   A set of equilibrium requirements and a least-energy limitation, remotely similar to those applying for the plasma, determine for any required current the normal values of cathode fall of potential and of area of cathode spot.

As in the plasma, the equilibrium conditions could be satisfied by a discharge cross section (in this case, cathode spot area) of almost any value. For one particular area, corresponding to what is called the *normal* current density, the cathode fall of potential is a minimum. This minimum is the value that exists normally and is called the *normal* cathode fall of potential. In laboratory glow discharges at gas pressures of modest fractions of a millimeter of mercury, cathode spots of a few square centimeters area will usually pass normal currents measured in milliamperes through normal cathode fall potentials of a few hundred volts, the cathode fall spaces extending outward a very few millimeters from the cathodes.

As the current increases, the cathode spot enlarges, the current density and cathode fall of potential remaining at the normal values. If the electrode area is restricted, so that the current density is compelled to be abnormally large, the cathode fall of potential also becomes abnormally large, and an *abnormal glow discharge* is said to exist.

The normal value of the cathode fall of potential of a glow discharge is determined by the nature of the gas and the material of the cathode, but is unaffected by changes in gas pressure. Normal cathode fall voltages range between perhaps 50 and 500 volts.[15C-136] Cathodes made of the alkali metals, sodium and potassium, permit a low cathode fall of potential with any gas, because they have small work functions. Glow discharges in the inert gases, helium, neon, and argon, have low cathode fall potentials with any cathode material. The neon-sodium combination has a 75-volt cathode fall of potential, and the mercury-vapor–iron combination is at the other extreme with a normal cathode fall of potential of about 390 volts. These values are considerably modified by small amounts of impurities, either on the surface or in the gas. Slepian gives empirical formulas for determining the abnormal cathode fall in terms of the normal cathode fall and abnormal current densities.[15C-137]

The distinguishing feature of a glow discharge is the mechanism it provides for releasing electrons from the cathode. Therefore a glow discharge with a thermionic cathode cannot exist, because the thermionic cathode provides its own electron release mechanism.

16.2 The Effect of Changes of Gas Concentration in a Glow Discharge; Similitude. In electrical discharges in which ionization and the obstruction to movement of charged particles are due to collisions with other particles, the mean free path is a yardstick by which the discharge lays out its own pattern. This expresses the "principle of similitude" [15C, D, E, f] for electrical discharges in which collision mechanisms exercise a controlling influence; see also Sections 15.9 and 14.14. According to this principle the pattern of a discharge remains geometrically *similar* for extensive changes in gas concentration; only the dimensional scale is altered by gas concentration changes.

The cathode fall space of a normal glow discharge illustrates similitude nicely. The nature of the gas and the cathode material determine the cathode fall space voltage. If the external circuit maintains

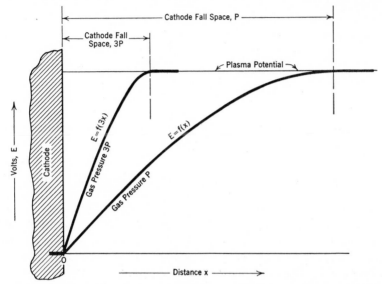

Fig. 16.2 Change in potential distribution within glow discharge cathode fall space as a result of increase in gas pressure, illustrating the principle of similitude.

the current constant, the mean free path is varied by changing the gas pressure, and dimensions change accordingly.

In a common type of laboratory demonstration of glow discharge the mean free path is made to grow from a few hundredths of a millimeter to several centimeters by a gradual reduction in pressure. The associated increase in extent of the cathode fall space is made evident by the receding of the negative glow and Faraday dark space to greater and greater distances from the cathode. At a sufficiently low pressure, the cathode fall space occupies the entire distance between electrodes many centimeters apart.

The mean free path can serve as a yardstick in measuring distances along the potential distribution curve extending outward from the cathode. This curve must have the same *shape* regardless of the scale. The curve in Fig. 16.2 marked $E = f(x)$ illustrates a type of potential variation that might exist originally. Suppose the gas concentration to be tripled, so that the yardstick shrinks by a 3 to 1 ratio. The new curve is the one labeled $E = f(3x)$. It is evident that:

(a) The electric field $(- dE/dx)$ at any given potential is 3 times its original value;

(b) Therefore the force that accelerates electrons and ions is 3 times its former value; yet *the velocity of the charged particles at any given potential is the same as before.* This is obvious for an electron that traverses the entire cathode fall space without collision. It is also true of electrons and ions that experience collisions; although the force accelerating them between collisions is 3 times its original value, the distance between retardations due to collisions is $\frac{1}{3}$ its former value. Driving force and retardation are both tripled, so that the velocity at any given *potential* along the new curve is the same as along the old one. This is indicated mathematically by the constancy of Fl_i. As ion velocities are unchanged, the energy of impact at cathode surface is unchanged.

(c) The scale factor (3 in this illustration) occurs twice in obtaining d^2E/dx^2. Thus the flexion, therefore the *space-charge density* (by Poisson's equation) is 9 times as great as originally. Current density, being $J = \rho v$, is increased in a 1 to 9 ratio. As the total current is unchanged, the cathode spot area is reduced by 9 to 1, and its diameter in the ratio 3 to 1, the original scale factor.

Note that, while the gas particle concentration is increased by the scale factor 3, the space-charge density and ion concentration are increased by 9, as the *square* of the scale factor. The percentage of ionization is increased by 3, that is, in proportion to the scale factor. With a sufficiently large pressure increase, this undermines the similitude relation; the nature of the discharge changes, not merely its dimensions. This is undoubtedly a factor in determining at what current density the transition from glow to arc occurs, in Fig. 15.1.

16.3 Sputtering of Cathode Material.[16c] The bombardment of a glow-discharge cathode surface by positive ions is often severe enough gradually to wear away the surface material. The wearing-away process is called "cathode sputtering," and it results in a deposit of cathode material appearing on the interior walls of the tube. Surfaces near the cathode are more rapidly affected than remote ones.

Sputtering wears away the electrodes, giving them limited life. It forms an opaque conducting deposit on the interior of the glass walls, cutting down the passage of light, and increasing electric leakage current along the interior walls. Because the sputtered deposit is gas absorbant, it accelerates the process of "clean-up," or disappearance of gas from the tube. Sputtering has been usefully employed to produce surfaces having unique optical and rectifying properties.

The major problem in early glow-discharge light sources was the avoidance of blackening of the tube walls caused by sputtering.[15H, I, J, r, 16c]

16.4   The Cathode Spot and Cathode Fall Space of an Arc.[15A, C, 16d]
As indicated in Section 15.5, in an arc the cathode fall of potential is
approximately equal to or less than the ionizing potential of the active
gas or vapor, hence almost invariably less than 25 volts.   In an arc, as
in a glow discharge, the electron emergence from the cathode is limited
to a well-defined area called the cathode spot, but cathode-spot current densities in arcs are very much larger than in glow discharges.   A
1-square-millimeter cathode spot may pass scores or hundreds of
amperes, depending on the gas pressure.

The details of the mechanism of electron emergence from an arc's
cathode spot are not fully understood.[15A, C, 16d]   The mechanism is
not the same for all arcs but is in all cases very different from that in
glow discharges.   Thermionic emission of the usual sort cannot be
considered the prevailing mechanism, for copper, brass, aluminum,
nickel, and many other metals used for arc electrodes vaporize at
temperatures below those necessary for appreciable thermionic emission.   Furthermore, there is evidence that an arc can exist momentarily
on a practically cold surface; in the Westinghouse Deion circuit breakers, arcs carrying many thousands of amperes are driven by magnetic
fields so rapidly over copper electrodes that the electrode surfaces are
scarcely marked.   The heating of the cathode spot may be an incidental
result rather than a necessary part of the electron-releasing mechanism.   However, cathode spots on refractory materials, such as carbon,
tungsten, molybdenum, and platinum, become so hot that thermionic
emission can provide the required current.

Whatever its details, the arc's cathode fall space mechanism performs two more or less distinct functions:

(a) It results in the emergence of electrons from the cathode.

(b) It gives these electrons enough kinetic energy, directed, or random, or both,
to enable them to maintain ion production equal to ion loss, and power input
equal to power loss, in the terminating end portion of the plasma immediately
adjacent to the cathode fall space.

If the cathode is an electrically heated thermionic emitter, as in
various thermionic gas rectifiers, the electron-release function is accomplished more or less independently of the action of the arc.   The electron emergence is not then limited to a well-defined cathode spot but
occurs over as much of the thermionic surface as is exposed to the
plasma.   The cathode current density is then much less than in a typical arc cathode spot.   The emission from oxide-coated thermionic
surfaces is materially increased by an electron-accelerating electric
gradient; see Section 7.14.   The arc cathode fall space provides such a
gradient, so that the current density at a thermionic arc cathode

can be greater than is usual for high-vacuum devices with similar cathodes.

The energy-giving function must be accomplished whether the electrons come from an electrically heated thermionic surface or from a hot spot maintained by the arc. Therefore the cathode fall of potential has approximately the same upper limit for either type of cathode.

The distance that the cathode fall space extends outward from the cathode is extremely short; [15A] see measurements by C. G. Smith.[16d] Hot cathode spots with extremely thin cathode fall spaces exist at pressures so low that the electron mean free path is measured in millimeters or even in centimeters. Thus there is no well-established dependence of the thickness of an arc's cathode fall space on mean free path. A glow discharge having a cathode fall space thickness of several millimeters may abruptly collapse into an arc whose cathode fall space is a very small fraction of a millimeter, at the glow-to-arc transition illustrated in Fig. 15.1.

Any discussion of the electron release mechanism at an arc's cathode spot is necessarily speculative. However, in general it is believed that the cathode fall space is so thin that the gradient within it is steep enough to produce the observed current by one or the other or a combination of the following effects: [15A, 16d]

(a) Field emission *through* the work function barrier, made thin by the extreme gradient; see Section 8.23.

(b) Reduction of the work function, as described in Section 8.22, to a value permitting a high thermionic current density at a modest electrode temperature.

16.5 The Anode Fall Space. In passing out of the plasma into the anode the main electron stream passes through the "anode fall space" within which it traverses the "anode fall of potential." Electrons are receivable at any part of the anode exposed to the plasma; thus there does not exist a limitation to an anode spot whose area is independent of the plasma cross section. The electrons "fall into" the anode; the work function aids their entrance.

The anode fall of potential may be either positive or negative,[15A, C] and it is usually not more than a few volts. The anode is not in general a positive ion source, and the electric field tends to drive positive ions away from it. The consequent scarcity of ions near the anode may require the main electron stream to pass from plasma to anode as a space-charge-limited current, which demands an electron-accelerating potential. On the other hand, the large random electron current density in the plasma tends toward a large random electron current into the anode, if the area of exposure of anode surface to plasma is very large. A small negative anode fall of potential may then be required to limit the rate of electron entrance to the anode to the current called for by the circuit.

16.6 Sheaths ("Inactive Boundaries"). "Inactive" boundary regions, enveloping all the surfaces of a plasma except those through which the main electron stream enters and leaves, are usually referred to as *sheaths*, or *positive ion sheaths*. They are called sheaths because they surround (form sheaths around) any objects, such as grids or exploring electrodes, that intrude into plasmas. They are called positive ion sheaths because they are practically free from electrons but contain positive ions in concentrations that are substantial, though on the average less than in adjacent plasmas.

Where there are no material bounding surfaces, as in an open-air arc, the inactive boundary region (flame) that surrounds the plasma may occupy a much greater volume than the plasma, and it merges gradually into the surrounding atmosphere.[15C, h] The extent of a plasma may be limited by its own equilibrium requirements, as in open-air arcs, or by physical boundaries, such as the glass walls of a tube, the arc chutes of an air circuit breaker, the oil of an a-c oil circuit breaker, or the grid of a thyratron. A sheath study may conveniently distinguish between:

(a) *Current-Carrying Sheaths:* The sheaths separating plasmas from conducting boundary surfaces which are electrically connected into the discharge circuitry, as by means of a high resistance and battery. The sheaths between plasma and grid of a grid-controlled gas rectifier, and between any plasma and an exploring electrode, or probe, are illustrations. Analysis of such sheaths follows the probe study principles developed by Langmuir [16f] and others.[16e]

(b) *Insulating Sheaths:* Similar to (a) except that the boundary surfaces are insulated from the main electric circuits, so that no current can pass through the sheaths. The boundary wall material may be either a conductor or an insulator. The sheath between a plasma and a "floating" metal grid (one having no external connections), and that between the plasma of a laboratory glow discharge and its enclosing glass tube are examples of these conditions.

(c) *Flaming Sheaths:* Boundary regions surrounding plasmas whose cross sections are determined by their own equilibrium conditions.[15C, g, h]

16.7 Current-Carrying Sheaths; Probes and Probe Characteristic Curves.* Consider a plasma contained within a long cylindrical glass tube, perhaps 2 inches in diameter, the cathode being at one end, the anode at the other. At a location reasonably remote from either end a small flat metal plate is mounted flush with the interior wall of the tube, to serve as an exploring electrode, employed to investigate plasma properties. Such an exploring electrode may be called a collec-

* See bibliography references 15A, B, C, D, G, 16a (Emeleus), e, f, 17n, 18m.

tor, or more commonly a probe. Because the circumferential extent
of the probe is small relative to tube radius, the probe may, in analysis,
be treated as having a plane surface (a planar probe).

Probes may have other shapes and locations; fine wires, spheres,
rings, and hollow cylinders may be used, located variously within the
plasma.

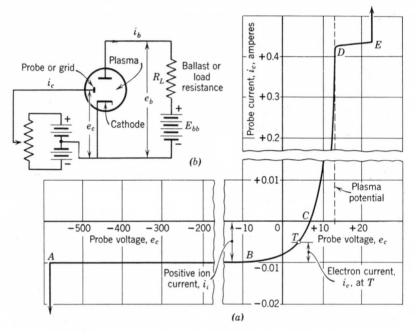

(*a*) Volt-ampere curve for probe or grid introduced into a plasma.
(*b*) Circuit diagram.

FIG. 16.3 Properties of a current-carrying sheath adjacent to a probe or grid
immersed in a plasma. The bend at *D*, shown as somewhat more abrupt than is
usually observed experimentally, occurs when the probe is at plasma potential;
plasma potential is often determined experimentally as the potential at this bend. .

Figure 16.3*a* may be thought of as the volt-ampere curve (voltages
measured relative to the cathode) for a side-wall planar probe. However, a probe of almost any shape and location will give a qualitatively
similar volt-ampere characteristic. The grid of a thyratron (Section
18.9) exhibits a similar volt-ampere characteristic; a thyratron's grid
may very satisfactorily be thought of as a large-area probe immersed
in a plasma.

The circuit of Fig. 16.3*b* may be used to obtain experimentally the
volt-ampere characteristic curve for either probe or grid, and from

this curve many significant facts about the plasma may be learned; see Chapter XI, in *Fundamentals of Physical Electronics*. In particular, plasma potential and electron temperature (Section 16.11), electron and ion density, and in some cases ion temperature are determinable by careful interpretation of data taken with properly designed probes.

For reasons stated later, the high-current bend at D, Fig. 16.3a, indicates that at that point probe and plasma have the same potential. Note the breaks in the vertical and horizontal scales; the current density at D may be numerically several hundred times the negative current along the AB horizontal. As the current density at D is very large, a probe of appreciable area would at that potential draw a current comparable with the main discharge current, thereby seriously altering the properties of the plasma being investigated. Thus if the point D is to be reached on an investigational volt-ampere curve, the probe area must be very small. The area of the grid of a thyratron is always substantial; therefore the grid volt-ampere curve of a thyratron can never be measured out to D, or to anywhere near that point.

16.8 Planar Sheath Potential Distributions.[15A, B, n, 16f, 18m] Figure 16.4b shows a typical potential distribution curve for the insulating sheath adjacent to the glass wall enclosing a plasma. The current

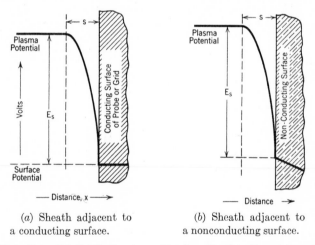

(a) Sheath adjacent to a conducting surface.

(b) Sheath adjacent to a nonconducting surface.

FIG. 16.4 Potential distribution in positive ion sheaths adjacent to surfaces.

through such an insulating sheath must be zero; the potential of the wall must therefore be as at point C, in Fig. 16.3a, because only at point C is the current zero. Thus the potential of the surface must be lower than the plasma potential, because point C is lower in potential than point D.

Figure 16.4a illustrates the potential distribution through a sheath adjacent to a conducting surface, such as the grid of a thyratron or a planar side-wall probe. Note particularly that:

(a) The wall is an equipotential in Fig. 16.4a, whereas it sustains a substantial gradient in Fig. 16.4b.

(b) The value of E_s in Fig. 16.4a may be anything at all, from a few volts to a few hundred volts, whereas in Fig. 16.4b E_s must be the potential difference between points C and D in Fig. 16.3a.

In Figs. 16.4a and 16.4b, the short horizontal potential curve portions marked "plasma potential" may be thought of as near-the-sheath portions of the plasma potential curve in Fig. 15.2c, but to such a scale as to appear perfectly horizontal in Figs. 16.4a and 16.4b.

It is apparent from the flatness of these portions of the potential curves that there is little or no space charge in the plasma, and that therefore $N_i \cong N_e$, where N_i and N_e stand for electron and ion concentrations. More definitely, a basic fact of the plasma is that $(N_i - N_e) \ll N_i$. The analysis used later for the potential distribution curve of Fig. 16.4a employs, *within the sheath*, the *opposite* extreme assumption, that $N_e \ll N_i$. In the sheath the ion density is about the same as in the plasma, but the electron density is essentially zero.

The overwhelming ion predominance in the sheath results from the fact that only very few (high-random-energy) electrons can enter the sheath from the plasma, because of the retarding field they encounter in the attempt. On the other hand, all the ions that reach the plasma face of the sheath fall through it to the probe. Thus the plasma face of the sheath, distant s from the probe surface, identifies a location where the transition takes place from the $(N_i - N_e) \ll N_i$ condition to the opposite extreme, $N_e \ll N_i$. The Boltzmann relation (12–113) governs the change in electron density; the exponential nature of this relation calls for a very rapid response of N_e to spatial changes in potential. Therefore the transition between these extremes may be thought of as occurring within a distance modest in comparison with s.

The plasma face of any such flat sheath as here discussed is an "ion sink." Any plasma positive ion whose motion brings it to the face of the sheath falls through the sheath to the probe, or grid, or glass-wall surface, and recombines there. If the wall surface is conducting, each ion steals an electron from the surface to become a neutral gas particle. If the wall surface is an insulator, the ion may have to wait on the wall until a high-random-energy electron penetrates through the sheath to the wall in the immediate neighborhood of the waiting ion, before recombination can occur.

The rate of entry of positive ions into the sheath from the plasma is determined *by the ion motions in the plasma*, and not in any way by the potential difference E_s across the sheath. Therefore, the potential of a grid or probe may be lowered to several hundred volts below cathode potential without appreciable change occurring in the ion current; this is why the probe volt-ampere characteristic of Fig. 16.3a is essentially horizontal between A and B, a range of several hundred volts. Throughout this entire range the probe or grid potential E_c is so low that no plasma electrons are able to penetrate through the sheath; hence within this A to B range the current to the probe or grid is just that corresponding to the plasma-determined ion flow from the plasma into the sheath. See Chapter X in *Fundamentals of Physical Electronics* for an analysis of this flow.[15n]

When the grid or probe potential rises above values in the neighborhood of B, the potential across the sheath becomes small enough to permit an appreciable fraction of the plasma electrons to penetrate to the probe or grid. The resulting electron current flow is opposite in polarity to that due to ion flow. As the total current is the algebraic sum of that due to ions and to electrons, the growth of the electron current is indicated by a rise in the curve. At some such point as T the electron and ion currents combine algebraically to give a net current smaller numerically than either alone. At C the two are equal, so that the total grid or probe current is zero.

At D the probe and plasma potentials are equal, so that neither electrons nor ions experience any force action in passing from plasma to probe; in fact, $E_s = 0$, so that there is no sheath. The entire random electron current density is entering the probe, therefore a rise of probe potential above its value at D will produce very little if any increase in electron current. Hence there is a more or less sharply defined bend in the probe volt-ampere curve at the plasma potential; this fact may be used to determine experimentally the plasma potential at the probe location.

At E, only a few volts above plasma potential, the grid or probe abruptly becomes a new anode of the discharge and can then no longer properly be called a probe. The grid or probe becomes a new cathode only when pushed to several hundred volts below the original cathode's potential, as at A. The difference is due to the fact that electrons pass freely into a metal but are removed from it with difficulty.

16.9 Sheath Voltage and Thickness.[15A, B, 16e,f, 18m] For thin planar sheaths as illustrated in Fig. 16.4, especially at relatively large sheath potentials, the following adaptation of (5–11) provides good approximations [16f] relating sheath potential E_s, sheath thickness s, and ion current density through the sheath, J_i:

$$J_i = \frac{4\epsilon_0}{9} \sqrt{\frac{2q_e}{m_g}} \frac{E_s^{\frac{3}{2}}}{s^2} \tag{16-1}$$

Numerically:

$$J_i = \frac{2.33 \times 10^{-6}}{\sqrt{m_g/m_e}} \frac{E_s^{\frac{3}{2}}}{s^2} \tag{16-2}$$

Note that J_i is the ion current from plasma to sheath, governed *by conditions in the plasma*. These space-charge-limited forms apply here because:

(a) The sheath is assumed thin enough so that the *ions* fall freely through it, just as the *electrons* fall freely from cathode toward anode in Section 5.4; also, the ions start falling from the plasma with negligible initial energies ($E_{Ti} \ll E_s$) just as the electrons leave the cathode of Section 5.4 with negligible initial velocities. Therefore, the energy equation (5–2) applies to the ions of the sheath, but with m_g used rather than m_e.

(b) Carriers of one sign only are present in the sheath, because the retarding field largely excludes electrons from the sheath; therefore Poisson's equation (5–1) and the equation of flow (5–4) apply in the planar sheath, as in Section 5.4, except that here ρ becomes $\rho_i = N_i q_e$.

(c) The potential gradient is essentially zero at the plasma face of the sheath, where the ions begin their rapidly accelerated free fall, just as the electrons of Section 5.4 start falling from a cathode at which the potential gradient is zero.

These (a), (b), and (c) conditions lead to a differential equation and boundary conditions identical with those leading to (5–11), except that m_g replaces m_e, hence the validity of (16–1) and (16–2). This validity has been demonstrated experimentally by visual observations of the sheath thickness. The sheath outline can be observed because very little light originates in the sheath in comparison with that originating in the adjacent plasma, owing to there being very few electrons, and therefore very little excitation of atoms, in the sheath.

Note that the gentle radial gradient in the plasma [15n] and the plasma random ion current govern J_i, and circuit operating conditions govern E_s; thus (16–2) *is usually employed as an equation for the determination of* s.

16.10   Thyratron Grid Shut-Off; Recovery Time. [18m]   In many thyratrons (see Sections 18.9 through 18.16) it is possible to cause shut-off of small plate currents by driving the grid strongly negative. This happens when the sheath around the grid becomes so thick that it entirely fills the openings of the grid. This prevents passage of the main plasma electron current, because the grid sheath is a low-potential region that electrons of the plasma cannot enter.

This grid shut-off action is ordinarily of no great utility, because it occurs easily only at small plasma currents. It does, however, often play an important part in the periodic extinction of current in the small thyratrons (Tube Nos. 2050, 2051) used for cathode-ray oscilloscope sweep circuits; see Section 18.16.

If, in a thyratron, plate current goes out because of normal plate circuit behavior, there remains in the interelectrode spaces a dying plasma. In course of time the ion concentration of the plasma decays, because of continuing loss of ions to the lateral boundaries. With far fewer ions present, the ion current J_i to the wall is much reduced; (16–2) then requires that s become greater, for given E_s. This continues until eventually the sheath around the grid wires or other conducting surfaces entirely fills the grid openings. If the plate voltage of the thyratron is driven positive before this closure of the grid holes occurs, the plasma will become re-established immediately in spite of a negative grid voltage; the grid has not yet recovered its normal control function. Thus the least value of the "recovery time," also called the "deionization time" (time required for the grid to regain control), is the time required for the ion concentration to decay to such a value that the sheath fills the grid holes. By employing this criterion it is possible to coordinate satisfactorily with theory the observed dependence of recovery time on grid voltage, plate current, condensed-mercury temperature, etc.[18l, m] See Chapter XI in *Fundamentals of Physical Electronics* for a detailed discussion of recovery or deionization time.

16.11   Probe Measurements of Plasma Electron Temperature and Plasma Potential.[15A, B, D, G, 16e, f, 18m] An experimental volt-ampere curve from either a probe or a thyratron grid can be used to measure the plasma electron temperature, and such a curve from a sufficiently small probe can be used to determine plasma potential.

The ion current is not affected by sheath potential, so that its value at some such point as T, Fig. 16.3a, can be determined by prolonging the line AB toward the right beyond the B region. This prolongation is shown lightly in the figure. The total current and the ion current for any such point are then known, so that the electron current can be found. The natural logarithm of the experimentally determined electron current is then plotted vs. the probe or grid voltage E_c, as in Fig. 16.5. In general, with Maxwellian electrons, this plot will establish a straight line, whose slope is $1/E_{Te}$, as will now be shown.

The behavior of Maxwellian velocity electrons entering the retarding electric field of the sheath was anticipated, for illustrative purposes, in connection with (12–100b), which states the random electron current density within the plasma, and (12–103), which states the electron current density penetrating through the sheath to the grid or probe. Using the notation employed there, the electron current i_e to

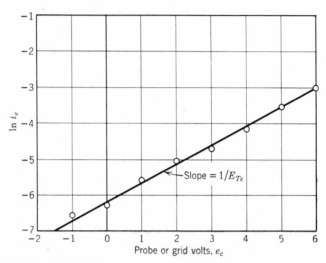

FIG. 16.5 Experimental determination of the electron temperature in a plasma.

a probe surface exposed where the electron density is N_e, is obtained by multiplying J_{es} by the surface area S of the probe. Thus, with e_s signifying the potential drop across the sheath,

$$i_e = \frac{N_e \bar{\zeta}_e q_e S}{2\sqrt{\pi}} \exp \frac{-e_s}{E_{Te}} \qquad (16\text{--}3)$$

If E_{pl} symbolizes plasma potential, and e_c probe or grid potential, it is evident from Fig. 16.4 that

$$e_s = E_{pl} - e_c \qquad (16\text{--}4)$$

Therefore the probe current can be expressed as

$$i_e = \frac{N_e \bar{\zeta}_e S}{2\sqrt{\pi}} \exp \left(- \frac{E_{pl} - e_c}{E_{Te}} \right) \qquad (16\text{--}5)$$

Taking natural logarithms gives

$$\ln i_e = \ln \frac{N_e \bar{\zeta}_e q_e S}{2\sqrt{\pi}} - \frac{E_{pl}}{E_{Te}} + \frac{e_c}{E_{Te}} \qquad (16\text{--}6)$$

This represents a straight line, if the variables are $\ln i_e$ and e_c. The slope of this straight line is $1/E_{Te}$, hence the interpretation given above to Fig. 16.5.

This general method of determining electron temperature is valid for almost any shape or placement of probe, and for both long-mean-free-path (very low pressure) and short-mean-free-path (only moderately low pressure) conditions. There are, however, many plasma conditions in which the plot of $\ln i_e$ vs. e_c does not give a very close approach to a straight line. In such cases the slope, even though not

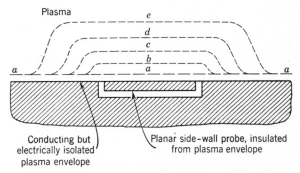

Fig. 16.6   Planar (flat) side-wall probe. Dashed curves a, b, c, d, and e describe probe sheath outlines for successively more negative values of probe voltage e_c. Curve a is for the zero-current sheath, having the same thickness as the sheath adjacent to the conducting but electrically isolated envelope.

constant, can still be used to give a general measure of the mean electron energy; the concept of temperature may then not be significant because of departures from a Maxwellian electron energy distribution.

Care must be exercised in the extrapolation of the AB portion of the volt-ampere curve, Fig. 16.3a, preliminary to determining the electron current. For example, Fig. 16.6 indicates how the sheath of a planar side-wall probe may grow as e_c goes more negative. This sheath thickening obviously exposes more sheath surface area to the plasma and so causes an increase in ion collection by the plasma. The AB portion of the characteristic in that case is a straight line sloping gently upward from left to right, and the extrapolation should exhibit the same continued gentle upward slope.[16f]

The potential of a low-pressure plasma can often be determined as the potential of the probe at the bend at D, Fig. 16.3a. Usually an experimentally obtained probe characteristic exhibits enough rounding-off of the bend to introduce a modest uncertainty as to the precise value of plasma potential. However, measurements at longitudinally separated probes behave similarly, so that relative potentials, and therefore potential gradients, can sometimes be rather well determined when absolute plasma potentials cannot. The probe surface area must be very small, because the electron current density to the probe is very large, yet the total probe current must be a very small fraction of the main plasma anode current, in order not to modify the plasma being studied.

16.12 Flaming Sheaths around Unrestricted Plasmas.[15A, C, D, g, h] Perhaps the most important difference between current-carrying and insulating sheaths on one hand and the flaming sheaths that surround open-air arcs on the other hand (see Fig. 15.2b) is in the manner and place of recombination of ions.[15A, B, u]

Any plasma ion that enters any of these sheaths is lost from the plasma; it is certain to recombine. In a sheath adjacent to a wall, the recombination takes place at the wall. In flaming sheaths the ions continue to diffuse outward for varying distances before recombining. Such sheaths do not have sharply defined outer boundaries; they merge gradually into the surrounding atmosphere. It may be that the two-stage mechanism mentioned in Section 15.7 accounts for much of the recombination in flaming sheaths.

The electrons that take part in the recombination, like the positive ions, move outward from the plasma into the flaming sheath. This diffusion-like movement takes place in spite of the electric force due to the radial potential gradient in the sheath, and because of the very considerable temperature energies of the electrons. In case the two-stage recombination process is important, a flaming sheath will contain negative ions in appreciable concentration.

The potential distribution curve for a flaming sheath must merge gradually into the space-charge-free potential distribution pattern established by the circuit as a whole. Both positive and negative space charge may exist in a flaming sheath, the latter enveloping the former, because there must always be a hollow cylinder of positive space charge immediately surrounding the plasma.

PROBLEMS

1. Tests on a certain mercury-vapor thyratron show that, as the grid voltage is decreased below about -12 volts (relative to the cathode), the grid current reaches a constant value of about 114 ma (positive ion current); grid current is zero when grid voltage is -2. Assume that ion and gas temperatures are both $500°$ K; grid area of 20 sq cm is exposed to the plasma. Plasma is 16 volts above cathode potential. Find: (a) the electron temperature; (b) the sheath thickness when grid voltage is -100.

2. To what electron temperature does Fig. 16.5 correspond?

3. A flat "probe," surface area 0.3 sq cm, is exposed to a plasma in mercury vapor at a point where there are 10^{12} ions per cu cm and an equal electron concentration. The ion current density to the probe is 0.0012, and the random electron current density 2.80, both in amp per sq cm.

(a) Find the temperature of the electrons and v_i from plasma into sheath. (b) Assuming that the electrons in the plasma have a Maxwellian velocity distribution, determine the current to the probe when its potential is 3 volts lower than that of the plasma. (c) Determine the current to the probe and the sheath thickness when the probe is 225 volts below plasma potential. (d) At what potential, relative to the plasma, will the probe current be zero?

4. A low-pressure mercury vapor arc carrying a current of 4 amp is operating in a long glass tube of 6 cm diameter. The glass wall interior surface is 7 volts negative relative to the plasma; the ion current density to the glass wall is 2 ma per sq cm. Electron, ion, and gas temperatures are respectively 18,000° K, 9000° K, and 600° K.

(a) Find the power delivered to the glass wall, per centimeter length of tube, by the ions and electrons arriving at the wall. (b) The rate of ion production in the plasma must equal the rate of ion loss to the glass wall, per centimeter of tube length. Find the number of ions produced per second per cubic centimeter of plasma. (c) Assume that there are 8 times as many exciting as there are ionizing collisions, and that the average energy radiated following each exciting collision is 6 electron volts. Find the total power radiated from the plasma, per centimeter length. (d) Find the potential gradient necessary to maintain this plasma, taking into account all the (a), (b), (c), power losses.

5. In a certain thyratron the holes in the grid (see Section 18.9) are 3 mm in diameter. When the plate current i_b is 1 amp, the ion current density to the grid is 8 ma per sq cm.

(a) At about what negative value of grid potential will this plate current be extinguished? (b) When the grid potential is −80 volts, what is the *potential gradient* at the surface of a flat portion of the grid lying between the holes? (c) If the diameter of the holes in the grid were increased by 50 per cent, would the recovery time (see Sections 16.10 and 18.16) be made greater or less? Explain.

6. One hypothesis of electron emergence from the cathode hot spot of a metallic or mercury-vapor arc is that there exists a high-current-density positive ion sheath adjacent to the spot, that results in an extremely high gradient at the metal surface, with resulting "field emission," at very high current densities.

(a) On the basis of this hypothesis, determine what the voltage gradient at the emitting surface would be under the following conditions, in a mercury-vapor discharge, with a mercury-pool cathode: condensed-mercury temperature 40° C (see Section 18.8, flow equilibrium); 100 per cent ionization of gas particles in the gas adjacent to the cathode "sheath"; temperature of the ionized gas adjacent to and in the cathode sheath 800° K; ion current density entering the sheath is the random ion current density from the adjacent 100 per cent ionized gas; sheath potential is the cathode fall of potential, assumed to be 10.4 volts. (b) If under these conditions the field emission from the spot gives an electron emission 12 times the ion current to the spot, what is the total cathode spot current density?

CHAPTER XVII

ARC AND GLOW TRANSIENT PHENOMENA

17.1 Initiation and Extinction Considerations. In the majority of engineering devices employing gaseous conduction, important problems of design or of use center around the initiation or extinction of the gas discharge. The following types of such events occur commonly: *

(a) *Voltage breakdown,*[17a, b, c, d, e, f, g, h, 18h] that is, the initiation of either a glow or an arc discharge between an anode and a *cold* cathode. (A cold cathode is a cathode that does not emit electrons thermionically.) Illustrations of this are: lightning; transmission-line flashover due to high-voltage surges; the initiation of current flow in VR-type voltage regulator tubes, in neon and similar commercial display lights, in cold-cathode triggering triodes, and in sparks employed for switching purposes or for spectroscopic analysis of the electrode material; and the sudden appearance of a destructive glow discharge in a gas phototube.

(b) Abrupt transition from a glow discharge to an arc [15C, 17k] as from C' to D', Fig. 15.1.

(c) Arc initiation in the presence of a thermionic cathode, as in domestic fluorescent lights, in thermionic gas rectifiers (phanotrons), and in *thyratrons* (grid-controlled gas rectifiers).[15A, C, G, H, I, 18i, j, k]

(d) Initiation of an *electrodeless discharge,* that is, a high-frequency plasma sustained without entry or exit of electrons to or from active electrodes.[15t, 17h]

(e) Initiation of a hot-spot arc cathode resulting from an extreme local electric gradient set up by current flow across a surface discontinuity, as in an *ignitron*.[18a, b, c]

(f) Initiation of a hot-spot arc cathode at the moment of separation of a pair of contacts through which current is flowing, as at the opening of a knife switch or a circuit breaker, or the excitron igniter.[18d]

(g) Abrupt conversion of an inactive plasma boundary (sheath) to an arc cathode, as at point A in Fig. 16.3a; in a gas rectifier this is called *arc-back* or *back-fire*.[18h] It is very similar to the transition from glow to arc.

(h) Extinction of a d-c arc by the creation of a demand for a larger voltage gradient than the circuit can supply; this applies particularly to the long arcs in d-c circuit breakers.[17l, m]

(i) Extinction of an a-c arc by the creation of conditions unfavorable to arc reignition following the normal cyclic current zero.[17l, m, n]

Several kinds of plasma-initiating events exhibit a random time delay between the moment the initiating voltage is applied and the moment the plasma comes into being; [17d, 18b, m] see Sections 17.3 and 18.18.

---

* In the bibliography, see book references 15A, B, C, D, F, G, H, I, 17A, B, C.

508

17.2   Cold-Cathode Voltage Breakdown Mechanisms at Low Pressures.* Figure 14.6a is employed later, in Sections 17.6 and 17.7, in setting up analytical expressions for voltage breakdown at low gas pressures, in the presence of a cathode surface that is not a thermionic emitter. To begin with, it is customarily assumed that the cathode is illuminated. However, the end expressions derived are independent of the strength of the illumination, which can therefore be thought of as vanishingly small in the limiting case.

In the Fig. 14.6a situation, the voltage gradient causes gas amplification. If the *ions* resulting from the amplification process strike the cathode with sufficient kinetic energy, they will knock electrons out of the cathode surface,[16b] somewhat as electrons do in causing secondary emission from a dynode. If sufficient voltage is applied, this release of new electrons by ion bombardment will occur so rapidly that the charged particles more than reproduce themselves, quite independently of the initial photoelectric emission. When this condition is reached, the current flow grows very rapidly, resulting in the establishment of a plasma. *Voltage breakdown* has then occurred, and the current flow is thereafter determined primarily by the external circuit.

It is analytically imaginable that voltage breakdown may occur by a process involving at the cathode photoelectric action alone, electron release by ion bombardment playing no part in the process. As the electrons move toward the anode, there will be exciting as well as ionizing collisions. The exciting collisions produce photons; many of these photons will strike the cathode, and photoelectric emission will result. The charged particles may in this way more than reproduce themselves, with resulting initiation of a plasma.

Presumably in actual low-pressure devices the ion bombardment mechanism and the photoelectric mechanism act simultaneously. It is shown in Sections 17.6 and 17.7 that for the planar geometry of Fig. 14.6a the *form* of the equation for voltage breakdown is the same for the two mechanisms. This has made it difficult to establish experimentally the circumstances under which each mechanism predominates.

There is a difference in the geometrical dependence of the two mechanisms. All the *ions* produced will reach the cathode, both in the planar system of Fig. 14.6a, and in a system in which the cathode is the inner member of a pair of concentric cylinders, because the direction of ion motion is determined by the electric field. However, the photon directions are not affected by the electric field. Thus for an infinite planar system one-half of the photons will terminate on the cathode,

---

* In the bibliography, see especially 15A, B, C, also 15D, F, G, 17a, b, c, m.

whereas in an inner-cathode concentric system somewhat fewer than half will terminate on the cathode. It should therefore be possible to study the predominance of one mechanism over the other by comparing the relative performance in different geometries.

There is a third mechanism of ion replenishment, employing metastable atoms. In addition to producing ions and, indirectly, photons, the advancing electrons may excite atoms into metastable states. In course of time these metastable atoms diffuse to the boundaries, because of ordinary thermal motions. Some of these metastable atoms may release electrons on arrival at the cathode, providing the energy of the metastable state is greater than the work function of the metal. The analysis of this mechanism parallels closely that of the photon mechanism.

In the present discussion and in Section 17.6 no attention is paid to the possibility that the ion replenishment might result from volume ionization by positive ion impact with gas particles. Experiments have shown that the probability of such ionization, described quantitatively by Townsend's β coefficient, is in engineering environments so very small that it has no influence on breakdown processes.

17.3   Voltage Breakdown Time-Lag Mechanisms.[14k, 15A, B, 17b, d]   The ion bombardment mechanism for low-pressure voltage breakdown requires that the ions move from the interelectrode space to the cathode before the replenishment mechanism can be initiated. Ions move relatively slowly; therefore, this mechanism should exhibit an appreciable time lag, of the order of 10^{-5} second, between application of voltage and establishment of the plasma. In contrast, the photoelectric mechanism involves a time lag due only to the *electron* transit time. Electrons move very rapidly; therefore, the time lag for this mechanism should be very short, of the order of 10^{-10} second. Diffusion of metastable atoms occurs very slowly, suggesting a time lag of the order of 10^{-3} second for the metastable-atom mechanism.

Thus, the three mechanisms presumably exhibit different time-lag characteristics. However, these systematic time lags may be masked by statistically random time lags of different origin.

In most devices exhibiting low-pressure voltage breakdown, the cathode is not in fact illuminated by light capable of producing the initial photoelectric current. However, in any earthly environment there are randomly occurring processes producing occasional ionization. One such event at or near the cathode will trip off the chain of events leading to voltage breakdown; this first event occurs *randomly*, in time, after voltage application. This is one reason for the statistically random nature of the important time lag; with any given set of physical circumstances and applied voltage there will exist this random time lag. For this type of causation, the distribution of individual time lags about the mean for many observations will be of the same nature as in the firing of an ignitron; see Figs. 18.19, 18.20, and the associated equations.

As the gas pressure is increased, the presence of the larger number of gas particles leads to an increase in the probability of occurrence of the initial event, so that the mean time lag becomes less, other things being equal. At and near atmospheric pressure the streamer mechanism of voltage breakdown, discussed in the next two sections, supplants those described above, but the statistically random time-lag behavior persists.

The mean time lag is in all cases a declining function of the *excess* of the applied "step" voltage above a critical value called the breakdown voltage. The higher the pressure, the less is the excess voltage that corresponds to any given value of mean time lag.

17.4   Voltage Breakdown at Atmospheric Pressure; Corona. [15A, B, 17A, B, C, c, d, e, f, g]   As indicated in Fig. 17.1, the breakdown voltage in air at atmospheric pressure is, at high voltages, very nearly proportional to spacing, providing edge effects are eliminated as in a sphere gap. Also, just as at lower pressures (see Fig. 17.2), there is a minimum voltage of the order of 300 volts below which breakdown will not occur, no matter how small the spacing. The slope in Fig. 17.1 corresponds to an atmospheric-pressure flashover gradient of about 30,000 volts per centimeter, or a little over 70,000 volts per inch. Because of the general similitude dependence of conduction phenomena on Fl (volts per mean free path), the high-voltage flashover gradient changes in proportion to the pressure. Of course, at any pressure, the flashover gradient differs markedly as between different gases.

At pressures exceeding a modest fraction of an atmosphere, and for appreciable spacings and correspondingly high voltages, the mean free path is extremely short relative to the distance between conductors. When this is true, the method of electron release at the cathode becomes of secondary importance, as evidenced by the fact that the initial appearance of conductivity in the gas occurs wherever the gradient is the greatest, often remote from the cathode. This implies a new mechanism, involving *streamers* or *electron avalanches*, distinctly different from the mechanisms of Section 17.2.

First the gross aspects, subsequently the detail aspects, of this streamer mechanism will be discussed. Consider first a region possessing a markedly nonuniform gradient, as that between concentric cylinders (large diameter ratio) or between the conductors of a transmission line. With sufficient voltage applied, the gas becomes con-ducting locally in the region of greatest field strength. This local conducting volume becomes essentially an equipotential region, ad-jacent to the small cylindrical conductor (wire). This enlarges the effective diameter of the conductor, thereby decreasing the gradient at the effective conductor surface (the outer surface of the annular gaseous-conducting envelope). The diameter of the conducting en-velope increases until the gradient at its outer surface is inadequate to establish conductivity. Thus there is formed around the wire a conducting shell having a more or less stable diameter. The name *corona* is given to the type of gaseous conductivity represented by the presence of such a conducting shell around the wire.

Corona cannot exist between parallel flat electrodes, because the appearance of the layer of conducting gas adjacent to either electrode, or at any local region, causes the gradient in the remaining space to increase rather than decrease. Thus, once the gas becomes locally conducting anywhere, the conducting volume rapidly grows along electric flux lines, and flashover ensues.

Even in a corona-forming geometry, flashover will result at a suf-ficiently high voltage; the critical voltage is that at which a further increase in diameter of the corona envelope causes an increase rather than a decrease of the maximum gradient. Lightning is an extreme example of flashover.[15A, B, 17g]

A corona envelope bears little apparent resemblance to an ordinary arc plasma. It consists, at atmospheric pressure, of myriads of hair-like and luminous extremely short-lived *streamers*. Each positive streamer (adjacent to the more positive conductor) resembles a tiny river, draining electrons from the corona envelope into the conductor. Similarly each negative streamer resembles a tiny river taking electrons from the more negative conductor, by one or more of the mechanisms described in Section 17.2 and delivering them to the intervening space. Positive streamers resemble tiny, threadlike arcs, each complete with plasma and sheath. Negative streamers exhibit a more diffuse pattern, the detail structure being on a finer scale.

17.5   Corona Streamer and Avalanche Details.[15A, B, 17A, C, e, f, g]   There is always a small but finite probability of an ionizing event's occurring within any small gas volume and time increment, causing the appear-ance of a free electron. Under short-mean-free-path conditions, with a gradient exceeding the breakdown value, the value of volts per mean free path is large enough so that any free electron will produce ions. That is, Townsend's α (see Fig. 14.11) has a value appreciably greater than zero. Thus, while advancing a distance of a substantial number of l-units, the one randomly introduced electron produces several more, and each of these again many more, as in gas amplification in a photo-tube. Thus there is produced an *avalanche* of advancing electrons.

This avalanche, especially if near the anode, creates a local, plasma-like river of electrons flowing toward the anode, that is, a streamer. This drains electrons away from a local volume, leaving this local volume with a substantial positive ion space charge. This space charge, by virtue of Poisson's law as applied to cylindrical geometry, reduces the gradient that maintains the streamer; thus in due course the streamer has no further source of electrons and ceases to exist. The positive ions then move slowly toward the cathode, reducing the local space charge and ultimately allowing breakdown gradient to be re-established. A positive corona envelope consists of myriads of these streamers, each one of extremely short duration and small size.

Negative corona streamers take electrons from the cathode by a combination of mechanisms similar to those at the cathode of a glow discharge; a local and rather diffuse plasma is maintained to support the necessary cathode fall of potential. The electrons are delivered, by the negative streamers, to a gentle-gradient region outside the negative corona envelope, where the electric field is little enough so that Townsend's α is vanishingly small; the electrons advance toward the opposite electrode without causing ionization. These electrons may become quiescent enough to form negative ions by attachment to gas particles. Thus a low-current-density conduction between the corona envelopes exists, owing to the oppositely directed flow of positive and negative ions. These particles in due course experience neutralizing recombination, either in the between-envelope region, or on close approach to the conducting envelope toward which they move.

If the geometry and voltages permit the tips of a negative streamer and a positive streamer to make contact, an immediate local intense plasma is established at the junction, and both streamers rapidly grow indefinitely in strength and current; flashover has occurred. Magnus-son, employing Lichtenberg figures on photographic film, has carried out extremely interesting and suggestive experiments related to this behavior.[17c]

17.6   Equations for Low-Pressure Voltage Breakdown; Electrons Released by Ion Bombardment.[15A, B, C, D, F, G, 17a, b]   Consider a planar geometry as in Fig. 14.6a, with spacing s, the mechanism of voltage breakdown being the low-pressure type involving release of electrons at the cathode by ion bombardment, as discussed in Section 17.2. Let

J_0 = photoelectric emission current density from the cathode, due to light from an external source. The light must be ultraviolet if it is to produce photoelectric emission from an ordinary metal surface.

J_b = total current density, due to flow of both ions and electrons. At the anode surface this is wholly electron-borne.

J_{ea} = electron-borne current density just off the cathode, consisting of J_0 plus the current carried by electrons knocked out by ion bombardment.

α = the number of new electrons produced per unit distance of an electron's advance; see Fig. 14.11.

γ_i = the probability that an ion bombarding the cathode will release an electron. When a substantial rate of ion flow exists, this is

$$\gamma_i = \frac{\text{electrons released by ion bombardment per second}}{\text{ions striking the cathode per second}}. \quad (17\text{--}1)$$

It is reasonably evident that

$$\text{Ion current density arriving at cathode} = J_b - J_{ea} \quad (17\text{--}2)$$

Therefore

$$\left.\begin{array}{l}\text{Electron current density at cathode,} \\ \text{due to electrons knocked out by} \\ \text{ion bombardment.}\end{array}\right\} = \gamma_i(J_b - J_{ea}) \quad (17\text{--}3)$$

It follows immediately that

$$J_{ea} = J_0 + \gamma_i(J_b - J_{ea}) \quad (17\text{--}4)$$

Solving for J_{ea} gives

$$J_{ea} = \frac{J_0 + \gamma_i J_b}{1 + \gamma_i} \quad (17\text{--}5)$$

From (14–9)

$$J_b = J_{ea} \exp \alpha s \quad (17\text{--}6)$$

Therefore, from the last two equations,

$$J_b = \frac{J_0 + \gamma_i J_b}{1 + \gamma_i} \exp \alpha s \quad (17\text{--}7)$$

Solving for J_b gives

$$J_b = \frac{J_0 \exp \alpha s}{1 - \gamma_i(\exp \alpha s - 1)} \quad (17\text{--}8)$$

The usual criterion for voltage breakdown is the vanishing of the denominator in this expression. This criterion is independent of J_0, except that J_0 must be finite.   Practically, this implies that voltage breakdown should occur if one electron appears in the neighborhood of the cathode, because one electron is the smallest finite charge that can exist.   If there is no intentional ultraviolet illumination of the cathode, the appearance of this first electron is an event occurring randomly in time; therefore the time lag to *initiation* of breakdown should be of random duration, as discussed in Section 17.3.

The vanishing of the denominator in (17–8) requires that

$$\gamma_i = \frac{1}{\exp \alpha s - 1} \qquad \text{[criterion for breakdown]} \qquad (17\text{--}9)$$

At potentials respectively a little less than, equal to, or a little greater than that causing (17–9) to be satisfied, the *probability* of any initial electron's reproducing itself is a little less than unity, equal to unity, or a little greater than unity.   For such a probability concept, individual events will agree with (17–9) only on an average basis.   Thus an individual electron may occasionally produce breakdown at less than the critical voltage; also, an electron released into a field greater than the critical value may fail to produce voltage breakdown.   This behavior modifies in some details the statistical time lag discussed in Section 17.3.

The arguments associated with (17–9) imply circuitry "stiff" enough (low enough impedance in series with the voltage source) to maintain the electrode voltage close to breakdown value in spite of the current flow associated with the initial electron "avalanche."   Time constants are ordinarily such that this requirement involves attention to capacitances and inductances of wires leading to the electrodes and to measuring devices.   The details of the transient behavior after the appearance of the first electron, and before the final stable existence of a plasma, are relatively complex, and intimately related to the speed of response of the circuitry.

17.7   Equations for Breakdown; Electrons Released by Photons Originating in the Interelectrode Space.[15A, B, 17b]   Consider a situation as in the previous section, except that γ_i is now zero, and the breakdown mechanism is that of photoelectric emission at the cathode due to photons originating between the electrodes, as discussed in Section 17.2.   In addition to the symbolism of the previous section, let

ξ = the number of photons produced in the gas per unit distance of an electron's advance toward the anode, these photons resulting from excitation of the gas particles.

h = a geometrical coefficient describing the fraction of the photons that arrive at the cathode surface. For infinite parallel planes, as here considered, $h = \frac{1}{2}$.

η = the probability that one of the photons that is produced in the interelectrode space, and that arrives at the cathode, will release an electron by photoelectric emission.

dx = the thickness of a flat increment of space distant x from the cathode.

U_a = the flux of photons arriving at the cathode, having originated by excitation of the gas (the ξ mechanism).

dU = the flux of photons, destined to arrive at the cathode, that originates within dx.

J_{ea} = electron-borne current density just off the cathode, consisting of J_0 plus the current carried by photoelectrons emitted by the photons originating between the electrodes.

Absorption of photons by the gas will be neglected.

From the principles of gas amplification, especially equation (14–9),

$$\left.\begin{array}{r}\text{Electron-borne current density}\\ \text{at distance } x \text{ from cathode}\end{array}\right\} = J_{ea} \exp \alpha x \qquad (17\text{--}10)$$

Therefore

$$dU = \xi h J_{ea} \exp \alpha x \, dx \qquad (17\text{--}11)$$

Integration from 0 to s gives

$$U_a = \frac{\xi h}{\alpha} J_{ea}[\exp (\alpha s) - 1] \qquad (17\text{--}12)$$

Use of (17–6) makes this become

$$U_a = \frac{\xi h}{\alpha} J_b - \frac{\xi h}{\alpha} J_{ea} \qquad (17\text{--}13)$$

The counterpart of (17–4) is, of course,

$$J_{ea} = J_0 + \eta U_a \qquad (17\text{--}14)$$

Use of (17–13) to eliminate U_a leads to

$$J_{ea} = \frac{J_0 + (\eta h \xi / \alpha) J_b}{1 + (\eta h \xi / \alpha)} \qquad (17\text{--}15)$$

This is identical with (17–5) if γ_{ph} replaces γ_i, where

$$\gamma_{ph} = \frac{\eta h \xi}{\alpha} \qquad (17\text{--}16)$$

Treatment paralleling that subsequent to (17–5) leads, therefore, to the following counterpart of (17–8):

$$J_b = \frac{J_0 \exp \alpha s}{1 - \gamma_{ph}(\exp \alpha s - 1)} \qquad (17\text{–}17)$$

The formal criterion for low-pressure voltage breakdown is obviously the same as in the previous section, except for the replacement of γ_i by γ_{ph}. In the absence of intentional ultraviolet illumination the time lag is dependent on the randomly occurring appearance of a first electron, just as in the previous case. However, as mentioned earlier, in Section 17.2, the photoelectric mechanism:

(a) Contains a geometric factor h, not present in the ion bombardment mechanisms; and

(b) Involves no time lag between the production of the photons and their appearance at the cathode, whereas the ions of the previous section do take appreciable time for transit to the cathode.

Note that for most electrically important gases a very substantial proportion of the photons will be in the ultraviolet portion of the spectrum and therefore easily capable of producing photoelectric emission, although at a relatively low quantum yield.

Analysis of the metastable-atom mechanism referred to in Section 17.2 leads to the derivation of a third coefficient γ_{ms} obeying an equation like (17–16), but with η describing the probability of release of an electron at the cathode by a metastable atom, and ξ describing the rate of production of metastable atoms in the space.

To cover the overall situation simply, the total current density for a short-of-breakdown condition is sometimes stated

$$J_b = \frac{J_0 \exp \alpha s}{1 - \gamma(\exp \alpha s - 1)} \qquad (17\text{–}18)$$

where

$$\gamma = \gamma_i + \gamma_{ph} + \gamma_{ms} \qquad (17\text{–}19)$$

Time constants associated with the establishment of the current by these various mechanisms have orders of magnitude as follows: for γ_i, 10^{-5} second; for γ_{ph}, 10^{-10} second; for γ_{ms}, 10^{-3} second; see Section 17.3.

17.8 Paschen's Law.[15A, B, C, D, E, F, G, 17A, B, C, a, b, h, m] Figures 17.1 and 17.2 illustrate, for air, the approximate dependence of breakdown voltage E_δ on the product of "pressure" P_0 by electrode spacing s. The

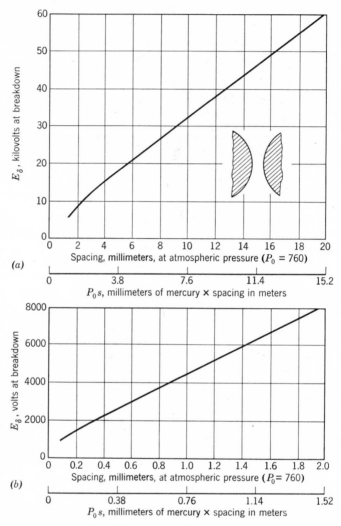

Fig. 17.1 Approximate breakdown voltages for air at atmospheric pressure, at about $20°$ C, as a function of distance between sphere gaps; data from Loeb [15B] (see also Fig. 17.2). (a) From 2 to 20 centimeters. (b) From 0.2 to 2 centimeters. Paschen's law distance coordinate $P_0 s$ also shown; see (17–20).

fact of the dependence on this product is known as *Paschen's law*, expressible formally as

$$E_\delta = f_p(P_0 s) \qquad (17\text{--}20)$$

where $f_p(P_0 s)$ is an empirically determined function of the product $P_0 s$. Actually, the dependence of E_δ is on the product of gas *concentration* by spacing; this is a similitude relationship, going back fundamentally

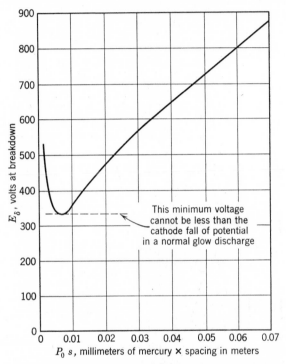

FIG. 17.2 Illustrative approximate graph of dependence of breakdown voltage E_δ in air on the product $P_0 s$ of pressure by electrode spacing s (Paschen's law); data from Loeb.[15B] This portion of the curve is experimentally observable only at low gas pressures. See also Fig. 17.1.

to a dependence on volts per mean free path Fl; details appear in Chapter IX, in *Fundamentals of Physical Electronics*. Therefore P_0 in (17–20) must describe in fact a concentration, not a pressure; for this reason P_0 is defined just as in Section 14.14, that is,

$$P_0 = P_g \frac{273}{T_g} = 2.83 \times 10^{23} N_g \qquad [\text{this defines } P_0] \quad (17\text{--}21)$$

where, as earlier, P_g and T_g are the actual observation-condition values of gas pressure in millimeters of mercury and of gas temperature in degrees Kelvin, and N_g is the number of gas particles per cubic meter.

Paschen's law indicates that a series of curves of breakdown voltage vs. pressure, taken at different electrode spacings, should coincide if plotted on the coordinates of Figs. 17.1 and 17.2. With sufficient care given to details of laboratory procedure, such curves do coincide very closely in the region to the right of the minimum in Fig. 17.2, and reasonably so to the left of the minimum.

The minimum value of E_δ is not less than and in general about the same in magnitude as the normal glow discharge cathode fall of potential, for any given gas and cathode surface.

For portions of Fig. 17.2 in the neighborhood of and to the left of the minimum, the analytical verification of Paschen's law rests on the vanishing of the denominator of (17–18) as a criterion for breakdown. For the higher P_0s values, cathode phenomena are not involved, but details of the emergence from zero of the Townsend's α curve of Fig. 14.11b are involved.

17.9 Cold-Cathode Diodes and Triodes.[17a, i] Cold-cathode glow discharge diodes, called VR (voltage regulator) tubes, are commonly used to maintain a nearly constant cathode-to-anode voltage over a wide range of currents, thus employing the constant-voltage property of the glow discharge portion of the general volt-ampere curve, Fig. 15.1. Design features are chosen to make the cathode fall of potential constitute practically the entire tube voltage. The cathode spot area increases in proportion to current.

Because the *operating* voltage is essentially the normal cathode fall of potential, it is determined by the material and processing of the cathode and the composition of the gas, but it is relatively independent of the geometry or pressure employed in the tube. However, the *starting* voltage obeys Paschen's law and is therefore considerably dependent on pressure and geometry, as well as on gas composition and cathode material and processing. Thus an important VR tube design problem is to make the starting voltage as little as possible above the operating voltage. This implies designing for operation near to the minimum on Fig. 17.2. In Fig. 15.1, the shift from A to B is illustrative of VR tube current initiation.

By placing a third electrode properly with respect to a suitably designed anode and cathode arrangement, it is possible to cause an impulse on the triggering electrode to establish a glow discharge in which the chief current flow is to the main anode. Design details as to electric gradients at electrode surfaces, proportioning of minor constituents in the gas, and cathode surface processing are very important. Such tubes are used in very large quantities to provide selective ringing on telephone lines serving two or four subscribers.

17.10 Radiation (Geiger) Counter Tubes.[17D, i] It is possible to select a combination of tube geometry, gas composition, gas pressure, and circuitry for which the random appearance of a single electron, or of several electrons simultaneously, will initiate an avalanche that does not result in a sustained discharge. The avalanche represents a current pulse that can be amplified by the methods of Section 14.11; the amplified pulse can excite a counting circuit to register the occurrence of these triggering events.

Tubes employing this principle, called radiation counter tubes or Geiger tubes, are employed to record the passage of various kinds of high-energy particles or photons of nuclear origin, including cosmic rays.

17.11 Static Arc and Glow Volt-Ampere Curves.[15A, C, G, c, d, e, g, k, 16a] Figure 17.3a presents an illustrative set of static arc and glow volt-ampere curves, for some definite electrode geometry and material, and

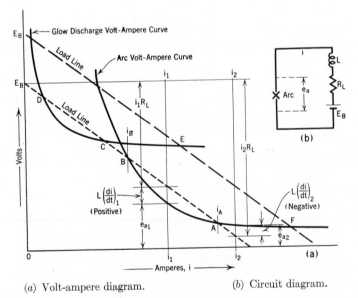

(a) Volt-ampere diagram.   (b) Circuit diagram.

Fig. 17.3 Static arc and glow discharge characteristic volt-ampere curves.

in a definite gas at definite values of gas pressure and ambient temperature. The axes are oriented in accordance with historical practice in engineering papers, in contrast with Fig. 15.1. The term static implies that such curves apply only in d-c or moderate-frequency a-c circuits.

A useful empirical formula for static arc volt-ampere curves is [15d]

$$e_a = A + \frac{B}{i_a{}^n} \qquad (17\text{--}22)$$

Here e_a is the arc voltage, i_a the current, and A, B, and n are empirical constants. n appears to vary directly with the boiling or sublimation temperature T_b of the *anode* material, according to the relation

$$n = 2.62 T_b \times 10^{-4} \qquad (17\text{--}23)$$

A and B vary with arc length, B more so than A. A is primarily characteristic of the electrode materials, and B of the gas in which the arc plays. If both electrodes are hot enough to supply vapor to the arc, that from the anode rather than from the cathode tends to become active in the discharge.

For the circuit of Fig. 17.3b:

$$E_B = e_a + iR_L + L\frac{di}{dt} \qquad (17\text{--}24)$$

The meanings of the symbols are evident from the figure. If the inductance is zero, or the current not changing, this can become

$$e_a = E_B - iR_L \qquad (17\text{--}25)$$

This describes a straight line, a *load line*, having zero-current and zero-voltage intercepts at E_B and E_B/R_L.

The circuit requires operation along the load line, while the device requires operation along an arc or glow volt-ampere curve. Therefore, steady d-c operation can occur only at an intersection of the load line with a volt-ampere curve.

Suppose that the device is operating at C along the glow discharge curve, with load line $DCBA$. If now E_B is increased, R_L remaining constant, the operating point shifts to the right, as to E, along a new load line through EF, corresponding to the new E_B. If the pressure is more than a few per cent of one atmosphere, and particularly if this shift has resulted in a change to an abnormal glow (in that case e_a should be materially higher at E than at C), a transition from glow to arc becomes probable. If such a transition occurs, there will be a fast circuit transient stabilizing at a higher-current point F on the load line EF and the arc volt-ampere curve.

17.12 Arc and Glow Stability; Oscillating Arc Circuits. Transients in the Fig. 17.3b circuit may result from abrupt changes in E_B, or of R_L, or of L, or by transition from glow to arc. Suppose that at a particular moment during a transient the current has the value i_1, and that E_B and R_L require the load line $DCBA$. During the transient the complete form (17–24) applies. The values of $i_1 R_L$ and e_a applicable to this moment are determinable from the figure. Evidently the gap between $i_1 R_L$ and e_a is the value that $L(di/dt)$ must have.

If the current has at any instant the value i_1, the quantity $L(di/dt)$ is not at that instant zero, so that the current must be *changing*. As $L(di/dt)$ is positive, the change is an increase of current, which must continue until the current has the value i_A, for only then does $L(di/dt)$ vanish. If the initial current is i_2, the rate of change of current is negative; the current decreases to the value i_A.

Evidently the intersection A is a point of *stable operation*, for, if any momentary departure from that point occurs, the circuit promptly forces the current back there. This occurs for any magnitude of L. If L is large, changes occur slowly, if small, they occur rapidly. Any real circuit has some inductance.

Intersection B is not a point of stable operation. Although $L(di/dt)$ has no value there, any slight increase in current above i_B makes $L(di/dt)$ positive, requiring travel along the curve to A. Similarly any slight decrease below i_B trips off a continued current decrease. Points B and D describe conditions of *unstable equilibrium; A* and C represent conditions of stable equilibrium.

This analysis shows why load ("ballast") resistors are needed to maintain steady operation of d-c arcs. The load line of a zero resistance circuit would be horizontal, the only intersections being at the unstable point B, and at $i_B \rightarrow \infty$. With a-c arcs, ballast reactors are used.

If an arc is connected to a resonant tank circuit, sustained pulsations of arc current may occur if the arc is operated under conditions that give the volt-ampere curve a negative slope in the operating range. The circuit analysis and equations for such an oscillating arc circuit are somewhat similar to those for a dynatron oscillator; see Section 10.13. The frequency of pulsation must be low enough so that the cyclic current-voltage locus lies along or near to the static characteristic curve, rather than along or near to a high-frequency characteristic, as discussed in the following section.

17.13 Voltage and Current Variations in a High-Frequency Pulsating Arc.[15A, C, G] During operation at any point along an arc's static volt-ampere characteristic there is a certain definite energy storage in the plasma. Each ion represents the storage of E_I electron volts of energy; also, the random energies of the gas particles, the electrons, and the ions all represent stored energy.

If either the voltage E_B or the resistance R_L in Fig. 17.3b is changed, operation shifts to some new point along the static volt-ampere curve. The electron-ion concentration, the various temperatures, and the plasma cross section all change; thus such a shift causes a change in the energy stored in the arc. Time is required to introduce or remove energy. Therefore static (equilibrium-condition) curves like those in Fig. 17.3a are obtained experimentally only if the current is altered

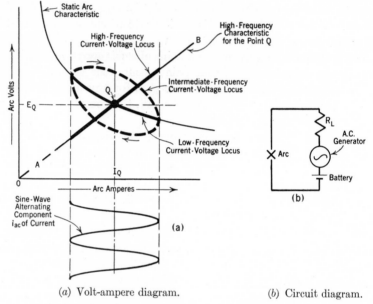

(a) Volt-ampere diagram. (b) Circuit diagram.

Fig. 17.4 Arc current-voltage loci at high, intermediate, and low frequencies.

slowly enough so that readjustments to the new energy and ion balance conditions can keep pace with changes in current. The cyclic variations of current and voltage in 60-cycle atmospheric-pressure pulsating arcs follow the static arc characteristics reasonably closely. Those in 600-cycle arcs depart considerably from the static curves.

The plasma of an arc has been compared to a metallic conductor; this comparison is especially apt when the arc current is unidirectional but rapidly pulsating, as in Fig. 17.4a. I_Q is the average current, and i_{ac} the a-c component. If the current pulsates very rapidly, the electron and ion concentrations and temperatures and the arc cross section remain steady at values corresponding to the I_Q, E_Q condition. The plasma resistance then remains constant, and the plasma gradient is proportional to the current (Ohm's law). If the arc is long enough so that the voltage drop in the plasma provides most of the arc drop, the high-frequency dynamic characteristic becomes practically a straight line directed away from the origin, as AB in Fig. 17.4a.

At an intermediate frequency the current-voltage locus pursues a loop, as indicated. During current down-swing, the existing plasma is one originally provided for a larger current. During the up-swing, it is one originally provided for a smaller current. At any given current the plasma gradient must be greater for current growth than for current decay. During growth the higher gradient is building in energy toward a high-current plasma; during decay it is permitting the plasma to shrink, so that full energy maintenance is not necessary.

17.14 Voltage and Current Relations in A-C Arcs; Reignition.[15A, C, 17l, m, n] If the current in an arc is alternating, not pulsating, a current

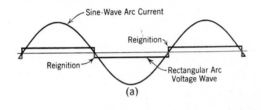

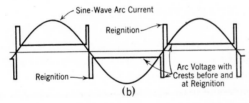

Fig. 17.5 Wave forms of voltage and current in a-c arcs.

reversal occurs at the end of each half-cycle. Ordinarily the arc voltage is a small fraction of the total circuit voltage. The magnitude, wave form, and phase position of the *current* are therefore controlled by the circuit external to the arc, whereas at each moment the arc *voltage* has the value specified by the arc characteristic, for the current flowing at that moment. Most power arcs operate at currents so large that the arc voltage is practically independent of the current; see Fig. 15.1. Therefore the arc voltage wave form is rectangular, as in Fig. 17.5a. Some a-c arcs have high-voltage peaks of short duration at the beginning and end of each half-cycle, as in Fig. 17.5b.

All significant problems relative to the extinction or continuance of a-c arcs have to do with the mechanism of reignition of the arc following the cyclic current zero. If after any given current zero reignition occurs, the arc continues; if reignition fails, the arc is extinguished. An ordinary metallic electrode that has been serving as an anode prior to current zero will not develop a "cathode spot" for electron release in the new direction until a potential of at least 250, sometimes 400 or more, volts appears between the electrodes in the new direction, this being the minimum-voltage condition for maintenance of a glow discharge in the new direction. Circuit capacitances cause the voltage rise to reignition to require appreciable time, so introducing a brief zero-current interval. Westinghouse Deion (not deion grid) circuit breakers make use of the minimum reignition voltage requirement. Subsequent to reignition to the glow discharge condition, a transition from glow to arc reduces the voltage abruptly to the low arc-drop value. This completes the explanation of the rise and fall of voltage just following current zero,[17n] in Fig. 17.5b.

A 110-volt a-c circuit never reaches the required reignition value, so that such a circuit will not support an arc between nonrefractory electrodes. Electrodes of refractory materials, such as carbon and tungsten, become and remain hot enough to supply electrons thermionically; this behavior permits reignition at relatively low voltages after current zero. Therefore a 110-volt a-c circuit will support an arc between such electrodes.

To explain the voltage crest *before* current zero, in Fig. 17.5b, note that an electric arc cannot persist at a current below some minimum value, of the order of a few tenths of an ampere to a few amperes. When in its approach to zero the arc current reaches this minimum value, the arc cathode spot disappears. There is always some little series inductance, and some little shunt capacitance. The series inductance demands momentary persistence of the current in the external circuit, thereby charging the shunt capacitance in the old direction. This causes the voltage to rise in the old direction until the glow discharge voltage is reached. The glow discharge then formed persists until cyclic current zero is reached.

Thus in Fig. 17.5b the voltage crests before and after reignition both represent short-duration atmospheric-pressure glow discharges.[17n]

PROBLEMS

1. Data for a curve of α/F vs. P_0/F, as in Fig. 14.11a, are as follows:

α/F	0.008	0.028	0.022	0.004	0.0005
P_0/F	10^{-4}	10^{-5}	10^{-6}	10^{-7}	10^{-8}
α/P_0	80	2800	22,000	40,000	50,000

Also, γ in the voltage breakdown equation obeys the relation

$$\gamma = 1 - \exp\left(\frac{-F/P_0}{A}\right)$$

where A is an empirical constant. When $P_0/F = 8 \times 10^{-8}$, $\gamma = 0.2$.

Determine points for, and plot approximately to scale, a Paschen's law curve of breakdown volts E_δ vs. $P_0 s$ (pressure $\times$ distance).

2. (a) From each of the three sawtooth diagrams of Fig. 14.10 determine a point on a curve of αl vs. Fl, therefore also on a curve of α/P_0 vs. F/P_0, assuming that the gas involved is air, and that the electron mean free path is 5×10^{-5} cm at 760 mm pressure and $273°$ K. Sketch in an estimated form of this curve, passing through these three points.

(b) From the curve so prepared, determine what would be the breakdown voltage in air at atmospheric pressure, between sphere gaps, expressed in volts per unit distance (state the distance unit carefully). There is no reason to expect the result to agree with the known value, because the data do not have that firm a basis.

3. The static arc characteristic for a certain gas and electrode arrangement passes through these points: (1) $I_a = 10$ amp, $E_a = 40$ volts; (2) $I_a = 50$ amp, $E_a = 15$ volts. Boiling temperature of the anode material $2000°$ K.

(a) Evaluate A and B in (17–22). (b) Plot a graph of the static arc characteristic. (c) This arc is part of a circuit as in Fig. 17.3b. If $E_B = 220$ volts, find values of R_L to give arc currents of 50 amp and of 10 amp.

4. Arc static characteristic as in Prob. 3, circuit like that in Fig. 10.14a. Select circuit constants to produce small-amplitude dynatron oscillations at a frequency of 300 cycles about a point Q for which $E_a = 30$ volts.

5. Find mathematically the low-frequency, also the high-frequency, a-c resistance of the arc of the two preceding problems at the point for which $E_a = 30$ volts.

6. Show that the intermediate-frequency loop, Fig. 17.4a, must have vertical tangents at the intersections with the static characteristic.

CHAPTER XVIII

GASEOUS-CONDUCTION RECTIFYING DEVICES

18.1 Gas Rectifiers Are High-Speed Switching Devices. The name rectifier applies to any device that can pass current freely in the "forward" direction but does not permit equally free flow in the "inverse" direction. Rectifying devices employing low-pressure arcs in mercury vapor, or in an inert gas, or in hydrogen, are used for a great variety of engineering services.

Ratings of gas (or vapor-arc) rectifying devices range from a few milliamperes at a hundred or so volts to a few thousand amperes at a few thousand (inverse) volts. The basic principles of operation are the same regardless of the size, type of cathode, or purpose for which they are used. All are essentially high-speed switching devices.

It is important to keep constantly in mind the sharp contrast between the current-throttling action of high-vacuum devices and the simple switching action of gas rectifiers. A throttle controls rate of flow; a switch either denies passage or permits flow at an unlimited rate. A gas rectifier has no more control over the magnitude of the instantaneous current through it than a knife switch has.

The circuit through a gas rectifier is closed when the arc exists, open when it does not exist. The closing and opening can be controlled by creating conditions that permit or forbid the existence of the arc. The device is an imperfect switch because of the "arc drop," which (a) uses some power which might otherwise be usefully employed, and (b) demands that the device itself be able to dissipate power. Gas rectifiers are expensive, and they require auxiliary apparatus which costs money, occupies space, and requires more or less attention. Thus radio receiver rectifier tubes require auxiliary filament transformers; 10,000-kilowatt steel-tank rectifiers for the metallurgical industries require vacuum pumps and arc-initiating and keep-alive rigs.

However, these various gas or vapor switches can close and open circuits repeatedly and with extreme rapidity, and the time and rate of such switching can be subject to the will of the operator. The extremely rapid, quiet, and easily controlled switching more than compensates for the cost and complication, for many services.

528

18.2   Classifications of Gas Rectifiers.[9L, 18A, B, C, D, E, F, G]   Gas rectifiers may be classified as to type of cathode. Thus there are:

I. Mercury-pool rectifiers, in which the electrons enter the arc through a hot wandering cathode spot on the surface of a pool of mercury. The pool must contain enough mercury to permit continuous evaporation at the cathode spot. The evaporated mercury returns to the pool by gravity after condensation on the walls. An important limitation in mercury-pool rectifier applications is the fact that a more or less definite minimum current, of the order of 2 to 4 amperes, is necessary to maintain the cathode spot. If the current momentarily drops below this minimum value, the spot disappears and the arc must be re-initiated. Thus for light-load operation an excitation or keep-alive arc is necessary, operating to a separate anode connected to a low-power-level d-c auxiliary source. The following methods of initially producing the cathode spot have been employed:

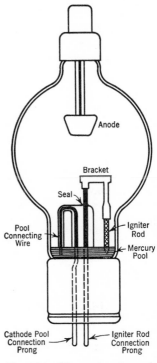

FIG. 18.1   Illustrative electrode arrangement in an ignitron rectifier; an early model.

(*a*) Mechanical tilting of the entire rectifier tube or tank, causing separation between the main mercury pool and an auxiliary mercury well in a side-arm, at a time when d-c current of modest value from an auxiliary source is flowing from the well to the main pool. At the point of separation an arc is drawn, which establishes the cathode spot. After this initiation the cathode spot is maintained either by an excitation or keep-alive arc, or by having the arc positive terminal shift cyclicly between two or more anodes. Initiation by tilting is industrially obsolete.

(*b*) In devices called Excitron rectifiers,[18d] made by the Allis-Chalmers Manufacturing Company, by using an excitation anode connected to the cathode through an external circuit, which is provided with a source of direct current. The arc-starting device consists of an iron plunger having at its upper end a graphite tip, the bottom end of the plunger extending into a "well" in the bottom of the mercury tank; a solenoidal coil surrounds the well. When the coil is not energized, the plunger is maintained in contact with an excitation anode by the flotation action of the mercury. When the coil is energized, the plunger is pulled down against the flotation action, thus breaking its contact with the excitation anode. When this contact is broken, an arc starts between plunger and excitation anode, with its cathode spot on the plunger. As the plunger is drawn down it becomes submerged in the mercury, the cathode spot then transferring to the mercury surface. Thus a keep-alive or excitation arc is established.

(c) Use of devices called *ignitrons*, or *ignitron rectifiers*,[18a, b, c] manufactured by the Westinghouse Electric Corporation and the General Electric Company, which employ tapered *igniter rods*, of sintered material physically and electrically resembling boron carbide or silicon carbide (Carborundum), extending from above to a little below the mercury surface, in the manner illustrated in Fig. 18.1. A momentary auxiliary rod current (usually from a few to a score or so amperes), sufficient to establish an average gradient in the rod of the order of 15 to 150 volts per centimeter, will initiate a hot cathode spot at the rod-mercury junction, in a manner described in Section 18.17. In apparatus employing ignitron rectifiers each anode may have its own cathode pool in its own separate chamber, without necessarily employing a keep-alive arc, because arc initiation may take place anew at the beginning of each positive half-cycle of arc.

(d) Use of devices incorporating initiating electrodes completely outside the enclosing walls of glass-envelope pools, and just above the pool level. By applying an impulse or high-frequency voltage of the order of 5000 to 10,000 volts to such an external electrode, an electric gradient is established at the cathode surface sufficient to initiate the spot. This may set up a keep-alive arc to an auxiliary anode, or such a voltage impulse may initiate an arc at the proper moment during each cycle. A modification of this principle employs a more modest voltage applied to small rods encased in very thin glass and floating on the mercury surface, and there are other related methods.[18e] Devices in this general (d) class tend to exhibit deterioration of the properties of the insulating dielectric, demanding progressively higher firing voltages.

There are also:

II. Thermionic gas or vapor rectifiers, in which the electrons enter through the oxide-coated surfaces of electrically heated cathodes. In the larger devices of this type, included in the category of industrial electron tubes, cathodes are used that approach the inward-radiating ideal described in Section 7.10. Their electron-emitting efficiencies are therefore very much higher than for the cathodes in high-vacuum devices. There is, however, the inconvenience of having to wait for one to several minutes after turning on cathode heating power before drawing anode current. There is no lower limit to stable current flow.

Evaporation from droplets of mercury, introduced during manufacture, supplies the necessary mercury vapor, in thermionic mercury-vapor rectifiers.

Gas rectifiers may be classified as to the manner in which current conduction to the anode may be initiated, that is, according to the nature of the fast switching-on mechanism. A low-power-level control circuit may be enabled to compel or forbid *initiation* of anode current by the following means:

(a) In a mercury-pool rectifier, an exciting or keep-alive arc may be employed to maintain a cathode spot, with a grid interposed between the keep-alive arc plasma and the anode. With the keep-alive arc excited, but no anode current flowing, a grid at a moderately negative potential can maintain a positive ion sheath thick enough to occlude the grid wires (see Section 16.10), thus preventing extension of the plasma into the grid-anode region, even with a very substantial positive anode voltage. If the grid potential is driven up to or near to cathode potential, the sheath becomes thin, no longer occluding the grid holes; the plasma at once extends into the grid-anode region, closing the circuit to the anode. The ion density near the grid is thereafter very large, because of the high current density through it to the main anode, so that reducing the grid potential will not produce sheaths thick enough to shut off the anode current.

(b) In a thermionic gas or mercury-vapor rectifier, by interposing a grid between the hot thermionic cathode and the anode. Figure 18.2 illustrates the arrangement of parts in such a device, called a *thyratron*.[18i, j, k, l, m, n] With no current flowing to the anode, a modest negative potential on the grid prevents initiation of anode current; when the grid swings up to or near to cathode potential, an arc is established in the tube as described later in Sections 18.9 and 18.10. Once this arc is established, reducing the grid potential will not ordinarily interrupt the anode current.

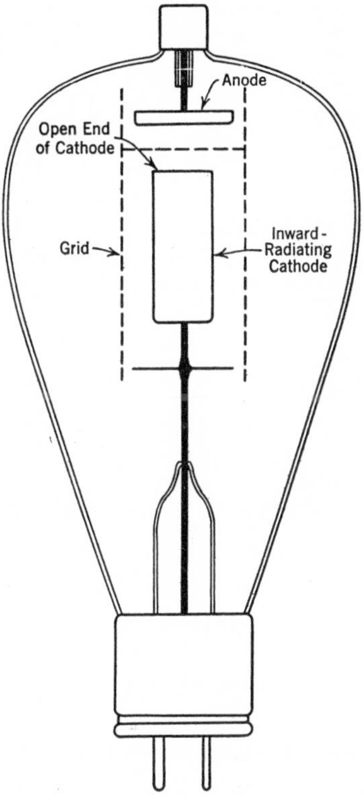

(c) In an *ignitron* rectifier, the igniter rod initiates an arc as ordered, as discussed in Section 18.17. In an ignitron rectifier the arc cathode spot will disappear if the load current drops below some minimum value. This offers no problem in resistance welder applications,[18D, E] where there is never a need for small continuous current flow, but in industrial power rectifiers it may make necessary an excitation arc in addition to the igniter rod.

FIG. 18.2 Typical electrode arrangement in a thyratron.

(d) In mercury-pool rectifiers, one or more glass-insulated electrodes may be so placed that when a control impulse consisting of a high voltage at high frequency is applied to them an arc-initiating gradient appears at the mercury surface, establishing conduction to the anode; see I(d) above.

(e) By magnetically affecting the flow of current.[18f]

Uses of gas and mercury-vapor rectifiers include: [9L, 18A, B, C, D, E, F, G]

1. Power rectification, that is, conversion of electric power from alternating to direct current.

2. Switching, and speed and voltage control, of electrical machinery.

3. Providing finely graded, efficient control of average power flow, as for welding, by passing current during controllable fractions of each a-c half-cycle; rectification may or may not be simultaneously provided.

4. Permitting control of the flow of substantial power in response to sensitive instruments, which provide low-energy signals.

5. Instrumentation services, as for counting impulses and for providing intermittent condenser charge and discharge in stroboscopic and cathode-ray sweep circuits.

6. Inversion of electric power from direct to alternating current.

7. Applying high-energy brief impulses, as in radar modulators.

Applications employing single-phase alternating current, either at the input or output or both, ordinarily provide for full-wave operation, that is, operation during both halves of each cycle. For full-wave single-phase rectification, one cathode and two anodes in a common glass or metal envelope may be used. For full-wave single-phase switching, or for current control without rectification, two separate envelopes are required, each with its own cathode and anode. In either case current passes through one arc in positive half-cycles, and through the other arc in negative half-cycles.

18.3 Commercial Classification of Gas Rectifiers. Probably the most familiar classification of gaseous conduction rectifiers is a semicommercial one, which distinguishes between the fields of engineering work in which the various types are used. Thus there are:

I. Polyphase Steel-Tank Mercury-Arc Rectifiers. These rectifiers are built in units rated in hundreds or thousands of kilowatts, requiring complex control and auxiliary apparatus, including vacuum-pumping systems for the tanks. They provide d-c power for electrolytic uses in the metallurgical and chemical industries, and for electric railway service. The rectifying elements are mercury-pool devices and may have control grids, or igniter rods, or the Excitron provisions. They are multiphase rectifiers, operated from three-phase power supply circuits. In the type of six-phase rectifier that does not use igniter rods or exciting electrodes, six anodes may operate from a common mercury-pool cathode, as illustrated in Fig. 18.3a. The arc transfers from one anode to another, then to the next, and so on, but has its cathode always on the one mercury pool. This particular circuit illustrates various essential principles very simply, but it is less economical of equipment than other comparable arrangements.[18A, B, C, E, F]

II. Industrial Electron Tubes.[9L, 18D, E, F, G] The devices belonging in this class are used for a great variety of rectifying, switching, and current-control purposes in industrial plants and power stations. Indus-

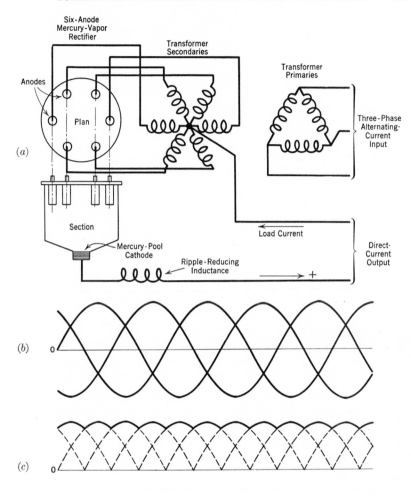

(a) Circuit diagram of six-phase mercury-arc rectifier and transformers.

(b) Three-phase a-c input voltages.

(c) The heavy wavy line is the voltage between transformer neutral and rectifier cathode; it is also the voltage at the terminals under no load conditions.

(d) Voltage at the load, full-load operation.

F IG. 18.3   Six-phase diametrical type of mercury-arc steel tank rectifier.

trial electron tubes are available having average current ratings from a few tenths to a hundred or more amperes, and they may have either glass or metal envelopes. The following types are of special interest:

(a) Thermionic gas or vapor rectifiers, without either grids or igniter rods.

(b) Thyratrons, that is, grid-controlled thermionic gas or mercury-vapor rectifiers; see Fig. 18.2.[9L, 18D, E, F, G, j, k, n, q]

(c) Ignitrons, that is, igniter-controlled mercury-pool type rectifiers, with or without grids or keep-alive arcs.[18D, E, F, G, a, b, c]

Thermionic thyratrons (class b) employ by far the most flexible combination of type of cathode and method of control. It is not, however, an especially cheap or durable combination. Thermionic cathodes are expensive in large current ratings, require continuous power input for heating, are easily damaged by overloads, short circuits, and continued vibration, and have limited life. Mercury-pool cathodes are relatively not expensive (per ampere), have large reserve capacities, and are mechanically rugged and long-lived.

As ordinarily used, neither grids, as in thyratrons, nor igniter rods, as in ignitrons, will interrupt forward current flow, once it is established. However, the lack of circuit-opening or "shut-off" control is not serious in a-c switching applications, for in all a-c circuits the current automatically goes to zero twice in every cycle. Each new half-cycle presents an opportunity to open the circuit permanently by preventing the restarting of the arc. The grids or igniter rods may be excited so as to initiate arcs at controllable phase points in every half-cycle, thus making current flow take place during an adjustable fraction of each half-cycle. The average current is controlled by changing this adjustable fraction; see Section 18.13 for details.

In many applications involving control of substantial currents, as in resistance welding equipment, ignitrons carry the main current, but their ignition is governed by thyratrons. This utilizes both the flexibility of thyratron grid control, and the economy and reliability of mercury-pool cathodes. It reduces the overload and short-circuit hazard on the thermionic cathodes by placing them in auxiliary rather than in the main circuits.

III. Low-Power Gas Tubes, for Communication and Instrumentation Uses.[9L] Devices in this class have been developed primarily for the radio and communication fields, but they are extensively used for a great variety of laboratory purposes and in measuring and recording apparatus. Ratings are from a few score to a few hundred milliamperes; the 2050 and 83 tubes are examples.

18.4   Rectifying and Filtering. Rectification without voltage control can be accomplished without either grids or igniter rods. A rectifier for such use may have a single cathode with as many anodes as the circuit requires. Two anodes are needed for full-wave single-phase operation, six anodes for the particular type of six-phase operation illustrated in Fig. 18.3a.

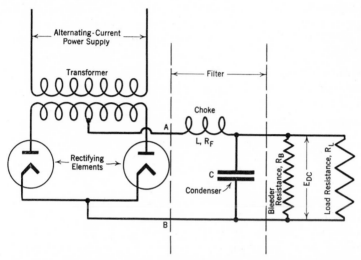

FIG. 18.4 Single-phase full-wave rectifier circuit with choke input filter.

Figure 18.4 is an illustrative full-wave single-phase rectifier circuit, including *filtering* provisions. The switching function performed by the rectifying elements automatically interchanges in alternate half-cycles the source voltage terminals connected to the load. In the

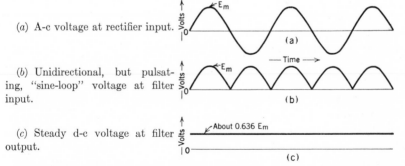

(a) A-c voltage at rectifier input.

(b) Unidirectional, but pulsating, "sine-loop" voltage at filter input.

(c) Steady d-c voltage at filter output.

FIG. 18.5 Rectified and filtered voltages at full load, in a full-wave single-phase rectifier circuit, Fig. 18.4. Ripple completely suppressed by the filter.

simplest operation no filter is used, the load is purely resistive, and a *sine loop* voltage, illustrated in Fig. 18.5b, appears at the load terminals.[18g]

The rectification is completed by a *filter circuit* which stores some of the energy from the source during peaks of periodic power input and delivers it during the valleys. The simplest filter consists only of a low-resistance high-inductance choke in series with the load, as if the condenser and bleeder resistance were omitted in Fig. 18.4. Figures 18.5a, 18.5b, and 18.5c contrast the a-c input voltage, the sine loop voltage at filter input, and the d-c voltage at the load when such a simple filter is used under large-load-current conditions that permit excellent filtering.

For light loads, good filtering will result from using a circuit like that of Fig. 18.4 except that the choke and bleeder are omitted. The solid-line curve of Fig. 18.6 then describes the voltage at filter input

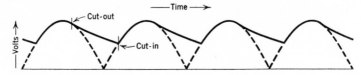

FIG. 18.6 Load and condenser voltage, for a rectifier using a filter consisting of condenser only. Circuit as in Fig. 18.4, except that choke is omitted. Dotted lines follow the sine-loop voltage. $f = 60$ cycles, $R_L = 2,000$ ohms, $C = 4$ microfarads, $R_B = \infty$.

for a modest load current. The condenser is charged through one of the tubes while the a-c wave is rising toward its crest. Purely because of circuit behavior, the tube current goes to zero at the cut-out point; as the tube cannot carry reverse current, it then remains an open switch while the condenser discharges through the load resistance. During this discharge period, between cut-out and cut-in, both tubes are open switches, because their anodes are both negative relative to their common cathode potential. Cut-in occurs when the anode of one of the tubes is driven by the circuit up to and a little above the cathode potential; the tube then becomes conducting (a closed switch) until its next current zero at the subsequent cut-out point. Thus the circuit behavior, in combination with the rectifying properties of the tubes, causes the switching action to take place, without the aid of either grids or igniter rods.

The higher the load resistance, the less the voltage declines during the discharge period. Thus such a circuit filters very well at light loads, and its limiting light-load d-c voltage is the sine loop crest.

With both choke and condenser in the circuit, as in Fig. 18.4, the overall d-c volt-ampere behavior is as in Fig. 18.7. At light loads the condenser filtering action predominates, providing good light-load filtering at a voltage close to the sine loop crest; at heavy loads the choke filtering action predominates, providing good heavy-load filtering close to the sine loop average.   In practice, a bleeder resistance R_B is employed which draws the current corresponding to point B in Fig. 18.7, thus insuring good voltage regulation for any externally connected load.   Such an arrangement filters well at all loads and provides a d-c voltage approximating the sine loop average.

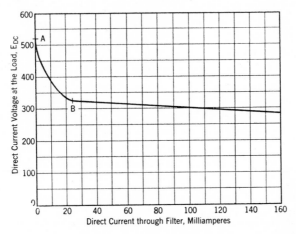

FIG. 18.7   Experimentally observed volt-ampere curve for a rectifier with choke-input filter, circuit diagram as in Fig. 18.4, $I_B = 24$ milliamperes, E_{DC} at $B = 328$ volts.

Figure 18.3b illustrates the voltage waves of the three-phase power supply for the six-phase rectifying arrangement of Fig. 18.3a.[18A, B, C, F] The solid line in Fig. 18.3c is the corresponding voltage between transformer neutral and rectifier cathode, and in Fig. 18.3d the voltage across the load if the "ripple" is completely suppressed by the inductance in series with the load.   In general, in a circuit containing n rectifier anodes, each anode is in service during the $1/n$th of each cycle for which its circuit voltage is greater than that of any other anode. Therefore the greater the number of anodes, the smaller is the ripple to be filtered out.

18.5   Inverse Voltage Rating of Rectifiers; Arc-Back.[9L, 15A, 18A, B, C, D, E, F, G, h]   As ordinarily used, the anode of a rectifying circuit element becomes strongly negative relative to the cathode in alternate half-cycles.   The inverse voltage rating specifies the maximum safe instantaneous value of this negative anode voltage.   All such circuit elements, large and small, with and without grids and igniter rods, are given inverse voltage ratings, although the word "inverse" may not always be used.

In multianode rectifiers, failure in the inverse direction may result from unwanted initiation of a cathode spot on an idle anode, called arc-back. This constitutes an internal short circuit between anodes. In spite of the placement of the several anodes in "anode arms," or in partially partitioned-off cells, the presence in the main chamber of the plasma carrying current to the active anode occasionally results in arc-back to an idle one. Grids enclosing the anodes discourage arc-back but increase the arc drop undesirably; see Section 18.7.

Arc-back to idle anodes does not occur in polyphase rectifiers of the igniter type, because the anodes are located in separate chambers, each chamber having its individual cathode pool. However, if a keep-alive or excitation arc is necessary in order to permit light-load operation of a rectifier, the excitation plasma may encourage arc-back. Even without a keep-alive arc, a large load current may produce a plasma so intense as to result in arc-back due to residual ionization. Therefore it is desirable to design large-current ignitrons for maximum rate of ion removal, that is, a maximum surface-to-volume ratio in the plasma enclosure.

In a multianode pool-type device, Fig. 18.3, the main current-carrying plasma tends to spread throughout the arc chamber and to form sheaths at all surfaces. Each idle anode is, during part of each cycle, at a very low potential relative to this plasma. During these cyclic periods the positive ion sheath that forms at an idle anode (see Fig. 16.4a) terminates in a very steep gradient at the face of the sheath adjacent to the idle anode surface. Experiments by Slepian [18h] show that the presence of this steep idle-anode surface gradient results in some definite momentary probability of arc-back. This probability is much greater for large than for small inverse voltages, and for large than for small load currents, and is otherwise dependent on various operating conditions and design details. It appears likely that this probability is increased by the presence of impurities or mercury droplets on the idle anode surface. The initiation, at arc-back, of a cathode spot on an idle-anode surface is very similar to the transition from a glow discharge to an arc.

Ignitrons employed for control of resistance welders, used very extensively in the automobile industry, are never required to operate at light load and therefore do not require keep-alive provisions. This makes the probability of anode-to-cathode arc-back relatively low, permitting close anode-to-cathode spacing and generally small arc drop.

The concept of probability of arc-back is very similar, as to statistical consequences, to that of the probability of firing of an igniter rod, discussed in Section 18.17; (18–7) is the significant underlying equation.

However, the mean time $1/p$ to arc-back is measurable in days or weeks or months, rather than in microseconds. In principle, the objective of attacks on the arc-back problem is that of increasing this mean time as much as possible without introducing excessive arc drop and associated severe power dissipation problems.

18.6 Forward Voltage Rating of Gas Rectifiers.[9L, 18D, E, F, G] The forward voltage rating of a rectifier specifies the maximum safe instantaneous voltage when the anode is positive but the anode circuit is being held open by the rectifier. Because only grid- or igniter-controlled rectifiers (thyratrons or ignitrons) are expected to maintain open circuits in spite of forward anode voltages, only these types are given forward voltage ratings.

Failure of a thyratron to maintain an open circuit in the forward direction when its grid is negative can result if the grid does not limit to a sufficiently small rate the entrance of electrons into the anode field. Various types of abuse, particularly overloads that cause transfer of cathode material onto the grid, making it a weak source of free electrons when heated by proximity to the discharge, can cause gradual decrease of the maximum safe forward voltage.

18.7 Current Ratings of Gas Rectifiers.[9L, 18D, E, F, G] Gas rectifiers are given average (not rms) current ratings, which specify the greatest average current that can be carried continuously without overheating. Such ratings are made subject to specified limits of ambient temperature. As with all electrical devices, the heating depends on the rate at which energy must be dissipated. Physical size, therefore cost, is in high-current mercury-pool devices largely governed by power dissipation requirements, so that any design change that increases the required dissipation increases the cost, for given current.

Power to be dissipated is the product of arc drop by current, plus any necessary filament heating power. The arc drop is usually affected very little by cyclic changes in load current, within normal operating limits; therefore the average power dissipation is proportional to the average current rather than to the rms current. The arc drop is rarely less than 5 or more than 25 volts.

If, for a given current rating, grids are introduced to provide control or to reduce arc-back frequency in a mercury-pool device, the arc drop will be materially increased. Should this change double the arc drop (as from 12 to 24 volts), the dissipation doubles; therefore the size, weight, and cost increase by some comparable factor. Thus provision of grid control and reduction in arc-back frequency may be expensive. It is the added equipment cost, not the reduction in efficiency, that has economic significance.

Thus the small anode-to-cathode spacing permissible in welder-control ignitrons, which have anodes in separate chambers and no keep-alive provisions (because light-load operation is never required), favors a small arc drop, therefore low power dissipation, therefore low cost per tube.

Ratings usually express, in one way or another, permissible short-time overload currents.

Industrial thermionic-cathode gas rectifiers are usually given the following ratings:

(a) *Average current* ratings, together with specifications of the maximum time, usually between 10 and 30 seconds, over which the average is to be taken. Tubes overheat if operated continuously at greater than the rated average currents.

(b) *Maximum instantaneous* or *crest* ratings, which specify the maximum value the current should be permitted to reach in each duty cycle. The crest rating is likely to be several times the average current rating.

(c) *Surge current* ratings, which specify the maximum momentary current the device can carry, in event of short circuits or other untoward events, without immediate destruction or major shortening of useful life.

The arc drop in such devices is an approximate measure of the energy with which ions strike the cathode surface, and at large currents the arc drop becomes a rising function of current. Progressive destruction of the coating on the surface by ion bombardment sets in if this energy exceeds a critical value, which usually corresponds to an arc drop between 20 and 25 volts. The crest current rating must be small enough to keep the energy of ion bombardment always below the critical value.[18i, k]

If the current continues, either steadily or intermittently, to exceed the crest rating, the coating on the cathode surface is gradually destroyed. As a result (a) the maximum safe instantaneous current becomes smaller, (b) the life of the tube is shortened, and (c) cathode material may be scattered onto the grid, making the grid surface a partial emitter, thereby encouraging false current initiation.

The smaller thermionic cathode rectifiers (those developed for radio and communication work) are sometimes given only maximum average current ratings, that take care both of temperature and cathode life restrictions.

18.8   Concentration of Mercury Atoms in Mercury-Vapor Rectifiers. During the manufacture of thermionic mercury-vapor rectifiers there is introduced a droplet of mercury, which remains permanently at the bottom of the tube. Thus in these devices as well as in mercury-pool apparatus there is present within the tube an exposed liquid mercury surface. The temperature of this surface controls the pressure of mercury vapor within the tube.

In a closed basement containing a pool of water the humidity eventually reaches 100 per cent.   This means that the water-vapor pressure becomes that at which condensation into the pool takes place just as

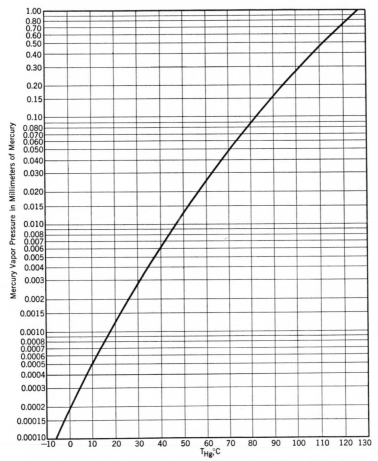

Temperature of Condensed Mercury, also of Mercury Vapor, in Degrees Centigrade

Fig. 18.8   Dependence of mercury-vapor pressure on temperature.[IX]   See Table XVII.

rapidly as evaporation from it.   Similarly the mercury-vapor pressure inside a mercury-vapor rectifier is always that at which the rate of condensation into the pool or droplet just equals the rate of evaporation.

The rate of evaporation, therefore also the mercury-vapor pressure, depends on the temperature of the condensed mercury pool or droplet. The relation between mercury-vapor pressure and temperature when vapor and condensed mercury have a common temperature is described in Fig. 18.8 and Table XVII. This dependence is essentially exponential in character and is similar to the dependence of thermionic emission current on cathode temperature.

In a thermionic gas rectifier the droplet is in intimate contact with the base of the tube, whereas the vapor is in intimate contact with the upper parts of the tube that may have been heated by its own discharge. Therefore, the vapor in the plasma may be at a higher temperature than the droplet. A similar situation can exist in a pool-type device because of the high level of energy interchange in a large-current plasma. If the temperature of the mercury vapor within the plasma is not the same as that of the pool or droplet, the vapor pressure in the plasma will differ a little, but relatively only a little, from that given in Fig. 18.8 and Table XVII.

Suppose the mercury-pool temperature to be T_{Hg}, the mercury-vapor temperature T_g. If the mean free path of a vapor particle in the plasma region is *short* relative to the dimensions of the enclosure, the vapor in the plasma, at temperature T_g, will be in *pressure* equilibrium with the vapor, at temperature T_{Hg}, located immediately adjacent to the pool or droplet surface.

In that case the gas law applies, so that

$$\text{Pressure} = N_g k T_g = N_{Hg} k T_{Hg} \tag{18-1}$$

where k is Boltzmann's gas constant; pressure is in newtons per square meter. Therefore,

$$N_g = N_{Hg}\frac{T_{Hg}}{T_g} \tag{18-2}$$

If, however, the mean free path of a vapor particle is *long* relative to the dimensions of the enclosure, the vapor in the plasma will be in *flow* equilibrium with the droplet, leading by the use of (12-91) to the relation

$$\frac{N_g \zeta_g}{2\sqrt{\pi}} = \frac{N_{Hg}\zeta_{Hg}}{2\sqrt{\pi}} \tag{18-3}$$

which gives

$$N_g = N_{Hg}\sqrt{\frac{T_{Hg}}{T_g}} \tag{18-4}$$

Relative to other factors of change and uncertainty, the difference between (18-2) and (18-4) is usually minor.

T_{Hg} can be measured with reasonable accuracy by a thermometer at the base of the tube. If T_{Hg} is known, N_{Hg} can be calculated, from the data of Table XVII or Fig. 18.8, by using the ideal gas law and N_q

as given in (15–15a). Often only a rough estimate of the value of T_g can be made; see comments on gas temperature in Section 15.14.

The effect on gas concentration of variations in T_g is not important, but that of variations in T_{Hg} is very important, because of the exponential nature of the dependence of N_{Hg} on T_{Hg}.

The gas concentration is of interest chiefly because it determines the electron mean free path; use (15–20) for obtaining approximate magnitudes.

18.9   Grid Control of Current Conduction in a Thyratron.[18i, j, k, n]

The cathode, grid, and plate of a thermionic thyratron, Fig. 18.2, are arranged so as to provide, before arc initiation, the same sort of control over the electric field between cathode and grid as exists in a high-vacuum triode. Figure 18.9a illustrates a mutual characteristic curve for a high-vacuum triode, with cut-off at plate and grid voltages of 600 and -2.25 respectively. The corresponding diagram for a typical thyratron is shown in Fig. 18.9b. If the thyratron grid voltage is brought up toward zero from strongly negative values, the arrival at the arc initiation point, comparable with a high-vacuum triode cut-off point, is marked by an abrupt establishment of current flow through the tube.

This current appears abruptly because an arc has formed between cathode and anode. The value of current after arc formation depends entirely on the circuit external to the tube. The cathode-to-anode voltage after arc initiation is the normal tube drop, usually between 8 and 20 volts.

Arc initiation occurs when the grid potential rises high enough to permit an appreciable "dark" electron current to flow to the plate. This dark electron current is the same kind of current as that flowing in a high-vacuum triode at grid voltage values in the neighborhood of cut-off. Discussions of the conditions that govern the magnitude of this type of current appear in Sections 8.17 through 8.19. A discussion of its triggering effect appears in the next section.

At the moment of arc initiation the voltage difference between cathode and anode decreases with extreme rapidity to the normal arc drop of the tube. The cathode-ray oscillogram reproduced in Fig. 18.10 records a typical collapse of plate voltage. In that operation the tube voltage dropped from several hundred volts to a very small value in less than half a microsecond. A corresponding current oscillogram showed that growth of the tube current to its steady-state value required some 20 to 30 microseconds, because of the small series inductance of the plate circuit. In principle, the tube voltage will collapse very rapidly at arc initiation if the plasma can be established more rapidly than the circuit permits the current to grow. This situation, illustrated in Fig. 18.10, exists commonly in industrial electronic control circuits.

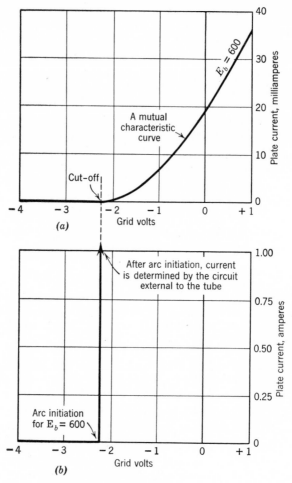

(a) Cut-off in a high-vacuum thermionic triode.
(b) Arc initiation in a thyratron.

Fig. 18.9 High-vacuum triode at cut-off, and thyratron at arc initiation, in geometrically similar devices.

With a small thyratron in a low-impedance circuit, as with a 2050 tube used in the Fig. 3.9 circuit, the tube voltage may decline more slowly, because the plasma may not grow in current-carrying capacity as fast as the external circuit permits the current to grow.

Once the arc has been initiated, a decrease of grid potential ordinarily has no effect on the current in the tube. The grid is immersed in a plasma, and a decrease of the grid potential to a low negative value merely increases the thickness of the positive ion sheath that forms around it, in the manner discussed in Section 16.9. In the extreme case of a low-ion-density plasma, small-diameter grid holes, and a grid voltage many hundreds of volts negative, the sheath may occlude the grid holes, thus shutting off the plate current; this is not, however, an industrially useful functioning.

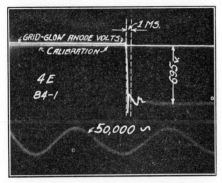

Fig. 18.10   Cathode-ray oscillogram of the collapse of anode-to-cathode voltage at arc initiation in a thyratron (at one time called by some authors a grid-glow tube). The irregular oscillations after collapse probably were caused by reflections in the lead-in circuit to the oscillograph. From Dow and Powers.[18b]

In practice, grid control is re-established only when changes in the plate circuit external to the tube bring the arc current to zero, as at the end of a half-cycle of a-c current flow. Any marked rise of grid potential occurring after arc initiation makes the grid become a second anode, as described in Section 18.11.

18.10   Mechanism of Arc Initiation in a Thyratron; Grid Control Curves.[9L, 18i, j, k]   It was pointed out toward the end of Section 8.18 that there is no such thing as mathematically defined cut-off in a triode. High-vacuum triode mutual characteristic curves like that in Fig. 18.9a are merely rapidly asymptotic to zero, in the neighborhood of a value of grid voltage that is called the cut-off value.

As the grid voltage is made to fall below this cut-off value, the negative potential dip outside the cathode (curves 3 and 4, Fig. 8.9) becomes very pronounced, and E_m correspondingly large. At each value of grid voltage in the neighborhood of cut-off the plate current is some small but definite fraction of the thermionic current, in accordance with an equation having the form of (8–26).

In a similar way there is a very small, but definite, plate current due to electron flow at each value of grid voltage just below the arc initiation point of Fig. 18.9b. Of course the electrons that constitute this current produce ions along their rapid flight to the anode; these ions move relatively slowly to the grid. The positive space charge due to their presence tends to lift the bottom of the negative potential dip. As the bottom of the negative dip rises, the electron current is increased. The increased electron flow makes the positive ion space

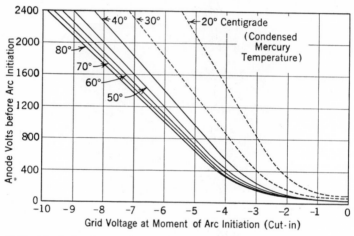

Fig. 18.11   Typical grid control curves for a General Electric type FG-17 thyratron.

charge become larger, this growth in space charge lifts the bottom of the dip higher, so permitting more electrons to flow, giving rise to more positive space charge, and so on. At the value of dark electron current that corresponds to the arc initiation point this pyramidal growth becomes unstable and accelerates indefinitely, the end condition being the plasma of an arc.

The electron mean free path is usually greater than the cathode-to-anode spacing, so that only a small percentage of the dark-current electrons hit gas particles during flight to the anode. Furthermore, the high plate voltage that exists prior to arc initiation makes practically all electrons that do hit gas particles acquire much more than ionizing energy before they hit. Under these conditions the rate of ion production depends primarily on how many gas particles are hit per second, rather than on the electron energy at impact.

If the gas concentration is low, many electrons must flow in order to make enough hits per second to initiate a plasma. If the gas concentration is high, each electron has a considerable chance of making a hit, so that only a few electrons may need to flow in order to make the same number of hits per second. Therefore when the gas concentration in a tube is high, the critical triggering current is less, and arc initiation occurs at a more negative potential than when the gas concentration is low.

Each of the various slant lines in Fig. 9.2 describes combinations of a triode's plate and grid voltages necessary to give the plate current

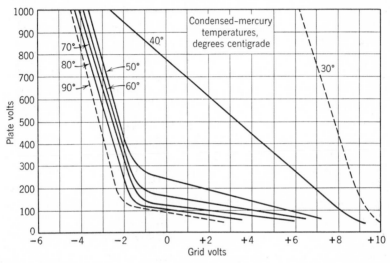

Fig. 18.12   Typical grid control curves for a General Electric type FG-67 thyratron.

some definite value. The larger the definite value, the farther to the right is the slant line. The thyratron grid control curves illustrated in Fig. 18.11 are essentially the same kind of slant lines as those in Fig. 9.2. They describe combinations of plate voltage and grid voltage that produce definite dark electron currents just sufficient to trigger the initiation of a plasma. High condensed-mercury temperature corresponds to high mercury-vapor concentration, and so to a considerable chance of any electron's hitting an atom, and so to little triggering current. Therefore, the high-temperature grid control curves lie to the left of the low-temperature ones.

In tubes containing inert gases instead of mercury vapor, the gas concentration is unaffected by temperature. Therefore each such tube has a single grid control curve rather than a family of them.[18j]

As an example of grid control curve use, suppose the Fig. 18.11 tube is dark, a strongly negative grid potential holding the circuit open in spite of a plate potential of 800 volts. Condensed-mercury temperature is 50° C. If now the grid potential is gradually raised toward zero, no change is noticed either in tube appearance or in readings of meters in the plate circuit until the 800-volt point on the 50° grid control curve is reached at about −5 grid volts. At this point the tube abruptly closes the plate circuit, as a result of the formation of an arc between cathode and anode. Driving the grid negative will not subsequently reopen the plate circuit.

The grid control curves of the General Electric FG–67 type of tube, Fig. 18.12, are less regular in shape than those in Fig. 18.11.

18.11   Current-Limiting Grid Circuit Resistors. After the arc in a thyratron is initiated, the grid is immersed in a plasma and is surrounded by a current-carrying sheath. Any attempt to raise the grid potential appreciably above that of the anode makes the grid become a second arc anode, as at E in the grid or probe volt-ampere curve shown in Fig. 16.3a. After this the current in the grid circuit depends almost wholly on the grid circuit external to the tube. For this reason it is essential to use current-limiting resistors in the grid circuits of thyratrons. Such grid resistors are chosen to limit average grid currents to not more than the permissible rated values.

18.12   Shield-Grid Thyratrons. The grids of thyratrons must exercise electrostatic control over all possible paths of emergence of electrons from cathode toward anode, because the production of ions along any such path can result in arc initiation. The grids therefore have rather large areas.

In a *shield-grid* thyratron the shield grid forms an enclosure around the cathode except at the anode exposure, and is kept at a low enough potential (usually the cathode potential) to prevent arc initiation anywhere except at the anode exposure. The arc is initiated by varying the potential of the control grid, which is small and so designed and placed as to have electrostatic control of the dark electron flow along the direct cathode-to-anode path.

The operation of some very sensitive grid circuits is undesirably affected by small dark currents that flow to negative grids, if single-grid thyratrons are used. Shield-grid thyratrons serve advantageously under such conditions, because their control grids have small areas and are otherwise so designed that dark currents to them are very small. Also, the capacitance between the control grid and other electrodes is less than in a single-grid thyratron.

18.13   Phase-Shift Control of Thyratrons.[9L, 18D, E, F, G, j, k] To understand certain thyratron design problems it is necessary to have in mind various circuit aspects of one of the commonest uses of thyratrons: to produce phase-shift control of current.

Figure 18.13a is a diagram of a circuit that uses a thyratron to deliver rectified current of easily adjustable magnitude to a load resistance R_L. The load current is varied by controlling the phase position at which the grid of the thyratron swings positive, thereby closing the load circuit. The grid circuit voltage phase position is varied by changing the variable resistance R. The heavy line in Fig. 18.14a is illustrative of the resulting load current wave form, if no filter is used.

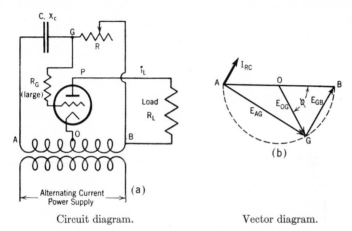

Circuit diagram.   Vector diagram.

FIG. 18.13   Thyratron current control by means of phase shift of grid circuit relative to power supply circuit. Half-wave operation.

If a filter is introduced between thyratron and load, the wave forms of filter and load currents both change markedly, but the average value of load current does not, if the filter constants are properly chosen. A condenser input filter cannot be used, for the abrupt application of circuit voltage to the condenser would pass such a large charging current as to damage seriously the cathode surface of the thyratron.

The abrupt rise at the beginning of each current wave occurs when the grid swings positive. It is evident that if this occurs earlier in each cycle than shown in the figure the average load current will be increased, whereas if it occurs later in the cycle the average load current will be decreased.

Figure 18.13b is a vector diagram of the current and voltages in the grid control circuit AGB, Fig. 18.13a. The current I_{RC} in this circuit leads the applied voltage E_{AB} by some phase angle that depends on the relative values of R and X_C. I_{RC} of course leads the voltage across the condenser by 90° and is in phase with the voltage E_{GB} across the resistance R. The grid-circuit voltage is E_{OG}; Fig. 18.13b shows that

E_{OG} lags behind the load-circuit voltage E_{OB} by some angle ϕ that depends on the relative values of R and C. As the angle AGB must always be 90°, variations in relative values of R and C cause point G, Fig. 18.13b, to trace an arc of a semicircle. The grid voltage E_{OG} has therefore a constant magnitude but a varying angle of lag relative to the load-circuit voltage.

Figure 18.14a illustrates the relations between grid voltage and load circuit currents and voltages. The voltage e_{OG} is applied to the cath-

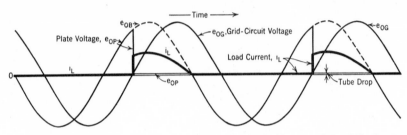

(a) Typical voltage and current variations in the half-wave phase-shift thyratron circuit of Fig. 18.13.

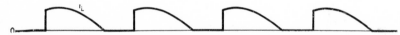

(b) Typical load current wave form for the full-wave rectifying phase-shift circuit of Fig. 18.16a.

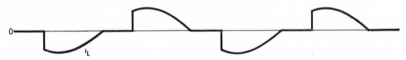

(c) Typical load current wave form for the full-wave non-rectifying phase-shift circuit of Fig. 18.16b.

FIG. 18.14   Voltage and current waves in phase-shift thyratron current control circuits, with resistive loads.

ode-to-grid path in series with a current-limiting resistor R_G. During the negative half-cycle of e_{OG}, no current flows between cathode and grid, because the grid is negative and the tube dark. After e_{OG} becomes positive, the tube contains an arc, and current would flow as freely to the grid in its positive swing as to the plate, if no current-limiting resistor were provided. R_G must limit grid current to not more than the rated value for the tube.

Similar operation can be obtained by replacing the grid-control-circuit condenser by a resistance, and the resistance by an inductance.

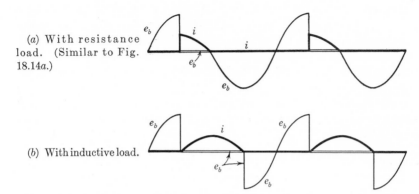

(a) With resistance load. (Similar to Fig. 18.14a.)

(b) With inductive load.

FIG. 18.15 Plate voltage and current variations in a thyratron arranged to provide current control by phase shift in the grid circuit. Arc initiated at the crest of the applied voltage wave. Half-wave operation.

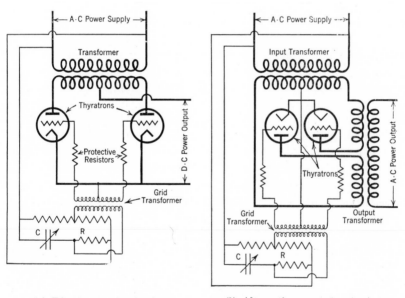

(a) Direct-current output; see Fig. 18.14b.

(b) Alternating-current output; see Fig. 18.14c.

FIG. 18.16 Circuit diagrams for full-wave phase-shift current control by means of thyratrons. Variable condenser in the grid circuit shifts the phase.

The vector diagram is then the same as in Fig. 18.13b except that the current vector lies along the E_{AG} vector.

Figure 18.15 contrasts the behavior of the Fig. 18.13a circuit with a similar one having an inductive load. With both inductive and non-inductive loads, current flow begins as soon as the grid swings positive. However, with an inductive load the current grows gradually rather than abruptly and persists well into the negative half-cycle. As soon as the current reaches zero in its normal transient course, the plate potential drops abruptly to a position along the e_{OB} voltage wave.

The Fig. 18.13a circuit provides only half-wave operation; that is, load current flows during a controllable portion of each alternate half-cycle. The Fig. 18.16a circuit provides similar full-wave operation. The Fig. 18.16b circuit provides phase-shift control of a-c current magnitude, used extensively in resistance welding equipment.

18.14   Large Grid Swing Necessary for Mercury-Vapor Thyratrons. It is evident from Figs. 18.11 and 18.12 that the grid voltage necessary to "fire" a thyratron in a given circuit is very sensitive to the temperature of the mercury droplet. The droplet temperature will in practice vary markedly from time to time, depending on ambient temperature, duty cycle of the tube, and other environmental factors. Therefore it is never practical to employ a mercury-vapor thyratron in a circuit in which operation is sensitive to small variations of grid control voltage.

It is thus universal practice, in applications of mercury-vapor thyratrons, to employ grid voltage swings of large amplitude, so that the grid voltage *swings up through zero rapidly*. For example, with a 1200-volt plate potential in Fig. 18.11, if the grid swings from -6.5 volts to -3 volts in a couple of degrees of the a-c cyclic period, the operation is not appreciably affected by a change of condensed-mercury temperature from 70° to 20° C. This suggests why phase shift circuits employ grid circuit voltages of the same general order of magnitude as industrial power voltages.

This requirement of a fast-swinging grid voltage is an important limitation to the usefulness of mercury-vapor thyratrons. The use of other gases, such as helium, argon, neon, and hydrogen, eliminates this difficulty; there is for each of such tubes only a single grid control curve. However, such tubes have suffered from a different and equally serious limitation, the "clean-up" or disappearance of the conducting gas, discussed in the following section. For many years the clean-up limitation has led to the almost universal employment of mercury rather than inert-gas thyratrons for industrial applications, where long life under continuous service with minimum maintenance is essential, and where large grid swings are easily provided. For many instrumentation uses inert gas tubes are preferable, and for radar modulator thyratrons hydrogen has been most commonly used.

18.15   "Clean-Up" of the Conducting Gas.[18o]   A primary reason for the extensive employment of mercury-vapor thyratrons is their freedom from deterioration due to "clean-up," that is, from gradual disappearance of the conducting gas, as occurs with all other gases.   In a mercury-vapor thyratron, the mercury droplet within the tube at the base is an adequate reservoir of mercury to replace that lost by clean-up.

Note from Fig. 18.15b that a thyratron in the usually employed inductive type of circuit experiences an abrupt and severe drop in plate voltage at the moment when the plate current goes to zero.   As long as the plate *current* is dropping rapidly, the plate voltage appears as an $L(di/dt)$ across the inductance, but as soon as the plate current is stable at zero there is neither $L(di/dt)$ nor iR across the load, so that at that moment the a-c circuit *voltage* appears abruptly between cathode and plate, the plate thus being driven strongly negative.

At this moment there is a large residual ion content in the now decaying plasma between grid and anode.   Many ions of this plasma fall freely through the positive ion sheath adjacent to the anode; each one reaches the anode with an energy in electron volts about equal to the anode-to-cathode voltage.   A small but appreciable fraction of them, perhaps one in 1000 or in 10,000, are caused by this high energy to become permanently embedded either in the anode or one of the other material boundaries of the plasma.

Over many millions of operations, the occasional permanent embedding of ions in the anode or elsewhere constitutes a serious cause of clean-up.   For many years this was overcome only by the use of mercury-vapor tubes.   It has, however, been found possible to minimize the rapid plate voltage drop as a cause of clean-up by the use of auxiliary "snubber" circuits, which employ small condensers to limit the rate of decline of anode voltage following current zero.

Less serious clean-up occurs continually to the cathode; of course if the grid is operated at a strongly negative voltage during current conduction there may be serious clean-up to the grid, but most circuits avoid such operation.

To overcome the clean-up limitation, thyratrons have been developed that employ an inert gas present in sufficient concentration to permit extensive clean-up without reaching an early end of life.[18j] This makes the use of snubber circuits unnecessary, yet the day-to-day control stability inherent in inert gas thyratrons is retained.   One of the important design problems in such tubes was to make certain spacings within the tube *small enough* to prevent failure due to voltage breakdown. The point is that gas pressures within these tubes are such as to place the breakdown voltage to the *left* of the minimum on the Paschen's law curve, Fig. 17.2. Thus, in order to keep the breakdown voltage adequate, these spacings must be very small, if the initial pressure is large enough to permit clean-up without rapid end of life.

In employing any inert gas or hydrogen thyratron, care must be taken to make applications only within the rating limits based on end-of-life due to clean-up.

18.16 Thyratron Recovery Time, in Timing Circuits.[16e, 18m, n]   In various types of electronic control apparatus, particularly resistance

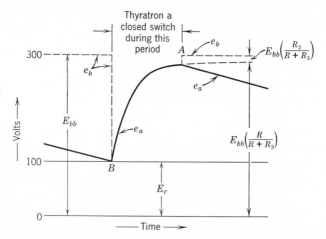

Fig. 18.17   Detail of rise of a timing-circuit cathode voltage, Fig. 3.9a, drawn to a greatly expanded time scale, for circumstances in which the thyratron is extinguished (at A) by the grid shut-off mechanism.

welder controls, circuits very similar to Fig. 3.9 are employed for governing the time intervals between the operation of fast relays or of gas control tubes. The overall behavior of such circuits is described in Section 3.8, but the explanation of the extinction of current flow at moments A of Fig. 3.9a was postponed to the present discussion.

First consider the manner of extinction of current in a circuit just such as shown in Fig. 3.9. After the thyratron fires at moment B, the cathode potential rises exponentially, as indicated in Fig. 18.17, aiming toward a d-c condition in which e_a would be determined by the potential-divider action of R and R_3 in series, if the tube drop is ignored. Of course $R_3 \ll R$. The transient behavior is determined by replacing the battery E_{bb} by its own internal resistance, which in the ideal case being discussed is zero. In the transient circuit so set up, R and R_3 are in parallel; therefore

$$\left.\begin{array}{c}\text{The time constant of the rising}\\ \text{exponential transient}\end{array}\right\} = \frac{RR_3}{R + R_3}\,C \qquad (18\text{--}5)$$

Note that the current in the tube is at moment B quite large, whereas if the thyratron were to remain a closed switch indefinitely the ultimate tube current would be very small. Thus very shortly after the firing moment B one would find a rapidly increasing thickness of the sheath around the grid, because (a) the tube current, therefore with it the ion density, is declining rapidly, and (b) the grid potential is rapidly becoming more negative than that of the cathode. If the design and operational parameters are properly chosen, grid shut-off due to the sheath occluding the grid holes will occur at some such moment as A in the figure. After this moment the cathode potential falls exponentially, the time constant being RC.

Under certain circumstances the tube current declines so rapidly during the rise of e_a that the extinction moment A occurs much too early, that is, at a potential very substantially below E_{bb}. If a suitably chosen resistor R_5, shown dotted in Fig. 3.9b is introduced, the grid potential is controlled by a potential-divider action involving R_1, R_2, R_4, R_5; this makes the grid potential tend to follow e_a up during the exponential rise, so that the sheath potential remains modest. In this way the value of cathode potential at extinction can be adjusted to be more nearly E_{bb}.

In many industrial electronic timing circuits it is necessary to use thyratrons and currents for which the grid shut-off characteristics do not permit extinction in the manner just described, chiefly for reasons related to reliability of performance. A *commutating inductance* may then be introduced; this is merely a small inductance in series with R_3, Fig. 3.9b. The voltage rise after the firing moment A is then a part of an oscillatory transient, as indicated in Fig. 18.18. At and near moment G the current in the inductance represents enough energy storage to charge the condenser to a potential considerably greater than E_{bb}; hence the cathode potential overshoots E_{bb}. Note, however, that the condenser current obeys the relation

$$i_c = C\,\frac{de_c}{dt} \qquad (18\text{--}6)$$

Therefore at some moment such as A the *declining* condenser potential causes a discharging current in C just equal to the current in R; therefore the tube current becomes zero; the thyratron has now become an open switch. After this extinction moment A the circuit is a simple RC combination; the voltage declines exponentially toward zero, along the line AH.

Prior to moment A, the anode potential e_b (relative to zero potential in the figure) has of course been greater than e_a by the amount of the tube drop. At moment A the anode potential drops abruptly to E_{bb}, because after A there is neither current in R_3 nor rate of change of

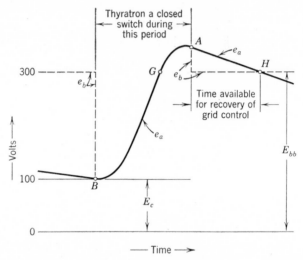

Fig. 18.18   Similar to Fig. 18.17, except that the thyratron is extinguished (at A) by the current going to zero during the oscillatory transient produced by the presence of a commutating inductance in series with R_3, Fig. 3.9b.

current in the commutating inductance. Therefore, during the A to H period the cathode is at a higher potential than the anode; the tube will obviously remain an open switch, because it is inherently a rectifier. After the moment H, however, the anode is positive relative to the cathode, and the thyratron will remain an open switch only because of the grid control over initiation of plate current.

The grid is of course strongly negative, tending to prevent firing. If, however, there are at moment H enough residual ions present in the decaying plasma so that the grid sheath does not occlude the holes in the grid, the tube will fire at once, and cathode potential will remain constant at about the value E_{bb}. The circuit has then failed to function properly.

Thus the period A to H may be called the *time available for recovery* (of grid control); or, in an older phraseology, the time available for deionization. Only if the *recovery time* of the tube (see Section 16.10), for the existing application is less than the time AH will the circuit function properly.

Note that the time available for recovery is a property of the *circuit*, while the recovery time is primarily a property of the *tube*.

Recovery time is, however, much longer for small grid voltages than for large grid voltages, because of the increase of sheath thickness with sheath potential. Thus, with a commutating inductance, introduction of a resistor such as R_5 in Fig. 3.9b would substantially *increase* the recovery time, thus lessening the dependability of the circuit.

Power *inverters*, that is, equipments employing gas tubes for changing d-c power to a-c power, possess limitations involving recovery time, both for thyratrons and for ignitrons.[9L, 18p, q]

18.17   Igniter-Rod Control of Arc Initiation.[18D, E, F, G, a, b, c]   Figure 18.1 illustrates (schematically only) the arrangement of parts in an ignitron that falls into the industrial electron tube classification. Ignition of the arc occurs if the potential gradient in the igniter rod at the junction with the mercury surface reaches or exceeds a critical gradient that may be expected to be between 15 and 150 volts per centimeter. The critical gradient is likely to be considerably smaller when the rod has been heated by continuous operation than when at room temperature. Ignitrons are very extensively used in welder control phase-shift circuits following the principles of Section 18.13; usually thyratrons are used to cause firing of the ignitron at controllable phase moments.

The potential gradient in the rod is established by the passage of an auxiliary current of several amperes. This current may be provided by connecting the rod to the anode through a resistance or by an auxiliary igniting circuit. The energy required for ignition may be very small, for, although the instantaneous power in the igniting circuit may be several hundred watts, ignition is usually accomplished in a few microseconds.

When the rod gradient exceeds the critical value, an arc forms at the rod-mercury junction. The lower terminal of this arc, a hot cathode spot, moves away from the rod along the surface of the pool. The upper arc terminal travels upward along the rod with extreme rapidity; when it reaches the metal of the supporting bracket the rod is of course short-circuited by the arc, which now plays between bracket and pool.

Experiments have shown that the arc between cathode pool and anode forms within a small fraction of a microsecond after the cathode spot is initiated at the rod-mercury junction. However, the time required for the formation of the cathode spot, after establishment of

the gradient in the rod, follows a simple statistical law,[18b] very similar
to that found by Slepian and Ludwig [18h] to describe arc-back frequency
in mercury-arc rectifiers. There exists for both situations a probability
of cathode-spot initiation which is presumably some reasonably simple
function of the gradient at the location of interest. In one situation
the location of interest is the rod-mercury junction; in the other the
surface of the idle anode.

18.18   Statistical Variation of Firing Time in Ignitrons.[18b]   The
mathematical analysis which appears below, for the variation in time
to arc ignition by an igniter rod, applies with slight modifications to
the arc-back situation; see Section 18.5. The mathematical method
employed is very similar to that used in Section 15.11, dealing with
mean free paths, but in the present application time rather than
distance is the important variable.

Experiments have shown that for any given set of igniter-rod operating conditions there is a definite probability $p\,dt$ of ignition of an
arc within a brief time interval dt, where p is primarily a function of
the gradient in the rod. If P is the probability that ignition occurs
later than t seconds after the application of the gradient,

$$-dP = P \cdot p\,dt \qquad (18\text{-}7)$$

or

$$d \ln P = p\,dt \qquad (18\text{-}8)$$

Equation (18–7) is based on the following reasoning: The chance of
ignition's occurring at some time later than t is by definition P, and the
chance of ignition in the particular interval dt *immediately following* t
is $p\,dt$; the product $P \cdot p\,dt$ is therefore the chance that ignition will
not occur until t seconds have passed but will occur in dt seconds
immediately thereafter. This product is therefore the negative
differential change in P, negative because P must become less for
longer times. The solution for P, if p is independent of time, is

$$P = \exp\,(-pt) \qquad (18\text{-}9)$$

If p is a function of time, the solution is

$$P = \exp\left[-\int_{t=0}^{t=t} p\,dt \right] \qquad (18\text{-}10)$$

In arriving at these expressions it is recognized that $P = 1$ when $t = 0$.

Below a rather definite critical gradient the momentary ignition
probability p is vanishingly small. Above this critical gradient it
depends on the actual value F of the gradient. With limited experimental data available it is possible to devise a considerable variety of

hypothetical forms of the mathematical dependence of p on F, all of which are consistent with the data. Among many such suggested forms the following two will be discussed here:

$$p = \frac{1}{t_0} \left(\frac{F - F_c}{F_0} \right)^3 \qquad (18\text{--}11)$$

$$p = \frac{1}{t_a} \exp \frac{F}{F_a} \qquad (18\text{--}12)$$

where t_0, F_c, F_0, and t_a, F_a are empirical quantities. F_c and F_a can be identified with the critical gradient. Corresponding expressions for P, in case F is zero before $t = 0$ *and has a constant value after* $t = 0$, are obtained by simple integration, giving

$$\ln P = -\frac{t}{t_0} \left(\frac{F - F_c}{F_0} \right)^3 \qquad (18\text{--}13)$$

$$\ln P = -\frac{t}{t_a} \exp \frac{F}{F_a} \qquad (18\text{--}14)$$

Here F and t are rod gradient and time delay to reignition.

The three step curves in Fig. 18.19 represent experimental data taken with abruptly applied gradients, respectively 86, 124, and 157 volts per centimeter, for a particular (rather early) ignitron. The three dashed straight lines in the figure represent the expected straight-line dependence of $\ln P$ on t, *as described by* (18–14), for the three gradients 86, 124, 157, and employing values of t_a and F_a chosen to maximize the agreement between the family of dashed lines and the experimental step curves.

Three lines can similarly be drawn based on (18–13), using values of F_c and $t_0 F_0{}^3$ chosen to maximize agreement with experiment. The three lines so drawn agree just as well with the experimental data as do those shown in the figure, which were based on (18–14).

However, a preference exists for (18–11) and (18–13), discussed by Rigrod,[18b] as compared with other suggested forms, because:

(a) A reasonably rational theory of the physics of igniter operation has been devised which leads to the form (18–11), and, subsequently,

(b) The form (18–11) has been shown to be in agreement with a great deal of the experimental data accumulated by various observers over a period of years.

Reason (a) illustrates the importance of analytical study of physical processes in the process of correlating experimental data.

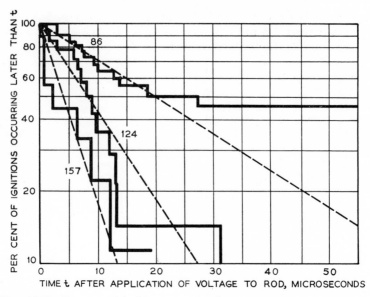

FIG. 18.19   Per cent of ignitions occurring later than time t, with igniter-rod gradients of 86, 124, and 157 volts per centimeter, in an ignitron.   Logarithmic per cent scale.

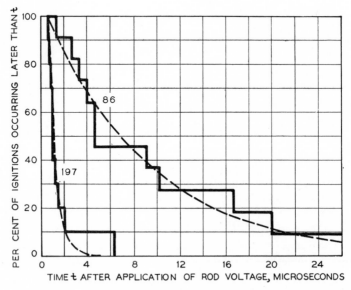

FIG. 18.20   Per cent of ignitions occurring later than time t, with igniter-rod gradients of 86 and 197 volts per centimeter, in an ignitron.

Figure 18.20 is another way of presenting the same kind of information as that contained in Fig. 18.19, the difference being in the vertical scale used.

PROBLEMS

1. In a certain mercury-vapor plasma the electron-and-ion concentration is 10^{11} per cu cm; ion and electron temperatures are respectively $11,600°$ K and $23,200°$ K. The condensed-mercury temperature is $80°$ C, the mercury-vapor temperature $400°$ K; there is pressure equilibrium between the gas in the plasma region and that adjacent to the condensed mercury. Find: (a) the percentage ionization, (b) the ion mean free path, (c) the electron mean free path.

2. Figure 18.21 illustrates the type of relation to be expected between metal case potential (relative to the cathode), and density of current flow from plasma

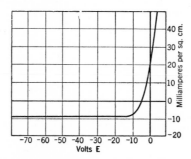

Fig. 18.21   Current density to the case of a mercury-arc rectifier.

to case, in a metal-enclosed mercury-arc rectifier. Note the resemblance to Fig. 16.3a. For Fig. 18.21, determine: (a) case potential when insulated from the rest of the circuit, (b) current density to the case when at cathode potential, (c) electron temperature.

3. Conditions as in the preceding problem. Determine the rate at which the plasma delivers energy (heat) to the walls of the case, in watts per square centimeter, with the case at cathode potential. Plasma is 12 volts above cathode potential. The following items should be accounted for, each calculable by multiplying a properly chosen current by a properly chosen voltage:

(a) Kinetic energy acquired by the positive ions in falling through the sheath.

(b) Energy released by recombination of positive ions at the surface.

(c) Residual kinetic energy of the electrons after penetrating the sheath.

(d) Heat produced by entrance into the metal of the case, sliding down the work function hill, of the electrons not needed for recombination at the surface. Work function of the case is 4 volts.

4. Conditions as in the two preceding problems. (a) Determine the thickness of the sheath adjacent to an idle anode whose potential is 2000 volts below that of the plasma. (b) Determine the potential gradient at the surface of this idle anode.

5. Suppose that in a mercury-arc rectifier the probability of arc-back follows the law $P = \exp(-t/\tau)$ where P is the chance that an arc-back will occur later than time t after the last one, and τ is a constant, measured in days, weeks, or months.

(a) The last arc-back occurred 6 weeks ago on rectifier 1; on rectifier 2, identical with rectifier 1 in every detail, the last arc-back occurred 3 days ago. For which one is there the greatest chance that arc-back will occur in the next 24 hours?

(b) If the average time between arc-backs is 3 months, how many times in 10 years should it be expected that an arc-back will follow the last previous one by ⅓ month or less?

6. Consider a neon gas thyratron operating under 60-cycle inductive-load phase-shift conditions as in Fig. 18.15b. At the moment the current goes to zero the anode potential drops abruptly to −150 volts. The plasma volume is 8 cu cm; while carrying current its ion density is 3×10^{12} per cu cm. All the ions run out to the enclosing grid and plate boundaries within perhaps 200 microseconds after each current-zero moment. The anode occupies 17 per cent of this boundary area, and 0.02 per cent of the ions that fall through the 150-volt drop then existing stay permanently in the anode metal. Total volume in the tube is 19 cu cm. If when new the tube contains 3×10^{16} neon atoms per cu cm, how many weeks of 60-cycle operation, 24 hours per day, will reduce the neon content to ⅕ of its original value?

7. Figure 18.22 is a diagram of a circuit that employs a mercury-vapor thyratron to produce a sawtooth voltage wave of the Fig. 3.8a type. If the tube used

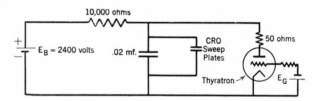

Fig. 18.22   Sweep circuit for cathode-ray oscilloscope.

is an FG17 thyratron (Fig. 18.11) at a condensed-mercury temperature of 40° C, and the crest of each sawtooth is to occur at 800 volts, find (a) the grid voltage required, (b) the frequency, and (c) approximate time required to discharge the condenser during the vertical drop from the crest of each sawtooth.

TABLE I

Charge carried by an electron (q_e)	1.602×10^{-19} coulomb
Ratio of charge to mass of an electron (q_e/m_e)	1.759×10^{11}
Mass of an electron (m_e)	9.11×10^{-31} kilogram
Velocity of an electron whose kinetic energy is 1 electron volt	5.932×10^5 meters per second
Mass of a proton	1.672×10^{-27} kilogram
Mass of a hydrogen atom	1.681×10^{-27} kilogram
Mass of an atom of unit atomic weight (no such atom exists)	1.660×10^{-27} kilogram
Ratio of the mass of an atom of unit atomic weight to that of an electron	1822
Atomic weights: Oxygen	16.0000
Hydrogen	1.00777 ± 0.00002
Helium	4.0022 ± 0.0004
Velocity of light	2.99776×10^8 meters per second
Planck's quantum of action (h)	6.624×10^{-34} joule second
Boltzmann's gas constant (k)	1.3803×10^{-23} joule per degree Kelvin
Stefan-Boltzmann radiation constant	5.672×10^{-8} joule per square meter per second per (degree Kelvin)^4
Pressure of any gas at 0° C and 760 mm of mercury pressure	1.013×10^5 newtons per square meter
Avogadro's number (number of molecules per kilogram molecule of any gas)	6.025×10^{26}
Loschmidt number (the number of molecules per cubic meter of any gas at 0° C and 760 millimeters of mercury pressure)	2.687×10^{25} molecules per cubic meter
The number of molecules per cubic meter of any gas at 0° C and 1 millimeter of mercury pressure	3.536×10^{22} molecules per cubic meter
Ice point (degrees Kelvin)	273.18° K
Ratio of temperature in degrees Kelvin to voltage equivalent of temperature	11606 degrees Kelvin per electron volt
Wavelength of a photon whose energy is 1 electron volt	12404 angstrom units 1.2404 microns
Ionizing potential of a hydrogen atom	13.68 electron volts
Wavelength of red cadmium line (at 15° C, atmospheric pressure)	6438.4696 angstrom units
Density of mercury at 0° C, 760 millimeters of mercury pressure	13.595 grams per cubic centimeter

* Values of the atomic constants used in this table are as given by DuMond and Cohen, *Revs. Mod. Phys.*, **20**, 106 (1948); **21**, 651 (1950).[1b]

TABLE II

Properties of Atoms of the Elements

Atomic Number	Symbol	Element	Atomic Weight	Ionizing Potential	Isotopes	Shell Distribution of Electrons						
						1	2	3	4	5	6	7
1	H	Hydrogen	1.0078	13.53	1, 2	1						
2	He	Helium	4.002	24.46	4	2						
3	Li	Lithium	6.940	5.37	7, 6	2	1					
4	Be	Beryllium	9.02	9.28	9	2	2					
5	B	Boron	10.82	8.28	11, 10	2	3					
6	C	Carbon	12.006	11.22	12, 13	2	4					
7	N	Nitrogen	14.008	14.48	14, 15	2	5					
8	O	Oxygen	16.000	13.55	16, 18, 17	2	6					
9	F	Fluorine	19.00	18.6	19	2	7					
10	Ne	Neon	20.18	21.47	20, 22, 21	2	8					
11	Na	Sodium	22.997	5.12	23	2	8	1				
12	Mg	Magnesium	24.32	7.61	24, 25, 26	2	8	2				
13	Al	Aluminum	26.97	5.96	27	2	8	3				
14	Si	Silicon	28.06	8.12	28, 29, 30	2	8	4				
15	P	Phosphorus	31.02	10.3	31	2	8	5				
16	S	Sulphur	32.065	12.96	32, 34, 33	2	8	6				
17	Cl	Chlorine	35.457	15.69	35, 37	2	8	7				
18	A	Argon	39.94		40, 36, 38	2	8	8				
19	K	Potassium	39.10	4.32	39, 41, 40	2	8	8	1			
20	Ca	Calcium	40.08	6.09	40, 44, 42, 43	2	8	8	2			
21	Sc	Scandium	45.10	6.7	45	2	8	9	2			
22	Ti	Titanium	47.9	6.81	48, 46, 47, 50, 49	2	8	10	2			
23	V	Vanadium	50.95	6.76	51	2	8	11	2			
24	Cr	Chromium	52.01	6.74	52, 53, 50, 54	2	8	13	1			
25	Mn	Manganese	54.93	7.41	55	2	8	13	2			
26	Fe	Iron	55.84	7.83	56, 54, 57, 58	2	8	14	2			
27	Co	Cobalt	58.94	8.5	59	2	8	15	2			

TABLE II (*Continued*)

Atomic Number	Symbol	Element	Atomic Weight	Ionizing Potential	Isotopes	Shell Distribution of Electrons						
						1	2	3	4	5	6	7
28	Ni	Nickel	58.69	7.61	58, 60, 62, 64	2	8	16	2			
29	Cu	Copper	63.57	7.68	63, 65	2	8	18	1			
30	Zn	Zinc	65.38	9.36	64, 66, 68, 67, 70	2	8	18	2			
31	Ga	Gallium	69.72	5.97	69, 71	2	8	18	3			
32	Ge	Germanium	72.60	8.09	74, 72, 70, 73, 76	2	8	18	4			
33	As	Arsenic	74.93	10	75	2	8	18	5			
34	Se	Selenium	78.96	9.5	80, 78, 76, 82, 77, 74	2	8	18	6			
35	Br	Bromine	79.916	11.80	79, 81	2	8	18	7			
36	Kr	Krypton	83.7	13.94	84, 86, 82, 83, 80, 78,	2	8	18	8			
37	Rb	Rubidium	85.44	4.16	85, 87	2	8	18	8	1		
38	Sr	Strontium	87.63	5.67	88, 86, 87, 84	2	8	18	8	2		
39	Y	Yttrium	88.92	6.5	89	2	8	18	9	2		
40	Zr	Zirconium	91.22	6.92	90, 92, 94, 91, 96	2	8	18	10	2		
41	Nb, Cb	Niobium, Columbium	93.3		93	2	8	18	12	1		
42	Mo	Molybdenum	96.0	7.35	98, 96, 95, 94, 92, 100, 97	2	8	18	13	1		
43	Ma	Technetium				2	8	18	14	1		
44	Ru	Ruthenium	101.7	7.7	102, 101, 104, 100	2	8	18	15	1		
45	Rh	Rhodium	102.91		103	2	8	18	16	1		
46	Pd	Palladium	106.7	8.3	102–110	2	8	18	18			
47	Ag	Silver	107.880	7.54	107, 109	2	8	18	18	1		
48	Cd	Cadmium	112.41	8.96	114, 112, 116, 110, 111, 113, 106, 108	2	8	18	18	2		
49	In	Indium	114.8	5.76	115, 113	2	8	18	18	3		
50	Sn	Tin	118.70	7.30	120, 118, 116, 119, 124, 117, 122, 121, 112, 114, 115	2	8	18	18	4		

TABLE II (Continued)

Atomic Number	Symbol	Element	Atomic Weight	Ionizing Potential	Isotopes	Shell Distribution of Electrons						
						1	2	3	4	5	6	7
51	Sb	Antimony	121.76	8.5	121, 123	2	8	18	18	5		
52	Te	Tellurium	127.6		120–130	2	8	18	18	6		
53	I	Iodine	126.92	10	127	2	8	18	18	7		
54	Xe	Xenon	131.3	12.08	132, 129, 131, 134, 136, 128, 130, 126, 124	2	8	18	18	8		
55	Cs	Cesium	132.81	3.87	133	2	8	18	18	8	1	
56	Ba	Barium	137.36	5.19	138, 130–137	2	8	18	18	8	2	
57	La	Lanthanum	138.92		139	2	8	18	18	9	2	
58	Ce	Cerium	140.13		140, 142	2	8	18	19	9	2	
59	Pr	Praseodimium	140.92		141	2	8	18	20	9	2	
60	Nd	Neodymium	144.27		142, 144, 146, 145	2	8	18	21	9	2	
61	Il	Promethium				2	8	18	22	9	2	
62	{Sm Sa}	Samarium	150.43		144–154	2	8	18	23	9	2	
63	Eu	Europium	152.0		153, 151	2	8	18	24	9	2	
64	Gd	Gadolinium	157.3		155–160	2	8	18	25	9	2	
65	Tb	Terbium	159.2		159	2	8	18	26	9	2	
66	{Ds Dy}	Dysprosium	162.46		164, 163, 162, 161	2	8	18	27	9	2	
67	Ho	Holmium	163.5		165	2	8	18	28	9	2	
68	Er	Erbium	167.64		166, 168, 167, 170	2	8	18	29	9	2	
69	{Tm Tu}	Thulium	169.4		169	2	8	18	30	9	2	
70	Yb	Ytterbium	173.5		174, 172, 173, 176, 171	2	8	18	31	9	2	
71	Lu	Lutetium	175.0		175	2	8	18	32	9	2	

TABLE II (Continued)

Atomic Number	Symbol	Element	Atomic Weight	Ionizing Potential	Isotopes	Shell Distribution of Electrons						
						1	2	3	4	5	6	7
72	Hf	Hafnium	178.6		180, 178, 177, 179	2	8	18	32	10	2	
73	Ta	Tantalum	181.4		181	2	8	18	32	11	2	
74	W	Tungsten	184.0		184, 186, 182, 183	2	8	18	32	12	2	
75	Re	Rhenium	186.31		185, 187	2	8	18	32	13	2	
76	Os	Osmium	190.8		192, 190, 189, 188	2	8	18	32	14	2	
77	Ir	Iridium	193.1		191, 193	2	8	18	32	15	2	
78	Pt	Platinum	195.23	8.9	192–198	2	8	18	32	16	2	
79	Au	Gold	197.2	9.2	197	2	8	18	32	18	1	
80	Hg	Mercury	200.61	10.38	202, 200, 199, 198, 201, 204, 196	2	8	18	32	18	2	
81	Tl	Thallium	204.4	6.07	205, 203	2	8	18	32	18	3	
82	Pb	Lead	207.22	7.38	208, 206, 207, 204, 203, 205	2	8	18	32	18	4	
83	Bi	Bismuth	209.00	8.0	209	2	8	18	32	18	5	
84	Po	Polonium				2	8	18	32	18	6	
85	At	Astatine				2	8	18	32	18	7	
86	Rn	Radon	222	10.69		2	8	18	32	18	8	
87	Fr	Francium				2	8	18	32	18	8	1
88	Ra	Radium	225.97	10.2		2	8	18	32	18	8	2
89	Ac	Actinium				2	8	18	32	18	9	2
90	Th	Thorium	232.12		232	2	8	18	32	18	10	2
91	Pa	Protactinium				2	8	18	32	18	11	2
92	U	Uranium	238.14		238, 235	2	8	18	32	18	12	2

Ionizing Potentials chiefly from *Atomic Energy States*, by Bacher and Goudsmit, McGraw-Hill, 1932. They are for atoms, not molecules.

TABLE III

(See Section 5.14)

DEPENDENCE OF β^2 ON r/r_k, IN EXPRESSIONS FOR SPACE-CHARGE-LIMITED CURRENTS FROM CYLINDRICAL CATHODES OF RADIUS r_k

β^2 applies where $r > r_k$,

$-\beta^2$ applies where $r < r_k$

r/r_k or r_k/r	β^2	$-\beta^2$	r/r_k or r_k/r	β^2	$-\beta^2$
1.00	0.0000	0.0000	3.8	0.6420	5.3795
1.01	0.00010	0.00010	4.0	0.6671	6.0601
1.02	0.00039	0.00040	4.2	0.6902	6.7705
1.04	0.00149	0.00159	4.4	0.7115	7.5096
1.06	0.00324	0.00356	4.6	0.7313	8.2763
1.08	0.00557	0.00630	4.8	0.7496	9.0696
1.10	0.00842	0.00980	5.0	0.7666	9.887
1.15	0.01747	0.02186	5.2	0.7825	10.733
1.20	0.02815	0.03849	5.4	0.7973	11.601
1.30	0.05589	0.08504	5.6	0.8111	12.493
1.40	0.08672	0.14856	5.8	0.8241	13.407
1.50	0.11934	0.2282	6.0	0.8362	14.343
1.60	0.1525	0.3233	6.5	0.8635	16.777
1.70	0.1854	0.4332	7.0	0.8870	19.337
1.80	0.2177	0.5572	7.5	0.9074	22.015
1.90	0.2491	0.6947	8.0	0.9253	24.805
2.0	0.2793	0.8454	8.5	0.9410	27.701
2.1	0.3083	1.0086	9.0	0.9548	30.698
2.2	0.3361	1.1840	9.5	0.9672	33.791
2.3	0.3626	1.3712	10.0	0.9782	36.976
2.4	0.3879	1.5697	12.0	1.0122	50.559
2.5	0.4121	1.7792	16.0	1.0513	81.203
2.6	0.4351	1.9995	20.0	1.0715	115.64
2.7	0.4571	2.2301	40.0	1.0946	327.01
2.8	0.4780	2.4708	80.0	1.0845	867.11
2.9	0.4980	2.7214	100.0	1.0782	1174.9
3.0	0.5170	2.9814	200.0	1.0562	2946.1
3.2	0.5526	3.5293	500.0	1.0307	9502.2
3.4	0.5851	4.1126	∞	1.000	∞
3.6	0.6148	4.7298			

TABLE IV

(See Section 5.17)

DEPENDENCE OF α^2 ON r/r_k, IN EXPRESSIONS FOR SPACE-CHARGE-LIMITED CURRENTS FROM SPHERICAL CATHODES OF RADIUS r_k

α^2 applies where $r > r_k$

$-\alpha^2$ applies where $r < r_k$

r/r_k or r_k/r	α^2	$-\alpha^2$	r/r_k or r_k/r	α^2	$-\alpha^2$
1.0	0.0000	0.0000	5.4	1.213	9.315
1.1	0.0086	0.0096	5.8	1.280	10.73
1.2	0.0299	0.0372	6.0	1.311	11.46
1.3	0.0591	0.0809	6.5	1.385	13.35
1.4	0.0931	0.1396	7.0	1.453	15.35
1.5	0.1302	0.2118	7.5	1.516	17.44
1.6	0.1688	0.2968	8.0	1.575	19.62
1.7	0.208	0.394	9.0	1.682	24.25
1.8	0.248	0.502	10.0	1.777	29.19
1.9	0.287	0.621	12.0	1.938	39.98
2.0	0.326	0.750	14.0	2.073	51.86
2.2	0.402	1.036	16.0	2.189	64.74
2.4	0.474	1.358	20.0	2.378	93.24
2.6	0.543	1.712	30.0	2.713	178.2
2.8	0.608	2.098	40.0	2.944	279.6
3.0	0.669	2.512	50.0	3.120	395.3
3.4	0.783	3.421	60.0	3.261	523.6
3.8	0.886	4.429	80.0	3.482	813.7
4.2	0.979	5.528	100.0	3.652	1144
4.6	1.063	6.712	500.0	4.829	13015
5.0	1.141	7.976	1000.0	5.324	

TABLE V

(See Section 5.22)

VALUES OF $f(E_s/E_f)$ WHICH GOVERNS DEPENDENCE OF TRIODE PLATE CURRENT
ON THE VOLTAGE DROP E_f ALONG THE FILAMENT

$\dfrac{E_s}{E_f}$	$f\left(\dfrac{E_s}{E_f}\right)$	$\dfrac{E_s}{E_f}$	$f\left(\dfrac{E_s}{E_f}\right)$
0	0	5.0	24.1
0.25	0.031	6.0	32.5
0.50	0.177	8.0	52.5
0.75	0.414	10	74.0
1.00	1.000	15	138
1.50	2.57	20	211
2.00	4.65	40	622
2.50	7.13		
3.00	9.94	Higher	$\dfrac{5}{2}\left[\dfrac{E_s}{E_f}\right]^{3/2}$
4.0	16.51		

TABLE VI

(See Sections 7.2, 8.24, and 14.1)

ELECTRON EMISSION CONSTANTS

(This data was assembled and made available by H. F. Ivey and J. W. McNall, of the Lamp Division, Westinghouse Electric Corp., Bloomfield, N. J.)

Substance	Thermionic $A_0 \cdot 10^{-4}$	Thermionic E_W	Photoelectric E_W	Contact Potential E_W
Li			(2.42)[37]	2.49[5]
Na	(60)*	(1.76)[36]	2.28[27]	
K	(60)	(1.45)[36]	2.24[11]	
Rb	(60)	(1.23)[36]	2.19[11]	
Cs	162	1.81[25]	1.96[11]	
Mg			3.67[15]	3.65[2]
Sr			(2.42)[37]	
Ba	60	2.11[35]	2.48[27]	2.39[1]
Ca			3.21[26]	
Zr	330	4.12[43]	3.92[33]	
Zr	120	4.00[23]		
Mo	55	4.20[42]	4.15[18]	
Ta	55	4.19[19]	4.15[8]	
W	72	4.52[31]	4.49[7]	
W	60	4.52[28]		
Pt	32	5.32[41]	(6.30)[16]	
Th	70	3.38[43]	3.36[33]	
U	6	3.27[22]	3.65[32]	
Cr	48	4.60[40]		
Fe(β)	26	4.48[39]	4.72[29]	
Fe(γ)	1.5	4.21[39]		
Co	41	4.41[39]	4.25[13]	
Ni	50	5.24[14]	5.05–5.20[14]	
Ni	30	4.61[39]		
Al			4.20[38]	
Cu	(65)	(4.33)[21]		4.46[6]
Ag			4.51[10]	4.47[4]
Au	(40)	(4.32)[21]	4.90[20]	
Hg			4.52[34]	
Pd	60	4.99[17]	4.97[17]	
Zn			4.31[38]	4.28[3]
Cd			4.10[38]	
Sn(β)			4.39[20]	
Sn(γ)			4.28[20]	
Sb			4.60[9]	
Te			4.76[8]	
Bi			4.34[9]	
B				4.6[8]
C	30	4.34[30]		
C	46	4.60[24]		
Si	5–11	3.59[12]		4.4–4.7[10]
Ge			4.8[8]	
As			4.72[9]	
Se				(5.15)[37]
BaO	0.004†		1.1[44]	
SrO	0.01†		1.4[44]	
CaO	0.4†		1.9[44]	
ThO_2	2.63		2.67[45]	

Reference List

1 Anderson, *Phys. Rev.*, **47**, 958 (1935).
2 *Ibid.*, **54**, 753 (1938).
3 *Ibid.*, **57**, 122 (1940).
4 *Ibid.*, **59**, 1034 (1941).
5 *Ibid.*, **75**, 1205 (1949).
6 *Ibid.*, **76**, 388 (1949).
7 Apker et al., *Phys. Rev.*, **73**, 46 (1948).
8 *Ibid.*, **74**, 1463 (1948).
9 *Ibid.*, **76**, 270 (1949).
10 Arsen'eval-Geil, *Doklady Akad. Nauk, SSSR*, **62**, 47 (1948).
11 Brady, *Phys. Rev.*, **41**, 613 (1932).
12 Braun and Busch, *Helv. Phys. Acta*, **20**, 33 (1947).
13 Cardwell, *Phys. Rev.*, **38**, 203 (1931).
14 *Ibid.*, **76**, 125 (1949).
15 Cashman, *Phys. Rev.*, **54**, 971 (1938).
16 Du Bridge, *Phys. Rev.*, **31**, 736 (1928).
17 Du Bridge and Roehr, *Phys. Rev.*, **39**, 99 (1932).
18 *Ibid.*, **42**, 52 (1932).
19 Fiske, *Phys. Rev.*, **61**, 513 (1942).
20 Fowler, *Phys. Rev.*, **38**, 45 (1931).
21 Goetz, *Z. Physik*, **43**, 531 (1927).
22 Hole and Wright, *Phys. Rev.*, **56**, 785 (1939).
23 Ivey, *Phys. Rev.*, **74**, 983 (1948).
24 *Ibid.*, **76**, 567 (1949).
25 Kingdon, *Phys. Rev.*, **25**, 892 (1925).
26 Liben, *Phys. Rev.*, **51**, 642 (1937).
27 Maurer, *Phys. Rev.*, **57**, 653 (1940).
28 Nottingham, *Phys. Rev.*, **47**, 806 (1935).
29 Olsen, *Phys. Rev.*, **56**, 210 (1939).
30 Reimann, *Proc. Phys. Soc. London*, **50**, 496 (1935).
31 Reimann, *Phil. Mag.*, **25**, 834 (1938).
32 Rentschler et al., *Rev. Sci. Instruments*, **3**, 794 (1932).
33 Rentschler and Henry, *Trans. Electrochem. Soc.*, **87**, 289 (1945).
34 Roller, *Phys. Rev.*, **36**, 738 (1930).
35 Ryde and Harris (Reimann [7B]).
36 Schulze, *Z. Physik*, **90**, 63 (1934).
37 *Ibid.*, **92**, 212 (1934).
38 Suhrmann and Pietrzyk, *Z. Physik*, **122**, 600 (1944).
39 Wahlin, *Phys. Rev.*, **61**, 509 (1942).
40 *Ibid.*, **73**, 1458 (1948).
41 Whitney, *Phys. Rev.*, **50**, 1154 (1936).
42 Wright, *Phys. Rev.*, **60**, 465 (1941).
43 Zwikker, *Physik. Z.* **30**, 578 (1929).
44 Blewett, *J. Applied Phys.*, **10**, 831 (1939).
45 Hanley, *J. Applied Phys.*, **19**, 583 (1948).

* Values enclosed in parentheses must be considered as only approximate. Only measurements made most recently, or considered most reliable, are listed.

† Average values. Emission may be a factor of 10 larger or smaller, depending on processing details and state of activation.

TABLE VII
(See Section 7.8)

RATIO OF HOT TO COLD RESISTANCES OF FILAMENT MATERIALS

T, °K	$\dfrac{\text{Hot Resistance}}{\text{Cold Resistance}}$		
	*Combined-Type Oxide-Coated Cathode (W.E.Co.)	†*Konel Metal	‡Tungsten
300	1.00	1.00	1.00
700	1.80	1.11	2.85
800	1.96	1.13	3.36
900	2.12	1.16	3.88
1000	2.26	1.19	4.41
1100	2.40	1.21	4.95
1200	2.53	1.24	5.48
1300	2.65	1.27	6.03
1400	2.75	1.29	6.57
1500	2.85	1.32	7.13
1600			7.70
1800			8.99
2000			10.03
2200			11.22
2400			12.45
2600			13.70
2800			14.96
3000			16.30

* DUSHMAN, Rev. Modern Phys., **2**, 381 (1930).
† LOWRY, Phys. Review, **35**, 1367 (1930).
‡ Calculated from data given by Chaffee, Theory of Thermionic Vacuum Tubes, p. 100.

TABLE VIII

(See Section 8.8)

QUANTUM-NUMBER COMBINATIONS FOR RECTANGULAR QUANTIZATION

n_u	n_v	n_w	n^2 (proportional to energy)	n	Number of Possible Arrangements	Number of Electrons
0	0	0	0	0	1	2
1	0	0				
0	1	0	1	1	3	6
0	0	1				
1	1	0				
1	0	1	2	1.414	3	6
0	1	1				
1	1	1	3	1.732	1	2
2	0	0				
0	2	0	4	2.000	3	6
0	0	2				
2	1	0				
2	0	1				
0	2	1	5	2.236	6	12
1	2	0				
1	0	2				
0	1	2				
2	1	1				
1	2	1	6	2.449	3	6
1	1	2				

and so on

TABLE IX

(See Chapter XII)

INTEGRALS CONTAINING ϵ^{-r^2}

A. The various integrals given below can in general be derived from the simple forms first given by a process of integration by parts, as follows:

$$\int_r^\infty \epsilon^{-r^2} r^2\, dr = \int_r^\infty \frac{r}{2}\,(2r\epsilon^{-r^2})dr = -\int_r^\infty \frac{r}{2}\, d\epsilon^{-r^2}$$

$$= -\frac{r\epsilon^{-r^2}}{2}\Big]_r^\infty + \int_r^\infty \frac{\epsilon^{-r^2}}{2}\, dr$$

$$= +\frac{r\epsilon^{-r^2}}{2} + \frac{1}{2}\int_r^\infty \epsilon^{-r^2}\, dr$$

B. Definite integrals of the form $\int_0^\infty \epsilon^{-r^2} r^n\, dr$.

n even	n odd
$\dfrac{2}{\sqrt{\pi}}\displaystyle\int_0^\infty \epsilon^{-r^2}\, dr = 1$	$2\displaystyle\int_0^\infty \epsilon^{-r^2} r\, dr = 1$
$\dfrac{2}{\sqrt{\pi}}\displaystyle\int_0^\infty \epsilon^{-r^2} r^2\, dr = \dfrac{1}{2}$	$2\displaystyle\int_0^\infty \epsilon^{-r^2} r^3\, dr = 1$
$\dfrac{2}{\sqrt{\pi}}\displaystyle\int_0^\infty \epsilon^{-r^2} r^4\, dr = \dfrac{3}{4}$	$2\displaystyle\int_0^\infty \epsilon^{-r^2} r^5\, dr = 2$
$\dfrac{2}{\sqrt{\pi}}\displaystyle\int_0^\infty \epsilon^{-r^2} r^n\, dr = \dfrac{1\cdot 3\cdot 5\cdots(n-1)}{2^{n/2}}$	$2\displaystyle\int_0^\infty \epsilon^{-r^2} r^n\, dr = 1\cdot 2\cdot 3\cdot 4\cdots\dfrac{n-1}{2}$

C. Indefinite integrals of the form $\int \epsilon^{-r^2} r^n\, dr$, n being *odd*.

$$2\int \epsilon^{-r^2} r\, dr = -\epsilon^{-r^2}$$

$$2\int \epsilon^{-r^2} r^3\, dr = -\epsilon^{-r^2}(r^2 + 1)$$

$$2\int \epsilon^{-r^2} r^5\, dr = -\epsilon^{-r^2}(r^4 + 2r^2 + 2)$$

$$2\int \epsilon^{-r^2} r^n\, dr = -\epsilon^{-r^2} r^{n-1} + (n-1)\int \epsilon^{-r^2} r^{n-2}\, dr$$

D. Indefinite integrals of the form $\int_r^\infty \epsilon^{-r^2} r^n\, dr$, n being *even*.

Definition:

$$\operatorname{erf} r = \frac{2}{\sqrt{\pi}}\int_0^r \epsilon^{-r^2}\, dr \qquad \text{(this is called the \emph{error function})}$$

TABLE IX (*Continued*)

Therefore, also using the definite integral in case $n = 0$, Part B, above

$$1 - \operatorname{erf} r = \frac{2}{\sqrt{\pi}} \int_r^\infty \epsilon^{-r^2} dr, \quad \text{so that}$$

$$\frac{2}{\sqrt{\pi}} \int_r^\infty \epsilon^{-r^2} dr = 1 - \operatorname{erf} r$$

$$\frac{2}{\sqrt{\pi}} \int_r^\infty \epsilon^{-r^2} r^2 dr = \frac{r\epsilon^{-r^2}}{\sqrt{\pi}} + \frac{1}{2}(1 - \operatorname{erf} r)$$

$$\frac{2}{\sqrt{\pi}} \int_r^\infty \epsilon^{-r^2} r^4 dr = \frac{r\epsilon^{-r^2}}{\sqrt{\pi}}\left(r^2 + \frac{3}{2}\right) + \frac{3}{4}(1 - \operatorname{erf} r)$$

$$\frac{2}{\sqrt{\pi}} \int_r^\infty \epsilon^{-r^2} r^n dr = \frac{\epsilon^{-r^2}}{\sqrt{\pi}} r^{n-1} + \frac{(n-1)}{\sqrt{\pi}} \int_r^\infty \epsilon^{-r^2} r^{n-2} dr$$

E. Miscellaneous.

$$\int_0^\infty \frac{r\,dr}{B\epsilon^{r^2} + 1} = \frac{1}{2} \log\left(\frac{1}{B} + 1\right)$$

(This is obtained by expansion into an infinite series, in two steps, one for the range $B\epsilon^{r^2} < 1$, one for the range $B\epsilon^{r^2} > 1$, with subsequent term-by-term integration.)

TABLE X

POSSIBLE COMBINATIONS OF POLAR QUANTUM NUMBERS; ALSO, GROUPS AND SUBGROUPS OF ELECTRONS IN SHELLS

(See Sections 13.15, 13.16, 13.20 and Table II)

n	n_r	l	m_l	n_θ	m_s (spin)	Number of Electrons in Subgroup	Subgroup Symbol	Number of Electrons in Shell ($2n^2$)	Represented in Configuration Code as
1	1	$=0$	0	0	1 $\{$ clockwise / counter $\}$	2	s	2	$1s^2$
2	2	$=0$	$0 \;+$	0	$\{$ clockwise / counter $\}$	2	s	8	$2s^2 2p^6$
	1	$=1$	$\begin{Bmatrix} +1 \text{ clockwise} \\ 0 \\ -1 \text{ counter} \end{Bmatrix} +++$	$\begin{matrix} 0 \\ 1 \\ 1 \\ 0 \end{matrix}$ each	$\{$ clockwise / counter $\}$ each	6	p		
3	3	$=0$	$0 \;+$	0	$\{$ clockwise / counter $\}$	2	s	18	$3s^2 3p^6 3d^{10}$
	2	$=1$	$\begin{Bmatrix} +1 \text{ clockwise} \\ 0 \\ -1 \text{ counter} \end{Bmatrix} +++$	$\begin{matrix} 0 \\ 1 \\ 1 \\ 0 \end{matrix}$ each	$\{$ clockwise / counter $\}$ each	6	p		
	1	$=2$	$\begin{Bmatrix} +2 \text{ clockwise} \\ +1 \text{ clockwise} \\ 0 \\ -1 \text{ counter} \\ -2 \text{ counter} \end{Bmatrix} +++++$	$\begin{matrix} 0 \\ 1 \\ 2 \\ 1 \\ 0 \end{matrix}$ each	$\{$ clockwise / counter $\}$ each	10	d		
4	4	$=0$	$0 \;+$	0	$\{$ clockwise / counter $\}$	2	s	32	$4s^2 4p^6 4d^{10} 4f^{14}$
	3	$=1$	$[$ three possible combinations, as above $]$		$\{$ clockwise / counter $\}$ each	6	p		
	2	$=2$	$[$ five possible combinations, as above $]$		$\{$ clockwise / counter $\}$ each	10	d		
	1	$=3$	$\begin{Bmatrix} +3 \text{ clockwise} \\ +2 \text{ clockwise} \\ +1 \text{ clockwise} \\ 0 \\ -1 \text{ counter} \\ -2 \text{ counter} \\ -3 \text{ counter} \end{Bmatrix} +++++++$	$\begin{matrix} 0 \\ 1 \\ 2 \\ 3 \\ 2 \\ 1 \\ 0 \end{matrix}$ each	$\{$ clockwise / counter $\}$ each	14	f		

TABLE XI
TERM VALUES FOR THE NaI SPECTRUM*
(Arc Spectrum of Sodium)
The configuration of sodium's 11 electrons is as follows in the normal state:
$$1s^2\, 2s^2\, 2p^6\, 3s \quad {}^2S_{\frac{1}{2}}$$

Configuration	Symbol	J	Term Value (cm^{-1})
$3s$	${}^2S$	$\frac{1}{2}$	41449.0
$3p$	${}^2P^\circ$	$\frac{1}{2}$	*24492.83*
		$1\frac{1}{2}$	*24475.65*
$4s$	${}^2S$	$\frac{1}{2}$	15709.50
$3d$	${}^2D$	$1\frac{1}{2}, 2\frac{1}{2}$	12276.18
$4p$	${}^2P^\circ$	$\frac{1}{2}$	*11181.63*
		$1\frac{1}{2}$	*11176.14*
$5s$	${}^2S$	$\frac{1}{2}$	8248.28
$4d$	${}^2D$	$1\frac{1}{2}, 2\frac{1}{2}$	6900.35
$4f$	${}^2F^\circ$	$2\frac{1}{2}, 3\frac{1}{2}$	6860.37

SERIES OF LEVELS

m	${}^2P_{\frac{1}{2}}{}^\circ$	${}^2P_{1\frac{1}{2}}{}^\circ$
3	*24492.83*	*24475.65*
4	*11181.63*	*11176.14*
5	*6408.83*	*6406.34*
6	*4152.80*	*4151.30*
7	*2908.93*	*2907.46*
8	*2150.69*	*2149.80*
9	*1655.31*	*1654.08*
10	*1312.28*	*1312.28*
11	*1065.86*	*1065.86*
12	*883.40*	*883.40*

m	${}^2S_{\frac{1}{2}}$
3	41449.00
4	15709.50
5	8248.28
6	5077.31
7	3437.28
8	2480.65
9	1874.49
10	1466.0
11	1175.5
12	966.1

m	${}^2D_{1\frac{1}{2},\, 2\frac{1}{2}}$
3	12276.18
4	6900.35
5	4412.47
6	3061.92
7	2248.56
8	1720.88

m	${}^2F_{2\frac{1}{2},\, 3\frac{1}{2}}{}^\circ$
4	*6860.37*
5	*4390.37*

* This table is reproduced, by permission of the publishers, from page 307 of the book *Atomic Energy States*, by R. F. Bacher and S. Goudsmit, published by the McGraw-Hill Book Company, Inc. 1932.

TABLE XII

TERM VALUES FOR THE HgI SPECTRUM*

(Arc Spectrum of Mercury)

The configuration of mercury's 80 electrons is as follows in the normal state of the atom:

$1s^2\ 2s^2\ 2p^6\ 3s^2\ 3p^6\ 3d^{10}\ 4s^2\ 4p^6\ 4d^{10}\ 4f^{14}\ 5s^2\ 5p^6\ 5d^{10}\ 6s^2\ {}^1S_0$

Configuration	Symbol	J	Term Value (cm⁻¹)
$6s^2$	^1S	0	84178.5
$6s\ 6p$	$^3P^\circ$	0	_46536.2_
		1	_44768.9_
		2	_40138.3_
$6s\ 6p$	$^1P^\circ$	1	_30112.8_
$6s\ 7s$	^3S	1	21830.8
$6s\ 7s$	^1S	0	20253.1
$6s\ 7p$	$^3P^\circ$	0	_14664.6_
		1	_14519.1_
		2	_12973.5_
$6s\ 6d$	^1D	2	12848.3
$6s\ 6d$	^3D	1	12845.1
		2	12785.0
		3	12749.0
$6s\ 7p$	$^1P^\circ$	1	_12886.1_

* This table is reproduced, by permission of the publishers, from page 227 of the book *Atomic Energy States*, by R. F. Bacher and S. Goudsmit, published by the McGraw-Hill Book Company, Inc., 1932.

TABLE XIII

Term Values for the NeI Spectrum*

(Arc Spectrum of Neon)

The configuration of neon's 10 electrons is as follows in the normal state of the atom:

$$1s^2\ 2s^2\ 2p^6\ {}^1S_0$$

Old Notation	Configuration	Symbol	J	Term Value (cm^{-1})
$1P_0$	$2p^6$	${}^1S$	0	173930
$1s_5$	$2p^5\,({}^2P_{1\frac12})\,3s$	$1°$	2	39887.61
$1s_4$		$2°$	1	39470.16
$1s_3$	$2p^5\,({}^2P_{\frac12})\,3s$	$3°$	0	39110.81
$1s_2$		$4°$	1	38040.73
$2p_{10}$	$2p^5\,({}^2P_{1\frac12})\,3p$	1	1	25671.65
$2p_9$		2	3	24272.41
$2p_8$		3	2	24105.23
$2p_7$		4	1	23807.85
$2p_6$		5	2	23613.59
$2p_3$		6	0	23012.02
$2p_5$	$2p^5\,({}^2P_{\frac12})\,3p$	7	1	23157.34
$2p_4$		8	2	23070.94
$2p_2$		9	1	22891.00
$2p_1$		10	0	20958.72
$3d_6$	$2p^5\,({}^2P_{1\frac12})\,3d$	$1°$	0	12419.87
$3d_5$		$2°$	1	12405.23
$3d_4{}'$		$3°$	4	12339.15
$3d_4$		$4°$	3	12337.32
$3d_3$		$5°$	2	12322.26
$3d_2$		$6°$	1	12292.85
$3d_1{}''$		$7°$	2	12229.82
$3d_1{}'$		$8°$	3	12228.05
$3s_1{}''''$	$2p^5\,({}^2P_{\frac12})\,3d$	$9°$	2	11520.82
$3s_1{}'''$		$10°$	3	11519.26
$3s_1{}''$		$11°$	2	11509.50
$3s_1{}'$		$12°$	1	11493.78
$2s_5$	$2p^5\,({}^2P_{1\frac12})\,4s$	$1°$	2	15328.31
$2s_4$		$2°$	1	15133.47
$2s_3$	$2p^5\,({}^2P_{\frac12})\,4s$	$3°$	0	14549.47
$2s_2$		$4°$	1	14395.75

* This table is reproduced, by permission of the publishers, from page 312 of the book *Atomic Energy States*, by R. F. Bacher and S. Goudsmit, published by the McGraw-Hill Book Company, Inc., 1932.

TABLE XIV

TERM VALUES FOR THE CuI SPECTRUM*

(Arc Spectrum of Copper)

The configuration of copper's 29 electrons is as follows in the normal state of the atom:

$$1s^2\ 2s^2\ 2p^6\ 3s^2\ 3p^6\ 3d^{10}\ 4s\ ^2S_{\frac{1}{2}}$$

Configuration	Symbol	J	Term Values (cm⁻¹)
$3d^{10}\ 4s$	^2S	$\frac{1}{2}$	62308.000
$3d^9\ 4s^2$	^2D	$2\frac{1}{2}$ $1\frac{1}{2}$	51105.435 49062.577
$3d^{10}\ 4p$	$^2P°$	$\frac{1}{2}$ $1\frac{1}{2}$	*31772.698* *31524.314*
$3d^9\ 4s\ 4p$	$^4P°$	$2\frac{1}{2}$ $1\frac{1}{2}$ $\frac{1}{2}$	*23289.348* *22194.01* *21364.27*
$3d^9\ 4s\ 4p$	$^4F°$	$4\frac{1}{2}$ $3\frac{1}{2}$ $2\frac{1}{2}$ $1\frac{1}{2}$	*21398.862* *21154.567* *20745.105* *20005.53*
$3d^{10}\ 5s$	^2S	$\frac{1}{2}$	19170.791
$3d^9\ 4s\ 4p$	$^4D°$	$3\frac{1}{2}$ $2\frac{1}{2}$ $1\frac{1}{2}$ $\frac{1}{2}$	*18794.05* *17901.732* *17763.847* *17392.39*
$3d^9\ 4s\ 4p$	$^2F°$	$2\frac{1}{2}$ $3\frac{1}{2}$	*18581.809* *17344.777*
$3d^9\ 4s\ 4p$	$^2P°$	$\frac{1}{2}$ $1\frac{1}{2}$	*16487.00* *16428.689*
$3d^9\ 4s\ 4p$	$^2D°$	$1\frac{1}{2}$ $2\frac{1}{2}$	*16135.158* *15709.66*
$3d^{10}\ 5p$	$^2P°$	$\frac{1}{2}, 1\frac{1}{2}$	*12925.05*
$3d^{10}\ 4d$	^2D	$1\frac{1}{2}$ $2\frac{1}{2}$	12372.800 12365.943
$3d^{10}\ 6s$	^2S	$\frac{1}{2}$	9459.251
$3d^{10}\ 6p$	$^2P°$	$1\frac{1}{2}$ $\frac{1}{2}$	*7523.94* *7280.26*
$3d^{10}\ 5d$	^2D	$1\frac{1}{2}$ $2\frac{1}{2}$	6920.332 6916.708
$3d^{10}\ 4f$	$^2F°$	$3\frac{1}{2}$ $2\frac{1}{2}$	*6881.8* *6878.2*
$3d^9\ 4s\ 4p$	$^2F°$	$3\frac{1}{2}$ $2\frac{1}{2}$	*6278.05* *4188.72*
$3d^9\ 4s\ 4p$	$^2P°$	$1\frac{1}{2}$ $\frac{1}{2}$	*5964.26* *3943.27*
$3d^9\ 4s\ 4p$	$^2D°$	$2\frac{1}{2}$ $1\frac{1}{2}$	*5656.52* *3617.14*

* This table is reproduced, by permission of the publishers, from page 175 of the book *Atomic Energy States*, by R. F. Bacher and S. Goudsmit, published by the McGraw-Hill Book Co., Inc., 1932.

TABLE XV

Approximate Standard-of-Comparison Values of Mean Free Paths

(See Section 15.12)

The values of atomic or molecular radius b in this table are as given in *Kinetic Theory of Gases* by L. B. Loeb, published by the McGraw-Hill Book Company, 1934. As indicated, most of the mean free path values are obtained from these values of b. Because the underlying measurement methods are nonelectrical, the mean free paths as given are only first approximations to true mean free paths for electrically charged particles. However, for comparisons between the extremes of large and small molecules, for example, between mercury atoms and hydrogen molecules, the values have useful significance.

For details as to the dependence of electron mean free path on electron energy, see Table XVI, and Chapter VII in *Fundamentals of Physical Electronics*.

1	2	3	4	Approximate Standard-of-Comparison Values of Mean Free Path in the Stated Gas at a Pressure of 1 Millimeter of Mercury and a Temperature of 273° K	
Gas	Symbol	Gas-Particle Radius Determined from: Van der Waals' Ideal Gas Law Correction (given by Loeb 12B-643) b angstrom units (10^{-8} cm)	Viscosity Measurements (given by Loeb 12B-643) b angstrom units (10^{-8} cm)	l_{go} For gas particles, equation (15-14) millimeters	l_{no} For electrons, equation (15-20a) millimeters
Helium	He	1.15		0.21[1,2] 0.12[3]	1.20[1,2] 0.68[3]
Neon	Ne		1.17	0.115[4]	0.65[4]
Argon	A	1.43	1.43	0.076[2,4]	0.43[2,4]
Krypton	Kr	1.57	1.59	0.064[4]	0.36[4]
Xenon	Xe	1.71	1.75	0.054[4]	0.31[4]
Mercury	Hg	1.19	1.82	0.048[4] 0.024[1,6] 0.0165[5]	0.27[4] 0.135[1,6] 0.093[5]
Hydrogen	H$_2$	1.38	1.09	0.136[2,4]	0.77[2,4]
Nitrogen	N$_2$	1.57	1.58	0.063[4] 0.072[2]	0.36[4] 0.41[2]
Oxygen	O$_2$	1.45	1.48	0.072[4]	0.41[4]
Chlorine	Cl$_2$	1.65	1.85	0.046[4] 0.035[2]	0.26[4] 0.20[2]
Cyanogen	(CN)$_2$	1.89	2.04	0.039[4]	0.22[4]
Hydrochloric acid gas	HCl	1.59		0.062[3]	0.35[3]
Carbon monoxide	CO	2.28		0.030[3]	0.17[3]
Carbon dioxide	CO$_2$	1.61		0.047[2,4]	0.27[2,4]
Water vapor	H$_2$O	1.44	1.36	0.085[4]	0.48[4]

[1] Used by Compton and Von Voorhis [15q]
[2] In agreement with Loeb [15B-646]
[3] Calculated using b from Column 3.
[4] Calculated using b from Column 4.

[5] From Engel and Steenbeck, Vol. I, [15G-39] and used by German authorities.
[6] Frequently used in engineering studies of mercury discharge apparatus.

TABLE XVI

RAMSAUER COLLISION PROBABILITIES (SECTION 15.12)

p_{eo}, also described as $1/l_{eo}$, where l_{eo} is the electron mean free path, in centimeters, at 0° C and 1 millimeter of mercury pressure.[15v]

Gas	Symbol	Electron Velocity in Square Root Volts, $\sqrt{E}$ 1	2	3	4	5	7	10	Maxima	Minima
Neon	N	6	8	10	11	12	11	8	12 at 5.5	
Argon	A	4	28	68	72	49	28	21	83 at 3.6	1 at 0.6
Krypton	Kr	4	48	96	93	64	36	26	99 at 3.5	4 at 0.8
Xenon	Xe	6	107	132	102	71			140 at 2.6	6 at 0.9
Helium	He	19	18	15	11	8	5	4	52 at 2	
Hydrogen	H₂	47	52	35	25	19	12	7		
Nitrous oxide	N₂O	21	44	47	57	60	50		80 at 1.4 / 60 at 5.0	21 at 0.9 / 41 at 2.2
Carbon dioxide	CO₂	23	49	40	53	58	48		50 at 2.1 / 58 at 4.8	21 at 1.3 / 31 at 2.4
Nitrogen	N₂	29	33	36	40	41	33	24	89 at 1.6	32 at 2.3
Oxygen	O₂	22	23	32	37	36	32		42 at 4.4 / 37 at 4.0	
Carbon monoxide	CO	45	67	39	43	43	34	26	122 at 1.6 / 45 at 4.5	39 at 3.2
Mercury	Hg	380	180	76	57	55	58	50	60 at 6	54 at 4.5
Cadmium	Cd	780	340	177	136	123	120	88	125 at 6.2	123 at 5.2
Zinc	Zn	{about 550}	300	142	112	88	69	63	72 at 8.3	70 at 6.6
Sodium	Na	980	640	470	340	300	170	120	1280 at 1.3	870 at 1.1
Potassium	K	1630	1000	690	500	390	200	120	1710 at 1.1	1360 at 0.7
Rubidium	Rb	1300	860	670	550	430	230	130	1500 at 1.1	
Caesium	Cs	930	1100	900	680	510	310	150	2000 at 1.5	930 at 1.0
Methane	CH₄	10	60	82	67	54	35		86 at 2.7	8 at 0.8
	C₂H₆	25	76	114	91	74	56		116 at 2.7	
	C₃H₈	35	100	143	120	100	74		150 at 2.6	

TABLE XVII

VAPOR PRESSURE OF MERCURY VAPOR AT VARIOUS TEMPERATURES.[IX]
MERCURY-VAPOR AND CONDENSED-MERCURY TEMPERATURES THE SAME.
(FIG. 18.8)

T_{Hg}, °C	Vapor Pressure P in Millimeters of Mercury	T_{Hg}, °C	Vapor Pressure P in Millimeters of Mercury
−30	0.00000478	+200	17.287
−20	0.0000181	210	23.723
−10	0.0000606	220	32.133
0	0.000185	230	42.989
+10	0.000490	240	56.855
+20	0.001201	250	74.375
+30	0.002777	260	96.296
40	0.006079	270	123.47
50	0.01267	280	156.87
60	0.02524	290	197.57
70	0.04825	300	246.80
80	0.08880	310	305.89
90	0.1582	320	376.33
100	0.2729	330	459.74
110	0.4572	340	557.90
120	0.7457	350	672.69
130	1.186	360	806.23
140	1.845	370	960.66
150	2.807	380	1138.4
160	4.189	390	1341.9
170	6.128	400	1574.1
180	8.796		
190	12.423	From 400° C to 1300° C, use	
200	17.287		

$$\log_{10}P = \frac{-3065}{T_{Hg}} + 7.75$$

BIBLIOGRAPHY

See Section 0.2 for the number and letter code employed in making references to the bibliography from the text. For each chapter, book references appear first, followed by periodical references, arranged where possible according to subject matter.

The author knows the items marked with an asterisk (*) to be distinctly useful, without, however, prejudice to many other items, with which the author has less familiarity.

CHAPTER I

A. *Attwood, S. S., *Electric and Magnetic Fields*, 3rd ed. John Wiley & Sons, 1949.

B. Maxwell, J. C., *Electricity and Magnetism*, 4th ed. Clarendon Press, 1904.

C. *Jeans, J. H., *Mathematical Theory of Electricity and Magnetism*, 5th ed. Cambridge University Press, 1948.

D. Stratton, J. A., *Electromagnetic Theory*. McGraw-Hill Book Co., 1941.

E. Jordan, E. C., *Electromagnetic Waves and Radiating Systems*. Prentice-Hall, 1950.

F. Page, L., and N. I. Adams, Jr., *Electrodynamics*. D. Van Nostrand Co., 1940.

G. *Ramo, S., and J. R. Whinnery, *Fields and Waves in Modern Radio*. John Wiley & Sons, 1944.

H. Darrow, K. K., *Introduction to Contemporary Physics*. D. Van Nostrand Co., 1939.

I. *Haas, A., *Introduction to Theoretical Physics*, 2 volumes. Constable & Co., 1924.

J. *Richtmyer, F. K., and E. H. Kennard, *Introduction to Modern Physics*. McGraw-Hill Book Co., 1942.

K. *Slater, J. C., and N. H. Frank, *Introduction to Theoretical Physics*. McGraw-Hill Book Co., 1933.

L. Slater, J. C., and N. H. Frank, *Electromagnetism*. McGraw-Hill Book Co., 1947.

M. Sokolnikoff, I. S., and E. S. Sokolnikoff, *Higher Mathematics for Engineers and Physicists*. McGraw-Hill Book Co., 1941.

N. Doherty, R. E., and E. G. Keller, *Mathematics of Modern Engineering*, Vol. I. John Wiley & Sons, 1936.
Keller, E. G., *Mathematics of Modern Engineering*, Vol. II. John Wiley & Sons, 1942.

O. Murnaghan, F. D., *Introduction to Applied Mathematics*. John Wiley & Sons, 1948.

P. *Churchill, R. V., *Fourier Series and Boundary Value Problems*. McGraw-Hill Book Co., 1941.

Q. *Churchill, R. V., *Introduction to Complex Variables and Applications*. McGraw-Hill Book Co., 1948.

R. Walker, M., *Conjugate Functions for Engineers*. Oxford University Press, 1933.

S. Townsend, E. J., *Functions of a Complex Variable.* Henry Holt & Co., 1927.
T. Watson, G. N., *A Theory of Bessel Functions.* Cambridge University Press, 1944.
U. Pierce, B. O., *A Short Table of Integrals.* Ginn & Co., 1929.
V. Dwight, H. B., *Tables of Integrals and Other Mathematical Data,* rev. ed. The Macmillan Co., 1947.
W. Jahnke, E., and F. Emde, *Tables of Functions with Formulae and Curves.* Dover Publications, N. Y., 1945.
X. *International Critical Tables.* McGraw-Hill Book Co.
Y. *Handbook of Chemistry and Physics.* Chemical Rubber Publishing Co.

a. "Symposium of Papers on M.K.S. System of Units." *Proc. IEE,* **97,** 235 (Sept. 1950).
b. *DuMond, J. W. M., and E. R. Cohen, "Our Knowledge of the Atomic Constants in 1947." *Revs. Modern Phys.,* **20,** 82 (Jan. 1948); **21,** 651 (Oct. 1949).
c. *Dow, W. G., "Impacts of Electronics on Engineering Education." *Trans. AIEE,* **68,** 58 (Jan. 1949).

CHAPTER II

A. Strong, J., *Procedures in Experimental Physics.* Prentice-Hall, 1938.
B. Yarwood, J., *High Vacuum Technique.* John Wiley & Sons, 1945.
C. Harnwell, G. P., and J. L. Livingood, *Experimental Atomic Physics.* McGraw-Hill Book Co., 1938.
D. Dushman, S., *Scientific Foundations of Vacuum Technique,* 2nd ed. John Wiley & Sons, 1951.
E. Dushman, S., *Production and Measurement of High Vacuum,* published by the *General Electric Review,* Schenectady, N. Y., 1922.

a. Jonker, J. L. H., "Electron Trajectories in Multigrid Valves." *Philips Tech. Rev.,* **5,** 131 (May 1940).
    Kleynen, P. H. J. A., "The Motion of an Electron in a Two-Dimensional Electrostatic Field." *Philips Tech. Rev.,* **2,** 338 (Nov. 1937).
b. *Dow, W. G., "Transit-Time Effects in Ultra-High-Frequency Class-C Operation." *Proc. IRE,* **35,** 35–42 (Jan. 1947).
    Hollmann, H. E., "Theoretical and Experimental Investigations of Electron Motions in Alternating Fields with the Aid of Ballistic Models." *Proc. IRE,* **29,** 70 (Feb. 1941).
c. Langmuir, D. B., "An Automatic Plotter for Electron Trajectories." *RCA Rev.,* **11,** 143 (Mar. 1950).
    Clark, J. W., and R. E. Neuber, "A Dynamic Electron Trajectory Tracer." *Proc. IRE,* **38,** 521 (May 1950).
    Liebmann, G., "An Improved Method of Numerical Ray Tracing through Electron Lenses." *Proc. Phys. Soc. London,* **62B,** 753, 869 (Dec. 1949).
    *Liebmann, G., "Field Plotting and Ray Tracing in Electron Optics—A Review of Numerical Methods." *Advances in Electronics,* Vol. II, Academic Press, 1948.
d. MacColl, L. A., "The Fundamental Equations of Electron Motion." *Bell System Tech. J.,* **22,** 153 (July 1943).
e. Weimer, P. K., and A. Rose, "The Motion of Electrons Subject to Forces Transverse to a Uniform Magnetic Field." *Proc. IRE,* **35,** 1273 (Nov. 1947).

f. *Hull, A. W., "The Effect of a Uniform Magnetic Field on the Motion of Electrons between Coaxial Cylinders." *Phys. Rev.*, **18**, 31 (July 1921).
*Hull, A. W., "The Path of Electrons in the Magnetron." *Phys. Rev.*, **23**, 112 (Jan. 1929).
Hull, A. W., "The Motions of Electrons between Coaxial Cylinders under the Influence of Current along the Axis." *Phys. Rev.*, **25**, 645 (May 1925).

CHAPTER III

A. *Pierce, J. R., *Theory and Design of Electron Beams.* D. Van Nostrand Co., 1949.
B. Cosslet, V. E., *Introduction to Electron Optics.* Clarendon Press, 1946.
C. *Zworykin, V. K., G. A. Morton, E. G. Ramberg, J. Hillier, and A. W. Vance, *Electron Optics and the Electron Microscope.* John Wiley & Sons, 1946.
D. *Maloff, I. G., and D. W. Epstein, *Electron Optics in Television.* McGraw-Hill Book Co., 1938.
E. Myers, L. M., *Electron Optics, Theoretical and Practical.* D. Van Nostrand Co., 1939.
F. Klemperer, Otto, *Electron Optics.* Cambridge University Press, 1939.
G. Picht, Johannes, *Einführung in die Theorie der Elektronenoptik.* Johann Ambrosius Barth, 1939. (Theory of lenses, mirrors, aberrations.)
H. Busch, H., and E. Bruche (eds.), *Beiträge zur Elektronenoptik.* Johann Ambrosius Barth, 1937. (Aberration, in theory and experimentally; electron microscopes and image tubes; illustrated.)
I. Bruche, E., and O. Scherzer, *Geometrische Elektronenoptik.* Julius Springer, 1934. (The initial electron optical treatise; finely illustrated.)
J. *Soller, T., M. A. Starr, and G. E. Valley, Jr. (eds.), *Cathode Ray Tube Displays.* McGraw-Hill Book Co., 1948. (Vol. 22, M.I.T. Radiation Laboratory Series.)
K. *Leverenz, H. W., *An Introduction to Luminescence of Solids.* John Wiley & Sons, 1950.
L. Kroger, F. A., *Some Aspects of the Luminescence of Solids.* Elsevier Publishing Co., 1948.
M. Rider, J. F., and S. D. Uslan, *Encyclopedia on Cathode Ray Oscilloscopes and Their Uses.* J. F. Rider Publishing Co., 1950.
N. Zworykin, V. K., and G. A. Morton, *Television, the Electronics of Image Transmission.* John Wiley & Sons, 1940.

a. *Grivet, P., "Electron Lenses." *Advances in Electronics*, Vol. II, Academic Press, 1949.
*Hutter, R. G. E., "The Deflection of Beams of Charged Particles." *Advances in Electronics*, Vol. I, Academic Press, 1948.
Langmuir, D. B., "Theoretical Limitations of Cathode Ray Tubes." *Proc. IRE*, **25**, 977 (Aug. 1937).
Thompson, H. C., "Electron Beams and Their Applications in Low-Voltage Devices." *Proc. IRE*, **24**, 1276 (Oct. 1936).
Johnson, J. B., "The Cathode Ray Oscillograph." *J. Franklin Inst.*, **212**, 687 (Dec. 1931); also *Bell System Tech. J.*, **11**, 1 (Jan. 1932).
b. Bamford, H. S., "Multigun Cathode Ray Oscillography." *Electronic Inds.*, **2**, 10 (May 1948).

588	BIBLIOGRAPHY

c. Iams, H. A., R. L. Burtner, and C. H. Chandler, "Stereoscopic Viewing of Cathode Ray Tube Presentations." *RCA Rev.*, **9**, 149 (Mar. 1948).
Schmitt, O. H., "Cathode Ray Presentation of Three Dimensional Data." *Proc. IRE*, **35**, 174 (Feb. 1947).
d. *Moss, H., "Cathode Ray Tube Progress in the Past Decade with Special Reference to Manufacture and Design." *Advances in Electronics*, Vol. II, Academic Press, 1948.
Christaldi, P. S., "Cathode Ray Tubes and Their Applications." *Proc. IRE*, **33**, 373 (June 1945).
Beers, J. R., "Cathode Ray Tube Development; Early History, Mathematical Concepts, Present-Day Problems." *Communications*, **24**, 43 (July 1944). See also reference 6f.
e. Garlick, G. F. J., "Cathodoluminescence." *Advances in Electronics*, Vol. II, Academic Press, 1948.
Strange, J. W., and S. T. Henderson, "Cathodo-Luminescence: Part I—Growth and Decay Processes; Part II—Current Saturation and Voltage Effects; Part III—Discussion of Results." *Proc. Phys. Soc. London*, **58**, 369 (July 1, 1946).
Nottingham, W. B., "Notes on Photometry, Colorimetry, and an Explanation of the Centibel Scale." *M.I.T. Radiation Lab. Rept.* 804 (Dec. 17, 1945).
Seitz, F., and H. W. Leverenz, "Luminescent Materials." *J. Applied Phys.*, **10**, 479 (July 1939).
f. Jesty, L. C., H. Moss, and R. Puleston, "War-Time Developments in Cathode-Ray Tubes for Radar." *J. IEE London*, Pt. IIIA, **93**, 149 (1946).
g. Bull, E. W., and V. A. Stanley (summary of discussion), "Comparison of Electrostatic and Electromagnetic Deflection in Cathode-Ray Tubes." *J. IEE London*, Pt. III, **93**, 364 (Sept. 1946).
h. Lampert, I. E., and R. Feldt, "The 5RP Multiband Tube: An Intensifier-Type Cathode Ray Tube for High-Voltage Operation." *Proc. IRE*, **34**, 432 (July 1946).
*Pierce, J. R., "After Acceleration and Deflection." *Proc. IRE*, **29**, 28 (Jan. 1941).
de Gier, J., "Cathode Ray Tube with Post Acceleration." *Philips Tech. Rev.*, **5**, 245 (Sept. 1940).
i. Flory, L. E., J. E. Dilley, W. S. Pike, and R. W. Smith, "A Storage Oscilloscope." *RCA Rev.*, **12**, 220 (June 1951).
Benner, A. H., and L. M. Seeberger, "Graphechon Writing Characteristics." *RCA Rev.*, **12**, 220 (June 1951).
Hopkinson, R. G., "The Photography of Cathode Ray Tube Traces." *J. IEE London*, Pt. IIIA, **93**, 808 (1946).
j. Janes, R. B., and A. A. Rotow, "Light-Transfer Characteristics of Image Orthicons." *RCA Rev.*, **11**, 364 (Sept. 1950).
Weimer, P. K., S. V. Forgue, and R. P. Goodrich, "The Vidicon Photoconductive Camera Tube." *Electronics*, **23**, 70 (May 1950).
Janes, R. B., R. E. Johnson, and R. R. Handel, "A New Image Orthicon." *RCA Rev.*, **10**, 586 (Dec. 1949).
Janes, R. B., R. E. Johnson, and R. S. Moore, "Development and Performance of Television Camera Tubes." *RCA Rev.*, **10**, 191 (June 1949).
*Rose, A., "Television Pick-Up Tubes and the Problem of Vision." *Advances in Electronics*, Vol. I, Academic Press, 1948.

Zworykin, V. K., G. A. Morton, and L. E. Flory, "Theory and Performance of the Iconoscope." *Proc. IRE*, **25**, 1071 (Aug. 1937).

Farnsworth, P. T., "Television by Electron Image Scanning." *J. Franklin Inst.*, **218**, 411 (Oct. 1934).

See also various papers in *Proc. IRE*, **39**, 1124–1332 (Oct. 1951), relative to the use of cathode-ray tubes for color television.

k. Ackermann, O., "A Cathode Ray Oscillograph with Norinder Relay." *Trans. AIEE*, **49**, 467 (Apr. 1930).

l. Sears, R. W., "Electron Beam Deflection Tube for Pulse Code Modulation." *Bell System Tech. J.*, **27**, 44 (Jan. 1948).

Skellett, A. M., "Electrostatically Focused Radial-Beam Tube." *Proc. IRE*, **36**, 1354 (Nov. 1948).

Greig, D. D., J. J. Glauber, and S. Moskowitz, "The Cyclophon: A Multi-purpose Electronic Commutator Tube." *Proc. IRE*, **35**, 1251 (Nov. 1947).

m. Field, L. M., K. Spangenberg, and R. Helm, "Control of Electron-Beam Dispersion at High Vacuum by Ions." *Elec. Commun.*, **24**, 108 (Mar. 1947).

Field, L. M., "High Current Electron Guns." *Revs. Modern Phys.*, **18**, 353 (July 1946).

Pierce, J. R., "Electron Beams in Strong Magnetic Fields." *Phys. Rev.*, **68**, 229 (Nov. 1945).

Skellett, A. M., "Beam Production in Radial Beam Tubes, Beam Power Tubes, and Other Low Voltage Electronic Devices." *Revs. Modern Phys.*, **18**, 379 (July 1946).

Skellett, A. M., "The Magnetically Focused Radial Beam Vacuum Tube." *Bell System Tech. J.*, **23**, 190 (Apr. 1944).

CHAPTER IV

A. Weber, Ernst, *Electromagnetic Fields, Theory and Application*, Vol. I, *Mapping of Fields*. John Wiley & Sons, 1950.

Bewley, L. V., *Two-Dimensional Fields in Electrical Engineering*. The Macmillan Co., 1948.

B. *Chaffee, E. L., *Theory of Thermionic Vacuum Tubes*. McGraw-Hill Book Co., 1933.

C. Van der Bijl, H. J., *Thermionic Vacuum Tubes*. McGraw-Hill Book Co., 1920.

D. *Spangenberg, K. R., *Vacuum Tubes*. McGraw-Hill Book Co., 1948.

E. Millman, J., and S. Seely, *Electronics*, 2nd ed. McGraw-Hill Book Co., 1951.

a. Frocht, M. M., and M. M. Levin, "A Rational Approach to the Numerical Solution of Laplace's Equation." *J. Applied Phys.*, **12**, 596 (Aug. 1941).

Shortley, G. H., and R. Weller, "Numerical Solution of Laplace's Equation." *J. Applied Phys.*, **9**, 339 (May 1938).

Knight, R. C., and B. W. McMullen, "The Potential of a Screen of Circular Wires between Two Conducting Planes." *Phil. Mag.*, **24**, 35 (1937).

b. Shah, J. R., and L. Jacob, "Investigation of Field Distribution in Symmetrical Electron Lens" [Using the electrolytic tank method]. *J. Applied Phys.*, **22**, 1236 (Oct. 1951).

Green, P. E., Jr., "Automatic Plotting of Electrostatic Fields." *Rev. Sci. Instruments*, **19**, 646 (Oct. 1948).

See also references 2c, 3A, B, C, D, E, F, I.

c. *Moore, A. D., "Fields from Fluid Flow Mappers." *J. Applied Phys.*, **20**, 790 (Aug. 1949).
   Moore, A. D., "Soap Film and Sandbed Mapper Techniques." *J. Applied Mechanics*, **17**, 291 (Sept. 1950).
   *Moore, A. D., "The Further Development of Fluid Mappers," and "Mapping Techniques Applied to Fluid-Mapper Patterns." *Trans. AIEE*, **69**, 1615 (1950) and **71** (1952).

d. *Vodges, F. B., and F. R. Elder, "Formulas for the Amplification Constant for Three Element Tubes." *Phys. Rev.*, **24**, 683 (Dec. 1924).

e. King, R. W., "Calculation of the Constants of a Thermionic Vacuum Tube." *Phys. Rev.*, **15**, 256 (Apr. 1920).

f. Rosenhead, L., and S. D. Daymond, "The Distribution of Potential in some Thermionic Tubes." *Proc. Roy. Soc. London*, A, **161**, 382 (1937).

g. Walker, G. B., "On Electric Fields in Multi-Grid Radio Valves." *Proc. IEE London*, Pt. III, **98**, 64 (Jan. 1951).

h. Bennett, W. R., and L. C. Peterson, "The Electrostatic Field in Vacuum Tubes with Arbitrarily Spaced Elements." *Bell System Tech. J.*, **28**, 303 (Apr. 1949).

i. Roberts, W. van B., "A Transformation for Calculating the Constants of Vacuum Tubes with Cylindrical Elements." *Proc. IRE*, **25**, 1300 (Oct. 1937).

j. Koizymi, S., "On the Amplification Constants of Multielectrode Tubes." *J. IEE Japan* (abstract), **10**, 18 (1934).

k. *"Standards on Electron Tubes: Definitions of Terms, 1950," **50 IRE 7.S1**; *Proc. IRE*, **38**, 426 (Apr. 1950).
   *"Standards on Electron Tubes: Methods of Testing, 1950," **50 IRE 7.S2** (Parts I and II); *Proc. IRE*, **38**, 919 (Aug. and Sept. 1950).
   See also reference 9a.

CHAPTER V

a. *Llewellyn, F. B., "Operation of UHF Vacuum Tubes." *Bell System Tech. J.*, **14**, 632 (Oct. 1935).

b. *Benham, W. E., "A Contribution to Tube and Amplifier Theory." *Proc. IRE*, **26**, 1093 (1938).

c. *Thompson, B. J., "Space-Current Flow in Vacuum Tube Structures." *Proc. IRE*, **31**, 485 (Sept. 1943).

d. Walker, G. B., "Theory of the Equivalent Diode." *Wireless Eng.*, **24**, 5 (Jan. 1947).

e. Van der Bijl, H. J., "Theory of the Thermionic Amplifier." *Phys. Rev.*, **12**, 171 (Sept. 1918).

f. Tellegan, B. D. I., "The Effect of the Emission Current in a Triode." *Physica*, **50**, 301 (1925).

g. Fremlin, J. H., "Calculation of Triode Constants." *Elec. Commun.*, **18**, 33 (July 1939); *Phil. Mag.*, **27**, 709 (1939).

h. *Dow, W. G., "Equivalent Electrostatic Circuits for Vacuum Tubes." *Proc. IRE*, **28**, 548 (Dec. 1940).

i. Glosius, T., "Calculation of the Characteristics of Triodes." *Hochfrequenztech. u. Elektroakustik*, **52**, 88 (Sept. 1938).

j. Herne, H., "Valve Amplification Factor." *Wireless Eng.*, **21**, 59 (Feb. 1944).
   Ollendorff, F., "Calculation of the Amplification Factor of Narrow Gratings." *Elektrotech. u. Maschinenbau*, **50**, 585 (Dec. 1934).

k. Fremlin, J. H., R. N. Hall, and P. A. Shatford, "Triode Amplification Factors." *Elec. Commun.*, **23**, 426 (Dec. 1946).

l. *Salzberg, B., "Formulas for the Amplification Factor of Triodes." *Proc. IRE*, **30**, 134 (Mar. 1942).

Oertel, L., "On the Theory of Vacuum Tubes in which the Grid-Cathode Distance is Small Relative to Grid-Wire Spacing." *Die Telefunkenröhre*, **12, 7** (Apr. 1938).

m. *Slonczewski, T., "Transconductance as a Criterion of Electron Tube Performance." *Bell System Tech. J.*, **28**, 315 (Apr. 1949).

n. Partridge, G. R., "Factors Influencing the Perveance of Power-Output Triodes." *Proc. IRE*, **37**, 87 (Jan. 1949).

o. *Chaffee, E. L., "Operating Characteristics of Power Tubes." *J. Applied Phys.*, **9**, 471 (July 1938).
See also references 11a, b.

p. *Langmuir, I., and K. Blodgett, "Currents Limited by Space Charge between Coaxial Cylinders." *Phys. Rev.*, **22**, 347 (Oct. 1923).

*Langmuir, I., and K. Blodgett, "Currents Limited by Space Charge between Concentric Spheres." *Phys. Rev.*, **24**, 49 (July 1924).

q. *O'Neill, G. D., "Concerning Space-Charge-Limited Currents." *Sylvania Technologist*, **3**, 22 (Apr. 1950).

r. *Kusunose, Q., "Calculation of Characteristics and Design of Triodes." *Proc. IRE*, **17**, 1706 (Oct. 1929).

s. Wenzel, J. A., and A. H. Waynick, "Microphonism in the Dynamically Operated Planar Triode." *Proc. IRE*, **38**, 524 (May 1950).

*Cohen, V. W., and A. Bloom, "Microphonism in a Subminiature Triode." *Proc. IRE*, **36**, 1039 (Aug. 1948).

*Feinstein, L., "Microphonism Investigation." *Sylvania Technologist*, **2**, 9 (July 1949).

Waynick, A. H., "The Reduction of Microphonics in Triodes." *J. Applied Phys.*, **18**, 239 (Feb. 1947).

t. Radio Corporation of America, " 'Vibrotron' Tube." *Rev. Sci. Instruments*, **17**, 282 (July 1946).

CHAPTER VI

A. *Spangenberg, K. R., *Vacuum Tubes*. McGraw-Hill Book Co., 1948.

B. Dart, H. F., *Vacuum Tube Testing and Design*. International Textbook Co., 1939.

C. Bruining, H., "The Secondary Emission of Solid Bodies." Julius Springer, 1942.

a. *Spitzer, E. E., "Principles of the Electrical Rating of High-Vacuum Power Tubes." *Proc. IRE*, **39**, 60 (Jan. 1951).

*White, W. C., "Trends in Electron Tube Design." *Elec. Eng.*, **67**, 517 (June 1948).

Mouromtseff, I. E., "Development of Electron Tubes." *Proc. IRE*, **33**, 223 (Apr. 1945).

Dreyer, J. F., Jr., "Factors Determining Industrial Tube Life." *Elect. Ind.*, **4**, 94 (Dec. 1945).

b. Chaffee, E. L., "The Characteristic Curves of the Triode." *Proc. IRE*, **30**, 383 (Aug. 1942).

c. Wood, G. W., "Positive-Grid Characteristics of a Triode." *Proc. IRE,* **36,** 804 (June 1948).

Hamaker, H. C., "Current Distribution in Triodes, Neglecting Space Charge and Initial Velocities." *Applied Sci. Res. Bl.,* **77** (1948).

Wallis, Clifford, "Space-Current Division in the Power Tetrode." *Proc. IRE,* **35,** 369 (Apr. 1947).

Jonker, J. L. H., and B. D. H. Tellegen, "The Current to a Positive Grid in Electron Tubes." *Philips Research Repts.,* **1,** 13 (Oct. 1945).

Jonker, J. L. H., "The Control of Current Distribution in Electron Tubes." *Philips Research Repts.,* **1,** 331 (Nov. 1946).

*Spangenberg, K., "Current Division in Plane-Electrode Triodes." *Proc. IRE,* **28,** 226 (May 1940).

*Everitt, W. L., and K. Spangenberg, "Grid Current Flow as a Factor in the Design of Vacuum Tube Power Amplifiers." *Proc. IRE,* **26,** 612 (May 1938).

d. Pomerantz, M. A., and J. F. Marshall, "Fundamentals of Secondary Emission." *Proc. IRE,* **39,** 1367 (Nov. 1951).

Diemer, G., and J. H. L. Jonker, "On the Time Delay in Secondary Emission." *Philips Research Repts.,* **5,** 161 (June 1950).

Koller, L. R., "Secondary Emission, Parts 1 and 2." *Gen. Elec. Rev.,* **51,** 33, 50 (Apr. and June 1948).

*McKay, K. G., "Secondary Electron Emission." *Advance in Electronics,* Vol. I, Academic Press, 1948.

Wooldridge, D. E., "Theory of Secondary Emission" and "Temperature Effects in Secondary Emission." *Phys. Rev.,* **56,** 562 (Sept. 1939); **58,** 316 (Aug. 1940).

Bruining, H. O., "Secondary Electron Emission—Parts I to VI." *Physica,* **5** (Jan. and Dec. 1938); **6** (Aug. and Oct. 1939).

e. Jonker, J. L. H., "Phenomena in Amplifier Valves Caused by Secondary Emission," and "Secondary Emission in Output Valves." *Philips Tech. Rev.,* **3,** 211 (July 1938); **10,** 346 (May 1949).

Myers, P. M., D. R. Hartree, and A. Porter, "The Effect of Space Charge on the Secondary Current in a Triode." *Proc. Roy. Soc. London,* A, **158,** 23 (Jan. 1937).

See also reference 10*b.*

f. Parker, C. V., "Charge Storage in Cathode Ray Tubes." *Proc. IRE,* **39,** 900 (Aug. 1951).

*Rajchman, J., "The Selective Electrostatic Storage Tube." *RCA Rev.,* **12,** 53 (Mar. 1951).

Miller, C. F., and W. S. McLean, "New Design for a Secondary Emission Trigger Tube." *Proc. IRE,* **37,** 952 (Aug. 1949).

*Williams, F. C., and T. Kilburn, "A Storage System for Use with Binary Digital Computing Machines." *Proc. IEE London,* Pt. III, **96,** 81 (Mar. 1949).

Jensen, A. S., J. P. Smith, M. H. Mesner, and L. E. Flory, "Barrier Grid Storage Tube and Its Operation." *RCA Rev.,* **11,** 112 (Mar. 1948).

McConnell, R. A., "Video Storage by Secondary Emission from Simple Mosaics." *Proc. IRE,* **35,** 1258 (Nov. 1947).

*Haeff, A. V., "A Memory Tube." *Electronics,* **20,** 80 (Sept. 1947).

Skellett, A. M., "Use of Secondary Emission to Obtain Trigger or Relay Action." *J. Applied Phys.*, **13**, 519 (Aug. 1942). See also references 3*i*, *j*.

g. *Buckland, B. O., "Basic Heat-Transfer Data in Electron Tube Operation." *Trans. AIEE*, **70**, Pt. I, 1079 (1951).

Harris, I. A., "The Calculation of Electrode Temperatures in the Radio Valve." *J. Brit. IRE*, **8**, 288–312 (Nov. and Dec. 1948).

Kauzmann, A. P., "Determination of Current and Dissipation Values for High-Vacuum Rectifier Tubes." *RCA Rev.*, **8**, 82 (Mar. 1947).

h. *Salzberg, B., and A. V. Haeff, "Effect of Space Charge in the Grid-Anode Region of Vacuum Tubes." *RCA Rev.*, **2**, 336 (Jan. 1938).

*Fay, C. E., A. L. Samuel, and W. Shockley, "On the Theory of Space Charge between Parallel Plane Electrodes." *Bell System Tech. J.*, **17**, 49 (1938).

Hernquist, K. G., "Space Charge and Ion Trapping Effects in Tetrodes." *Proc. IRE*, **39**, 1541 (Dec. 1951).

i. Schade, O. H., "Beam Power Tubes." *Proc. IRE*, **26**, 137 (Feb. 1938).

Harries, J. H. O., "Critical Distance Tubes." *Electronics*, **9**, 33 (May 1936).

j. Wing, A. H., "On the Theory of Tubes with Two Control Grids." *Proc. IRE*, **29**, 121 (Mar. 1941).

CHAPTER VII

A. Dushman, S. A., *The Elements of Quantum Mechanics*. John Wiley & Sons, 1938.

B. *Reiman, A. L., *Thermionic Emission*. John Wiley & Sons, 1934.

C. Richardson, O. W., *Emission of Electricity from Hot Bodies*. Longmans, Green & Co., 1916.

D. *Koller, L. R., *Physics of Electron Tubes*. McGraw-Hill Book Co., 1937.

E. Electrical Engineering Staff, The Massachusetts Institute of Technology, *Applied Electronics*, John Wiley & Sons, 1944.

F. *Moore, A. D., *Fundamentals of Electrical Design*. McGraw-Hill Book Co., 1927.

a. *Dushman, S. A., "Thermionic Emission." *Revs. Modern Phys.*, **2**, 381 (Oct. 1930).

b. Dushman, S. A., "Theory of Electronic Emission." *Trans. Am. Electrochem. Soc.*, **44**, 201 (1923).

c. King, R. W., "Thermionic Vacuum Tubes and Their Applications." *Bell System Tech. J.*, **2**, 31 (Oct. 1923).

d. *Herrings, C., and M. H. Nichols, "Thermionic Emission." (Complete bibliography.) *Revs. Modern Phys.*, **21**, 187 (Apr. 1949).

*Blewett, J. P., "Oxide Coated Cathode Literature, 1940–1945." *J. Applied Phys.*, **17**, 643 (Aug. 1946).

e. McElwee, Eleanor M., "Statistical Evaluation of Life Expectancy of Vacuum Tubes Designed for Long-Life Operation." *Proc. IRE*, **39**, 137 (Feb. 1951).

Waymouth, J. F., Jr., "Deterioration of Oxide-Coated Cathodes under Low Duty-Factor Operation." *J. Applied Phys.*, **22**, 80 (Jan. 1951).

Metson, G. H., "Poisoning Effects in Oxide-Cathode Valves." *Proc. Phys. Soc. London*, **62**, 589 (Sept. 1, 1949).

f. *Becker, J. A., "Phenomena in Oxide-Coated Filaments." *Phys. Rev.*, **34**, 1323 (Nov. 1939).

*Blewett, J. P., "Time Changes in Emission from Oxide-Coated Cathodes." *Phys. Rev.*, **55**, 713 (Apr. 1939).

g. *Eisenstein, A. S., "Oxide Coated Cathodes." *Advances in Electronics*, Vol. I, Academic Press, 1948; see also *J. Applied Phys.*, **20**, 776 (Aug. 1949), and **22**, 138 (Feb. 1951).

Loosjes, R., and H. J. Vink, "Conduction Processes in the Oxide-Coated Cathode." *Philips Tech. Rev.*, **11**, 271 (Mar. 1950).

Mahlman, G. W., "Work Functions and Conductivity of Oxide-Coated Cathodes." *J. Applied Phys.*, **20**, 197 (Feb. 1949).

Hamaker, H. C., H. Bruining, and A. H. W. Aten, Jr., "On the Activation of Oxide Coated Cathodes." *Philips Research Repts.*, **2**, 171 (June 1947).

h. Dailey, H. J., "Designing Thoriated Tungsten Filaments." *Electronics*, **21**, 107 (Jan. 1948).

i. Fan, H. Y., "Thermionic Emission from Sintered Cathode of Thoria and Tungsten Mixture." *J. Applied Phys.*, **20**, 682 (July 1949).

*Hanley, T. E., "Spectral Emissivity and Electron Emission Constants of Thoria Cathodes." *J. Applied Phys.*, **19**, 583 (June 1948).

j. Lyon, J. A. M., and C. E. Williams, "Amalgam-Cathode Materials for Power Tubes." *Trans. AIEE*, **67**, 627 (1948).

k. *Lafferty, J. M., "Boride Cathodes." *Phys. Rev.*, **79**, 1012 (Sept. 15, 1950).

l. *Lemmens, H. J., M. J. Jansen, and R. Loosjes, "Thermionic Cathodes for Heavy Loads." *Philips Tech. Rev.*, **11**, 341 (June 1950).

CHAPTER VIII

A. *Shockley, W., *Electrons and Holes in Semiconductors, with Applications to Transistor Electronics.* D. Van Nostrand Co., 1950.

B. Mott, N. F., and I. N. Sneddon, *Wave-Mechanics and Its Applications.* Oxford University Press, 1948.

C. Torrey, H. C., and C. A. Whitmer (eds.), *Crystal Rectifiers.* McGraw-Hill Book Co., 1948. (Vol. 15, M.I.T. Radiation Laboratory Series.)

D. *Seitz, F., *The Modern Theory of Solids.* McGraw-Hill Book Co., 1940.

E. *Mott, N. F., and R. W. Gurney, *Electronic Processes in Ionic Crystals.* Clarendon Press, 1940.

F. Wilson, A. H., *Semiconductors and Metals.* Cambridge University Press, 1939.

G. *Slater, J. C., *Introduction to Chemical Physics.* McGraw-Hill Book Co., 1939.

H. *Fowler, H. H., *Statistical Mechanics.* Cambridge University Press, 1936.

I. *Rittner, E. S., "I. Thermionic Emission from Oxide Cathodes;" "II. Photoconductivity in Semiconductors." Lectures at 1950 (Electrical Engineering) Summer Electronics Symposium, University of Michigan; also *Technical Report* 34, Philips Laboratories, Inc., Irvington-on-Hudson, New York.

J. *Becker, J. A., and J. N. Shive, "Theory of Semiconductor Devices." Lectures by J. A. Becker at 1950 (Electrical Engineering) Summer Electronics Symposium, University of Michigan.

K. deBoer, J. H., *Electron Emission and Adsorption.* The Macmillan Co., 1935. See also references 7A, B.

a. Hill, E. L., and R. Landshoff, "The Dirac Electron Theory." (Bibliography.) *Revs. Modern Phys.*, **10**, 87 (Apr. 1938).

*Slater, J. C., "The Electronic Structure of Metals." *Revs. Modern Phys.*, **6**, 209 (Oct. 1934).

*Karapetoff, V., "The Fermi-Dirac Hypothesis of Gas Degeneration." *Mech. Eng.*, **55**, 237, 290, 358 (Apr., May, and June 1933).

b. *Seitz, F., and R. P. Johnson, "Modern Theory of Solids" and "Basic Principles of Semiconductors." *J. Applied Phys.*, **8**, 186 (Mar. 1937); **16**, 553 (Oct. 1945).

c. Schultheiss, P. M., and H. J. Reich, "Some Transistor Trigger Circuits." *Proc. IRE*, **39**, 632 (June 1951).

*Wallace, R. L., Jr., and W. J. Pietenpol, "Some Circuit Properties and Applications of *n-p-n* Transistors." *Proc. IRE*, **39**, 753 (July 1951); *Bell System Tech. J.*, **30**, 530 (July 1951).

*Brown, C. B., "Magnetically Biased Transistors." *Phys. Rev.*, **76**, 1736 (Dec. 1949).

Webster, W. M., E. Eberhard, and L. E. Barton, "Some Novel Circuits for Three-Terminal Semiconductor Amplifiers." *RCA Rev.*, **10**, 5 (Mar. 1949).

Eberhard, E., R. O. Endres, and R. P. Moore, "Counter Circuits Using Transistors." *RCA Rev.*, **10**, 459 (Dec. 1949).

d. *Brown, C. B., "High Frequency Operation of Transistors." *Electronics*, **23**, 81 (July 1950).

Banbury, P. C., and H. K. Henish, "On the Frequency Response of PbS Transistors." *Proc. Roy. Soc. London*, B, **63**, 540 (July 1950).

e. Slade, B. N., "A High-Performance Transistor with Wide Spacing between Contacts." *RCA Rev.*, **11**, 517 (Dec. 1950).

Pfann, W. G., and J. H. Scaff, "The *p*-Type Germanium Transistor." *Proc. IRE*, **38**, 1151 (Oct. 1950).

*Hall, R. N., and W. C. Dunlap, "*p-n* Junctions Prepared by Impurity Diffusion." *Phys. Rev.*, **80**, 467 (Nov. 1, 1950).

*Becker, J. A., and J. N. Shive, "The Transistor, a New Semi-Conductor Amplifier." *Elec. Eng.*, **68**, 215 (Mar. 1949).

*Bardeen, J., and W. H. Brattain, "Physical Principles Involved in Transistor Action." *Bell System Tech. J.*, **28**, 239 (Apr. 1949).

Gebbie, H. A., P. C. Banbury, and C. A. Hogarth, "Crystal Diode and Triode Action in Lead Sulfide." *Proc. Roy. Soc. London*, B, **63**, 371 (May 1950).

f. Stansel, F. R., "The Characteristics and Some Applications of Varistors." *Proc. IRE*, **39**, 342 (Apr. 1951).

Bollman, J. H., and J. G. Kreer, "The Application of Thermistors to Control Networks." *Proc. IRE*, **38**, 20 (Jan. 1950).

Becker, J. A., C. B. Green, and G. L. Pearson, "Properties and Uses of Thermistors—Thermally Sensitive Resistors." *Trans. AIEE*, **65**, 711 (Nov. 1946).

g. Becker, M., and H. Y. Fan, "Optical Properties of Semiconductors: II—Infra-Red Transmission of Germanium; III—Infra-Red Transmission of Silicon" and "Photovoltaic Effects of *p-n* Junctions in Germanium." *Phys. Rev.*, **76**, 1530 (Nov. 15, 1949); **78**, 301 (May 1, 1950).

h. Scaff, J. H., and R. S. Ohl, "Development of Silicon Crystal Rectifiers." *Bell System Tech. J.*, **26**, 1 (Jan. 1947).

North, H. Q., "Properties of Welded Contact Germanium Rectifiers." *J. Applied Phys.*, **17**, 912 (Nov. 1946).

i. Henkels, H. W., "Electrical Properties of Selenium." *J. Applied Phys.*, **22**, 916, 1265 (July and Oct. 1951).

Dunlap, W. C., "Some Properties of High-Resistivity *p*-Type Germanium." *Phys. Rev.*, **79**, 286 (July 15, 1950).

Johnson, V. A., and K. Lark-Horowitz, "Theoretical Hall Coefficient Expressions for Impurity Semiconductors." *Phys. Rev.*, **79**, 176 (July 1, 1950).

Cleland, J. W., K. Lark-Horowitz, and J. C. Pigg, "Transmutation Produced Semiconductors." *Phys. Rev.*, **78**, 814 (June 15, 1950).

Lark-Horowitz, K., V. A. Johnson, and various associates, "Theory of Thermoelectric Power in Germanium," "Electrical Conductivity and Hall Effect in Germanium," "The Reflectivity of Germanium," and "Electronic Mobility in Germanium." *Phys. Rev.*, **69**, 259, 686 (Mar. 1946); **76**, 1530 (Nov. 15, 1949); **79**, 409 (July 15, 1950).

j. Ferris, W. R., "Some Characteristics of Diodes with Oxide-Coated Cathodes." *RCA Rev.*, **10**, 134 (Mar. 1949).

Waterman, A. T., and R. S. Bartlett, "Space Charge vs. Image Force in Thermionic Emission," "Fermi-Dirac Statistics Applied to the Problem of Space Charge in Thermionic Emission," and "The Equilibrium Distribution of Potential and of Electrons outside the Surface of a Conductor." *Phys. Rev.*, **37**, 279, 959 (Feb. and Apr. 1931); **38**, 1497 (Oct. 1931).

*Langmuir, I. L., "The Effect of Space Charge and Initial Velocities on the Potential Distribution and Thermionic Current between Parallel Plane Electrodes." *Phys. Rev.*, **21**, 419 (Apr. 1923).

*See also reference 12*b*.

k. Bowie, R. M., "This Matter of Contact Potential." *Proc. IRE*, **24**, 1501 (Nov. 1936).

Millikan, R. A., "The Distinction between Intrinsic and Spurious Contact E. M. F.'s and the Question of Absorption of Radiation by Metals in Quanta." *Phys. Rev.*, **18**, 236 (Sept. 1921).

Richardson, O. W., and F. S. Robertson, "Contact Difference of Potential and Thermionic Emission." *Phil. Mag.*, **43**, 557 (Mar. 1922).

See also reference 14*a*.

l. Ashworth, F., "Field Emission Microscopy." *Advances in Electronics*, Vol. III, Academic Press, 1951.

Bertein, F., "Cold Emission from Plane Metallic Surfaces." *Compt. rend.*, **223**, 475 (Sept. 23, 1946).

Jenkins, R. O., "Field Emission of Electrons." *Rept. Progr. Phys.*, **9**, 177–197 (1942 and 1943).

Guth, E., and C. J. Mullin, "Electron Emission of Metals in Electric Fields. I. Explanations of the Periodic Deviations from the Schottky Line." *Phys. Rev.*, **59**, 575 (Apr. 1941). "III. The Transition from Thermionic to Cold Emission." *Phys. Rev.*, **61**, 339 (Mar. 1942).

Haefer, R., "Theory of Field Electron Emission." *Z. Physik*, **116**, 604 (1940).

Henderson, J. E., and R. K. Dahlstrom, "Energy Distribution in Field Emission." *Phys. Rev.*, **55**, 473 (Mar. 1939).

m. *Pierce, J. R., "Theoretical Limitation to Transconductance in Certain Types of Vacuum Tubes." *Proc. IRE*, **31**, 657 (Dec. 1943).

n. Kilgore, G. R., "Beam-Deflection Control for Amplifier Tubes." *RCA Rev.*, **8**, 480–505 (Sept. 1947).

o. Victoreen, J., "Electrometer Tubes for the Measurement of Small Currents." *Proc. IRE*, **37**, 422 (Apr. 1949).

p. Munick, R. J., W. B. La Berge, and E. A. Coomes, "Periodic Deviation in the Schottky Effect for Tantalum." *Phys. Rev.*, **80**, 887 (Dec. 1, 1950).

Schottky, W., "Electron Emission der Metalle." *Physik. Z.*, **15**, 872 (Nov. 1914).
See also Guth and Mullin, in reference 8*l*.

CHAPTER IX

A. *Argimbau, L. B., *Vacuum-Tube Circuits.* John Wiley & Sons, 1948.
B. Chaffee, E. L., *Theory of Thermionic Vacuum Tubes.* McGraw-Hill Book Co., 1933.
C. *Cruft Laboratory Staff, Harvard University, *Electronic Circuits and Tubes.* McGraw-Hill Book Co., 1947.
D. *Everitt, W. L., *Communication Engineering.* McGraw-Hill Book Co., 1932.
E. Glasgow, R. S., *Principles of Radio Engineering.* McGraw-Hill Book Co., 1936.
F. *Guillemin, E. A., *Communication Networks.* John Wiley & Sons, Vol. 1, 1931; Vol. 2, 1935.
G. McIlwain, K., and J. G. Brainerd, *High Frequency Alternating Currents.* John Wiley & Sons, 1931.
H. *Electrical Engineering Staff, The Massachusetts Institute of Technology, *Applied Electronics.* John Wiley & Sons, 1944.
I. Millman, J., and S. Seely, *Electronics.* McGraw-Hill Book Co., 1941.
J. Peters, L. J., *Theory of Thermionic Vacuum Tube Circuits.* McGraw-Hill Book Co., 1927.
K. Rao, V. V. L., *The Decibel Notation.* Chemical Publishing Co., 1946.
L. *Reich, H. J., *Theory and Applications of Electron Tubes*, 2nd ed. McGraw-Hill Book Co., 1944.
M. *Terman, F. E., *Radio Engineering*, 3rd ed. McGraw-Hill Book Co., 1947.
N. *Terman, F. E., *Radio Engineers Handbook.* McGraw-Hill Book Co., 1943.
O. Van der Bijl, H. J., *Thermionic Vacuum Tubes.* McGraw-Hill Book Co., 1920.
P. National Bureau of Standards, "Radio Instruments and Measurements," *Bulletin 74.*

a. "Standards on Abbreviations, Graphical Symbols, Letter Symbols, and Mathematical Signs, 1948." **48 IRE 21.S1;** obtainable from The Institute of Radio Engineers, 1 E. 79th St., New York 21, N. Y. (See also reference 4*k.*)
b. Everitt, W. L., "Optimum Operating Conditions for Class B Radio-Frequency Amplifiers." *Proc. IRE*, **24**, 305 (Feb. 1936).
Thompson, B. J., "Graphical Determination of Performance of Push-Pull Audio Amplifiers." *Proc. IRE*, **21**, 591 (Apr. 1933).
Fay, C. E., "The Operation of Vacuum Tubes as Class B and Class C Amplifiers." *Bell System Tech. J.*, **11**, 28 (Jan. 1932).

CHAPTER X

a. Hull, A. W., "Description of the Dynatron." *Proc. IRE*, **6**, 5 (Feb. 1918).
Meinke, H. H., "Dynatron Characteristics." *Hochfrequenztech. u. Elektroakustik*, **50**, 50 (Aug. 1937).
Bakker, C. J., and C. J. Boers, "On the Influence of the Non-Linearity of Characteristics on the Frequency of Dynatron and Triode Oscillators." *Physica*, **3**, 649 (July 1936).

598 BIBLIOGRAPHY

Gager, F. M., and J. B. Russell, "A Quantitative Study of the Dynatron." *Proc. IRE*, **23**, 1536 (1935).

van der Pol, B., "The Non-Linear Theory of Electric Oscillations." (Bibliography.) *Proc. IRE*, **22**, 1051 (Sept. 1934).

b. Giacoletto, L. J., "Dynatron Oscillator Operation with Particular Emphasis on a New Saw-Tooth Current Oscillator." Ph.D. Thesis (Electrical Engineering), University of Michigan, 1951, available on microfilm.

CHAPTER XI

A. Beck, A. H. W., *Velocity-Modulated Thermionic Tubes.* The Macmillan Co., 1948.
B. Brainerd, J. G., G. Koehler, H. J. Reich, and L. F. Woodruff, *Ultra-High Frequency Techniques.* D. Van Nostrand Co., 1942.
C. Bronwell, A. B., and R. E. Beam, *Theory and Application of Microwaves.* McGraw-Hill Book Co., 1947.
D. *Collins, G. B. (ed.), *Microwave Magnetrons.* McGraw-Hill Book Co., 1947. (Vol. 6, M.I.T. Radiation Laboratory Series.)
E. *Llewellyn, F. B., *Electron Inertia Effects.* Cambridge University Press, 1941.
F. Hamilton, D. R., J. K. Knipp, and J. B. H. Kuper (eds.), *Klystrons and Microwave Triodes.* McGraw-Hill Book Co., 1947. (Vol. 7, M.I.T. Radiation Laboratory Series.)
G. Harrison, A. E., *Klystron Tubes.* McGraw-Hill Book Co., 1947.
H. *Pierce, J. R., *Traveling-Wave Tubes.* D. Van Nostrand Co., 1950.
I. Pollard, E. C., and J. N. Sturtevant, *Microwaves and Radar Electronics.* John Wiley & Sons, 1948.
J. Montgomery, C. G., R. H. Dicke, and E. M. Purcell (eds.), *Principles of Microwave Circuits.* McGraw-Hill Book Co., 1948. (Vol. 8, M.I.T. Radiation Laboratory Series.)
K. Silver, S. (ed.), *Microwave Antenna Theory and Design.* McGraw-Hill Book Co., 1949. (Vol. 12, M.I.T. Radiation Laboratory Series.)
L. *Radio Research Laboratory Staff, Harvard University, *Very High Frequency Techniques*, Vols. 1 and 2. McGraw-Hill Book Co., 1947.
M. Ramo, S., *Introduction to Microwaves.* McGraw-Hill Book Co., 1945.
N. *Sarbacher, R. I., and W. A. Edson, *Hyper and Ultra-High Frequency Engineering.* John Wiley & Sons, 1943.
O. Schelkunoff, S. A., *Electromagnetic Waves.* D. Van Nostrand Co., 1943.
P. *Slater, J. C., *Microwave Electronics.* D. Van Nostrand Co., 1950.
Q. *Slater, J. C., *Microwave Transmission.* McGraw-Hill Book Co., 1942.
R. *Spangenberg, K. R., *Vacuum Tubes.* McGraw-Hill Book Co., 1948.

a. McArthur, E. D., and E. F. Peterson, "The Lighthouse Tube; A Pioneer Ultra High Frequency Development." *Proc. Natl. Electronics Conf.*, **1**, 38 (1944).
b. Bowen, A. E., and W. W. Mumford, "New Microwave Triode: Its Performance as Modulator and as Amplifier." *Bell System Tech. J.*, **29**, 531 (Oct. 1950).
c. Salisbury, W. W., "The Resnatron." *Electronics*, **19**, 92–97 (Feb. 1946).
d. Nergaard, L. S., D. G. Burnside, and R. P. Stone, "A Developmental Pulse Triode for 200 KW Output at 600 MC." *Proc. IRE*, **36**, 412 (Mar. 1948.)

e. McArthur, E. D., "The Dyotron—a new Microwave Oscillator." *Proc. IRE*, **36**, 378 (Mar. 1948).
f. Foster, J., "Grounded-Grid Amplifier Valves for Very Short Waves." *J. IEE London*, Pt. IIIA, **93**, 868 (1946).
Jones, M. C., "Grounded-Grid Radio-Frequency Voltage Amplifiers." *Proc. IRE*, **32**, 423 (July 1944).
Dishal, M., "Theoretical Gain and Signal-to-Noise Ratio Obtained with the Grounded-Grid Amplifier at Ultra-High Frequencies." *Proc. IRE*, **32**, 276 (May 1934).
g. Kompfner, R., "Current Induced in an External Circuit by Electrons Moving between Two Plane Electrodes." *Wireless Engineer*, **19**, 59 (Feb. 1942).
*Ramo, S., "Currents Induced by Electron Motion." *Proc. IRE*, **32**, 276 (May 1934).
h. *Everitt, W. L., "Optimum Operating Conditions for Class C Amplifiers." *Proc. IRE*, **22**, 152 (Feb. 1934).
i. Haeff, A. V., "The Electron-Wave Tube—A Novel Method of Generation and Amplification of Microwave Energy." *Proc. IRE*, **37**, 4 (Jan. 1949).
j. Robinson, F. N. H., "Traveling-Wave Tubes with Dispersive Helices." *Wireless Engineer*, **28**, 110 (Apr. 1951).

CHAPTER XII

A. *Kennard, E. H., *Kinetic Theory of Gases*. McGraw-Hill Book Co., 1938.
B. *Loeb, L. B., *Kinetic Theory of Gases*. McGraw-Hill Book Co., 1934.
C. Loeb, L. B., *The Nature of a Gas*. John Wiley & Sons, 1931.
D. Jeans, J. H., *The Dynamical Theory of Gases*. Cambridge University Press, 1925.
E. *Lawson, J. L., and G. E. Uhlenbeck (eds.), *Threshold Signals*. McGraw-Hill Book Co., 1950. (Vol. 24, M.I.T. Radiation Laboratory Series.)

a. Tolman, R. C., "The Principle of Microscopic Reversibility." *Proc. Natl. Acad. Sci. U. S.*, **11**, 436 (1925).
b. *Thompson, B. J., D. O. North, and W. A. Harris, "Fluctuations in Space-Charge-Limited Currents at Moderately High Frequencies: Part I—General Survey; Part II—Diodes and Negative-Grid Triodes; Part III—Multi-Collectors; Part IV—Collision Ionization." *RCA Rev.*, **4**, 269, 441 (Jan. and Apr. 1940); **5**, 106, 244, 371 (July and Oct. 1940; Jan. 1941).

CHAPTER XIII

A. Bacher, R. F., and S. Goudsmit, *Atomic Energy States*. McGraw-Hill Book Co., 1932.
B. Pauling, L., and S. Goudsmit, *The Structure of Line Spectra*. McGraw-Hill Book Co., 1930.
C. Pollard, E. C., and W. L. Davidson, *Applied Nuclear Physics*, 2nd ed. John Wiley & Sons, 1951.
D. Herzberg, G., *Atomic Spectra and Atomic Structure*. Prentice-Hall, 1937.
White, H. E., *Introduction to Atomic Spectra*, McGraw-Hill Book Co., 1934.
E. Hume-Rothery, *Atomic Theory for Students of Metallurgy*. Clay and Co., Ltd., 1948.

CHAPTER XIV

A. Higbie, H. H., *Lighting Calculations*. John Wiley & Sons, 1934.
    Moon, P., and D. E. Spencer, *Lighting Design*. Addison-Wesley Press, 1948.
B. Hardy, A. C., and F. H. Perrin, *Principles of Optics*. McGraw-Hill Book Co., 1932.
C. Wood, R. W., *Physical Optics*, 3rd ed. The Macmillan Co., 1934.
D. Hughes, A. L., and L. A. Du Bridge, *Photoelectric Phenomena*. McGraw-Hill Book Co., 1932.
E. Campbell, N. R., and D. Ritchie, *Photoelectric Cells*. Isaac Pittman & Sons, 1934.
F. Zworykin, V. K., and E. P. Wilson, *Photocells and Their Applications*. John Wiley & Sons, 1934.
G. Sommer, A., *Photoelectric Cells*. Chemical Publishing Co., 1947.
H. Walker, R. C., and T. M. C. Lance, *Photoelectric Cell Applications*. Pitman Publishing Corp., 1938.

a. *Fan, H. Y., "Theory of Photoelectric Emission from Metals." *Phys. Rev.*, **68**, 43 (July 1945).
    *Apker, L., E. Taft, and J. Dickey, "Energy Distribution of Photoelectrons from Polycrystalline Tungsten," "Photoelectric Emission and Contact Potentials of Semiconductors," and "Some Semi-Metallic Characteristics of the Photoelectric Emission from As, Sb, and Bi." *Phys. Rev.*, **73**, 46 (Jan. 1, 1948); **74**, 1462 (Nov. 15, 1948); **76**, 270 (Jan. 15, 1948).
b. Rentschler, H. C., and D. E. Henry, "Photoelectric Emission." *J. Franklin Inst.*, **223**, 135 (Feb. 1937).
c. Linford, L. B., "The External Photoelectric Effect." *Revs. Modern Phys.*, **5**, 34 (Jan. 1933).
d. *Fowler, R. H., "The Analysis of Photoelectric Sensitivity Curves for Clean Metals at Various Temperatures." *Phys. Rev.*, **38**, 45 (July 1931).
e. Pakswer, S., "Fatigue of Ag-Cs$_2$O, Ag-Cs Photoelectric Surfaces." *J. Applied Phys.*, **18**, 203 (Feb. 1947).
    Prescott, C. H., Jr., and M. J. Kelly, "The Caesium-Oxygen-Silver Photo Cell." *Bell System Tech. J.*, **11**, 334 (July 1932).
f. Morton, G. A., "Photomultipliers for Scintillation Counting." *RCA Rev.*, **10**, 525 (Dec. 1949).
    Malter, L., "The Behavior of Electrostatic Electron Multipliers as a Function of Frequency" and "The Behavior of 'Magnetic' Electron Multipliers as a Function of Frequency." *Proc. IRE*, **29**, 587 (Nov. 1941); **35**, 1074 (Oct. 1947).
    Zworykin, V. K., and J. A. Rajchman, "The Electrostatic Electron Multiplier." *Proc. IRE*, **27**, 558 (Sept. 1939).
    Zworykin, V. K., G. A. Morton, and L. Malter, "The Secondary Emission Multiplier, a New Electronic Device." *Proc. IRE*, **24**, 351 (Mar. 1936).
g. *Druyvesteyn, M. J., "Calculation of Townsend's α for Neon." *Physica*, **3**, 65 (Feb. 1936).
h. Brattain, W. H., "The Copper Oxide Rectifier." *Revs. Modern Phys.*, **23**, 203 (July 1951).
    von Geel, W. C., "Blocking-Layer Photo Cells." *Philips Tech. Rev.*, **8**, 65 (Mar. 1946).

Grondahl, L. O., "The Copper-Cuprous Oxide Rectifier and Photo Cell." *Revs. Modern Phys.*, **5**, 141 (Apr. 1933).
See also references 8I, J, *b*, *i*.
i. Anderson, N., and S. Pakswer, "Comparison of Lead-Sulfide Photoconductive Cells with Photoemissive Tubes." *J. Soc. Motion Picture Engrs.*, **52**, 41 (Jan. 1949).
j. Starkiewicz, J., "Lead Selenide Photo-Conductive Cells." *J. Optical Soc. Am.*, **38**, 481 (May 1948).
Sosnowski, L., J. Starkiewicz, and O. Simpson, "Lead Sulphide Photo-Conductive Cells." *Nature*, **159**, 818 (June 1947).
von Hippel, A., F. G. Chesley, H. S. Denmark, P. B. Ulin, and E. S. Rittner, "Photoelectric Mechanism of the Thallous Sulfide Photo-Conductive Cell." *Phys. Rev.*, **69**, 685 (June 1946).
See also reference 8I.
k. Skellett, A. M., "The Time Lag in Gas-Filled Photoelectric Cells." *J. Applied Phys.*, **9**, 631 (Oct. 1938).
Kruithof, A. A., "Time Lag Phenomena in Gas-Filled Photoelectric Cells." *Philips Tech. Rev.*, **4**, 48 (Feb. 1938).
Houstoun, R. A., "Time Lag of Vacuum Photoelectric Cells." *Proc. Roy. Soc. Edinburgh*, **57**, 163 (1937).

CHAPTER XV

A. *Cobine, J. D., *Gaseous Conductors, Theory and Engineering Applications.* McGraw-Hill Book Co., 1941.
B. *Loeb, L. B., *Fundamental Processes of Electrical Discharge in Gases.* John Wiley & Sons, 1939.
C. *Slepian, J., "Lectures on Conduction of Electricity in Gases." Westinghouse Electric and Mfg. Co., East Pittsburgh, Pa., 1933.
D. Darrow, K. K., *Electrical Phenomena in Gases.* Williams & Wilkins Co., 1932.
E. Thomson, J. J., and G. P. Thomson, *Conduction of Electricity through Gases*, 2 volumes. Cambridge University Press, 1928.
F. Townsend, J. S., *Electricity in Gases.* Clarendon Press, 1915.
G. *Engel, A., and M. Steenbeck, *Elektrische Gasentladungen*, Vol. I and Vol. II. Julius Springer, 1934.
H. Forsythe, W. E., and E. Q. Adams, *Fluorescent and Other Gaseous Discharge Lamps.* Murray Hill Books, 1948.
I. Cotton, H., *Electric Discharge Lamps.* Chapman and Hall, 1946.
J. Miller, S. C., *Neon Signs.* McGraw-Hill Book Co., 1935.
K. Guthrie, A. K., and R. K. Wakerling, *Characteristics of Electrical Discharges in Magnetic Fields.* McGraw-Hill Book Co., 1949.

a. *Compton, K. T., and I. Langmuir, "Electric Discharge in Gases, Part I, Survey of Fundamental Processes." *Revs. Modern Phys.*, **2**, 123 (Apr. 1930).
b. *Langmuir, I., and K. T. Compton, "Electric Discharge in Gases, Part II. Fundamental Phenomena in Electrical Discharges." *Revs. Modern Phys.*, **3**, 191 (Apr. 1931).
c. *Compton, K. T., "The Electric Arc." *Trans. AIEE*, **46**, 868 (June 1927).
d. Myer, J. L., "New Studies of the Arc Discharge." (Bibliography.) *Trans. AIEE*, **52**, 250 (Mar. 1933).

e. Finkelnburg, W., "The High Current Carbon Arc and Its Mechanism." *J. Applied Phys.*, **20**, 469 (May 1949).

f. Elenbaas, W., "Similarity of High-Pressure Discharges of the Convection-Stabilized Type" also "On the Excitation Temperature, the Gas Temperature, and the Electron Temperature in the High-Pressure Mercury Discharge." *Philips Research Repts.*, **1**, 339 (Nov. 1946); **2**, 20 (Feb. 1947).

g. *Suits, C. G., "High Pressure Arcs in Common Gases in Free Convection." *Phys. Rev.*, **55**, 561 (Mar. 1939).

Kenty, C., "On Convection Currents in High Pressure Mercury Arcs." *J. Applied Phys.*, **9**, 53 (Jan. 1938).

Mason, R. C., "Probe Measurements on High Pressure Arcs." *Phys. Rev.*, **51**, 28 (Jan. 1937).

*Suits, C. G., "The Determination of Arc Temperature from Sound Velocity Measurements" and "Studies of Arc Temperature by an Optical Method." *Physics*, **6**, 190, 315 (June and Oct. 1935).

h. Slepian, J., "Flames from Arcs." *Trans. AIEE*, **49**, 56 (Jan. 1930).

i. Molnar, J. P., "Conduction Phenomena in Gases." *Elec. Eng.*, **69**, 1071 (Dec. 1950).

j. Kenty, C., M. A. Easley, and B. T. Barnes, "Gas Temperatures and Elastic Losses in Low-Pressure Mercury-Argon Discharges." *J. Applied Phys.*, **22**, 1006 (Aug. 1951).

k. von Gugelberg, H. L., "On the Growth, Reaction Mechanism, and Stability of Low-Current, Low-Pressure Discharges." (In German.) *Helv. Phys. Acta*, **20**, 307 (Aug. 4, 1947).

l. Chao, K. T., and T. Y. Yang, "Electron Temperatures in Electric Discharges." *Phys. Rev.*, **68**, 80 (July 1945).

m. Druyvesteyn, M. J., and F. M. Penning, "The Mechanism of Electric Discharges in Gases at Low Pressure." *Revs. Modern Phys.*, **12**, 87 (Apr. 1940).

Uyterhoeven, W., "Electrical Phenomena in the Positive Column at Low Pressure" and "Emission of Light in the Positive Column at Low Pressure." *Philips Tech. Rev.*, **3**, 156, 197 (June and July, 1938).

n. *Tonks, L., and I. Langmuir, "A General Theory of the Plasma of an Arc." *Phys. Rev.*, **34**, 876 (Sept. 1929). See also papers by Tonks in references 15s, y.

o. Schulz, P., "Der Einfluss der Positiven Ion auf die Elektronenbewiglichkeit." *Ann. Physik*, **1**, 318 (1947).

p. Killian, T. J., "The Uniform Positive Column of an Electric Discharge in Mercury Vapor." *Phys. Rev.*, **35**, 1238 (May 1930).

q. *Compton, K. T., and C. C. Van Voorhis, "Probability of Ionization of Gas Molecules by Electron Impacts." *Phys. Rev.*, **26**, 436 (Oct. 1925).

r. Townsend, M. A., "Electronics of the Fluorescent Lamp." *Trans. AIEE*, **61**, 607 (Aug. 1942).

*Dushman, S., "Low Pressure Gaseous Discharge Lamps." *Trans. AIEE*, **53**, 1204, 1283 (Aug. and Sept. 1934); "Production of Light from Discharge in Gases." *Gen. Elec. Rev.*, **37**, 260 (June 1934).

Founds, C. G., "Fundamental Phenomena in Sodium-Vapor Lamps." *Gen. Elec. Rev.*, **37**, 269 (June 1934).

Fonda, G. R., and A. H. Young, "The A-C Sodium-Vapor Lamp." *Gen. Elec. Rev.*, **37**, 331 (July 1934).

s. McBee, W. D., "A Study of the Influence of a Strong Transverse Magnetic Field on an Unconfined Glow Discharge at about 1 Mm. Pressure." Ph.D. Thesis (Electrical Engineering), University of Michigan, 1951, available on microfilm.

*Early, H. C., and W. G. Dow, "Supersonic Wind at Low Pressures Produced by an Arc in a [Strong] Magnetic Field." *Phys. Rev.*, **79**, 186 (July 1, 1950).

Beckman, L., "The Influence of a Transverse Magnetic Field on a Cylindrical Plasma." *Proc. Phys. Soc. London*, **61**, 515 (Dec. 1, 1948).

*Tonks, L., "Drift of Ions and Electrons in a Magnetic Field" and "Theory of Magnetic Effects in the Plasma of an Arc." *Phys. Rev.*, **51**, 744 (May 1937); **56**, 360 (Aug. 1939).

*Tonks, L., and C. S. Cummings, "Influence of a Longitudinal Magnetic Field on an Electrical Discharge in Mercury Vapor at Low Pressure." *Phys. Rev.*, **59**, 514 (Mar. 1941).

t. *Margenau, H., and L. M. Hartman, "Theory of High Frequency Gas Discharges: Part 1—Methods for Calculating Electron Distribution Functions; Part 2—Harmonic Components of the Distribution Function; Part 3—High Frequency Breakdown; Part 4—Note on the Similarity Principle." *Phys. Rev.*, **73**, 297, 309, 316, 326 (Feb. 15, 1948).

See also references 17h.

u. Cravath, A. M., "The Rate of Formation of Negative Ions by Electron Attachment" and "The Rate at which Ions Lose Energy in Elastic Collisions." *Phys. Rev.*, **33**, 605 (Apr. 1929); **36**, 248 (July 1930).

Mohler, F. L., "Recombination and Photo-Ionization." *Revs. Modern Phys.*, **1**, 216 (Oct. 1929).

Milne, A. E., "Statistical Equilibrium in Relation to Photoelectric Effect (and Recombination) and Its Application to the Determination of Absorption Coefficients." *Phil. Mag.*, **47**, 209 (Jan. 1924).

v. *Brode, R. B., "Quantitative Study of the Collisions of Electrons with Atoms." *Revs. Modern Phys.*, **5**, 257 (Oct. 1933).

Webb, G. M., "The Elastic Scattering of Electrons in Argon and Krypton" and "The Elastic Scattering of Electrons in Molecular Hydrogen." *Phys. Rev.*, **47**, 379, 384 (Mar. 1, 1935).

McMillen, J. H., "Elastic Electron Scattering in Potassium." *Phys. Rev.*, **46**, 983 (Dec. 1, 1934).

*Ramsauer, C., and R. Kollath, "Der Wirkungsquerschnitt von Gasmolekulen gegenüber langsamen Elektronen und langsamen Ionen." *Handbuch der Physik*, **22**, Pt. 2, 243, Julius Springer, 1933.

w. *Compton, K. T., "On the Motions of Electrons in Gases" and "Mobilities of Electrons in Gases." *Phys. Rev.*, **22**, 333, 432 (Oct. and Nov. 1923).

Mayer, H. F., "Kritik zur Wanderungsgeschwindigkeitsformael Herrn Langevin." *Ann. Physik*, **62**, 358 (1920).

*Langevin, M. P., "Nouvelle méthode" and "Une formule fondamentale de théorie cinetique." *Ann. chim. et phys.*, **28**, series 7, 495 (1903); **5**, series 8, 245 (1905).

x. Morse, P. M., W. P. Allis, and E. S. Lamar, "Velocity Distributions for Elastically Colliding Electrons." *Phys. Rev.*, **48**, 412 (Sept. 1935).

y. Wehner, G., "Plasma Oscillator" and "Electron Plasma Oscillations." *J. Applied Phys.*, **21**, 62 (Jan. 1950); **22**, 761 (June 1951).

Borgnis, F., "On the Theory of Electron-Plasma Oscillations." (In German.) *Helv. Phys. Acta*, **20**, 207 (Apr. 30, 1947).

*Tonks, L., "The High Frequency Behavior of a Plasma." (Bibliography.) "Plasma-Electron Resonance, Plasma Resonance, and Plasma Shape." *Phys. Rev.*, **37**, 1458 (June 1931); **38**, 1219 (Sept. 1931).

De Bye and Hückel, *Physik. Z.*, **24**, 185, 305 (1923).

CHAPTER XVI

a. Brewer, A. K., and J. W. Westhauer, "The Cathode Region in the Glow Discharge." *J. Applied Phys.*, **8**, 779 (Nov. 1937).

Emeleus, K. G., and O. S. Duffendack, "Spectral and Impact Phenomena in the Faraday Dark Space." (Bibliography.) *Phys. Rev.*, **47**, 460 (Mar. 1935).

b. Hill, A. G., W. W. Buechner, J. S. Clark, and J. B. Fisk, "Emission of Secondary Electrons under High Energy Positive Ion Bombardment." *Phys. Rev.*, **55**, 463 (Mar. 1939).

Allen, J. S., "Emission of Secondary Electrons from Metals Bombarded with Protons." *Phys. Rev.*, **55**, 336 (Feb. 1939).

Guntherschulze, A., and H. Betz, "Liberation of Electrons by Impact of Positive Ions of a Glow Discharge." *Z. Physik*, **108**, 780 (1937).

Guntherschulze, A., and W. Bar, "Emission of Electrons by Impact of Positive Ions of a Glow Discharge." *Z. Physik*, **109**, 1921 (1938).

c. Haworth, F. E., "Electrode Reactions in the Glow Discharge." *J. Applied Phys.*, **22**, 606 (May 1951).

Townes, C. H., "Theory of Cathode Sputtering in Low Voltage Gaseous Discharges." *Phys. Rev.*, **65**, 319 (1944).

Rockwood, G. H., "Current Rating and Life of Cold Cathode Tubes." *Trans. AIEE*, **60**, 901 (1941).

Starr, C., "Cathode Sputtering." (Abstract.) *Phys. Rev.*, **56**, 216 (1939).

Compton, K. T., and E. S. Lamar, "A Test of the Classical Momentum Theory of Accommodation Coefficients of Ions at Cathodes." *Phys. Rev.*, **44**, 338 (Sept. 1, 1933).

See also references 15A, 16b.

d. *Cobine, J. D., and C. J. Gallagher, "Current Density of the Arc Cathode Spot." *Phys. Rev.*, **74**, 1524 (Nov. 1948).

Smith, C. G., "Mercury Arc Cathode" and "Cathode Dark Space and Negative Glow of a Mercury Arc." *Phys. Rev.*, **62**, 48 (July 1942); **69**, 96 (Feb. 1, 1946).

Tonks, L., "The Pressure of Plasma Electrons and the Force on the Cathode of an Arc." *Phys. Rev.*, **46**, 278 (Aug. 15, 1934).

e. *Malter, L., and W. M. Webster, "Rapid Determination of Gas Discharge Constants from Probe Data." *RCA Rev.*, **12**, 191 (June 1951).

Johnson, E. O., and L. Malter, "A Floating Double Probe Method for Measurements in Gas Discharges." *Phys. Rev.*, **80**, 58 (Oct. 1, 1950).

Easley, M. A., "Probe Technique for the Measurement of Electron Temperature." *J. Applied Phys.*, **22**, 590 (May 1951).

Boyd, R. L. F., "The Collection of Positive Ions by a Probe in an Electrical Discharge." *Proc. Roy. Soc. London*, A, **201**, 329 (Apr. 26, 1950).

Anderson, T. A., "Dynamic Probe Characteristics." *Phil. Mag.*, **38**, 179 (Mar. 1947).

f. *Mott-Smith, H. M., and I. Langmuir, "The Theory of Collectors in Gaseous Discharges." *Phys. Rev.*, **28**, 727 (1926). [In equation 28a, factor exp η should appear in last term.]

  *Langmuir, I., and H. M. Mott-Smith, "Studies of Electric Discharges in Gases at Low Pressure." *Gen. Elec. Rev.*, **27**, 449, 538, 616, and 762 (July, Aug., Sept., and Nov. 1924).

  Langmuir, I., "Positive Ion Currents in the Positive Column of the Mercury Arc." *Gen. Elec. Rev.*, **26**, 731 (Nov. 1923); *J. Franklin Inst.*, **196**, 751 (1923).

CHAPTER XVII

A. Loeb, L. B., and J. M. Meek, *The Mechanism of the Electric Spark.* Stanford University Press, 1940.

B. Peek, F. W., Jr., *Dielectric Phenomena in High Voltage Engineering.* McGraw-Hill Book Co., 1929.

C. Strigel, R., *Electrische Stossfestigleit.* Julius Springer, 1939.

D. Korff, S. A., *Electron and Nuclear Counters.* D. Van Nostrand Co., 1946.

a. Lichtman, S. W., "High-Voltage Stabilization by Means of the Corona Discharge between Coaxial Cylinders." *Proc. IRE*, **39**, 419 (Apr. 1951).

  Quinn, R. B., "Sparking Potentials at Low Pressure." *Phys. Rev.*, **55**, 482 (Mar. 1939).

b. *Loeb, L. B., "Fundamental Mechanisms which Determine the Starting Potentials of the Low Pressure Corona Discharges." *J. Applied Phys.*, **8**, 495 (July 1937).

c. *Magnusson, C. E., "The Kindling of Electric Sparkover, Based on Lichtenberg Figures." *Trans. AIEE*, **51**, 74 (Mar. 1932).

d. Strigel, R., "Building-Up Period in the Spark Delay." *Elektrotech. Z.*, **59**, 33 (1938).

  *Tilles, A., "Spark Lag of the Sphere Gap." *Trans. AIEE*, **54**, 868 (1935); see also *Phys. Rev.*, **46**, 1015 (1934).

  See also references 15A and B.

e. Hurd, D. T., "Mechanism of Dielectric Breakdown." *Gen. Elec. Rev.*, **51**, 26 (Dec. 1948).

f. *Miller, C. G., and L. B. Loeb, "Positive [and Negative] Coaxial Cylindrical Corona Discharges in Pure N_2, O_2, and Mixtures Thereof." *J. Applied Phys.*, **22**, 494, 614, 740 (Apr., May, and June 1951).

  English, W. N., and L. B. Loeb, "Point to Plane Corona Onsets." *J. Applied Phys.*, **20**, 707 (July 1949).

  Loeb, L. B., and J. M. Meek, "Mechanism of the Spark Discharge in Air at Atmospheric Pressure." *J. Applied Phys.*, **11**, 438 (June 1940).

  See also references 15A and B.

g. Loeb, L. B., "The Mechanism of Lightning Discharge." *J. Franklin Inst.*, **246**, 123 (Aug. 1948).

  Flowers, J. W., "Lightning." *Gen. Elec. Rev.*, **47**, 9 (1945); and "Channel of the Spark Discharge." *Phys. Rev.*, **64**, 225 (Oct. 1943).

h. Brown, S. C., "High-Frequency Gas-Discharge Breakdown." *Proc. IRE*, **39**, 1493 (Dec. 1951).

Gill, E. W. B., and A. von Engel, "Starting Potentials of High-Frequency Gas Discharges at Low Pressures." *Proc. Roy. Soc. London*, A, **192**, 446 (Feb. 18, 1948).

Herlin, M. A., and S. C. Brown, "Electrical Breakdown of a Gas between Coaxial Cylinders at Microwave Frequencies." *Phys. Rev.*, **74**, 910 (Oct. 15, 1948).

See also reference 15*t*.

i. Townsend, M. A., "Construction of Cold-Cathode Counting or Stepping Tubes." *Elec. Eng.*, **69**, 810 (Sept. 1950).

Hough, G. S., and D. S. Ridler, "Multicathode Gas Tube Counters." *Elec. Commun. London*, **27**, 214 (Sept. 1950).

Chilcot, A. L., and F. G. Heymann, "Potassium-Activated Cold Cathode Tube." *J. Sci. Instruments*, **26**, 289 (Sept. 1949).

Depp, W. A., and W. H. T. Holden, "Circuits for Cold Cathode Glow Tubes." *Elec. Mf.*, **44**, 92 (July 1949).

Ingram, S. B., "Cold Cathode Gas Filled Tubes as Circuit Elements." *Elec. Eng.*, **58**, 342 (July 1939).

j. Friedman, Herbert, "Geiger Counter Tubes." *Proc. IRE*, **37**, 791 (July 1949).

Duffendack, O. S., and W. E. Morriss, "An Investigation of the Properties and Applications of the Geiger-Müller Photoelectron Counter." *J. Opt. Soc. Am.*, **32**, 8 (Jan. 1948).

Montgomery, C. G., and D. D. Montgomery, "Discharge Mechanism of the G. M. Counter." *Phys. Rev.*, **57**, 1030 (June 1940).

k. Fan, H. Y., "Transition from Glow Discharge to Arc." *Phys. Rev.*, **55**, 769 (Apr. 1939).

l. Boehne, E. W., "The Geometry of Arc Interruption" and "The Geometry of Arc Interruption—II, Current-Zero Phenomena." *Trans. AIEE*, **60**, 524 (1941); **63**, 575 (1944).

Suits, C. G., "Heat Transfer Methods in Arc Interruption." *Gen. Elec. Rev.*, **42**, 432 (Oct. 1939).

Van Sickle, R. C., and W. E. Berkey, "Arc Extinction Phenomena in High Voltage Circuit Breakers." *Trans. AIEE*, **52**, 850 (Sept. 1933).

Prince, D. C., "Theory of Oil-Blast Circuit Breakers." *Trans. AIEE*, **51**, 166 (1932).

Slepian, J., "The Electric Arc in Circuit Interrupters." *J. Franklin Inst.*, **214**, 413 (Oct. 1932).

*Slepian, J., "Extinction of an A-C Arc," "Theory of the Deion Circuit Breaker," and "Extinction of Long A-C Arcs." *Trans. AIEE*, **47**, 1398 (Oct. 1928); **48**, 523 (Apr. 1929); **49**, 421 (Apr. 1930).

m. *Slepian, J., and R. C. Mason, "The Experimental Validity of Paschen's Law and of a Similar Relation for the Reignition Potential of an A-C Arc." *J. Applied Phys.*, **8**, 619 (Sept. 1937).

Cobine, J. D., and R. B. Power, "The Application of Paschen's Law to the Reignition of an Arc." *J. Applied Phys.*, **8**, 287 (Apr. 1937).

n. Dow, W. G., S. S. Attwood, and G. S. Timoshenko, "Probe Measurements and Potential Distribution in Copper A-C Arcs." *Trans. AIEE*, **52**, 926 (Sept. 1933).

*Attwood, S. S., W. G. Dow, and W. Krausnick, "Reignition of Metallic A-C Arcs in Air." *Trans. AIEE*, **50**, 854 (Sept. 1931).

CHAPTER XVIII

A. Marti, O. K., and H. Winograd, *Mercury Arc Rectifiers*. McGraw-Hill Book Co., 1931.
B. Jolley, B. W., *Alternating Current Rectification and Allied Problems*. Chapman & Hall, 1926.
C. Prince, D. C., and F. B. Vodges, *Principles of Mercury Arc Rectifiers and Their Circuits*. McGraw-Hill Book Co., 1927.
D. *Chute, G. M., *Electronics in Industry*. McGraw-Hill Book Co., 1946.
E. *Cage, J. M., *Theory and Application of Industrial Electronics*. McGraw-Hill Book Co., 1951.
F. Bendz, W. I., *Electronics for Industry*. John Wiley & Sons, 1948.
G. Kloeffler, R. G., *Industrial Electronics and Control*. John Wiley & Sons, 1949.

a. Slepian, J., and L. R. Ludwig, "A New Method for Initiating the Cathode of an Arc." *Trans. AIEE*, **52**, 693 (June 1933).
b. *Rigrod, W. W., "Behavior of the Resistance Ignitor in Mercury." *J. Applied Phys.*, **22**, 787 (June 1951).
Cage, J. M., "Theory of the Immersion Mercury-Arc Ignitor." *Gen. Elec. Rev.*, **38**, 464 (Oct. 1935).
*Dow, W. G., and W. H. Powers, "Firing Time of an Ignitor Type of Tube." *Trans. AIEE*, **54**, 942 (Sept. 1935).
c. Herskind, C. C., and E. J. Remschei, "Excitation, Control, and Cooling of Ignitron Tubes." *Trans. AIEE*, **65**, 632 (Oct. 1946).
Herskind, C. C., and H. C. Steiner, "Rectifier Capacity." *Trans. AIEE*, **65**, 667 (Oct. 1946).
Steiner, H. C., J. L. Zehner, and H. E. Zuvers, "Pentode Ignitrons for Electronic Power Converters," *Trans. AIEE*. **63**, 693 (1944).
d. Winograd, H., "Development of the Excitron Type Rectifier." *Trans. AIEE*, **63**, 969 (1944).
e. Warmoitz, N., "The Ignition Mechanism of Relay Tubes with Dielectric Igniter." *Philips Tech. Rev.*, **9**, 105 (1947).
f. Makinsun, R. E. B., J. M. Somerville, and P. Thoneman, "Magnetically Controlled Gas Discharge Tubes." *J. Applied Phys.*, **17**, 567 (July 1946).
Overbeck, W. B., "The Permatron—A Magnetically Controlled Industrial Tube." *Trans. AIEE*, **58**, 225 (May 1939).
g. *Stout, M. B., "Analysis of Rectifier Filter Circuits." *Trans. AIEE*, **54**, 977 (Sept. 1935).
h. Hull, A. W., and F. R. Elder, "The Phase of Arc-Back." *J. Applied Phys.*, **13**, 171 (Mar. 1942).
White, J. E., "Back-Fires in Mercury-Arc Rectifiers" and "A New Approach to the Study of Arc Back." *J. Applied Phys.*, **11**, 507 (July 1940); **13**, 265 (Apr. 1942).
Kingdon, K. H., and E. J. Lawton, "The Relation of Residual Ionization to Arc-Back in Thyratrons." *Gen. Elec. Rev.*, **42**, 474 (Nov. 1939).
Slepian, J., and L. R. Ludwig, "Backfires in Mercury Arc Rectifiers." *Trans. AIEE*, **51**, 92 (Mar. 1932).
i. Hull, A. W., "Fundamental Processes in Gaseous Tube Rectifiers." *Elec. Eng.*, **69**, 695 (Aug. 1950).

j. *Coolidge, A. W., Jr., "New Line of Thyratrons." *Elec. Eng.*, **67**, 435 (May 1948).

k. *Hull, A. W., "Hot Cathode Thyratrons: Part I, Characteristics, Part II, Applications." *Gen. Elec. Rev.*, **32**, 213, 390 (Apr. and July 1929).

l. Harrison, A. H., "Ionization Time of Thyratrons." *Trans. AIEE*, **59**, 747 (1940).

Cance, J. C. R., "Note on the Ionization and Deionization Times of Gas-Filled Thyratrons." *J. Sci. Instruments*, **23**, 50 (Mar. 1946).

m. *Dow, W. G., and H. A. Romanowitz, "Statistical Nature and Physical Concepts of Thyratron Deionization Time." *Trans. AIEE*, **69**, 368 (1950).

*Malter, L., and E. O. Johnson, "Studies of Thyratron Behavior: Part I, The Effect of Grid Resistance on the Recovery Time of Thyratrons; Part II, A Study of the Effect of Grid Potential Variations during the Afterglow Period upon the Recovery Time of Thyratrons." *RCA Rev.*, **11**, 165, 178 (June 1950).

Wittenberg, H. H., "Pulse Measurements of Deionization Time." *Elec. Eng.*, **69**, 823 (Sept. 1950).

n. Wittenberg, H. H., "Thyratrons in Radar Modulator Service." *RCA Rev.*, **10**, 116 (Mar. 1949); also "Frequency Performance of Thyratrons." *Trans. AIEE*, **65**, 843 (1948).

de Knight, H. B., "Hot Cathode Thyratrons; Practical Studies of Characteristics." *Proc. IEE*, Part III, **96**, 361 (Sept. 1949).

de Knight, H. B., and L. Herbert, "The Development of Mercury-Vapour Thyratrons for Radar Modulator Service." *Proc. IEE*, Part IIIA, **93**, 949 (1946).

Heins, H., "Hydrogen Thyratrons." *Electronics*, **19**, 96 (July 1946).

o. *Rouse, G. F., and M. J. Reddan, "Clean-Up of a Noble Gas in an Arc Discharge." *Trans. AIEE*, **70** (1951).

Hull, A. W., and E. E. Burger, "The Disappearance of Gas in Discharge Tubes." *Phys. Rev.*, **46**, 1044 (June 1932).

p. Reich, H. J., "The Relaxation Inverter and D-C Transformer with Resistance Load." *Rev. Sci. Instruments*, **4**, 147 (Mar. 1933).

q. Wagner, C. F., "Parallel Inverter with Resistance Load" and "Parallel Inverter with Inductive Load." *Trans. AIEE*, **54**, 1227 (Nov. 1935); **55**, 970 (Sept. 1936).

Sabbah, C. A., "Series-Parallel Type Static Converters." Parts I, II, and III. *Gen. Elec. Rev.*, **34**, 288, 580, 738 (May, Oct., and Dec. 1931).

Willis, C. H., B. D. Bedford, and F. R. Elder, "Constant-Current D-C Transmission." *Trans. AIEE*, **54**, 103 (Jan. 1935).

INDEX

Probability integral, 369, 574
Probe measurements (plasma), 479–506
electric gradient, 479
electron temperature, 479, 504
planar sidewall probe, 498–502
plasma potential, 498, 501, 505
probe characteristic, 498
various geometries, 498
Proton, 397, 563
Push-pull amplifiers, 298–302

"q" plane and cylinder, 140ff, 173, 198
Quantization of action, 223, 399–407, 425
Quantum-number lattice, 225, 227
Quantum yield, 427, 429, 451

Radar, "A scope," "B scope," 65, 69
crystal detectors, 233
reflex klystron local oscillator, 343
plan position indicator (PPI), 66, 69
thyratron modulators, 532, 552
uhf triode transmitter, 341
Radiation counter tubes, 521
Radioactive aid to voltage breakdown, 440
Radius of gas particle, 441, 469, 473, 581
Raindrops (problem), 386
Ramsauer free paths, 476, 581ff
Random current density, anode fall space, 496
concept, 378
plasma, 378, 384, 486, 504
positive ion sheath, 379, 504
Random velocities, arrival at a boundary, 372ff
averaging procedure, 361, 368
electron volt measure of, 26, 202
Fermi distribution function, 230, 352, 359
Maxwellian distribution, affects mean free path, 470
averages, 308, 371, 372, 375
Boltzmann relation, 384
collision mechanism derivation, 353ff
detail balancing (microscopic reversibility), 356
energy, velocity, characteristic of temperature, 359, 362

Random velocities, Maxwellian distribution, equations, arrival at a surface, 373–376, 385
total velocity, 353, 361, 365
x-directed, 362ff, 370, 372
equipartition of energy, 203, 372
ideal gas law, 201, 376
of penetrating electrons, 381, 384, 504
of plasma electrons, 465, 476, 504
sign conventions, 367
symbolism, 362
temperature concept, 359
of thermionic electrons, 203, 245, 353, 374–376, 382
raindrop problem, 386
snapshot-throughout-a-volume, 202, 376
time-exposure-over-a-surface, 202, 375ff
velocity space, 353ff, 358, 362
vs. drift velocities, 480, 483–487
Randomly occasional ionization, 510, 512
Raster, 65, 75
Ratings, rectifier, 537–540
Recombination, none in plasmas, 465
occurs in boundary regions, 465, 500, 506
surfaces encourage, 465
Recovery time (thyratron), 503
Rectifier photocells, 428, 448–451
Rectifiers, gas, anode dissipation, 539
arc-back, 508, 538ff, 558, 562
arc drop, 457, 460, 528, 539, 543
arc-initiating provisions, 528, 530ff, 543ff, 557ff
circuits, filtering, 533ff, 537
phase-shift control, 543, 549ff
polyphase, 456, 460, 533
ripple, 537
single-phase, 535, 549–551
clean-up of gas, 553, 594
condensed-mercury temperature, 541ff, 546ff, 583
economic considerations, 534, 539
efficiency, 460, 539
arc-back and grids, 539
excitation arc, 528, 530, 538
Excitron initiation, 508, 529